The Living Ocean

Biology and Technology of the Marine Environment

HMSS, Hawai'i Marine Science Studies

Third Edition

E. Barbara Klemm

S. Arthur Reed

Francis M. Pottenger III

Christine Porter

Thomas W. Speitel

CRDG

A Publication of the University of Hawai'i's
Curriculum Research & Development Group
Honolulu, Hawai'i

CRDG Director: Arthur R. King, Jr.
Associate Director: Myrtle M. Yamada
Director, Science Projects: Francis M. Pottenger III
Managing Editor: Edith K. Kleinjans
Publications Coordinator: Gayle Y. Hamasaki

Production, Third Edition
***HMSS* Project Directors:** E. Barbara Klemm and Francis M. Pottenger III
Production Management: Christine Porter
Cover Design: Christine Porter
Illustrations: Christine Porter and Byron Inouye
Cover Photo: Heinz de Couet
Computer Layout: Christine Porter, Wayne M. Shishido, S. Arthur Reed, Edgar Ambrosio

Contributing Authors
Edith H. Chave
Mary Gullickson
Will Kyselka
Raymond K. Rounds
Barbara S. Siegel
Dorothy Wendt

Content Reviewers and Advisers, Third Edition
Dr. Isabella A. Abbott, Department of Botany, University of Hawai'i
Dr. John Bardach, East-West Center
Dr. Julie H. Brock, Department of Zoology, University of Hawai'i
Mr. Mark Brooks, Pacific Aquaculture, Heeia Fishpond
Dr. Bruce A. Carlson, Director, Waikiki Aquarium
Dr. Keith E. Chave, Department of Oceanography, University of Hawai'i
David E. Coleman, Head Librarian, University of Hawai'i
Dr. John P. Craven, Law of the Sea Institute, University of Hawai'i
Dr. Pierre J. Flament, Department of Oceanography, University of Hawai'i
Dr. Richard W. Grigg, Department of Oceanography, University of Hawai'i
David Gulko, Department of Zoology, University of Hawai'i
Dr. Michael G. Hadfield, Department of Zoology, University of Hawai'i
Dr. Carol Hopper, Director of Education, Waikiki Aquarium
Dr. Cynthia Hunter, Hawai'i Institute of Marine Biology, University of Hawai'i
Dr. M. Casey Jarman, Law of the Sea Institute, University of Hawai'i
Dr. Paul L. Jokiel, Associate Researcher, Hawai'i Institute of Marine Biology, University of Hawai'i
Dr. E. Alison Kay, Department of Zoology, University of Hawai'i
Dr. Michael R. Landry, Department of Oceanography, University of Hawai'i
Dr. Edward A. Laws, Department of Oceanography, University of Hawai'i
Marilyn Lee, Sea Life Park
Ricardo M. Letelier, Department of Oceanography, University of Hawai'i
Dr. Phillip S. Lobel, Associate Scientist, Woods Hole Oceanographic Institute
Dr. Sherwood D. Maynard, Director, Marine Options Program, University of Hawai'i
Dr. Harold Morowitz, Robinson Professor of Biology and Natural Philosophy, George Mason University
Dr. Paul G. Olin, Sea Grant Advisory Agent, University of Hawai'i
Olive Schoenberg, Hawai'i Malacological Society
Dr. Edward D. Stroup, Department of Oceanography, University of Hawai'i
Raymond S. Tabata, Coastal Research Agent, Sea Grant Extension Service, University of Hawai'i

Teacher Reviewers, Third Edition
Jack Crowley, Bingham High School, Maine
Jonathan D. Fudge, UH Laboratory School, Honolulu
Mary Ann Johnson, Greensboro, North Carolina
John Southworth, UH Laboratory School, Honolulu
Twylla Dawn Steer, 'Aiea High School, Hawai'i
Ann Weaver, UH Laboratory School, Honolulu
With many thanks to the 25 teachers who gave us their responses in our California and Hawai'i institutes of 1992 and many others whose contributions shaped this work.

Printed in the United States of America

Distributed by the *HMSS* Project
Curriculum Research & Development Group
1776 University Avenue
Honolulu, Hawai'i 96822

ISBN 0–937049–75–1

Contents

Preface

THE LIVING OCEAN: Biological Science and Technology of the Marine Environment offers students the opportunity to learn the basic concepts of science by investigating the oceans. They explore the biology of organisms that live in the ocean and in fresh water and investigate ecological, technological, and socioeconomic applications. In a companion text, *THE FLUID EARTH: Physical Science and Technology of the Marine Environment,* they explore the physics, chemistry, and geology of the oceans and related practical applications in ocean engineering.

The program was designed, developed, and revised by the staff of the *Hawaii Marine Science Studies (HMSS)* Project of the Curriculum Research & Development Group of the University of Hawaii under the co-direction of Francis M. Pottenger III and E. Barbara Klemm.

Since the first experimental edition of the program in 1975, the materials have been used by over 400 teachers. In 1982 the National Science Teachers Association selected *HMSS* as an "Exemplary Program in Science."

Funds for the project came from the University of Hawaii, the university's Sea Grant program, and other sources.

Introduction for Students

THE LIVING OCEAN: Biological Science and Technology of the Marine Environment has been designed to engage you in the activities of science. You will learn the skills, concepts, and methods used by oceanographers and other scientists and engineers who study the ocean. You will learn about the oceans by carrying out investigations, designing experiments, making observations, and interpreting your findings. To succeed in using this text, you will need a laboratory notebook for recording your data and conclusions. Much of what you learn will grow out of the findings recorded in your notebook.

Study Aids

The text contains some aids to study and understanding.

1. When a new science term is defined, it is printed in **boldface.**
2. Cautions and notes are highlighted by **BOLDFACED CAPITAL LETTERS.**
3. Some words have a pronunciation guide in parentheses following their first appearance.
4. Each topic has these parts:
   READING. An introduction to the topic.
   ACTIVITY. A statement of what you are to do in an investigation.
   MATERIALS. A list of supplies and equipment for the activity.
   PROCEDURE. Instructions for doing the activity.
   QUESTIONS. Helps in interpreting your findings.
   FURTHER INVESTIGATIONS. Suggestions for extending your study by following up on related activities.
   Ⓦ Indicates a table or figure that is included in the Student Workbook.

Laboratory Safety

These safety precautions apply to all laboratory classes.

1. Wear safety goggles whenever you are working with chemical reagents and Bunsen burners.
2. Wear a laboratory apron when you do laboratory investigations. If you spill chemicals, the apron protects both you and your clothing.
3. Stand when you do laboratory work. Standing prevents spilling chemicals in your lap.
4. Always wear shoes with closed tops.
5. If you spill chemicals on yourself or your clothing, rinse immediately with a large quantity of water to dilute and wash away the chemicals.
6. Never taste a chemical without your teacher's permission.
7. If your hair is long, pin it at the back of your head to keep it out of chemicals or flames.
8. Find out where the fire extinguisher, safety shower, and fire blanket are and learn how to use them.
9. Report all accidents to your teacher.

UNIT 1
FISH

"Another one!" shouted Michiko, pushing the thrashing silverside down the slippery water trough to her father. A deft blow across the head, fingers thrust into the gill slit, and the lifeless fish was thrown onto the heavy wooden cutting table. Seventy returning hatchmates had already been cleaned and put in baskets of ice for delivery to the cooperative. "She's big! Bring the egg bucket," called the father. Reaching under the blue tarpaulin, Michiko brought out a wooden bucket about a quarter full of cold stream water. With a quick knife thrust up the belly, the egg sac, gorged with pinkish spheres, slid onto the table. The blade touched the sac's straining membrane, and the eggs spilled into the bucket. In an instant one cycle of life ended and another was about to begin.

As the wild populations of the oceans and fresh waters are being depleted by pollution and industrial harvesting, aquaculture has begun to fill the markets of the world with tilapia, mullet, salmon, trout, eel, catfish, and other species. But the promise that aquaculture may keep our plates full tends to shut out our concern for the other inhabitants of the earth's waters. Yet these waters are alive with a huge diversity of organisms important to our global ecosystem. To preserve our environmental heritage, we need to know about these communities.

We begin our study of aquatic life by studying fish—their structure, physiology, and behavior. In units that follow we will look at other organisms and their interrelationships in the living ocean.

Francis M. Pottenger III

1. Fish Prints

To identify species of fish, assess their age and health, and learn about their structure and function, marine biologists measure fish and describe their external features. For measuring and describing, they use fresh fish, photographs, scientific drawings, or other kinds of detailed images—even fossils.

We will use a Japanese fish-printing method called ***gyotaku*** (GYOH tah koo) to make an accurate image of a fish. See Fig. 1–1. We will cover a fish with paint and press paper over it to make a print. *Gyotaku* is a popular art form in Japan. Color, arrangement, and detail give *gyotaku* its artistic qualities and its scientific value.

Fig. 1–1. A *gyotaku* print by artist Anne Machado

ACTIVITY

Experiment with ways of making fish prints. Prepare a collection of prints of common fish species.

MATERIALS

- newspapers
- 3- to 10-in long fresh, whole fish
- soapy water
- paper towels
- 8½ x 11-in sheet of cardboard or Styrofoam (or sand in a resealable plastic bag about 12 x 12 in)
- sharp-pointed scissors or scalpel
- 2 sheets of wax paper 10 x 10 cm or larger
- straight pins
- piece of modeling clay, marble-sized
- water-based block printing ink or tempera paint
- 2 paintbrushes with ½-in bristles (keep one brush dry)
- newsprint or paper towels
- rice paper or other good paper
- cleaning supplies

PROCEDURE

1. Cover a tabletop, lab bench, or floor area with newspapers.

2. Gently clean the outside of the fish with soapy water to remove any gelatinous covering. Rinse the fish and pat it dry with paper towels.

3. Cut a body-shaped "well" out of cardboard or Styrofoam. (Or make a well in a closed bag filled with sand.) See Fig. 1–2. For thick-bodied fish use several layers of cardboard. The body should lie

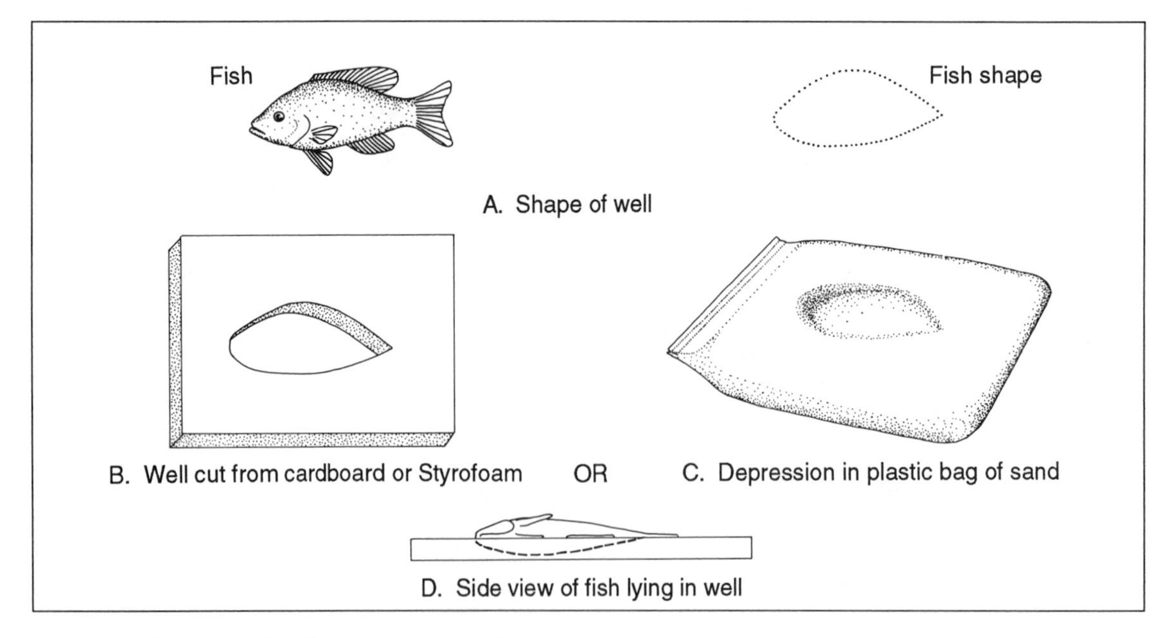

Fig. 1–2. Making a "well" to support the fish

in the well with the edges supporting the fins. Follow these steps:

a. Trace the outline of the fish's body, but not its fins, onto a piece of cardboard or Styrofoam.
b. Remove the fish.
c. Using scissors or a scalpel, cut the fish outline out of the cardboard or Styrofoam to form a well.
d. Tear one sheet of wax paper into pieces and line the well with them to keep paint out of the well.

4. Lay the fish in the well. Refer to Fig. 1–3 as you work.
   a. Spread out the fins. Decide how you want them to appear in your fish print. Hold each fin in place by inserting a straight pin behind the largest spine into the body of the fish. Be sure the pin doesn't show on the side of the fish to be covered with paint.
   b. If a fin needs more support, put a thin layer of modeling clay under it. The clay should not show from the top.
   c. Insert a small piece of clay or paper towel to hold the mouth open the way you want it to appear.
   d. Support the gill covers by putting a small, thin piece of clay or wadded paper towel under the gill opening. Keep the gill opening dry by blotting it with a paper towel.

5. Paint the fish. Refer to Fig. 1–4.
   a. Get a dab of one color of paint from the class supply. The paint should be thick, not watery. Carry it to your work area on the second piece

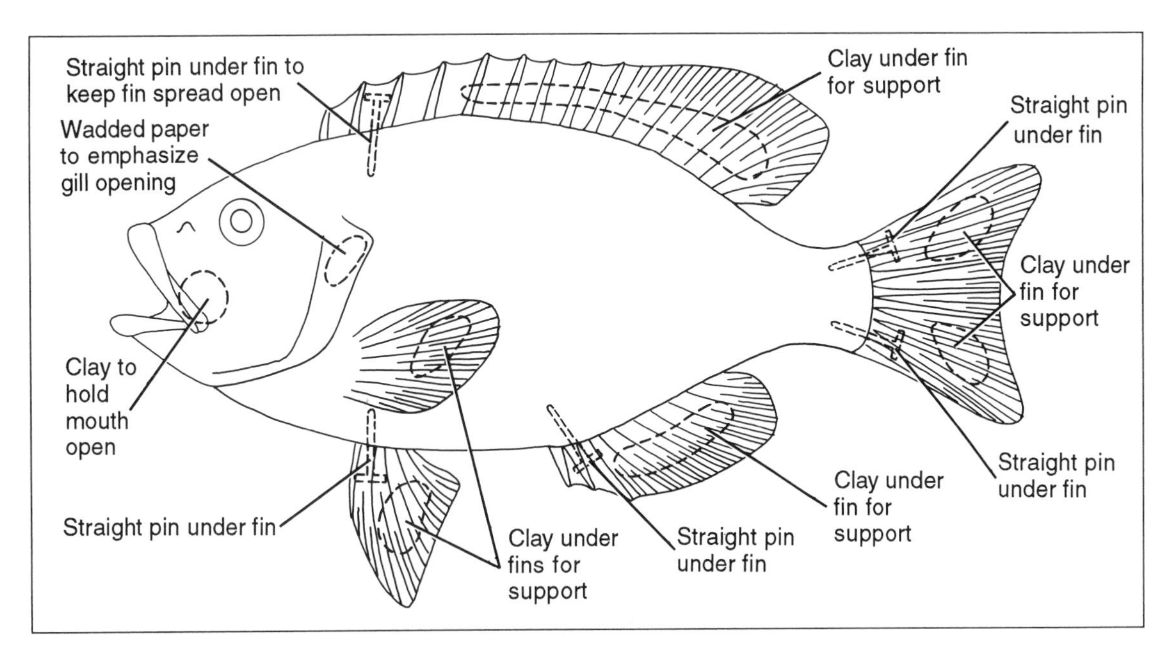

Fig. 1–3. Techniques for displaying fish features

of wax paper.

b. With a paintbrush, gently apply a thin, even coat of paint from the head to the tail of the fish. Do not put paint on the eye. Be careful not to damage the scales when applying the paint. You may need to dilute the paint. If you want to make the scales more prominent, apply the paint from tail to head to make them stand up more. Be careful not to damage them.

c. Remove and discard the pieces of wax paper that lined the well. Clean up any paint on the cardboard that might ruin the print.

6. Work with a partner to apply the paper to the fish. Practice with newsprint, paper towel, or other inexpensive paper. Later, when you are more practiced, use rice paper or other good paper.

a. Partner A positions the paper over the fish, holding the paper in place so that it does not slide. One end of the paper may be pinned to the cardboard to help hold it in place.

b. Partner B uses a clean, dry paintbrush or fingertips to gently press the paper onto the painted fish. Lightly stroke the fish in one direction only. The harder you press, the less detail you will get. Use the handle of the brush to reach the curved surfaces and to bring out the features of the fins.

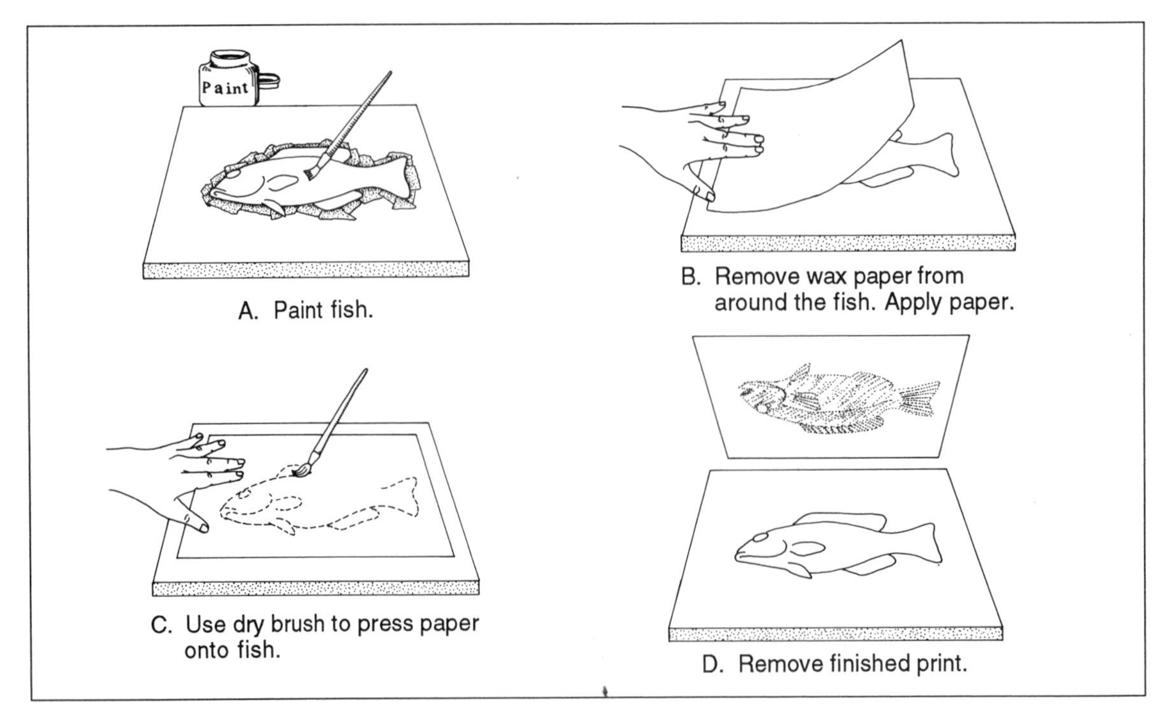

Fig. 1–4. Fish-printing process

7. Carefully lift the paper off the fish and let the print dry. Sign your names or initials on the paper.

8. Examine the print. Decide how to improve your technique. Usually the second or third print is better than the first.
   a. If some areas on the print are too light, decide whether you used too little paint or missed rubbing that area. Repaint the fish if necessary.
   b. If some areas on the fish have too much paint, lightly blot off the excess with a paper towel.
   c. Check for watery areas, especially around the eyes, gill openings, and anal openings. Blot these dry.
   d. When you are finished, clean the brushes thoroughly.

9. Try new techniques and explain them to the class. Here are some suggestions:
   a. Use more than one color on the fish.
   b. Make a group of prints of the same fish on one piece of paper.

10. Prepare a set of fish prints of common fish or of major fish groups.

QUESTIONS

1. How does *gyotaku* compare with photography as a means of getting and displaying information on the features of a fish? What are the advantages and disadvantages of each?

2. What techniques worked best to bring out the details in your prints?

3. What measurements can be made from a fish print?

4. Suggest other uses for the *gyotaku* printing technique.

FURTHER INVESTIGATIONS

1. Explore using fish prints as an art form for wall hangings, notepaper, place mats, and other decorations.

2. Try making fish prints on fabric with fabric paints.

3. Make copies of fish prints by using a silk-screening technique. Ask your art teacher or a seller of art supplies for details.

4. Using library references, look for the uses of fish as symbols in paintings and architecture.

5. Find out about career opportunities for
   a. wildlife artists.
   b. nature photographers.
   c. scientific illustrators.
   d. craft workers who use natural motifs.

6. Choose a wildlife artist or nature photographer and read about the artist's life and work.

7. What role(s) do wildlife artists and photographers play in making us aware of the environment and dangers to it? Find examples of environmental art that teach about specific plants or animals or ways to protect the environment.

2. The External Anatomy of Fish

Anatomy is the study of the structures of organisms and their arrangement in relation to each other. The external anatomy of a fish gives clues to where and how it lives. Variations in shape and size of body parts permit different fish to live in different environments or in different parts of the same environment.

In this investigation we will identify the outer anatomical structures common to most fish. Then we will observe how the shapes, sizes, and arrangements of anatomical structures differ among fish.

ACTIVITY

Identify the common external anatomical structures of several fish.

Compare the shapes, sizes, and locations of these structures.

MATERIALS

- fresh, whole fish
- newspaper or dissecting pan
- 8½ x 11-in plain white paper
- copies of Workbook Tables 2–1 and 2–2
- forceps
- microscope slide
- 10X dissecting microscope
- black paper
- microscope light (optional)
- cleaning supplies

PROCEDURE

1. Lay your fish on its side in a dissecting tray or on newspaper, orienting it as in Fig. 2–1 on the following page.

2. Draw the fish on plain paper. Make your drawing large.
   a. For the title of your drawing, write the name of your fish. Get the name from your teacher or use the key in Topic 4 to find its biological family name.
   b. Label the drawing with the following terms to show the orientation of the fish. See Fig. 2–1.
   ANTERIOR for the head end
   POSTERIOR for the tail end

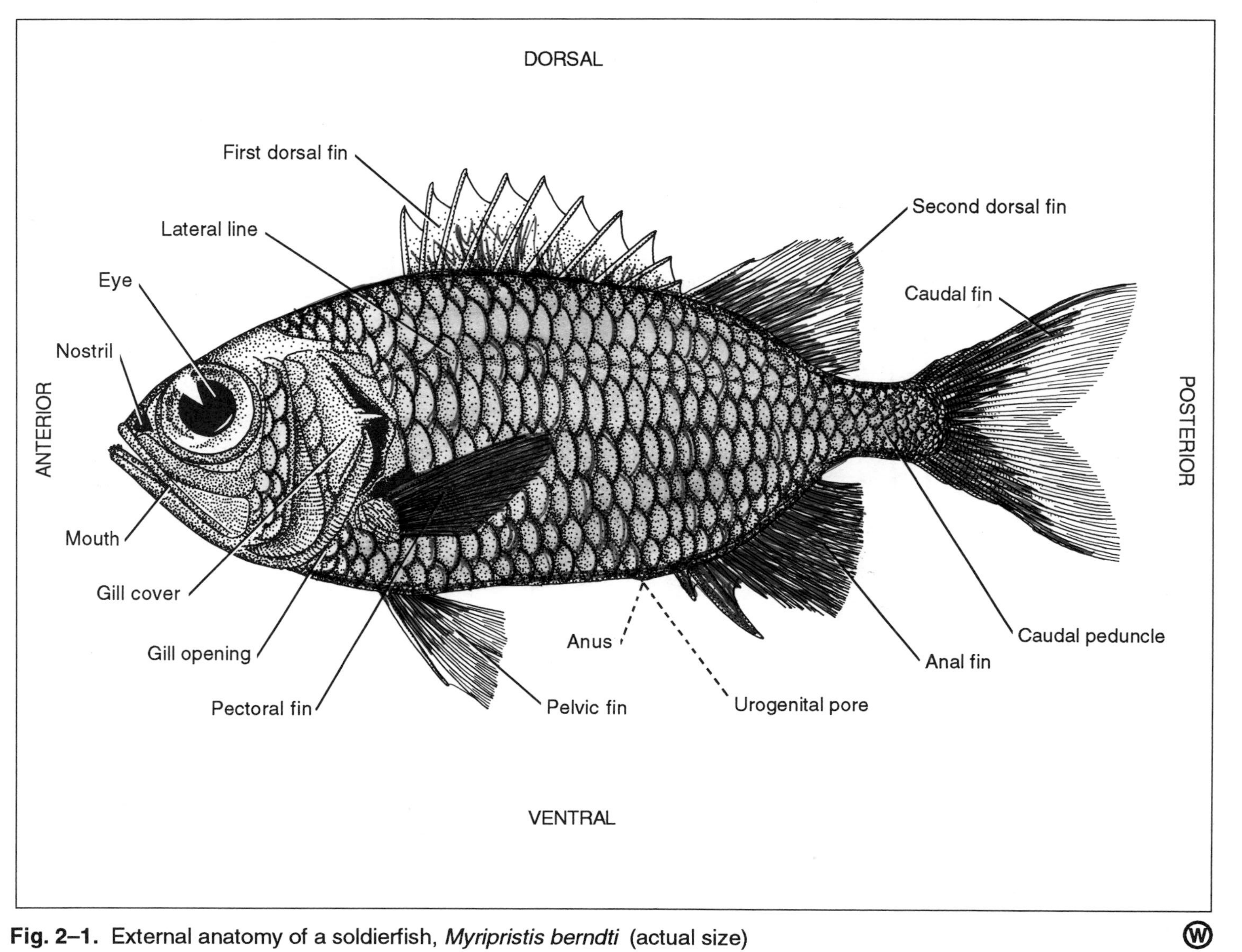

Fig. 2–1. External anatomy of a soldierfish, *Myripristis berndti* (actual size) Ⓦ

DORSAL for the upper or top side
VENTRAL for the lower or bottom side

3. Using the soldierfish diagram as a guide, identify and label the structures of your fish. See Fig. 2–1. (Some fish do not have all the structures shown in the figure; others have structures that vary from the ones in the figure.)

4. Complete Table 2–1.
   a. In the columns in Table 2–1, sketch the dorsal fin or fins and the anal fin of your fish. Label the first fin spine and first fin ray. See Fig. 2–2 for an example of a fin spine and a fin ray.
   b. Use forceps to remove a scale from the middle of the body (but not along the lateral line). Place it on a microscope slide and examine it under a

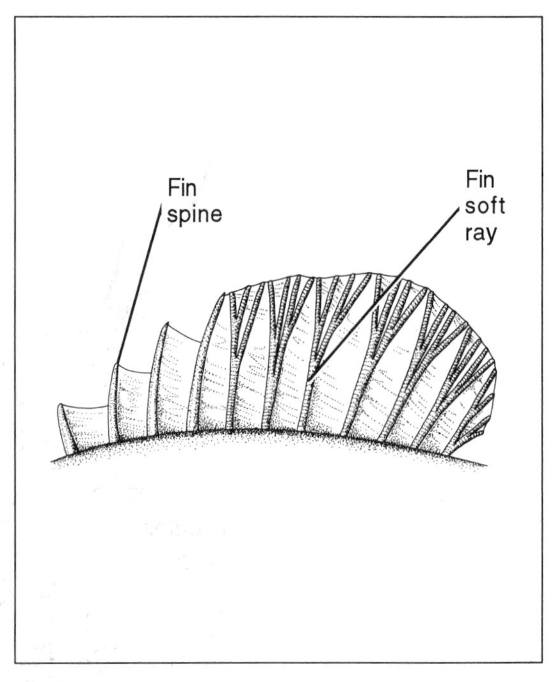

Fig. 2–2. A dorsal fin showing fin spines and rays (similar to the second dorsal fin of the soldierfish) Ⓦ

Table 2–1. Fish spines, rays, and scales 

Name of fish ______________________	
Sketch of dorsal fin	Sketch of anal fin
Sketch of scale from middle of body	Sketch of scale from lateral line

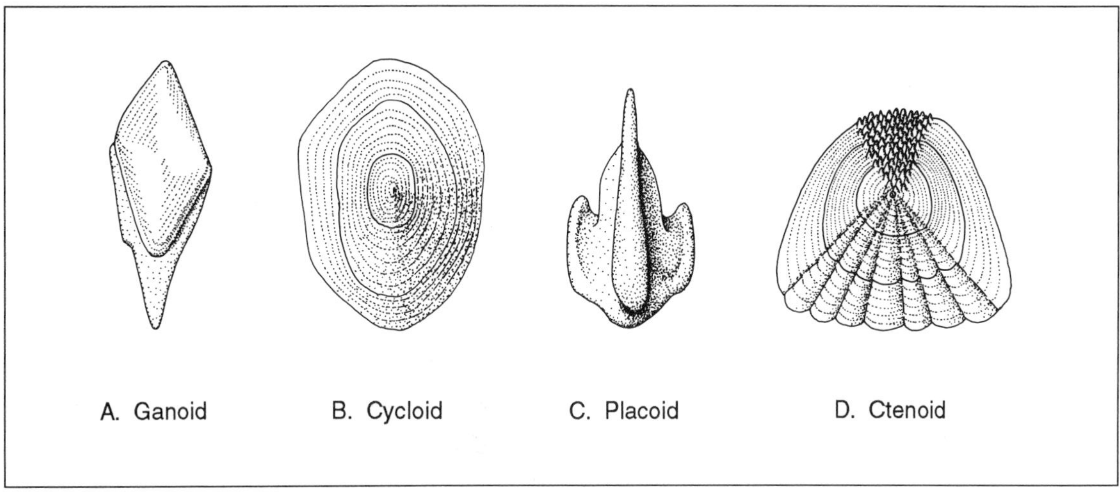

Fig. 2–3. Four types of fish scales

dissecting microscope at 10X. For better contrast, put the slide on black paper and beam a microscope light on it from the top.

c. Make a sketch of the scale in Table 2–1. Identify the scale type by comparing your drawing with the scales shown in Fig. 2–3 on the next page. Write the type of scale below the sketch.

d. Repeat Procedures 4.b. and 4.c. using a lateral line scale. (Note: Some fish do not have an obvious lateral line; others have no lateral line.)

5. Compare your fish with the soldierfish in Fig. 2–1, noting any difference in structures.
   a. Record your observations as sketches or descriptions in Table 2–2.
   b. Sketch or describe any structures of your fish not seen on the soldierfish.

6. Follow your teacher's instructions for preserving or discarding the fish and cleaning the microscope slide.

QUESTIONS

1. Which type of scale was most common among the fish your class examined?

2. Which structures would you use to differentiate any two kinds of fish? Explain why you chose these structures.

3. Hypothesize which of the two fish, yours or the soldierfish, is the faster swimmer. What structures of the fish might enable it to swim faster?

4. Check your understanding of these terms. Use a dictionary or reference book if you are not sure.
   a. anatomy
   b. external
   c. pectoral
   d. pelvic

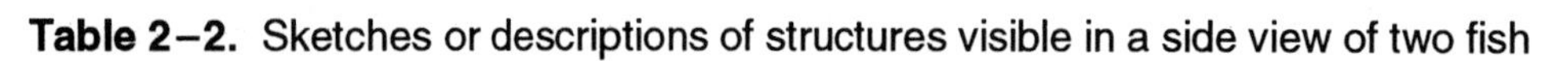
Table 2–2. Sketches or descriptions of structures visible in a side view of two fish

Structure	Soldierfish	Your fish
Dorsal fin(s)		
Pectoral fins		
Pelvic fins		
Anal fin		
Caudal fin		
Gill cover		
Gill opening		
Lateral line		
Anus		
Eye		
Mouth		
Nostrils	Two openings close together, between top lip and eye at front of head	
Body scale type	Ctenoid	
Fin spine		
Fin ray		
Features not found on soldierfish		

e. dorsal
f. ventral
g. anterior
h. posterior
i. internal

FURTHER INVESTIGATIONS

1. Observe how a fish in an aquarium uses each of its fins to move. Describe and sketch the movements.

2. Make a collection of preserved fish or fish photographs for classroom use.

3. How could external body parts affect cleaning fish for commercial food use? (Cleaning includes removing scales and fins.)

4. How are physical features of fish represented in
   a. cartoons?
   b. toys?

   What features are emphasized? In what ways are the fish given human attributes?

3. Classification, Nomenclature, and Keys

Biological classification is the orderly arrangement of organisms into identifiable groups. The most specific category is **species.** A species is a group of similar organisms that can interbreed to produce fertile offspring that as adults can reproduce.

The next larger category is **genus,** which has one or more species. Species within a genus have similar features. But sometimes a species is so unlike other species that it is put in a genus of its own. For example, humans are in a genus of their own. Groups of **genera** (the singular is *genus*) together form a **family.** Groups of families form an **order;** groups of orders form a **class;** groups of classes form a **phylum;** and groups of phyla form a **kingdom.**

All organisms in a kingdom have common features. The organisms making up a species have all the features of their kingdom, phylum, class, order, family, and genus, plus features unique to their species. Thus the raccoon butterflyfish—a species—can be classified as shown in Table 3–1.

Each classification level is described by a **key characteristic,** a distinctive and usually readily observable feature that can be used to separate animals or plants into groups. English translations of the terms that describe the raccoon butterflyfish are in the right column in Table 3–1.

Scientific Nomenclature

Scientific nomenclature is the system that scientists use for naming organisms. In this topic we use butterflyfish to show how to use scientific names. Butterflyfish are popular saltwater tropical aquarium fish. But there are more than a dozen species of butterflyfish. Common names are not adequate for identifying fish species for several reasons:

1. Different common names are often used for a single species. In English, for example, the fish in Table 3–1 is called a raccoon butterflyfish in Hawaii, a cross butterflyfish in other parts of Polynesia, and a red-striped butterflyfish in Melanesia.

2. A common name may refer to several similar but different species. In Hawaiian, for example, only two common names, *kikakapu* and *lauhau*, are used for the 15 species of butterflyfish listed in Table 3–4 and shown in Fig. 3–2.

3. Common names sometimes contain misleading descriptive words. For example, starfish, jellyfish, and crayfish are not fish. See Fig. 3–1.

Binomial Nomenclature

Scientists around the world, no matter what their language, use a two-name or **binomial** system for naming organisms. **Scientific names** usually combine word parts from Latin (L) or Greek (G). Table 3–2 shows Latin and Greek word parts used in naming the butterflyfish. A scientific name includes the

Table 3–1. Classification of the raccoon butterflyfish

A. Common names
In Hawaii: raccoon butterflyfish
In Polynesia: cross butterflyfish
In Melanesia: red-striped butterflyfish

B. Using biological classification

Category	Key characteristic		Meaning
Kingdom	Animalia	=	animal
Phylum	Chordata	=	has a notochord (a supporting bony rod)
Subphylum	Vertebrata	=	has a vertebral column (a "backbone")
Class	Osteichthyes	=	fish with a bony skeleton
Order	Perciformes	=	shaped like a perch
Family	Chaetodontidae	=	teeth shaped like bristles
Genus	*Chaetodon*	=	bristle teeth
Species	*lunula*	=	shaped like a moon

C. Scientific name: *Chaetodon lunula*
Abbreviated scientific name: *C. lunula*

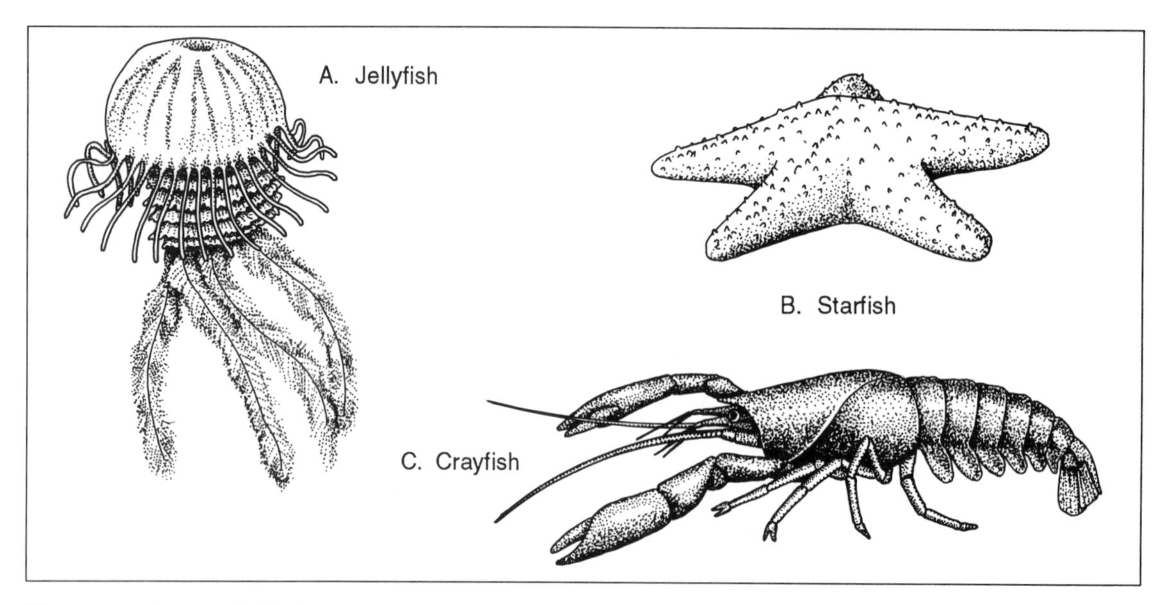

Fig. 3–1. Some "fish" that are not true fish

Table 3–2. Some Latin (L) and Greek (G) word parts

Word part and its meaning	
auri - (L). Gold, golden	***lineo*** (L). A line
bi- (L). Two	***lun-*** (L). The moon
chaet (G). Bristle	***macula*** (L). Spot, spotted
cinct (L). Girdled	***miliar*** (L). Millet (a grass) seed
citrin (G). A lemon	***multi-*** (L). Many
-ellus (L). Small	***-odon*** (G). Tooth
ephippi (G). A saddle	***ornat*** (L). Adorned
fasciat (L). Banded	***quadri-*** (L). Four
frem (L). Roar, murmur	***reticul*** (L). A network
-latus (L). Side, broad, wide	***tri-*** (L). Three

names of both the genus and the species. For example, the scientific name of the raccoon butterflyfish is *Chaetodon lunula.* The genus name comes before the species name. In writing, both names are either underlined or printed in italics (slanting type). The first letter of the genus name is always capitalized. If the genus has already been mentioned, its scientific name may be abbreviated: *C. lunula.*

When scientists identify a new animal species, they enter its scientific name and description in a registry used by scientists worldwide. All scientific names of animals must be approved by the International Commission on Zoological Nomenclature, whose records are kept at the British Museum of Natural History in London. At least one specimen of the new species is placed in a recognized museum.

QUESTIONS

1. Why do scientists classify organisms?
2. What could happen to the exchange of scientific information if organisms were not classified?
3. List the rules to follow for writing scientific names of organisms.

Identification Keys

Over 2 million species of organisms have been named by scientists; probably millions more are still unnamed. To distinguish species, biologists make keys using easily identifiable features. A **biological key** is a series of decisions for identifying a species by its features. A key may be shown as a diagram or explained in words. See Table 3–3.

Schematic Keys

In Table 3–3, (A) shows a schematic key for identifying oceanic **vertebrates** (animals with spinal columns). Such a key is called a **dichotomous key** because it has two choices at each decision point.

The decision at the first branch point in the key separates vertebrate from invertebrate animals. The second one separates animals that feed in the ocean from those that feed on land. The next one separates animals that have lungs from those that have gills.

Look at branch point 6, below "Has gills." It shows that an animal with one gill opening on each side of its body is a bony fish and that an animal with more than one gill opening on each side is a shark or a ray. A more detailed key would help us find the scientific name of a particular bony fish, shark, or ray.

Word Keys

Because schematic keys are often too large or complex to fit on paper, scientists usually convert them to word keys. In Table 3–3, (B) shows the word-key counterpart to the schematic key for oceanic vertebrates.

In a **word key**, each number on the left identifies a decision point related to a pair of descriptive statements. The user selects a decision point, then looks at the number on the right (at the end of the sentence) that tells where to find the next level of descriptions. A number in parentheses shows the previous decision point, the one that led to this point in the key.

ACTIVITY 1

Use a word classification key to identify several species of butterflyfish.

MATERIALS

- copy of Workbook Fig. 3–2
- scissors
- sheet of construction paper (optional)
- glue (optional)

PROCEDURE

1. (Optional) Cut out the fish cards from Fig. 3–2.
2. Select the butterflyfish M. Using the

Table 3–3. Keys for identifying oceanic vertebrates

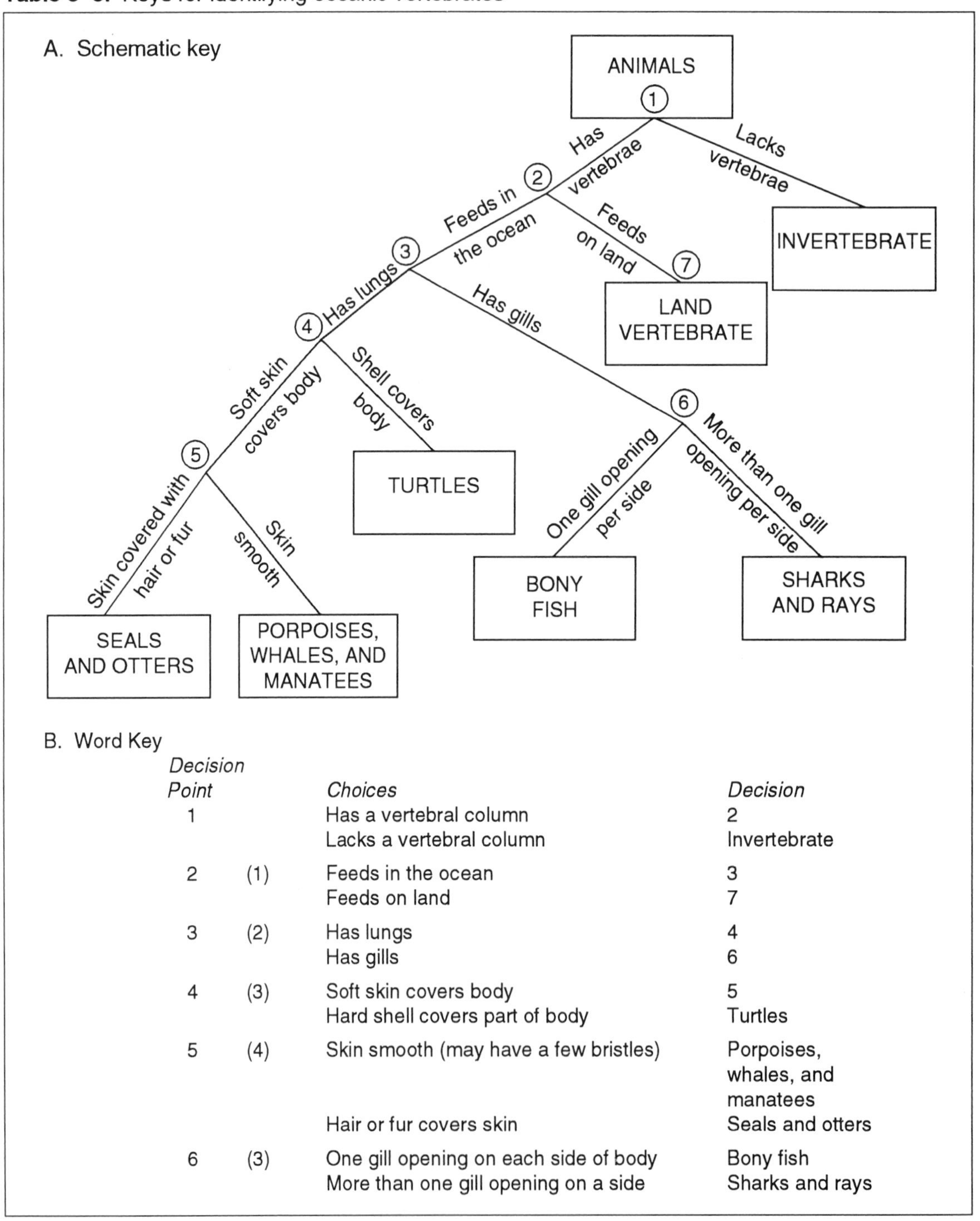

B. Word Key

Decision Point		*Choices*	*Decision*
1		Has a vertebral column	2
		Lacks a vertebral column	Invertebrate
2	(1)	Feeds in the ocean	3
		Feeds on land	7
3	(2)	Has lungs	4
		Has gills	6
4	(3)	Soft skin covers body	5
		Hard shell covers part of body	Turtles
5	(4)	Skin smooth (may have a few bristles)	Porpoises, whales, and manatees
		Hair or fur covers skin	Seals and otters
6	(3)	One gill opening on each side of body	Bony fish
		More than one gill opening on a side	Sharks and rays

word key in Table 3–4, key out butterflyfish M by following these steps:

a. Starting at decision point 1, read the two statements describing a feature of butterflyfish.
b. Decide which statement fits the picture of fish M. (The description "Pelvic fin dark" is the correct description for fish M.)
c. Note the number to the right side of this statement. It is 2.
d. Go to decision point 2. Read the two

Table 3–4. Word key to the butterflyfish of the genus *Chaetodon*

Decision Point		*Choices*	*Decision*
1		Pelvic fin dark	2
		Pelvic fin light	4
2	(1)	Two large white spots below dorsal fin	*C. quadrimaculatus*
		Lacks two large white spots below dorsal fin	3
3	(2)	Tail with two dark bars at tip	*C. reticulatus*
		Tail with one dark bar at tip	*C. kleini*
4	(1)	Posterior or dorsal fin has long filament extension	5
		Filament extension lacking from dorsal fin	6
5	(4)	Large dark spot on body near filament	*C. ephippium*
		Small dark spot on body near filament	*C. auriga*
6	(4)	No vertical band through eye	*C. fremblii*
		Vertical band through eye	7
7	(6)	Incomplete eyeband on face (does not go to top of head)	*C. multicinctus*
		Complete eyeband on face (extends to top of head)	8
8	(7)	Nose area with band	9
		Nose area lacks band	10
9	(8)	Fewer than eight diagonal bands on body	*C. ornatissimus*
		More than eight diagonal bands on body	*C. trifasciatus*
10	(8)	Distinct white spot splits eyeband above eye	*C. lineolatus*
		No white spot above eye; eyeband not split	11
11	(10)	Upper third of body under dorsal fin dark	*C. tinkeri*
		Upper third of body under dorsal fin not dark	12
12	(11)	Distinct small spots arranged in rows	13
		No distinct small spots; body has large spot or band	14
13	(12)	No black band on caudal fin	*C. citrinellus*
		Obvious black band on caudal peduncle	*C. miliaris*
14	(12)	Side with a large black teardrop; no dark bars on tail	*C. unimaculatus*
		Large black shoulder patch; tail with dark bars	*C. lunula*

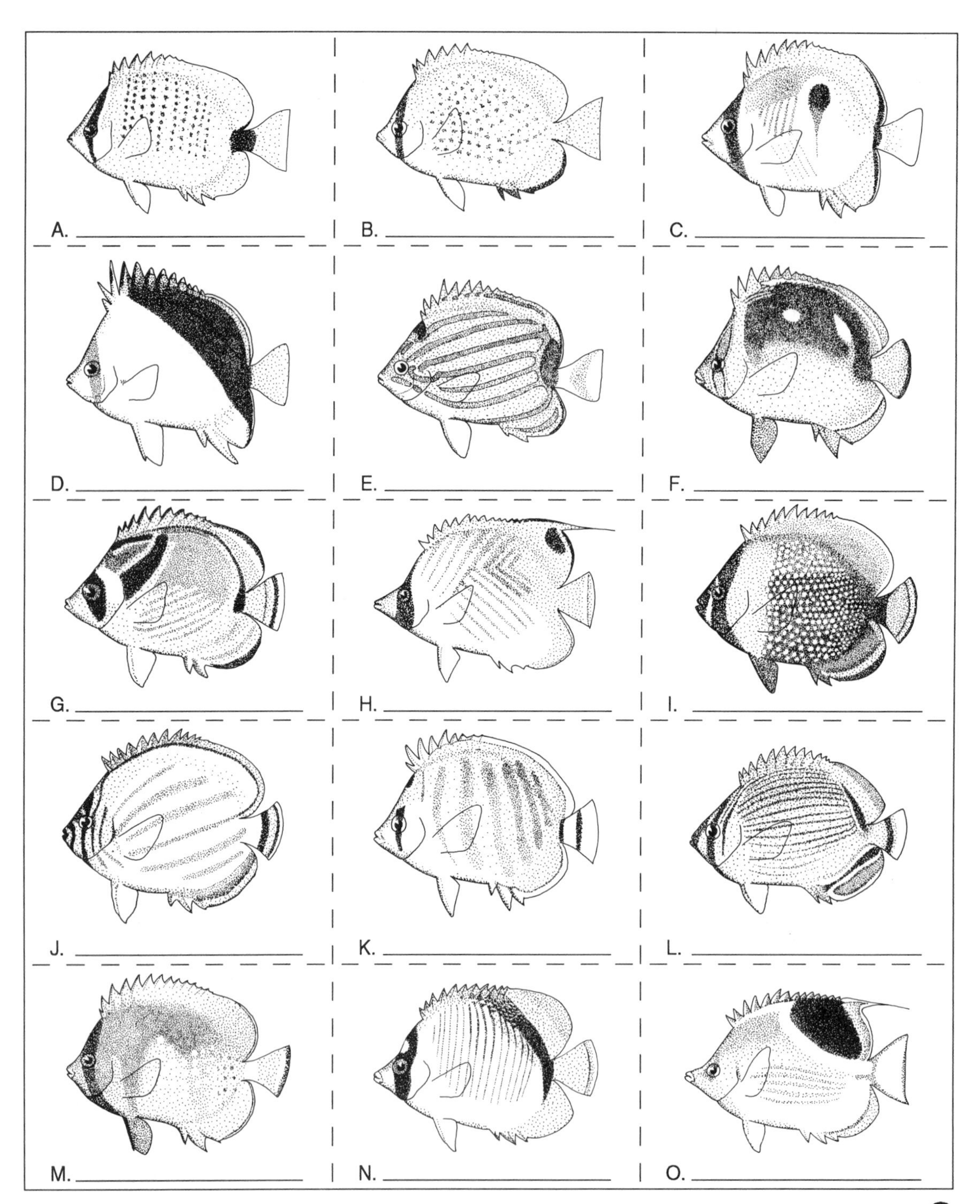

Fig. 3–2. Butterflyfish

descriptions. Decide which statement better describes fish M. (The second statement, "Lacks two large white spots below dorsal fin," is the correct choice.)

e. Find the number in the right-hand column for the statement you chose. Go to the decision point with that number at the left.

f. Again select the proper description. (Of the two choices there, "Tail with one dark bar at tip" is the correct choice.) This description identifies the organism, and its name appears: *Chaetodon kleini.*

g. Record the name of your fish below its picture in Fig. 3–2. (Because all fish in Fig. 3–2 are in the genus *Chaetodon,* the name of the genus may be abbreviated as *C* and *Chaetodon kleini* may be identified as *C. kleini.*)

3. Identify all the butterflyfish in Fig. 3–2.
   a. Read the two descriptions at each decision point, then select the description that matches the fish.
   b. When you identify a fish, write its scientific name under its picture. Continue until you identify all the fish.
   c. If you are using cards, remove each card from the deck when you identify the fish on it.

4. (Optional) Make a schematic key like (A) in Fig. 3–3 on a sheet of construction paper. Glue your cards at the correct locations on the key.

QUESTIONS

4. What kind of feature should be used for constructing a key for a group of animals or plants?

5. How might biological keys handle the problem of a species of fish that have different color patterns in juvenile and adult stages?

6. Color and markings are usually poor characteristics to use in identification keys. Why?

Hybrids

Different species rarely interbreed in nature, either because they live far apart or because they do not share mating habits. When two species do interbreed, the offspring, called a **hybrid**, is given a scientific name that indicates its genetic cross. For example, a male donkey (*Equus asinus*) and a female horse (*Equus caballus*), different species within the same genus, can mate to produce a hybrid mule (*Equus asinus* x *caballus*). Like most hybrids, mules are sterile; that is, they cannot produce offspring.

Sometimes scientists are surprised by new hybrids, such as the hybrid female **wholphin** born in 1985 at Sea Life Park in Hawaii. The wholphin's father is a false killer whale (*Pseudorca crassidens*) and its mother is an Atlantic bottlenose dolphin (*Tursiops truncatus*). What surprised the scientists was that the parents were not just different species but different genera. The scientific name given the wholphin is *Pseudorca* x *Tursiops,* showing that the wholphin is a cross between two genera. A similar hybrid born in Tokyo in

1981 lived only a short time.

When a wholphin was born in Hawaii, no one knew whether it would survive. But it proved healthy, grew rapidly, and soon was trained to perform with other dolphins and whales at Sea Life Park. An even more surprising thing happened in 1990, when the wholphin gave birth to a live 47-lb female calf that looked like its mother. Its father was thought to be an Atlantic bottlenose

Table 3–5. Characteristics of a hybrid wholphin and its parents

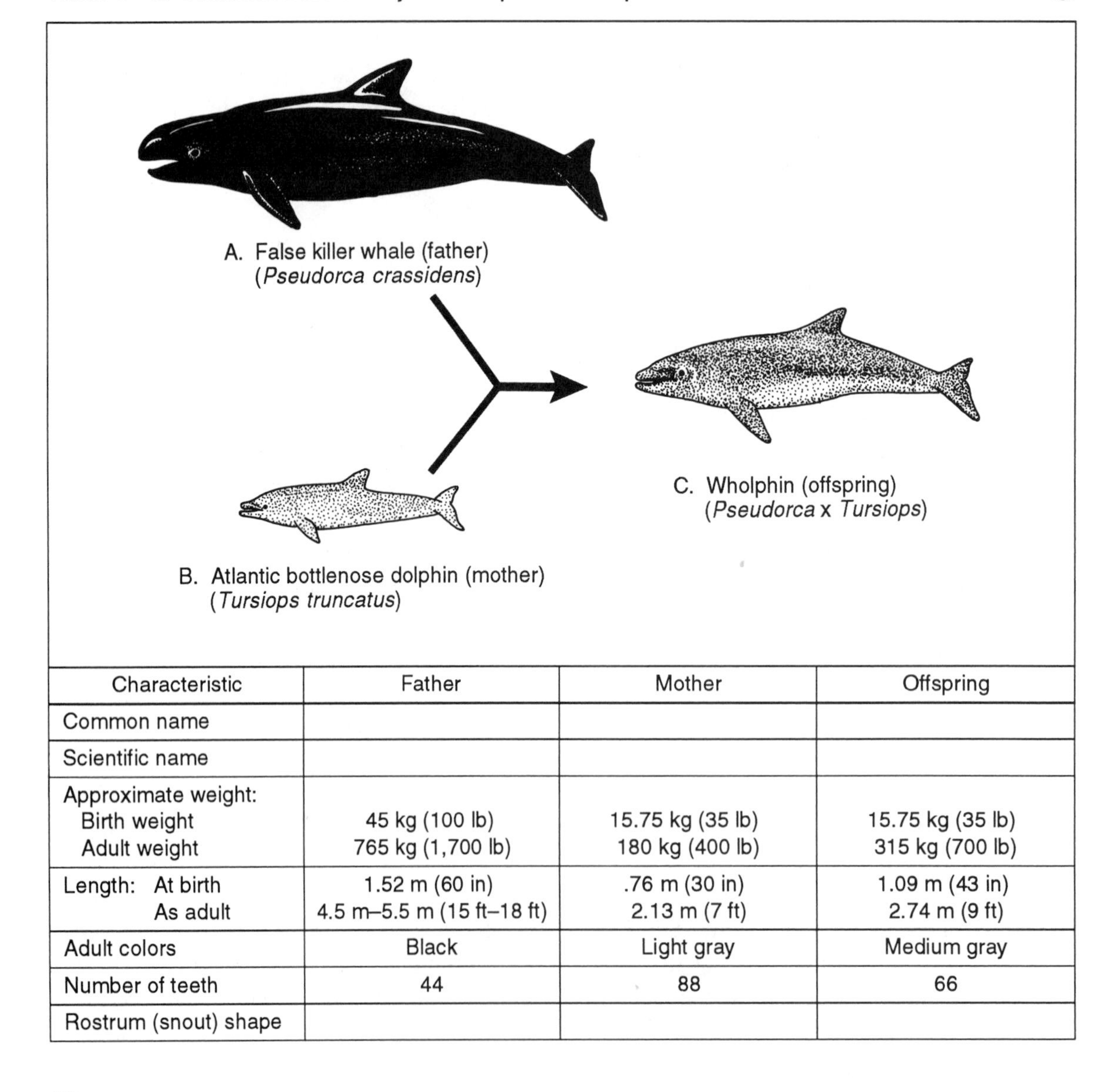

Characteristic	Father	Mother	Offspring
Common name			
Scientific name			
Approximate weight: Birth weight Adult weight	 45 kg (100 lb) 765 kg (1,700 lb)	 15.75 kg (35 lb) 180 kg (400 lb)	 15.75 kg (35 lb) 315 kg (700 lb)
Length: At birth As adult	1.52 m (60 in) 4.5 m–5.5 m (15 ft–18 ft)	.76 m (30 in) 2.13 m (7 ft)	1.09 m (43 in) 2.74 m (9 ft)
Adult colors	Black	Light gray	Medium gray
Number of teeth	44	88	66
Rostrum (snout) shape			

dolphin. But the calf lived only a few days because it did not nurse. Another female calf born the next year was bottle-fed by scientists. She has grown into a healthy animal, over a year old.

Table 3–5 summarizes the characteristics of a wholphin and its parents.

ACTIVITY 2

Describe the characteristics of a hybrid.

MATERIALS

- copy of Workbook Table 3–5

PROCEDURE

1. Examine the drawings and the information in Table 3–5. Record the common names and the scientific names of the wholphin and its parents in the table.

2. Compare and describe or sketch the rostrum (snout) of each organism.

QUESTIONS

7. How do the wholphin's features compare with the features of its mother? Its father?

8. What makes the wholphin such an unusual hybrid? Use the terms *genus* and *species* in your answer.

FURTHER INVESTIGATIONS

1. Make a schematic key or a word key to identify each person in your class. Use easily identified characteristics such as age, sex, height, hair color, eye color, and so on. Avoid descriptions that are hard to measure such as *pretty*, *handsome*, or *smart*.

2. **Taxonomy** (G. *taxis* = arrangement) is the study of theories, principles, and processes of establishing categories for classifying organisms.
   a. What kinds of talents or abilities does a taxonomist need? Explain your reasoning.
   b. Where and in what kinds of work might a taxonomist be employed? Give examples.

3. Collect keys to the common marine or aquatic organisms near your community. Learn how to use the keys. Check nearby museums and public aquaria as well as the library for information.

4. Plants and animals have been cross-bred for centuries to produce such characteristics as hardier species, larger bodies, and faster growth. Study cross-breeding techniques used in agriculture and animal husbandry. Find out how cross-breeding has increased world food production.

5. Find out about the application of cross-breeding techniques in
   a. developing desired aquaculture stocks such as trout or carp.
   b. breeding aquarium fish such as mollies or platys.

4. Keying Oceanic Bony Fish to Family

Thousands of species, hundreds of genera, and many families of fish inhabit the oceans. To get an idea of the diversity of fish, we will look at a key of fish families.

The pictorial key in Table 4–1 shows 51 families to which some common oceanic bony fish belong. By comparing your fish with the drawings and descriptions in this key, you can match your fish to its family. Then you can use a more detailed book on fish classification to learn about a particular fish.

ACTIVITY

Use a key to identify a fish to its family level.

MATERIALS

- fish (fresh or preserved)
- newspaper or dissecting pan
- copy of Workbook Table 4–2

PROCEDURE

1. Get a fish from your teacher. Sketch the fish if you have time.
2. Identify the family—the scientific name and the common name—to which the fish belongs.
   a. Look at Table 4–1. Find Primary Key A and the four subkeys B through E.
   b. Use Primary Key A in Table 4–1 to determine which subkey (B through E) applies to a given fish. This step will reduce the time you spend identifying a fish. The families are divided into four subkeys by the structure of their pelvic and dorsal fins.
   c. Continue using subkeys to identify your specimen to its family level.
3. Record the family name and common name of your fish in Table 4–2.
4. Repeat Procedures 1 through 3 to identify as many fish as you can. Review Topic 2 to identify external anatomical structures.

Table 4–1. Simplified key to selected oceanic bony fish families. Family names are in capital letters; common names are in parentheses.

Primary Key A

1		An eye on each side of head	2
		Two eyes on one side of head	***BOTHIDAE*** (Flatfish)
2		No lure in front of spines on head	3
		Lure in front of spines on head; paired pectoral and pelvic fins handlike	***ANTENNARIIDAE*** (Anglerfish)
3	(2)	Pelvic fins present	4
		Pelvic fins absent	**Go to Subkey B (p. 26)**
4	(3)	Pelvic fins with five or fewer soft rays	5
		Pelvic fins with more than five soft rays	**Go to Subkey C (p. 29)**
5	(4)	Dorsal fin with two or more completely separated sections	**Go to Subkey D (p. 32)**
		Dorsal fin single or incompletely divided into two lobes	**Go to Subkey E (p. 35)**

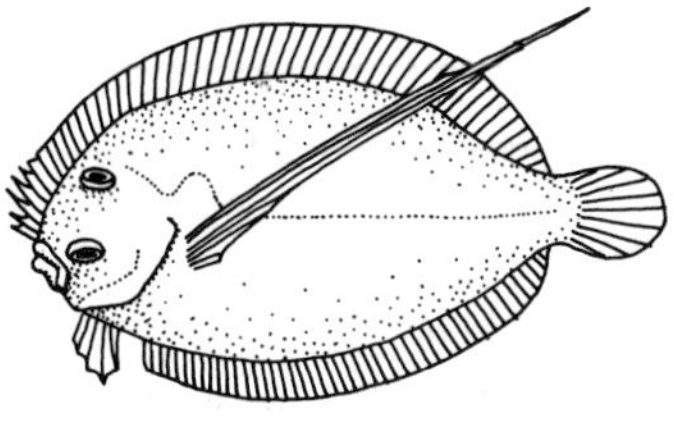

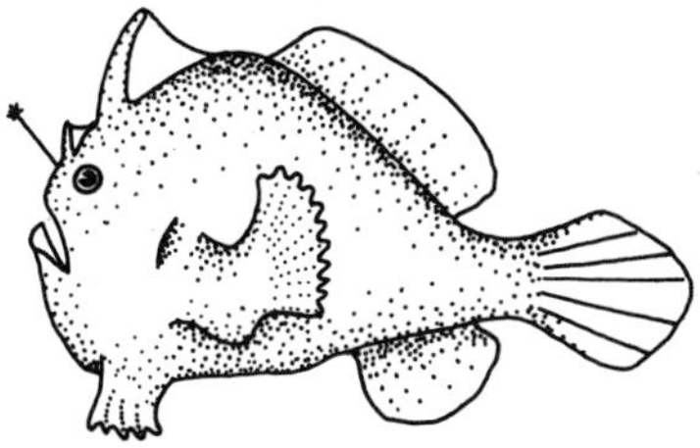

Table 4–1 *continued.* Simplified key to selected oceanic bony fish families. Subkey B

Subkey B

Pelvic fins absent

1		Has caudal fin	5
		No caudal fin	2
2	(1)	Body not encased in bony rings	3
		Body encased in bony rings	***SYNGNATHIDAE*** (Seahorse, pipefish)

3	(2)	Body eel-like, pectoral fins present	4
		Body eel-like, pectoral fins absent	***MURAENIDAE*** (Moray eel)

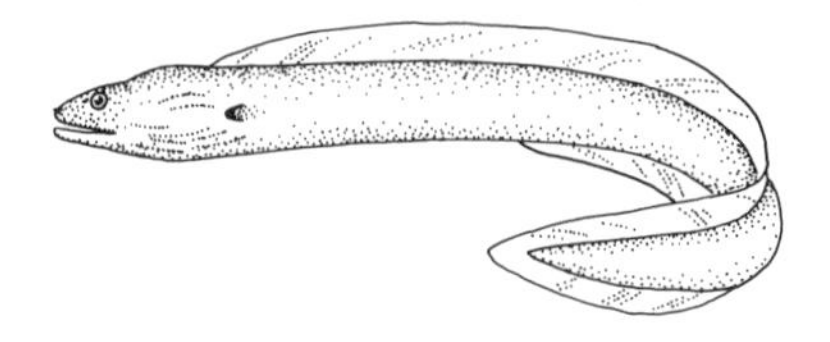

Table 4–1 *continued.* Simplified key to selected oceanic bony fish families. Subkey B

4	(3)	Dorsal fin longer than anal fin	***CONGRIDAE*** (Conger eel or white eel)
		Dorsal fin and anal fin equal in length	***ANGUILLIDAE*** (European eel)
5	(1)	Single dorsal fin	6
		Two separated dorsal fins; first dorsal fin composed of one large spine	***MONACANTHIDAE*** (Filefish)
		First dorsal fin composed of two or more spines	***BALISTIDAE*** (Triggerfish)

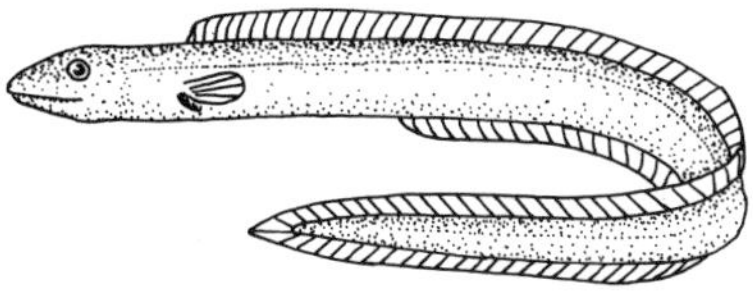

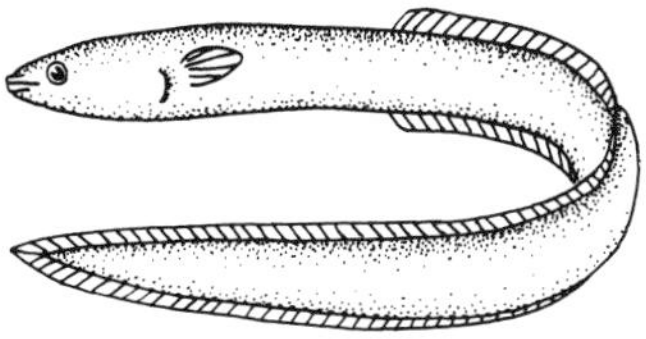

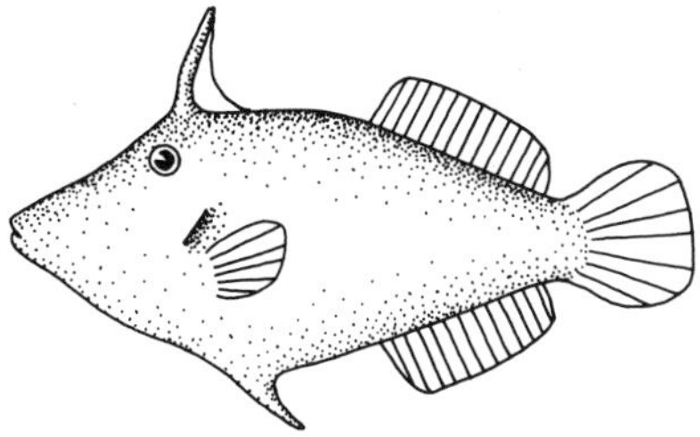

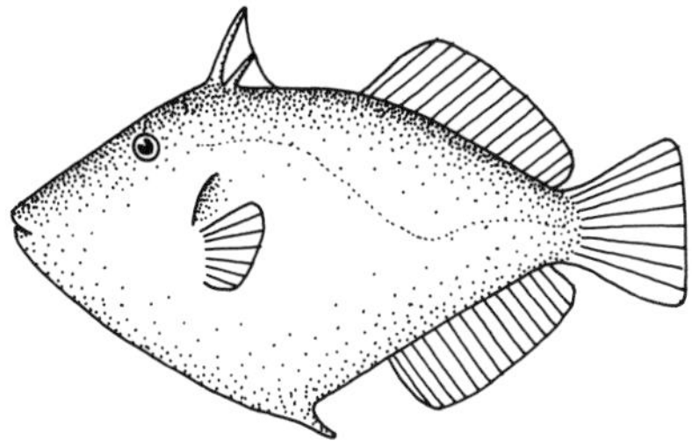

Table 4–1 *continued.* Simplified key to selected oceanic bony fish families. Subkey B

6	(5)	Body inflatable	7
		Body enclosed in noninflatable bony box	***OSTRACIONTIDAE*** (Trunkfish)
7	(6)	Body not spiny	8
		Spiny body	***DIODONTIDAE*** (Porcupinefish)
8	(7)	Erect flap on nostril	***TETRAODONTIDAE*** (Balloonfish)
		No erect flap on nostril	***CANTHIGASTERIDAE*** (Sharpback puffer; also called sharpnose puffer)

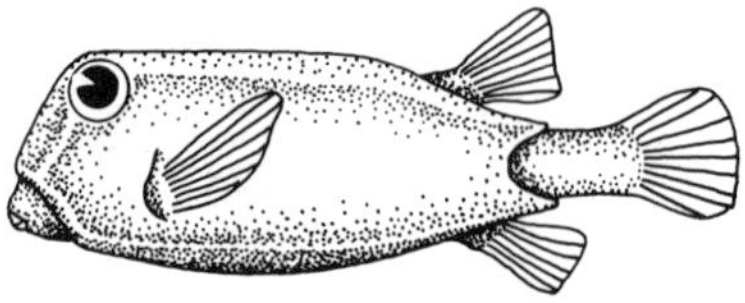

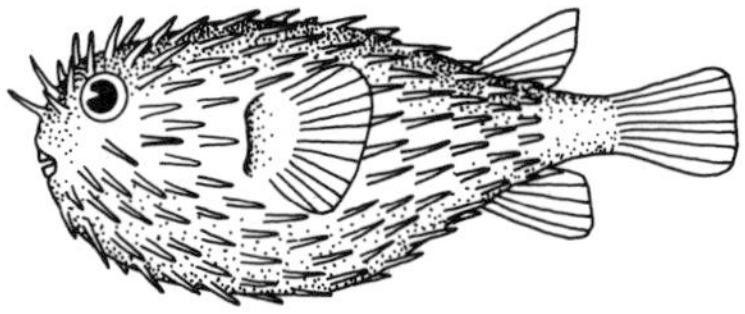

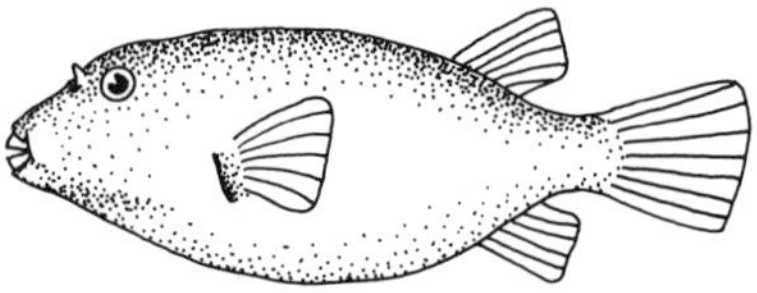

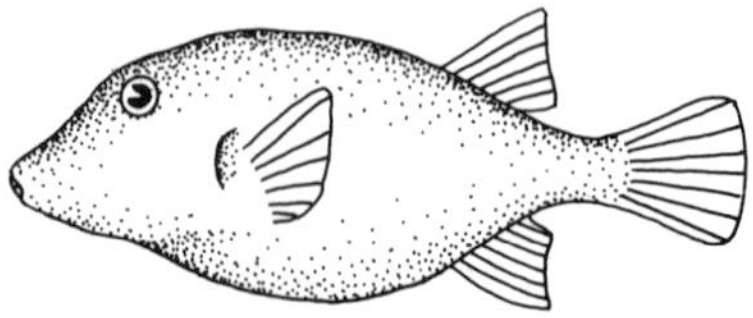

Table 4–1 *continued.* Simplified key to selected oceanic bony fish families. Subkey C

Subkey C

Pelvic fins with more than five soft rays

1 — No spines at the front of anal fin 2

One or more spines at the front of the anal fin .... ***HOLOCENTRIDAE*** (Squirrelfish)

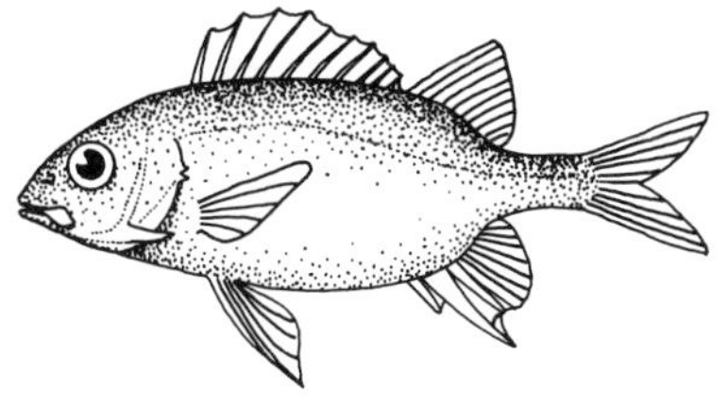

2 (1) — Without adipose (fatty) fin behind the dorsal fin 3

With adipose fin, pectoral fins high, pelvic fins forward of midbody .... ***SYNODONTIDAE*** (Lizardfish)

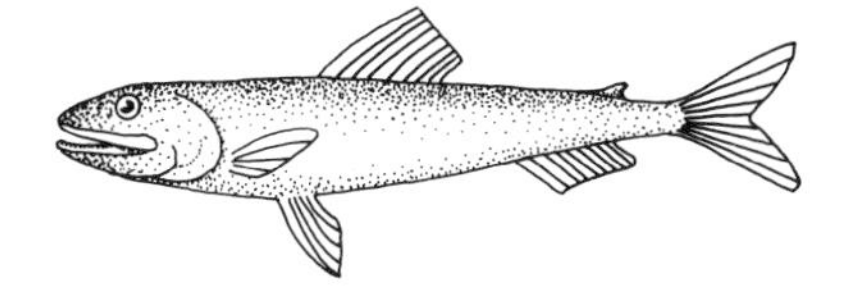

With adipose fin, pectoral fins low, pelvic fins midbody, caudal fin forked .... ***OSMERIDAE*** (Smelt)

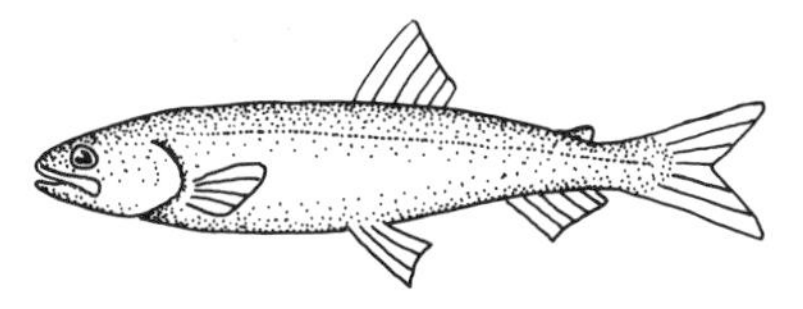

With adipose fin, pectoral fins low, pelvic fins midbody, caudal fin not forked .... ***SALMONIDAE*** (Salmon, trout)

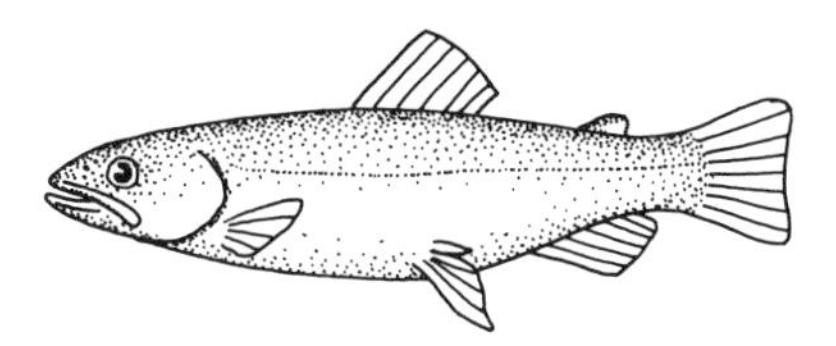

Table 4–1 *continued.* Simplified key to selected oceanic bony fish families. Subkey C

3	(2)	Snout not tubular	4
		Snout tubular; tail with medial filament	Fistulariidae (Cornetfish)
		Snout tubular with a barbel; tail without a medial filament	***AULOSTOMIDAE*** (Trumpetfish)
4	(3)	Lateral line obvious	5
		No lateral line; snout overhangs lower jaw	***ENGRAULIDAE*** (Anchovy)
		No lateral line; mouth terminal (*terminal* means "at the end of the snout"); prominent sharp keel (ridge) on belly	***CLUPEIDAE*** (Herring)
5	(4)	Both dorsal and anal fin not placed far back on body	6
		Dorsal and anal fin at rear of body	***EXOCOETIDAE*** (Flyingfish)

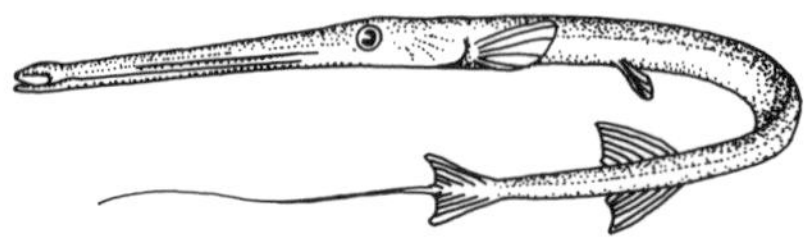

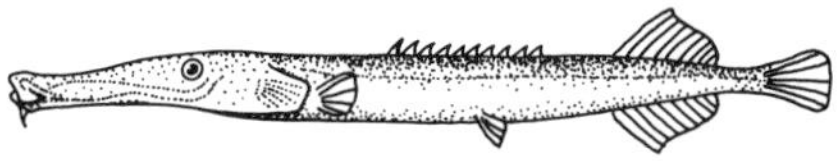

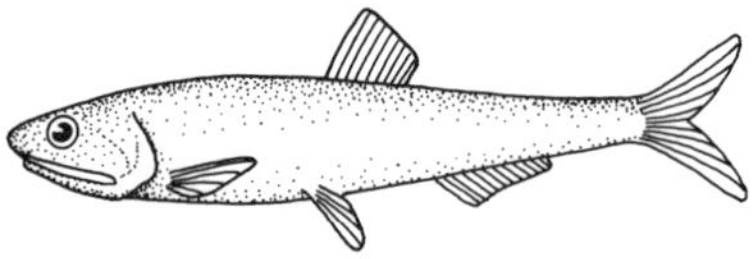

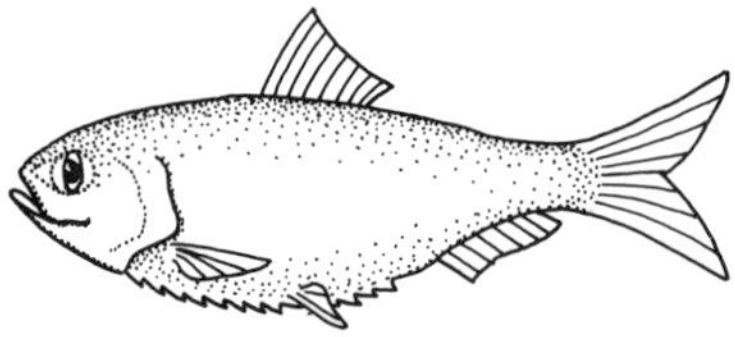

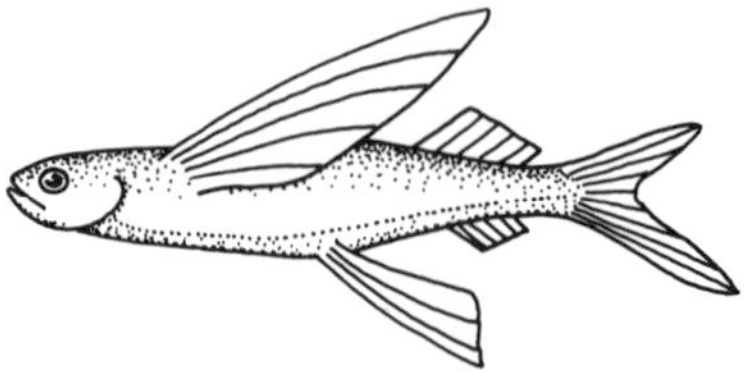

Table 4–1 *continued.* Simplified key to selected oceanic bony fish families. Subkey C

6	(5)	Caudal fin strongly forked	7
		Caudal fin not strongly forked; two or three dorsal fins	***GADIDAE*** (Codfish)
7	(6)	Mouth does not extend behind eye	8
		Mouth long, extending behind eye	***ELOPIDAE*** (Ladyfish)
8	(7)	Snout overhangs lower jaw	***ALBULIDAE*** (Bonefish)
		Snout and jaw equally aligned	***CHANIDAE*** (Milkfish)

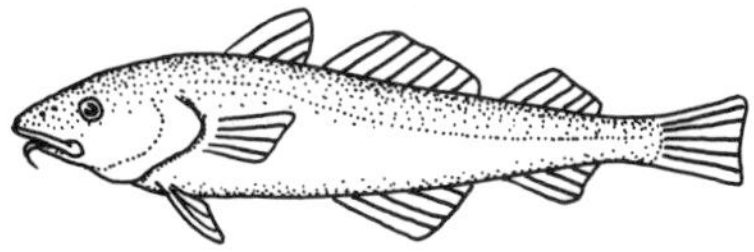

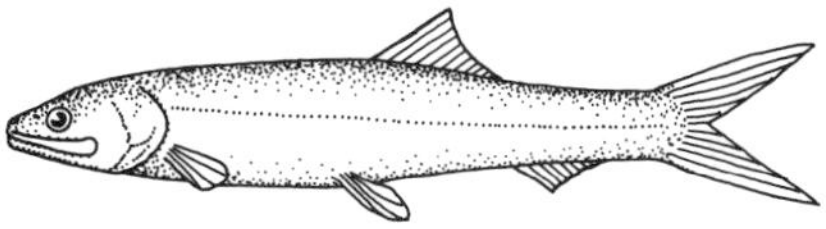

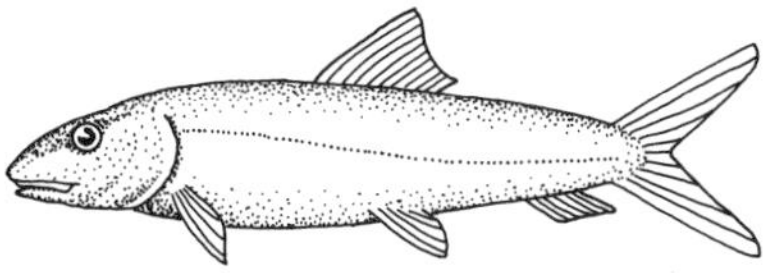

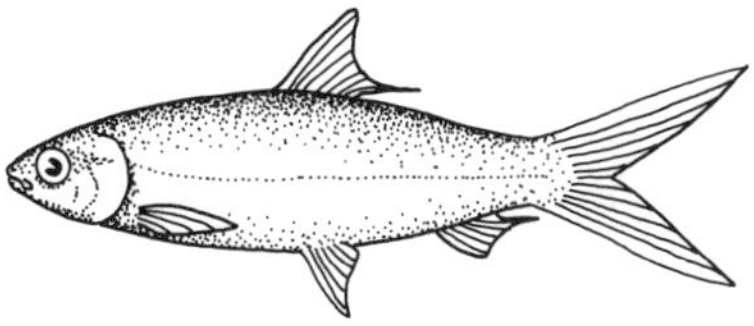

Table 4–1 *continued.* Simplified key to selected oceanic bony fish families. Subkey D

Subkey D

Dorsal fins with two or more completely separated sections
Pelvic fins with five or fewer soft rays

1		Pectoral fins not winglike	2
		Pectoral fins winglike; head completely armored	***DACTYLOPTERIDAE*** (Flying gurnard)

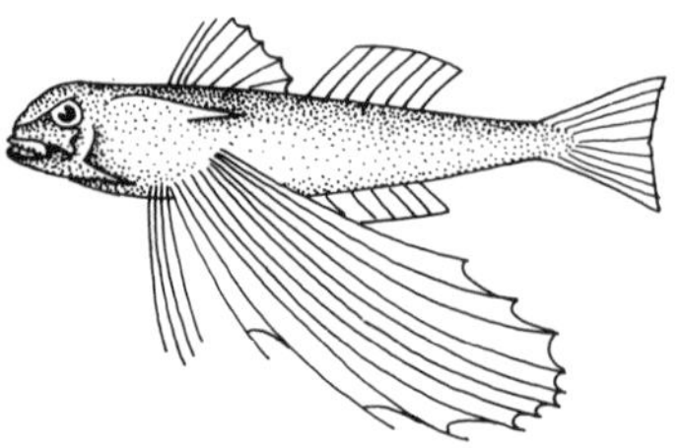

2	(1)	Upper jaw not projecting as a tapering bony spear	3
		Upper jaw projecting as a tapering spear, round in cross-section	***ISTIOPHORIDAE*** (Billfish)

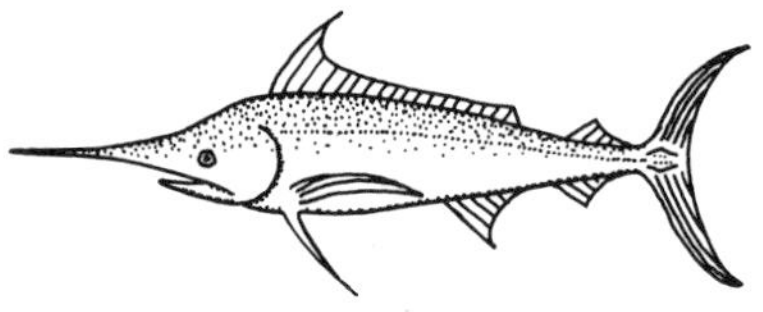

3	(2)	Pelvic fins separate	4
		Two pelvic fins fused to form a sucking disc	***GOBIIDAE*** (Goby)

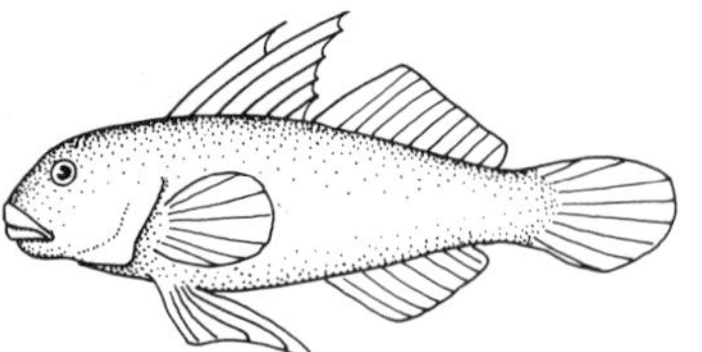

4	(3)	Pectoral fin without threads	5
		Base of pectoral fin divided into several threadlike rays....	***POLYNEMIDAE*** (Threadfin)

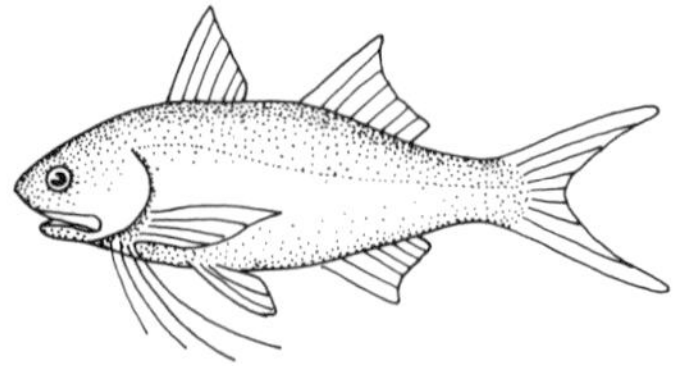

Table 4–1 *continued.* Simplified key to selected oceanic bony fish families. Subkey D

5	(4)	No finlets following dorsal spine; no separated spine on anal fin	6
		Two separate small, sharp spines in front of anal fin	***CARANGIDAE*** (Jack)
		Anal fin not preceded by two spines; finlets following dorsal spine	***SCOMBRIDAE*** (Tuna)
6	(5)	Pelvic fins not anterior to pectoral fins	7
		Pelvic fins anterior to pectoral fins; first dorsal fin anterior to pectoral fin	***TRIPTERYGIIDAE*** (False blenny)
		Pelvic fins anterior to pectoral fins; dorsal fin inserted above or behind pectoral fin	***GADIDAE*** (Codfish)

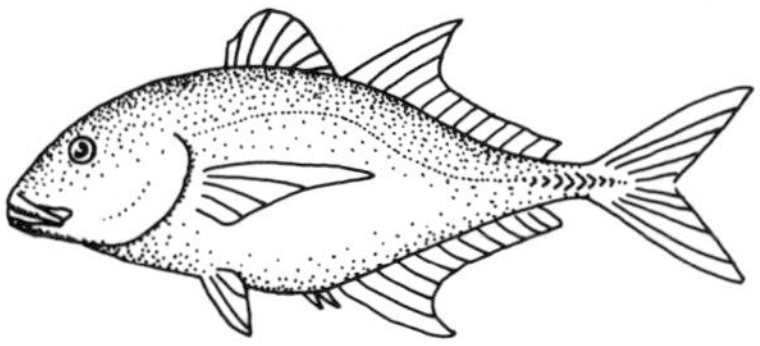

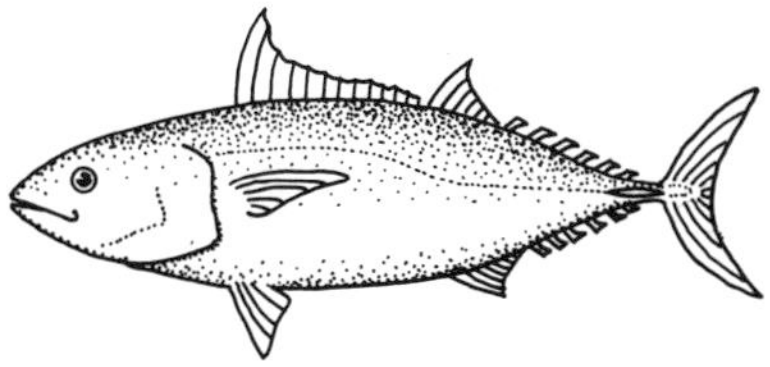

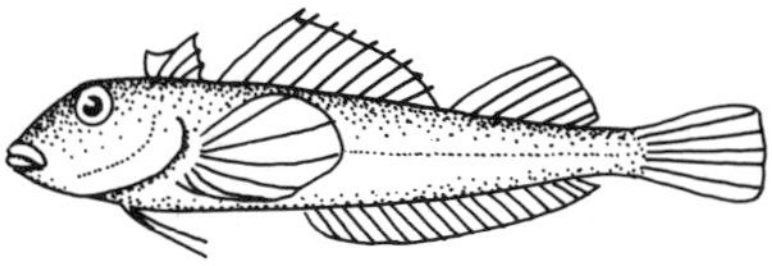

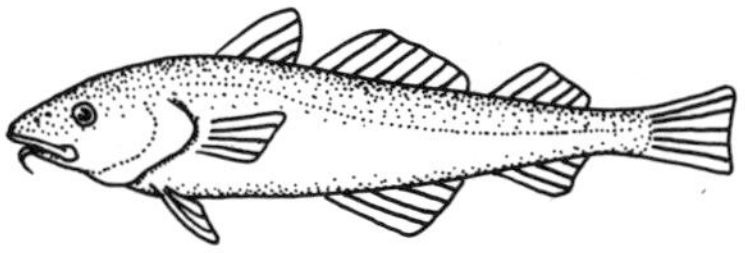

Table 4–1 *continued.* Simplified key to selected oceanic bony fish families. Subkey D

7 (6) No long barbel on chin 8

A pair of long barbels on chin .... ***MULLIDAE*** (Goatfish)

8 (7) Pelvic fins behind pectoral fin base 9

Pelvic fins below or in front of pectoral fin base .... ***APOGONIDAE*** (Cardinalfish)

9 (8) No lateral line 10

Lateral line present; teeth large; body long and cylindrical .... ***SPHYRAENIDAE*** (Barracuda)

Lateral line present; pectoral fin extremely broad; body apparently without scales .... ***COTTIDAE*** (Sculpin)

Table 4–1 *continued.* Simplified key to selected oceanic bony fish families. Subkeys D and E

10 (9)	Anal fin with about 17 soft rays	***ATHERINIDAE*** (Silverside)

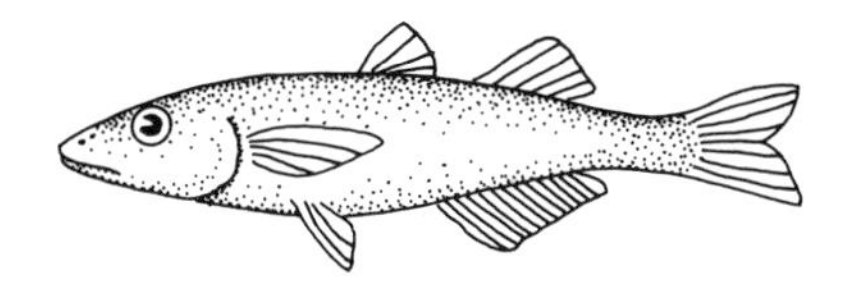

	Anal fin with about 10 soft rays	***MUGILIDAE*** (Mullet)

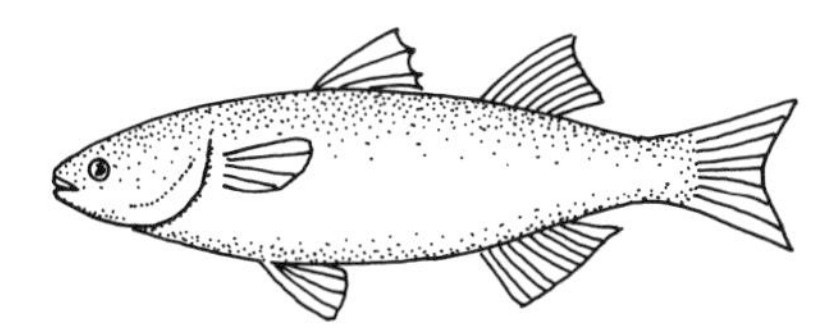

Subkey E

Dorsal fin single or incompletely divided into two lobes
Pelvic fins with five or fewer soft rays

1	Body scales present	2
	Body scales absent	***BLENNIIDAE*** (Blenny)

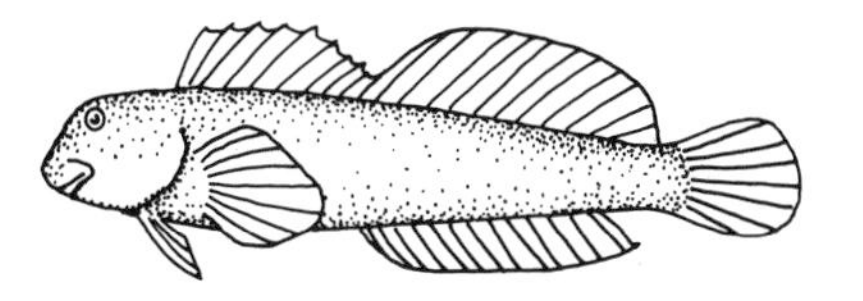

Table 4–1 *continued.* Simplified key to selected oceanic bony fish families. Subkey E

2	(1)	Gill openings reach under throat	3
		Gill openings not reaching throat (only on side of head); one or two pairs of spines on the caudal peduncle	***ACANTHURIDAE*** (Surgeonfish, tang)
		No spines on caudal peduncle; first few dorsal spines greatly elongated	***ZANCLIDAE*** (Moorish idol)
3	(2)	No spiny ridge running horizontally across cheek	4
		Spiny ridge running horizontally across cheek	***SCORPAENIDAE*** (Scorpionfish, lionfish, turkeyfish)
4	(3)	Branched caudal rays 14 or more	6
		Branched caudal rays 11 to 12	5

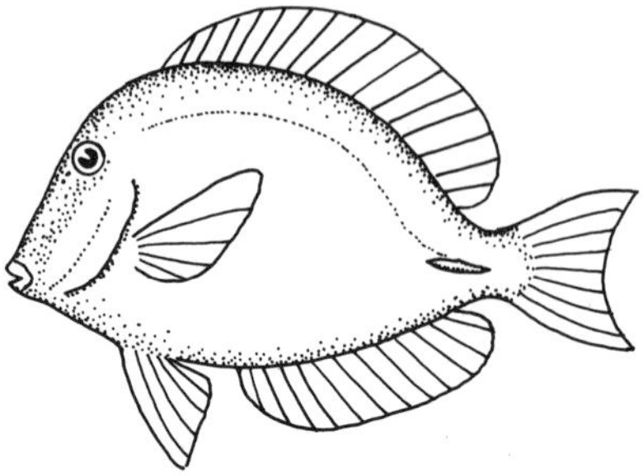

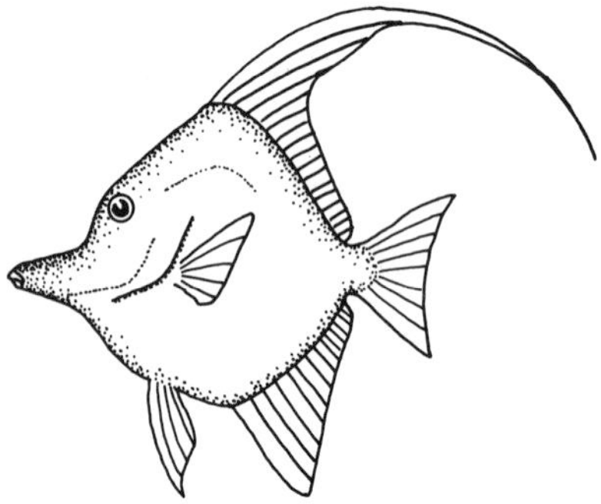

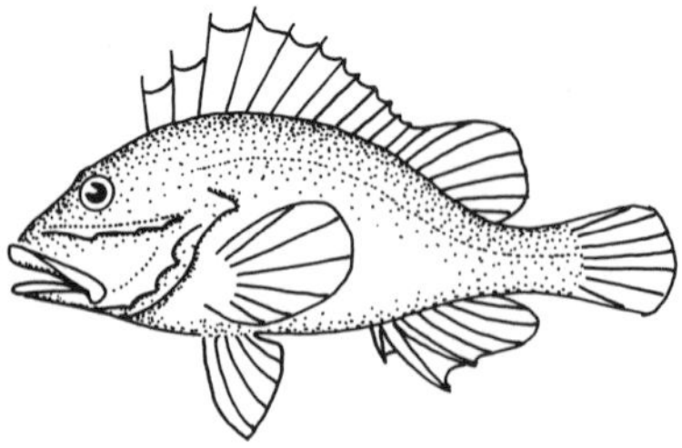

Table 4–1 *continued.* Simplified key to selected oceanic bony fish families. Subkey E

5	(4)	Two front teeth protruding and separated	***LABRIDAE*** (Wrasse)
		Teeth fused into beak or with two to several overlapping fused rows of front teeth	***SCARIDAE*** (Parrotfish)
6	(4)	Anal fin with 3 spines	7
		Anal fin with 2 spines	***POMACENTRIDAE*** (Damselfish)
7	(6)	Sides never plain or silvery	8
		Sides plain and silvery	***KUHLIIDAE*** (Flagtail)

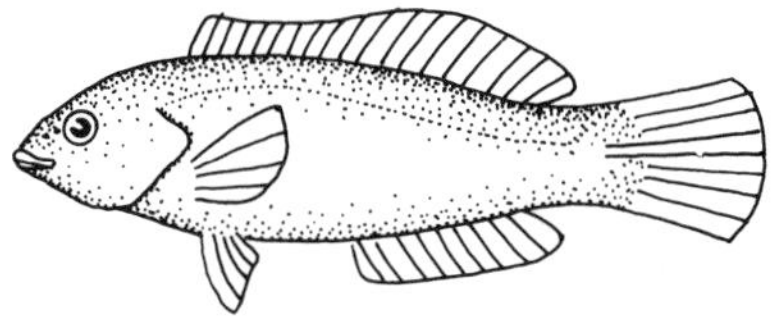

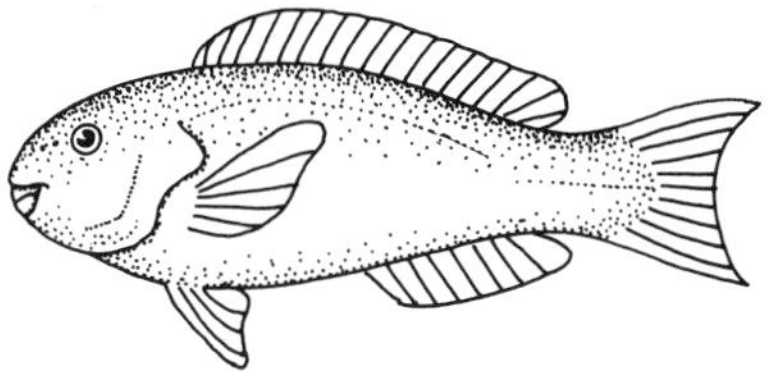

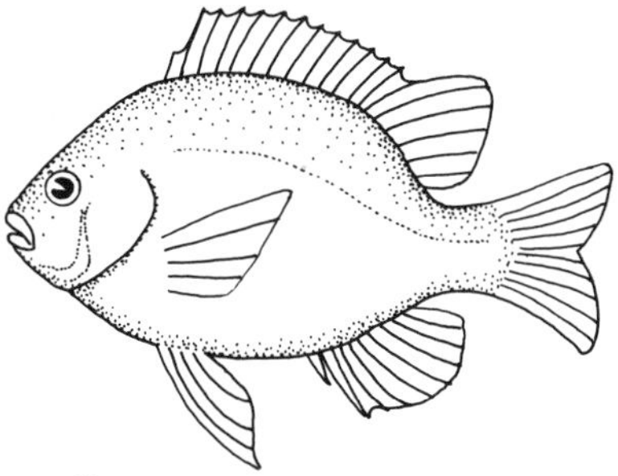

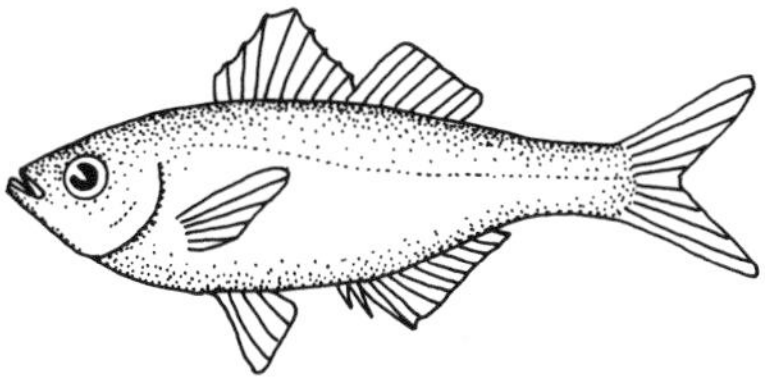

Table 4–1 *continued.* Simplified key to selected oceanic bony fish families. Subkey E

8	(7)	Mouth moderate to large; body depth no more than half the body length	9
		Mouth small; body about as deep as long; dorsal with 12 or more spines	***CHAETODONTIDAE*** (Butterflyfish)
		Dorsal with 11 spines	***SCORPIDIDAE*** (Convictfish)
9	(8)	Pelvic fin not attached to belly by a broad membrane	10
		Pelvic fin attached to belly by a broad membrane	***PRIACANTHIDAE*** (Bigeye)

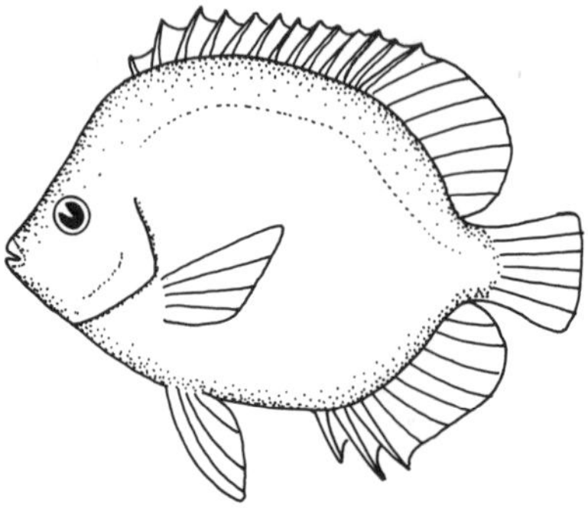

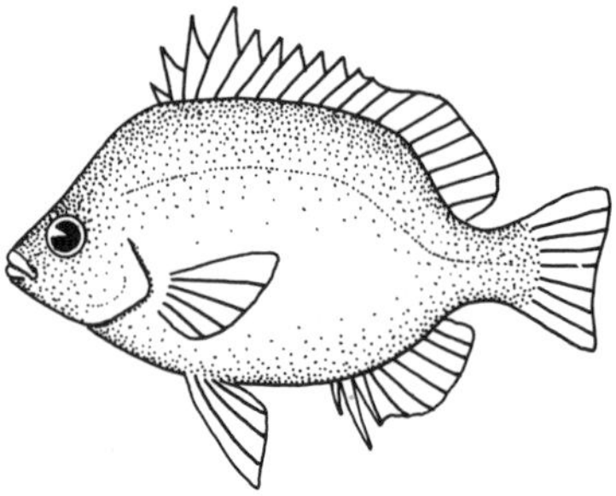

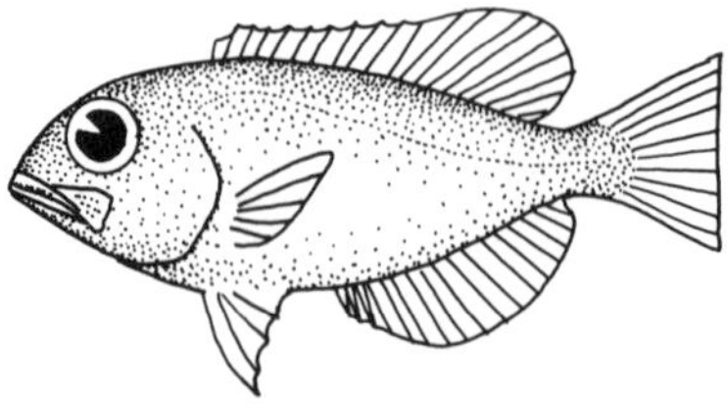

Table 4–1 *continued.* Simplified key to selected oceanic bony fish families. Subkey E

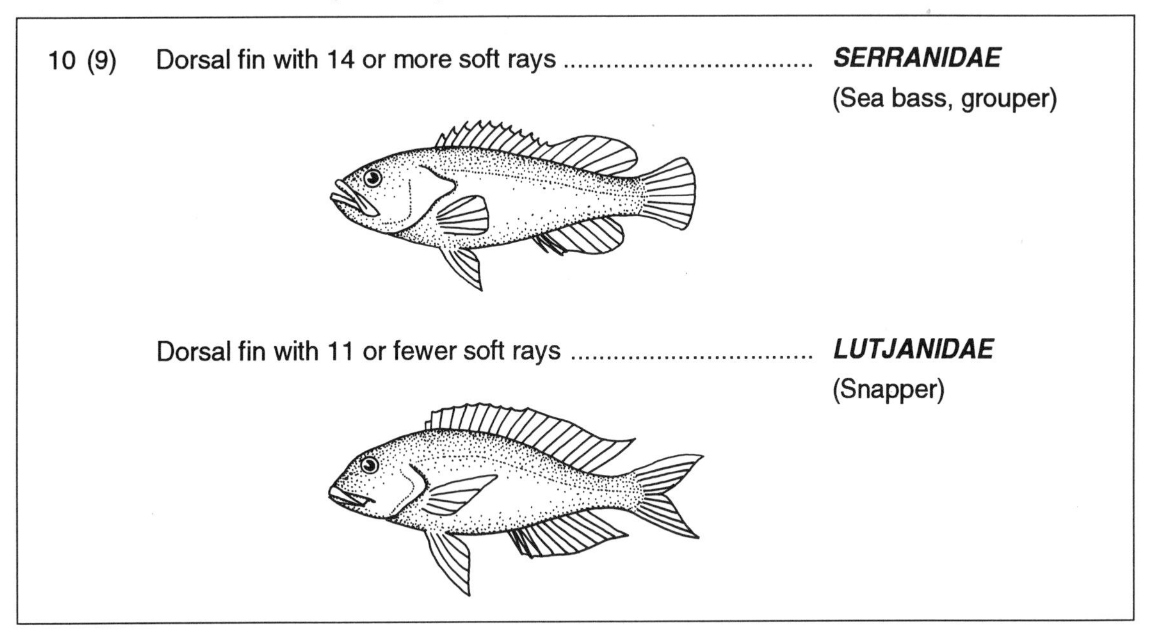

10 (9) Dorsal fin with 14 or more soft rays .... ***SERRANIDAE*** (Sea bass, grouper)

Dorsal fin with 11 or fewer soft rays .... ***LUTJANIDAE*** (Snapper)

Table 4–2. Family and common names of keyed fish Ⓦ

Family name	Common name

QUESTIONS

1. Using the bony fish family key, name a fish family
   a. with an adipose (fatty) fin behind the dorsal fin.
   b. without pectoral fins.
   c. with sharp spines over its body surface.
   d. with a medial caudal filament. (A **filament** is a flexible, threadlike structure.)
   e. with the upper jaw projecting as a tapering spear.
   f. with a tubular snout.
   g. with finlets.
   h. with a pair of long barbels on the chin. (The **barbel** is a soft, fleshy projection.)
2. How many families with more than five pelvic fin rays are included in the key?

3. In the key, how does
   a. a white eel differ from a moray eel?
   b. a triggerfish differ from a filefish?
   c. a wrasse differ from a parrotfish?

4. How many dorsal fins do the following have?
   a. mullet
   b. ladyfish
   c. butterflyfish
   d. triggerfish
   e. porcupinefish

5. Name fish families
   a. without caudal fins.
   b. with forked caudal fins.

6. The key to butterflyfish in Topic 3 is a dichotomous or two-choice key. How does Table 4–1, Simplified key to selected oceanic bony fish families, differ from a dichotomous key?

FURTHER INVESTIGATIONS

1. Get a key to fish in local waters. Use it to identify your fish to the species level. If you find no key, devise your own.

2. Using available keys, identify the fish sold in your local fishmarket. Ask where they come from and how they are caught and shipped to the market.

3. Using a dictionary of word roots, look up the meanings of the names of the families of bony fish listed in Table 4–1.

4. Some museums collect and classify species of organisms. What museums in your state serve these functions?

5. Fish Measurements and Counts of Structures

Researchers from your state's Division of Fish and Game and the National Marine Fisheries Service regularly survey fish populations to find how many fish and what species live in an area. They also try to find whether the area is being overfished and whether diseases or pollutants are harming fish populations. A scarcity of large, mature fish, for example, may indicate a short-term overfishing problem. A large number of underweight fish could warn of disease, a food shortage, or a long-term stress such as pollution. To make surveys, researchers must be able to identify fish species rapidly and to determine if individuals deviate from normal growth patterns.

A common way to classify fish and judge their health at the same time is to count and measure their external structures. Because males, females, and young of a species may be differently colored or patterned, scientists use features that are always present. They use information about variable features to judge the age and health of an organism. Data from several fish of the same species help them monitor the health and abundance of a whole population of that species.

In this activity you will count, measure, and compare the external structures of different fish species.

ACTIVITY

Count and measure some external structures of fish.
Construct fish polygraphs.
Compare polygraphs of fish of the same and different species.

MATERIALS

- large and small fish of several species
- newspapers or dissecting pan
- centimeter ruler
- dissecting microscope or hand lens
- copies of Workbook Table 5–2 and Fig. 5–3
- colored pencils
- centigram balance or spring scale

PROCEDURE

1. Use two fish of the same species but of different sizes.

2. Study Table 5–1 for a list of measurements. Make all the measurements shown in Table 5–1. Record them in Table 5–2.

3. Count the scales along the lateral lines of the two fish. Lateral line scales have **tubes** through them. The arrows in Fig. 5–1 show where to start and end the count. Record the information in Table 5–2.

Table 5–1. Fish measurements 

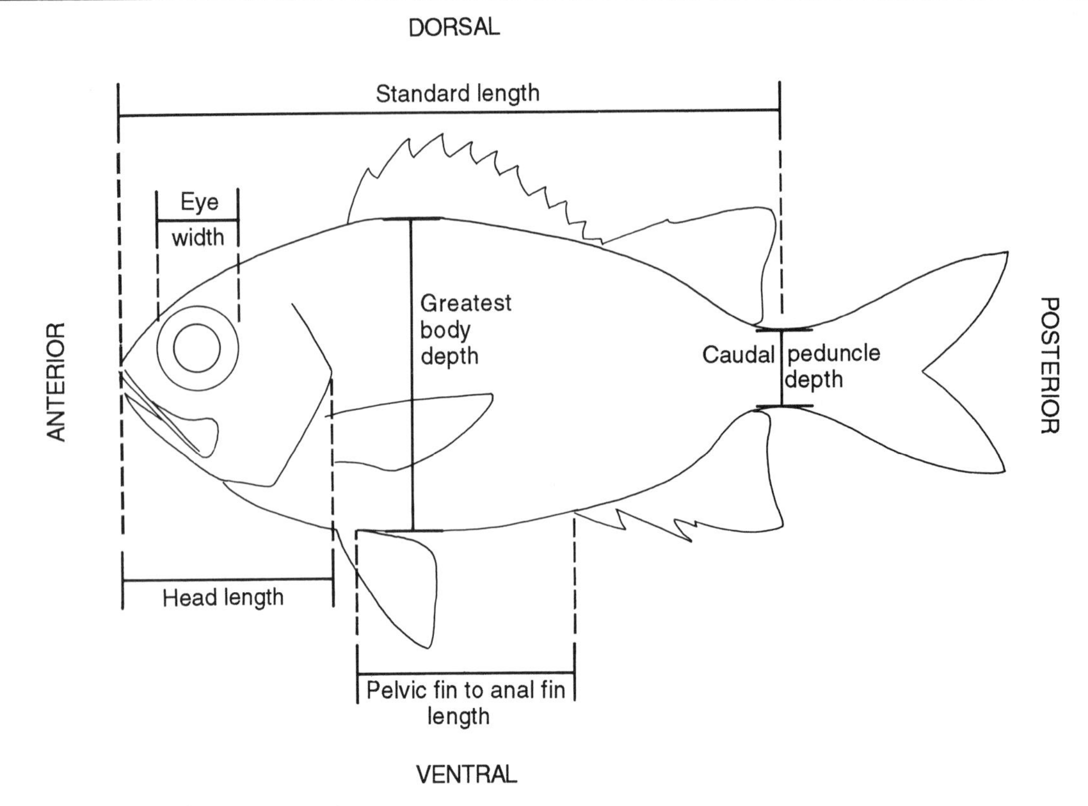

Length in centimeters; mass in grams

1. ***Standard length*** is the distance between the most anterior part of the head and the end of the vertebral column. (To find the end of the vertebral column, bend the caudal [tail] fin toward the head. A crease marks the end of the column.)
2. ***Head length*** is the distance from the most anterior part of the head to the farthest posterior edge of the gill cover.
3. ***Eye width*** is the distance from the anterior margin of the eye to its farthest posterior edge.
4. ***Greatest body depth*** is the widest vertical part of the body.
5. ***Caudal peduncle depth*** is the narrowest part of the caudal peduncle.
6. ***Pelvic fin to anal fin length*** is the distance along the body from the posterior base of the pelvic fin to the anterior base of the anal fin.
7. ***Total body mass*** is the mass of the entire fish to the nearest gram.
8. ***Lateral line scale count*** is the number of scales along the lateral line from its anterior origin behind the gill cover to its posterior end, usually the caudal peduncle. See Fig. 5–1.

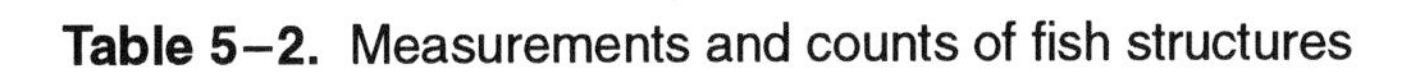

Table 5–2. Measurements and counts of fish structures

Measurement	Fish 1	Fish 2
1. Standard length (cm)		
2. Head length (cm)		
3. Eye width (cm)		
4. Greatest body depth (cm)		
5. Caudal peduncle depth (cm)		
6. Pelvic fin to anal fin length (cm)		
7. Total body mass (to nearest gram)		
8. Lateral line scale count		
9. Number of spines in first dorsal fin		
10. Number of soft rays in first dorsal fin		
11. Number of spines in second dorsal fin		
12. Number of soft rays in second dorsal fin		
13. Fin formula for dorsal fin(s)		

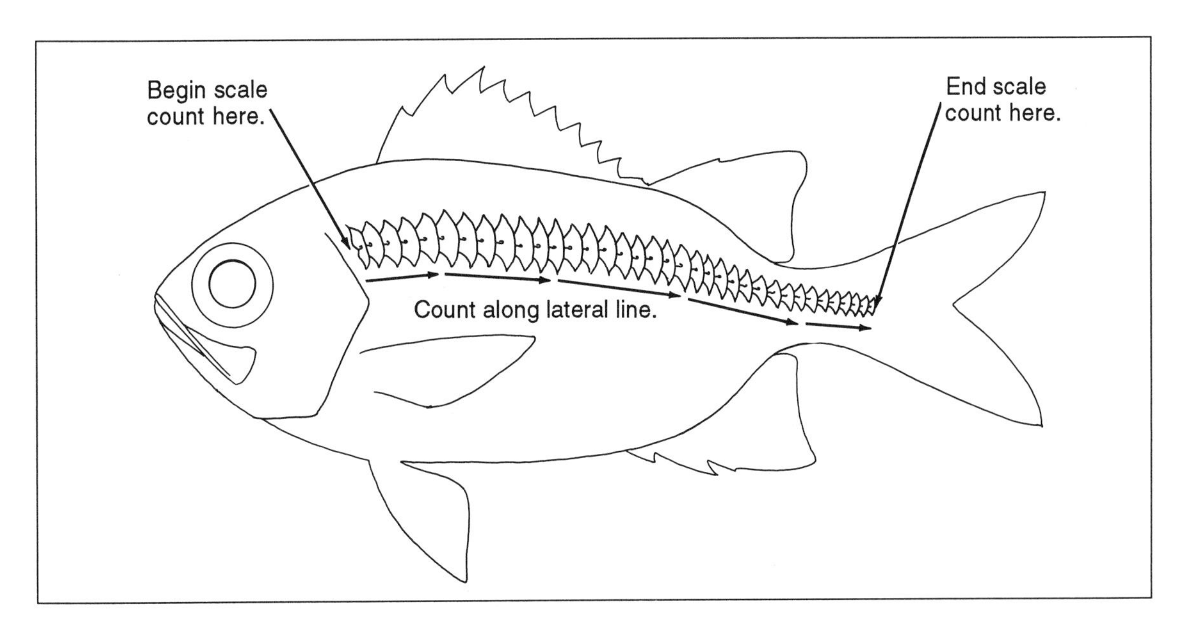

Fig. 5–1. Counting lateral line scales

4. Complete Table 5–2 by determining and recording the **fin formula** of each specimen. Look first at the examples in Fig. 5–2. Spines are indicated by roman numerals (I, IV, etc.); soft rays are indicated by arabic numbers (1, 2, 3, etc.). Count the bases of the rays, not the multiple tips.
   a. Using a dissecting microscope or a hand lens, examine your fish.
   b. Record the number of **spines** in the first dorsal fin. If this fin has soft rays, separate the spine count from the ray count with a comma (,). See (A) in Fig. 5–2.
   c. If the specimen has a second dorsal fin, record a dash (—) followed by the spine count (if any), then a comma (,) and the soft ray count (if any). See (B) and (C) in Fig. 5–2.

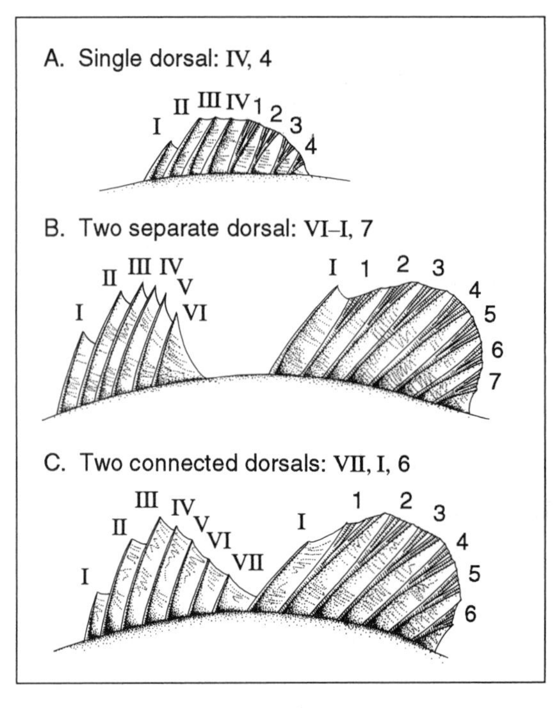

Fig. 5–2. Formulas for fin types

5. Plot the data from Table 5–2 on a polygraph. See Fig. 5–3. Use a different color for each fish.
   a. Start with the line for the standard length. On it make a large mark showing the length of the first fish. For example, if the fish is 35 cm long, make a mark on the line halfway between 30 and 40 cm. If the length is greater than 40 cm, extend the polygraph line beyond the circle.
   b. Plot the counts and measurements. Modify the scale units as necessary. For example, if your fish weighs more than 100 g, either extend the line beyond the circle or change the units on the scale.
   c. Use a ruler to connect adjacent marks with a straight line.
   d. In the color code box, record the name of each fish and lightly shade in its color code.

6. Compare your fish polygraphs with the polygraphs of other species constructed by other teams.

QUESTIONS

1. Refer to your team's data on different-sized fish of the same species.
   a. Decide which counts and measurements do not change as the fish grows. Why might they remain the same?

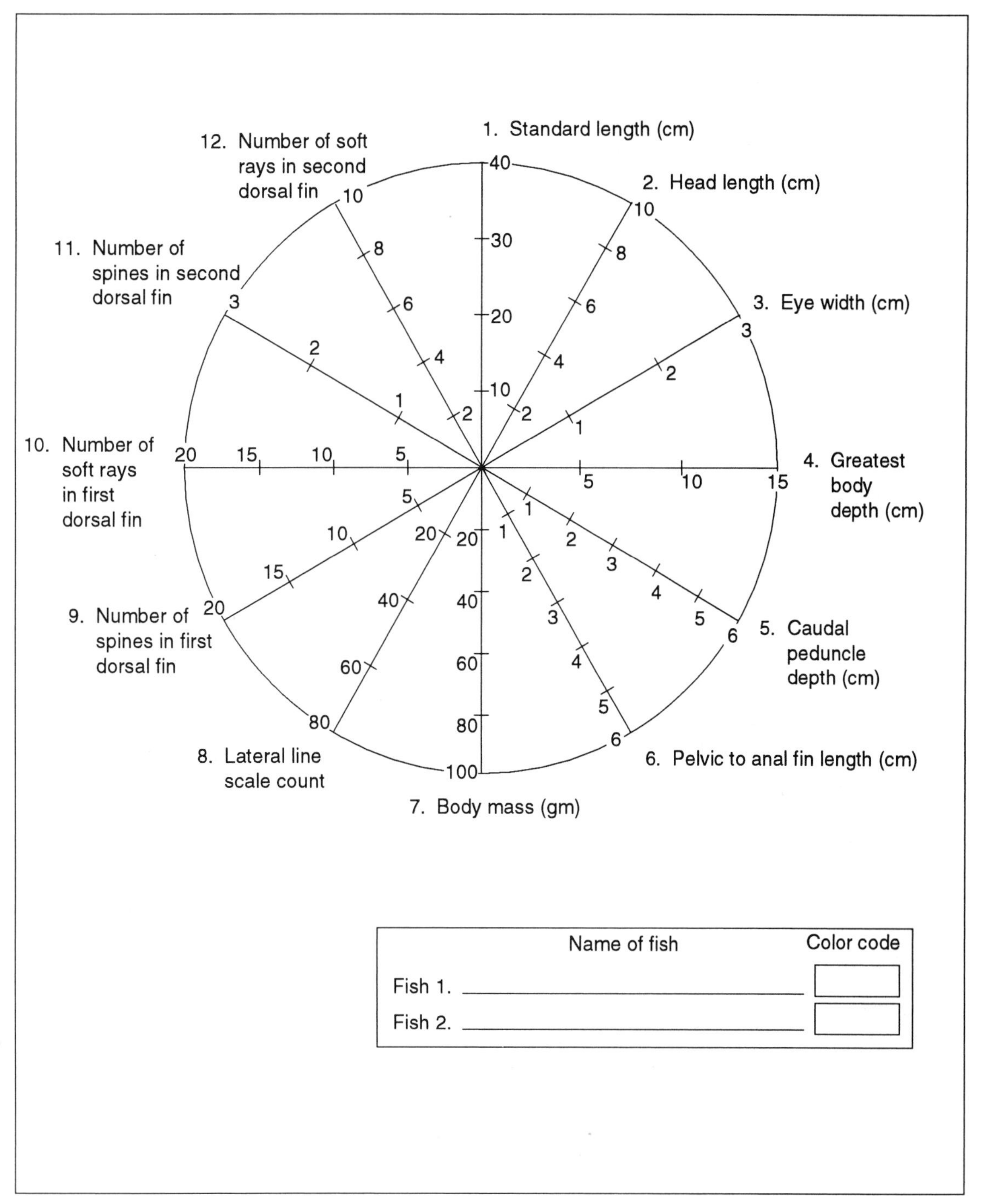

Fig. 5–3. Polygraph for comparing fish

Ⓦ

b. Decide which counts and measurements change as the fish grows. Why might they change?

2. Refer to polygraphs of different species. Where possible, compare fish of about the same length. Decide which counts and measurements could be used to tell the fish apart. What are they?

3. How does a polygraph help identify the differences between different but similar-sized species?

4. What counts or measurements might change if a fish were partially starved over the winter?

5. What counts or measurements might differ between a diseased fish and a healthy fish?

6. How is the fish polygraph like and unlike the fish key you used in Topic 4?

7. How might fish measurements be used to monitor populations of fish? Suggest how fish polygraphs could be used in fisheries management.

FURTHER INVESTIGATIONS

1. Visit local fishmarkets and tally the popular fish and fish species sold locally. Find out if the average size of any of the fish is becoming smaller each year.

2. Find out what local laws and regulations govern fishing. Which fish are seasonal? Which fish are protected? Report your findings to the class.

3. Invite a speaker from the Division of Fish and Game to explain the reasons for having closed fishing seasons on some local fish but not others.

4. What other methods do field biologists use to study fish in their natural environments (*in situ* research)? How do they estimate and monitor population size?

5. Learn more about national or international management of fisheries. What laws and technologies might be used to achieve sustainable yields? Investigate one type of fishery, such as cod, tuna, or anchovy.

6. Fish Form and Function

Fish have been swimming and reproducing in the waters of our planet for over 450 million years. During this time the body structures (external anatomy) of many fish groups have undergone changes that let them live better in some water environments than in others.

In this topic we examine how **body forms**—the shapes of parts—vary among fish. For example, we will examine the shape of the caudal fin on fast- and slow-moving fish. We will also investigate relationships between body form and **adapted functions**—how the parts are used. By observing the forms and functions of a fish's body parts, we can make some informed guesses about where it might live and how it might behave.

ACTIVITY

Compare the external anatomies of different species of fish.

From their external anatomy, predict behaviors of each fish.

MATERIALS

- 3 fish of different species
- newspapers or dissecting pan
- 3 copies of Workbook Table 6–1
- copy of Workbook Table 6–3
- dissecting microscope or hand lens (optional)

PROCEDURE

1. Obtain a fish.
   a. Identify its family by using the fish key in Table 4–1 in Topic 4.
   b. Record the family name in Table 6–1 on page 48.
2. Complete Table 6–1 by following these steps:
   a. Examine the fish closely. Use Table 6–2 to find and identify each of its external anatomical parts.
   b. Sketch each part or describe its shape in Table 6–1.
   c. Record the adapted function of each part from Table 6–2.
   d. If the features of your fish or its parts are not in Table 6–2, describe and sketch them. Try to guess what the adapted function is.
3. Predict the fish's behaviors and habitats. Record your predictions in Table 6–3.
4. Repeat Procedures 1 through 3 with two fish of other species. Record your data on separate copies of Table 6–1.

Table 6–1. Fish features and functions

Ⓦ

Fish number and name ______________________		
Sketch of feature	DESCRIPTION	Adapted function
A. BODY SHAPE AND COLOR		
1. BODY SHAPE		
2. COLOR OF BODY		
B. HEAD FEATURES		
1. MOUTH		
2. TEETH		
3. EYES		
C. FIN FEATURES		
1. TAIL		
2. DORSAL FIN		
3. PECTORAL FINS		
4. PELVIC FINS		
5. COMBINATION OF FINS		
D. SCALES AND OTHER ADAPTATIONS		
1. SCALES		
2. OTHER ADAPTATIONS		

Table 6–2. Fish forms and functions

SECTION A. BODY SHAPE AND COLOR. PART 1

1. BODY SHAPE Drawn example	DESCRIPTION	Adapted function
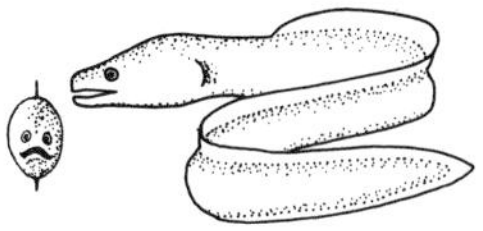	EEL SHAPE	Maneuvering in crevasses
	BULLET SHAPE	Lowering frictional resistance in fast swimmers
	BROAD, FLAT SHAPE	Lying on or below surface of sand
	TALL, THIN SHAPE	Entering vertical crevices
	VERTICALLY FLATTENED SHAPE	Bottom heavy for sitting on bottom, not casting a shadow
	PERCHLIKE SHAPE	General all-purpose shape
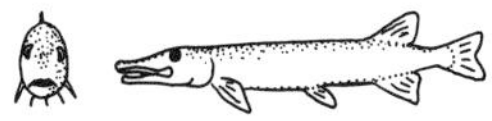	ELONGATED SHAPE	Ambush predators
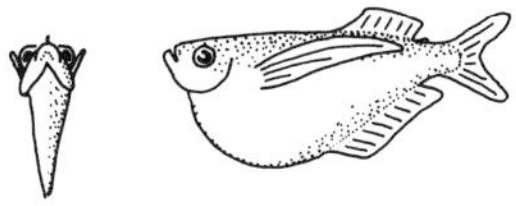	SURFACE–ORIENTED SHAPE	Feeding at water/air interface

Table 6–2 *continued*. Fish forms and functions

SECTION A. BODY SHAPE AND COLOR. PART 2

2. BODY COLOR Drawn example	DESCRIPTION	Adapted function
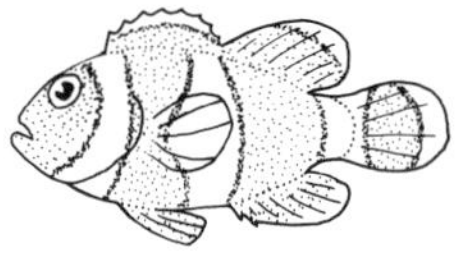	BOTH SEXES BRIGHTLY COLORED	A warning: not good to eat
	BRIGHTLY COLORED AREAS AROUND DEFENSIVE PARTS	Warning
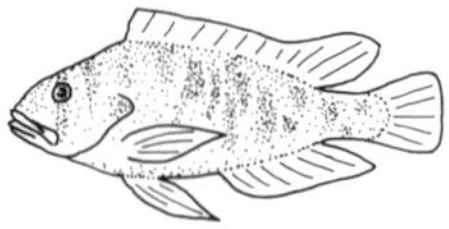	MOTTLED	Camouflage
	DARK ON TOP, LIGHTER ON BOTTOM	Camouflage in midwater
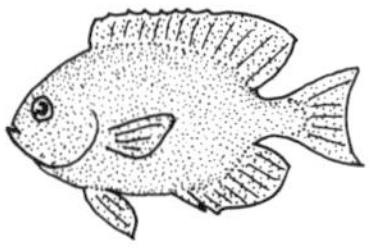	DARK ALL OVER	Camouflage in dark areas
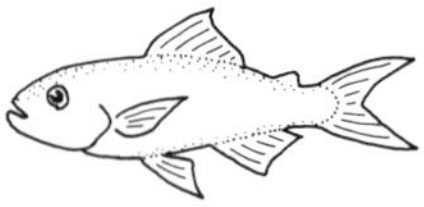	LIGHT ALL OVER	Camouflage in light areas
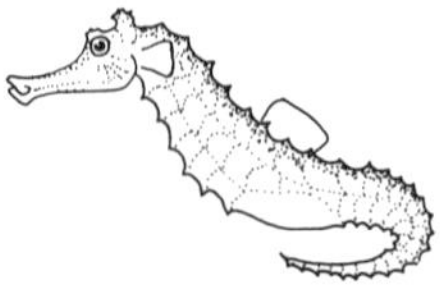	TRANSPARENT FINS	Concealing movement
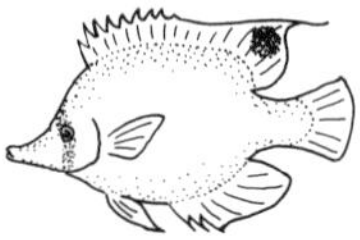	EYESPOT(S)	Leading predator away from head

Table 6–2 *continued.* Fish forms and functions

SECTION B. HEAD FEATURES. PART 1

1. MOUTH

Drawn example	DESCRIPTION	Adapted function
	TWEEZERLIKE SNOUT	Poking into crevices
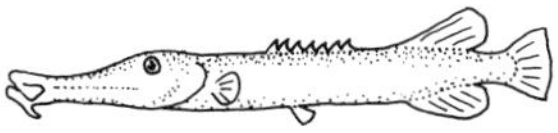	SUCTION TUBE	Slurping in prey
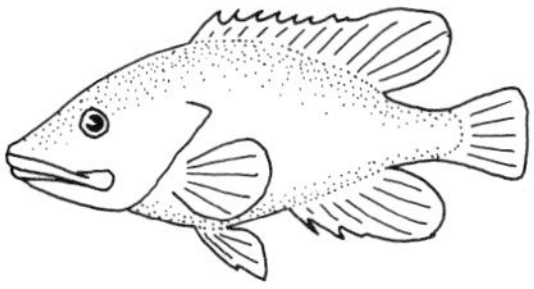	LARGE	Swallowing large prey
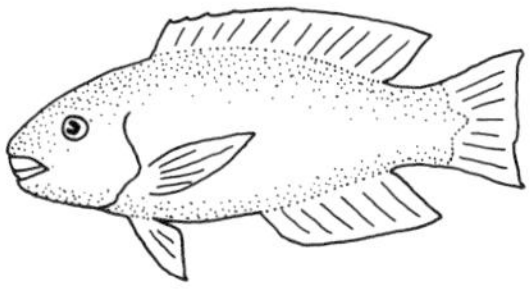	BEAKLIKE; NO DISTINCT TEETH	Biting hard objects
	TINY AND TURNED UP	Capturing plankton

Table 6–2 *continued.* Fish forms and functions

SECTION B. HEAD FEATURES. PART 2

1. TEETH Drawn example	DESCRIPTION	Adapted function
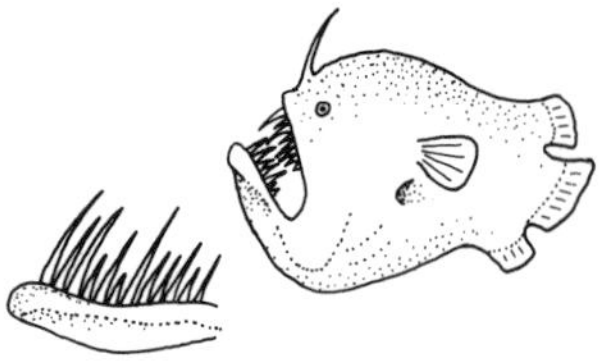	POINTED	Stabbing
	COMBLIKE	Scraping soft materials off rocks
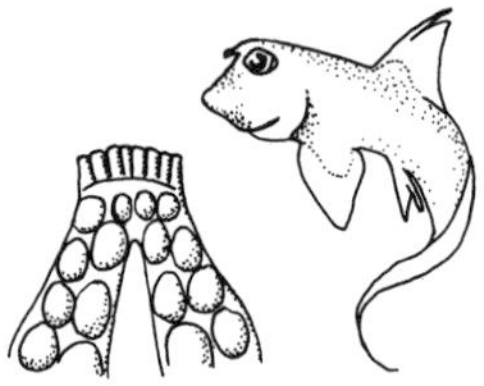	MOLARLIKE; HEAVY AND FLAT	Grinding
	FUSED LIKE A BEAK	Scraping hard materials off rocks
	INCISORLIKE	Cutting

Table 6–2 *continued.* Fish forms and functions

SECTION B. HEAD FEATURES. PART 3

3. EYES

Drawn example	DESCRIPTION	Adapted function
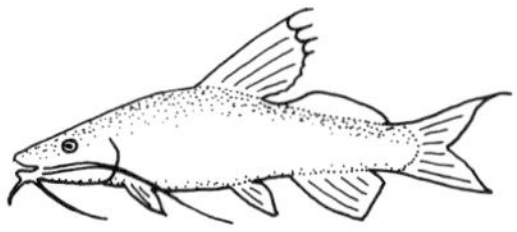	TINY EYES (HEAD LENGTH .6X EYE WIDTH)	Receiving high-intensity light
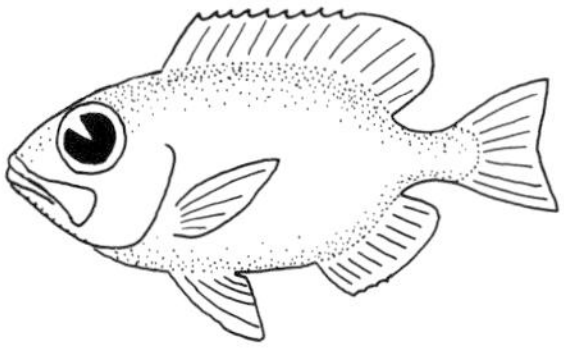	LARGE EYES (HEAD LENGTH 3X EYE WIDTH)	Receiving low-intensity light
	AVERAGE EYES (HEAD LENGTH 3–5X EYE WIDTH)	Receiving normal-intensity light
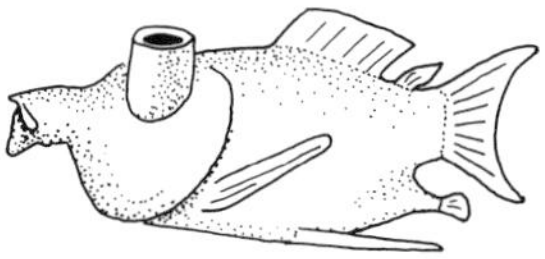	TUBULAR EYES IN DEEP–WATER FISH	Receiving low light from above

Table 6–2 *continued.* Fish forms and functions

SECTION C. FIN FEATURES. PART 1

1. TAIL (CAUDAL FIN AND CAUDAL PEDUNCLE)

Drawn example	DESCRIPTION	Adapted function
	ROUNDED TAIL	Slow swimming, accelerating, and maneuvering
	TRUNCATED (TRIANGU–LAR) TAIL	Turning quickly
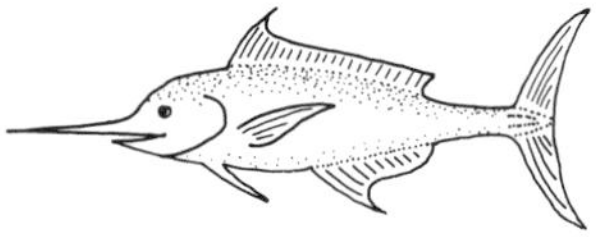	LUNATE (MOON–SHAPED) TAIL	Continuous long-distance swimming
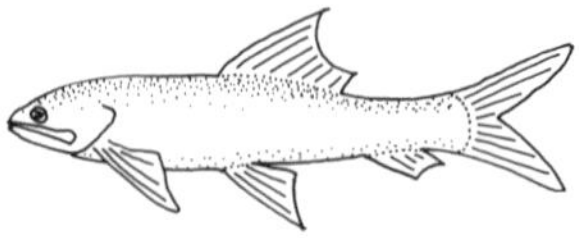	FORKED TAIL	Rapid swimming in bursts of speed

Table 6–2 *continued.* Fish forms and functions

SECTION C. FIN FEATURES. PARTS 2

2. DORSAL FIN Drawn example	DESCRIPTION	Adapted function
	SPINY AND SOFT–RAYED DORSAL FIN	Flared to make the fish look bigger
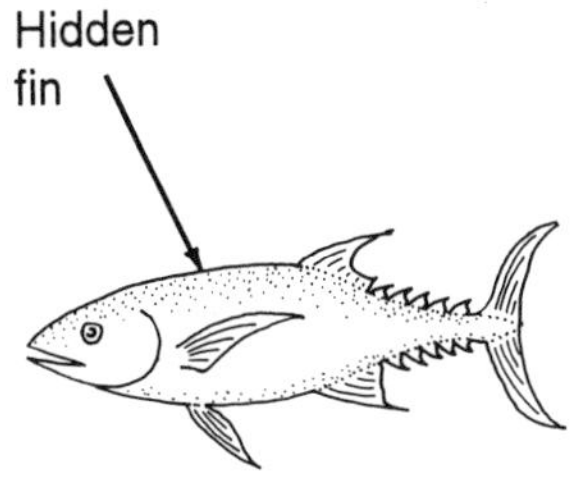 Hidden fin	TUCKED–IN DORSAL FIN	Reducing drag in fast swimmers
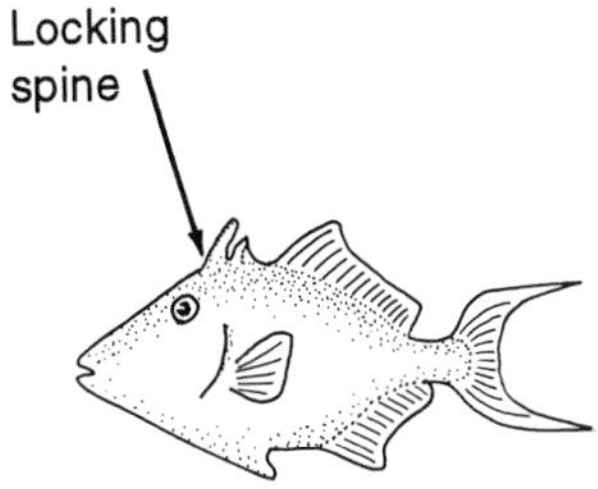 Locking spine	LOCKING SPINY DORSAL FIN	Locking itself into coral crevices
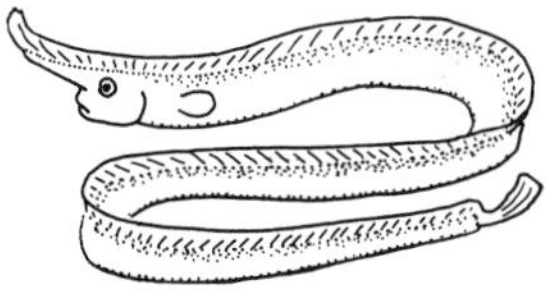	VERY LONG DORSAL FIN	Snakelike locomotion

Table 6–2 *continued.* Fish forms and functions

SECTION C. FIN FEATURES. PART 3

3. PECTORAL FIN Drawn example	DESCRIPTION	Adapted function
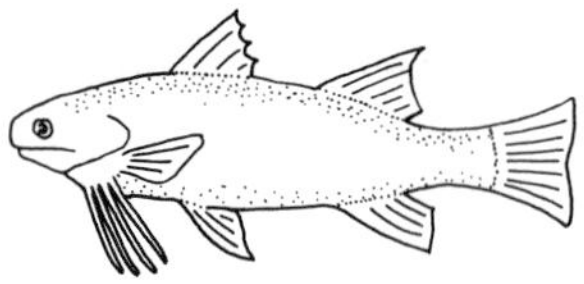	FRINGELIKE PECTORAL FINS	Probing substrate
	SPINY PECTORAL FINS	Propping on substrate
	HANDLIKE PECTORAL FINS	Crawling on substrate
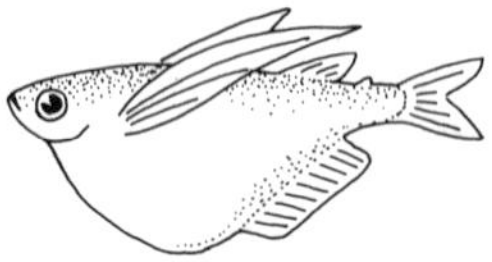	WINGLIKE PECTORAL FINS	Soaring and swimming

Table 6–2 *continued.* Fish forms and functions

SECTION C. FIN FEATURES. PARTS 4 & 5

4. PELVIC FINS Drawn example	DESCRIPTION	Adapted function
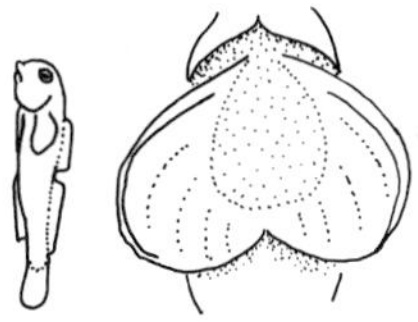	SUCKERLIKE PELVIC FINS	Grabbing rocks by suction
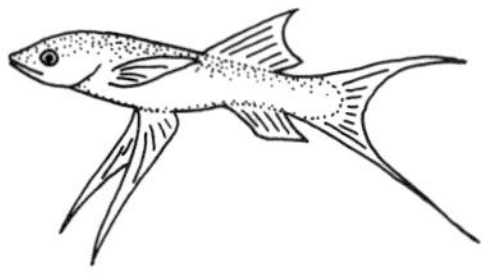	THICKENED RAYS ON PELVIC FINS	Sitting on substrate

5. COMBINATIONS OF FINS Drawn example	DESCRIPTION	Adapted function
	DORSAL AND ANAL FINS	Propulsion (Most other fish use their tails.)
	PECTORAL AND TAIL FINS	Soaring in air

Table 6–2 *continued.* Fish forms and functions

SECTION D. SCALES AND OTHER ADAPTATIONS. PART 1

1. SCALES

Drawn example	DESCRIPTION	Adapted function
	SPINES	Protection from predators
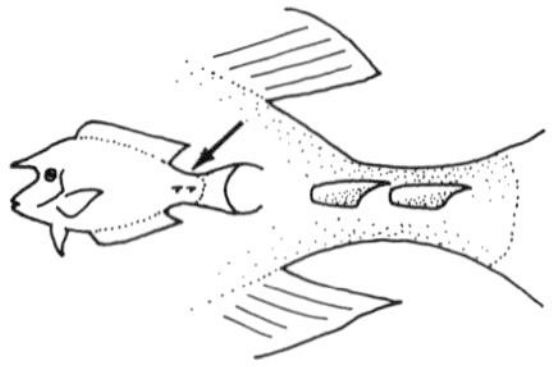	BLADES	Protection and defense
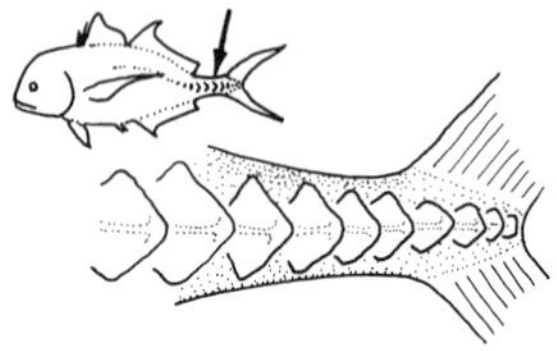	SCUTES (OR KEEL; NOT SHOWN)	Cuts through water, streamlines swimming
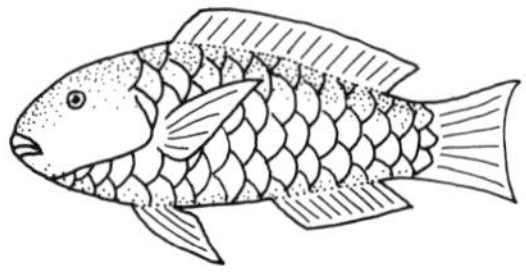	MANY LARGE SCALES	Body protection
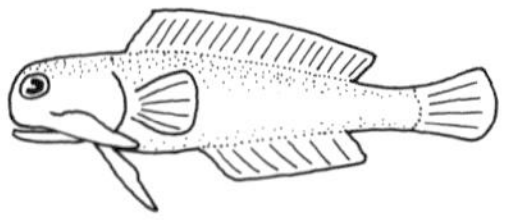	NO SCALES	Burrowing
	LEATHERY SCALES	Protection

Table 6–2 *continued.* Fish forms and functions

SECTION D. SCALES AND OTHER ADAPTATIONS. PARTS 1 7 2

1. SCALES *continued*

Drawn example	DESCRIPTION	Adapted function
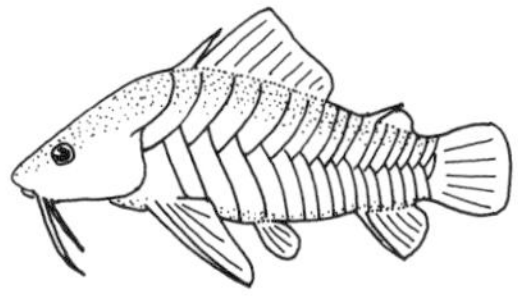	BONY ARMOR SCUTES	Protection from predators
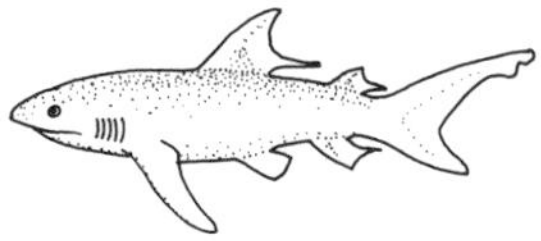	ROUGH SCALES	Protection from parasites

2. OTHER ADAPTATIONS

Drawn example	DESCRIPTION	Adapted function
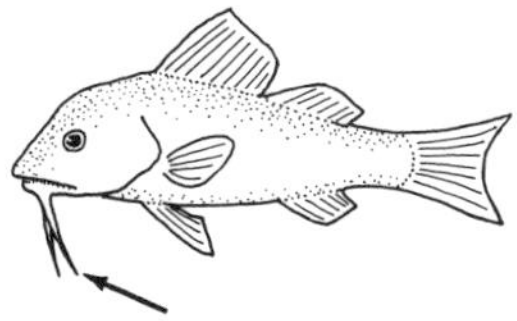	BARBELS	Probing for food in sand
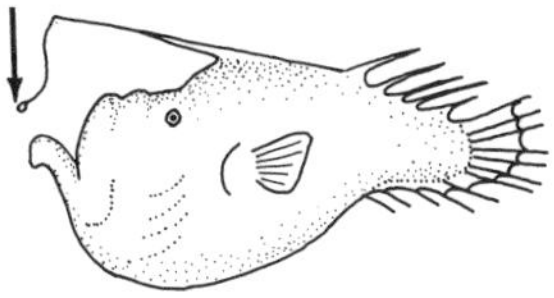	LURES	Attracting prey

Table 6–2 *continued.* Fish forms and functions

SECTION D. SCALES AND OTHER ADAPTATIONS. PARTS 1 & 2

2. OTHER ADAPTATIONS *continued* Drawn example	DESCRIPTION	Adapted function
	POISON SACS AT BASE OF SPINES	Protection
	TUBULAR NOSTRILS	Detecting small amounts of chemicals

Table 6–3. Behaviors and habitats predicted from anatomical forms

Predictions	Fish specimens (identified to family)		
	Fish 1 ________	Fish 2 ________	Fish 3 ________
Food eaten (algae, soft animals, large animals, coral, etc.)			
Swimming ability (fast/slow, short lunges, moderate distances, long distances)			
Method(s) of defense			
Most developed methods of sensing the world around it (sight, smell, touch, etc.)			
Probable habitat (where it lives under water: in holes, on sand, etc.)			

QUESTIONS

1. From Table 6 – 2, tell what structures and shapes might be best for
   a. **nocturnal** fish: ones active at night.
   b. **diurnal** fish: ones active during the day.
   c. **herbivorous** fish: ones that eat seaweeds or phytoplankton.
   d. **carnivorous** fish: ones that eat other animals.

2. Sketch or describe an ideal form for each kind of fish listed below. Include mouth, teeth, body shape, fin structures and shapes, and coloration—especially for camouflage.
   a. Fish 1: continuous swimming in open water
   b. Fish 2: hiding in seaweed to ambush small prey
   c. Fish 3: living among branches of coral
   d. Fish 4: finding food in or on open, flat sandy bottoms

3. What would be likely sources of food for each fish you drew or described?

FURTHER INVESTIGATIONS

1. Visit an aquarium during feeding time and make the following observations:
   a. Observe how the following fish use body parts for locomotion:
      1) jack
      2) triggerfish
      3) scorpionfish
      4) eel
      5) wrasse
      6) pufferfish
      7) butterflyfish
   b. Find and name at least one fish that usually
      1) rests on its pectoral fins.
      2) hangs in the water.
      3) swims continuously.
      4) lives in holes.
      5) "hops" along the substrate.
   c. Observe and describe the different ways that fish feed.
   d. Find out which fish are
      1) nocturnal (active at night).
      2) diurnal (active during the day).
      3) crepuscular (active in the morning and in the evening).

7. Anatomy and Function of Organ Systems in Fish

All living things are composed of one or more **cells.** See (A) in Fig. 7–1. Cells often become specialized to perform certain functions. For example, muscle cells contract, nerve cells transmit impulses, and gland cells produce and secrete chemicals.

A **tissue** is a group of similar cells performing a similar function. See (B) in Fig. 7–1. Muscle tissue, for example, is made of many muscle cells that contract. Groups of nerve cells form nervous tissue, which transmits information throughout the body.

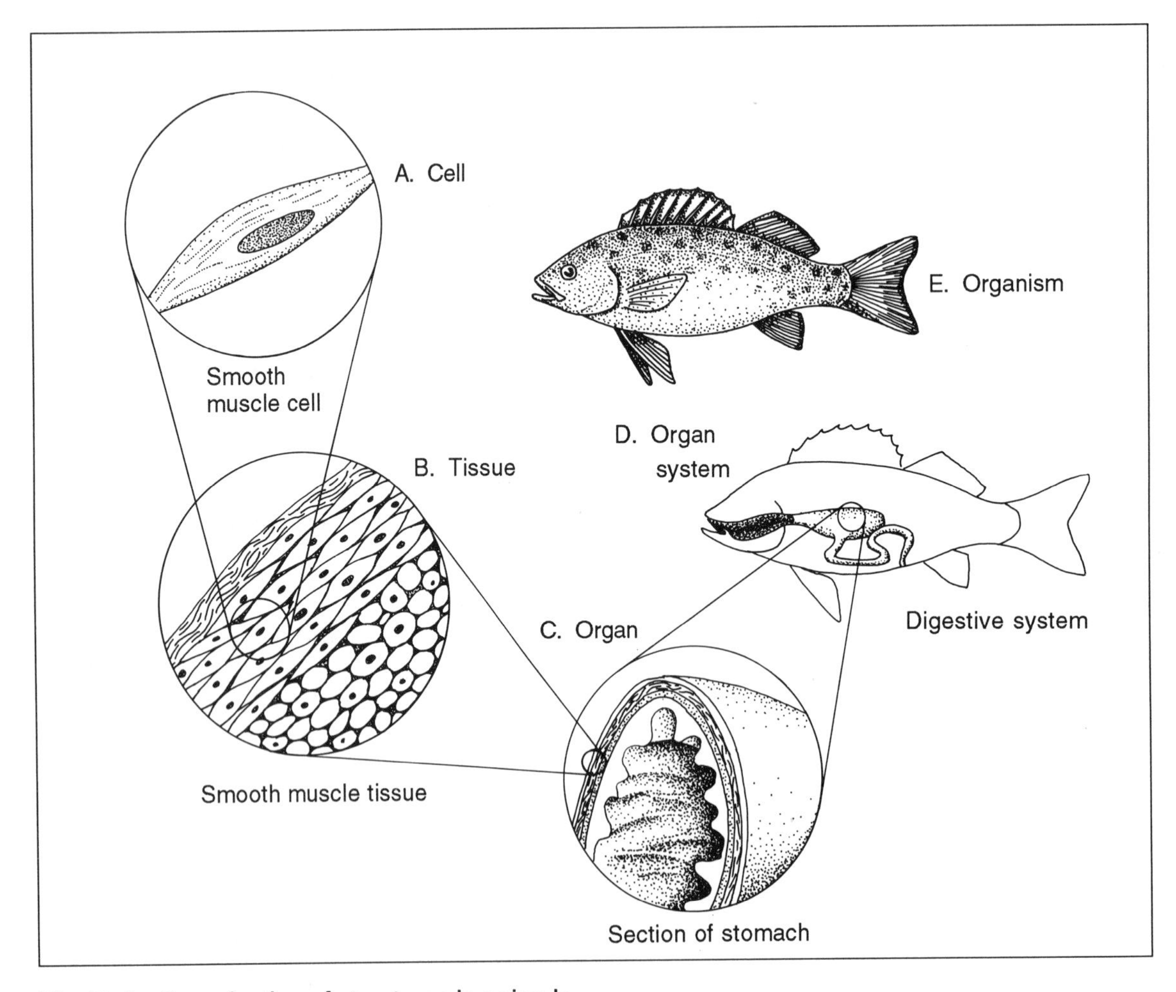

Fig. 7–1. Organization of structures in animals

Glandular tissue consists of gland cells that produce and secrete chemicals. There are many other kinds of tissues—bone, cartilage, blood, fat, tendon, skin, and scales.

An **organ** is a group of different kinds of tissues working together to perform a specific function. See (C) in Fig. 7–1. The stomach is an example of an organ made of several types of tissues. Muscle tissue in the wall of the stomach contracts to churn and mix food. Glandular tissue, the inner lining of the stomach, secretes digestive chemicals (enzymes). Nerve tissue in the wall of the stomach coordinates the mixing and digesting activities.

An **organ system** is a group of organs that together perform a function for the body. See (D) in Fig. 7–1. The digestive system, for example, consists of organs such as the mouth, the stomach, and the intestine.

An **organism** is an entire living thing with all its organ systems. See (E) in Fig. 7–1. A complex organism like a fish has digestive, nervous, sensory, reproductive, and many other systems.

Like humans, fish consist of interacting groups of organ systems that together enable a fish to function. We will investigate the 10 systems listed in Table 7–1 with their major parts and functions.

Table 7–1. Body systems

System	Body parts	General functions
1. Integumentary (outer covering)	Epidermis, dermis, scales, mucus cells, pigment cells	Protection, coloration
2. Skeletal	Skull, vertebrae, ribs, fin supports, spines, rays	Support, locomotion
3. Muscular	Tendons, skeletal muscle, heart muscle, smooth muscle	Movement, locomotion
4. Digestive	Mouth, teeth, tongue, stomach, intestine, anus, digestive glands	Food processing
5. Respiratory	Gill filaments, gill cover (operculum), gas bladder	Oxygen and carbon dioxide exchange
6. Circulatory	Heart, arteries, capillaries, veins, lymphatic ducts, blood	Body fluid transport
7. Excretory	Kidney, bladder, urinary duct	Waste removal from blood
8. Reproductive	Ovaries, testes, genital duct	Continuance of the species
9. Nervous	Brain, spinal cord, nerves, eyes, balancing mechanism, pressure receptors, nostrils, taste receptors, ears	Sensing, coordination, and response
10. Endocrine	Hormone-producing glands	Chemical regulation

ACTIVITY

Investigate the body systems of a fish.

MATERIALS

- copies of workbook tables assigned to your team

PROCEDURE

1. Your teacher will divide the class into teams and assign one body system for each team to investigate. Get your team assignment.

2. Work with your team members to
   a. read the information on the system assigned to you.
   b. prepare answers to questions about that system.
   c. present the information to the class and help others complete the table.

3. Listen as other teams present information on the other body systems of fish. Record data in the specified tables and write answers to all the questions with each table.

1. Integumentary System

The integumentary system is commonly called the skin. It consists of two layers, the epidermis or outer layer, and the dermis or inner layer. See Fig. 7–2. Beneath these are the muscles and other tissues that the skin covers.

A. The **epidermis** is made of several sheets of cells that cover the scales. As the cells age, new cells growing underneath push older cells toward the outer surface. Old surface cells constantly rub off. Young inner cells constantly divide, producing new cells that replace old outer cells.

   In the epidermis of most fish are cells that produce **mucus**, a slippery material, like runny gelatin, that helps the fish slide through the water. The mucus constantly wears off, carrying away microscopic organisms and other irritants that might harm the fish. (The odor typical of most fish comes from chemicals in the mucus.)

   In their epidermis, fish have cells containing **pigment grains** that give fish their color. Some fish can change color by expanding or contracting pigment cells. The changes are controlled by hormones produced by the endocrine system and regulated by the nervous system.

B. The **dermis** contains blood vessels, nerves for sensing touch and vibration, and connective tissue made of strong fibers.

   A special layer of dermal cells constantly secretes chemicals to produce scales, which grow larger as the fish grows. As the scales grow, they form concentric rings. In some fish these growth rings can be used to determine the fish's age.

   Most fish have covering scales that protect them from damage when they bump into things or are attacked. A few fish, such as catfish, have no scales.

QUESTIONS

1. What are the parts of the integumentary system and their functions? Fill in Table 7–2 with information from this reading.

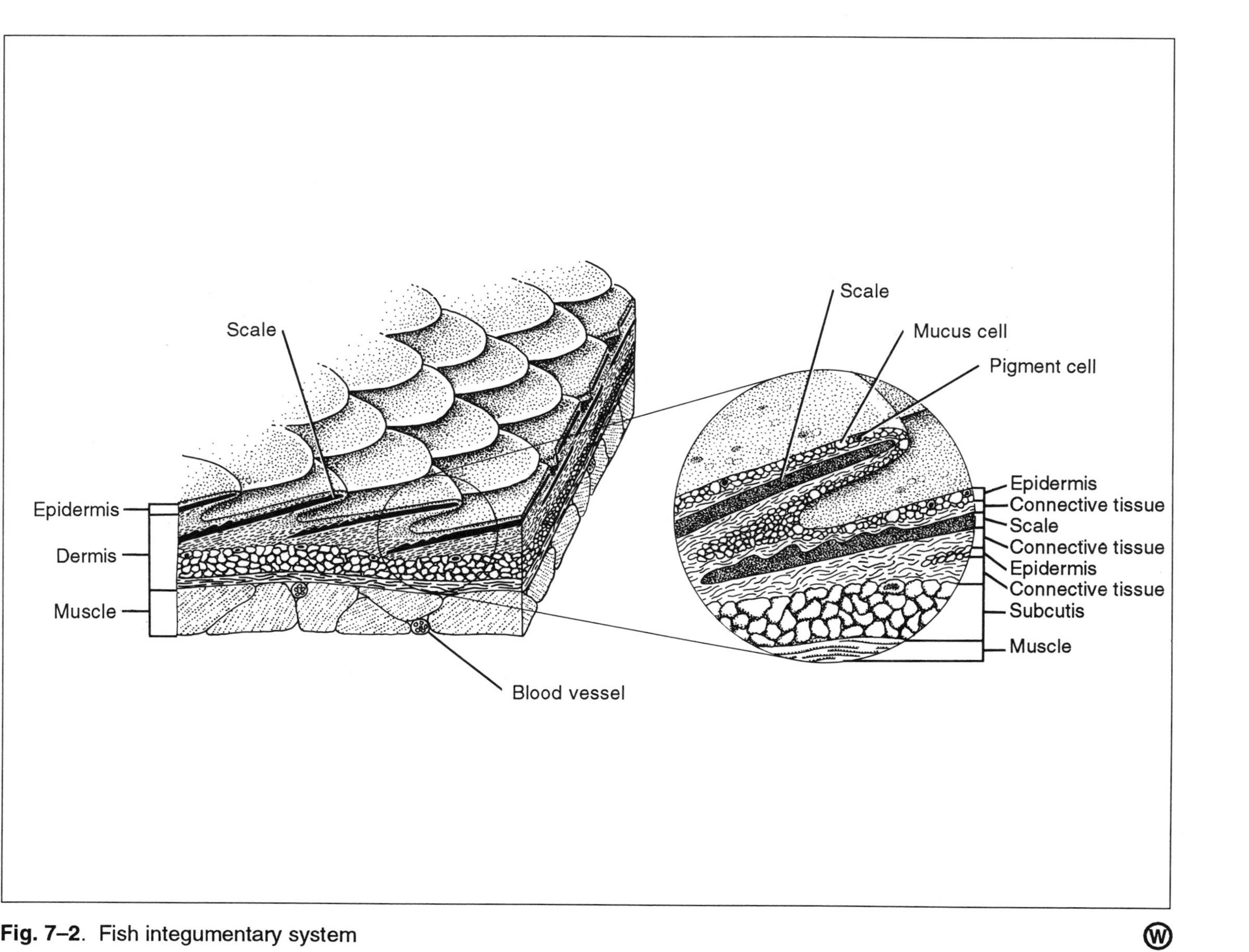

Fig. 7–2. Fish integumentary system

Ⓦ

2. How does the integumentary system of a fish respond to aging and to wear and tear from its environment?

3. How is the epidermis of fish like the skin of humans? How is it different?

4. What other animals besides fish have scales? Are there any fish that do not produce scales? If so, give examples.

5. Why is the integumentary system essential to fish?

Table 7–2. Parts of the integumentary system and their functions Ⓦ

General function of the integumentary system	Integumentary parts	Part functions

2. Skeletal System

The skeletal system supports the soft tissues and organs of the fish. See Fig. 7–3. The skeleton also protects organs and gives the body of the fish its basic shape. The many bones of the skull form a rigid box that protects the brain. Holes, hinges, and pockets in the skull allow room for the nostrils, mouth, and eyes. Muscles make some bones act as levers to move the body. Rib bones protect the body cavity. Bones also support fish spines and rays.

The **vertebral column**, or backbone, is not a solid rod but a string of small bones called **vertebrae.** See Fig. 7–4. Each vertebra has a small hole in it, forming a canal through which the spinal cord passes. The bone around the holes protects the spinal cord. Spaces between the vertebrae allow the nerves to reach the tissues and organs of the body.

QUESTIONS

6. What are the parts of the skeletal system and their functions? See Table 7–1. Write your answers in Table 7–3.

7. What bones of a fish skeleton correspond to those of a human skeleton?

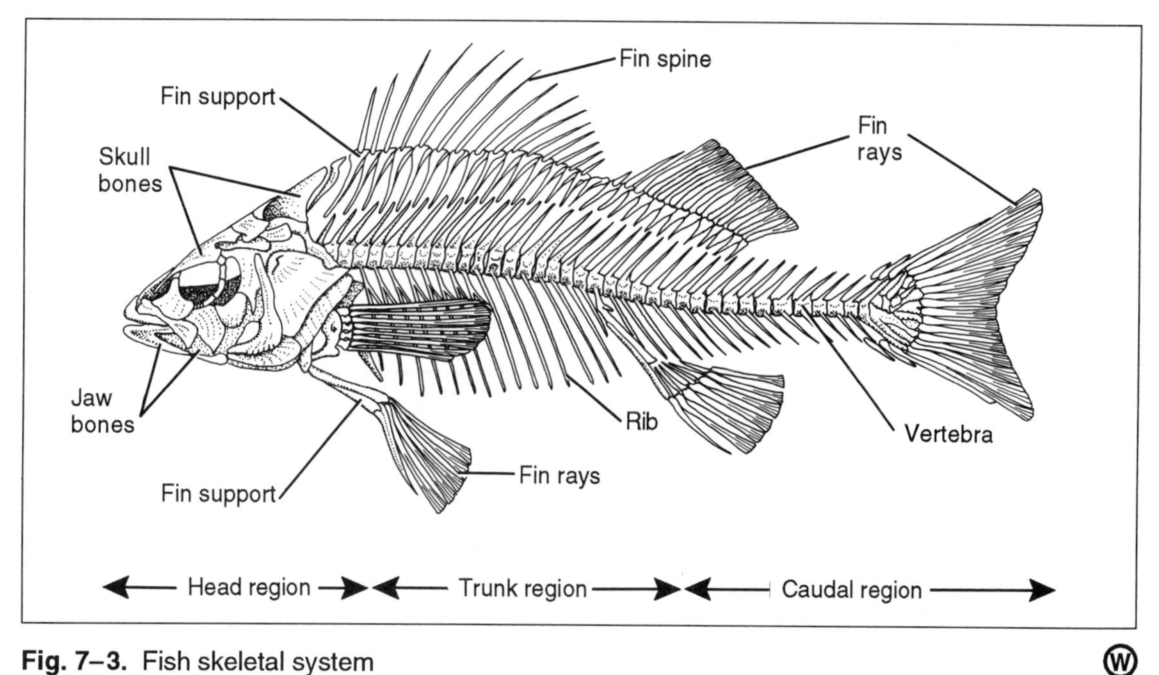

Fig. 7–3. Fish skeletal system

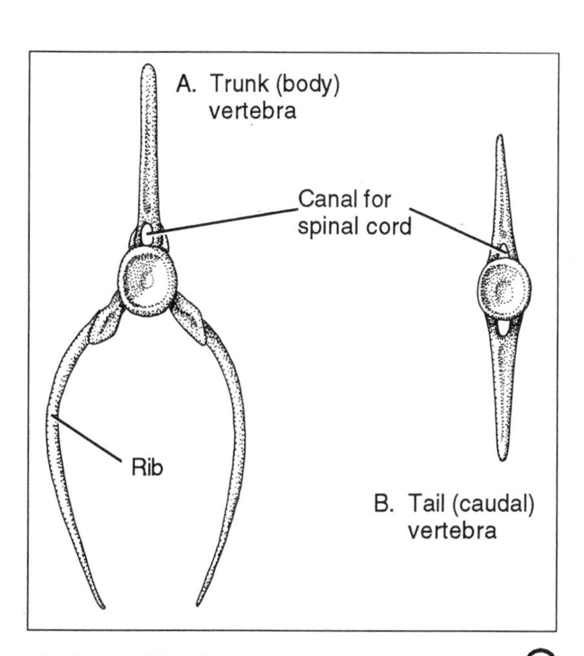

Fig. 7–4. Fish skeleton vertebrae viewed from the front

8. What parts of a fish skeleton are lacking in a human skeleton?

9. What kinds of changes in the skeleton would enable a fish to walk on land?

10. Joints are junctions between bones.
    a. Which joints on the fish skeleton are rigid? Suggest an advantage for their rigidity.
    b. Which joints on the fish skeleton are flexible? Suggest an advantage for their flexibility.

11. Which parts of the skeleton are not attached to the skull and vertebral column? How might unattached parts be held in place in a living organism?

Table 7–3. Bones and functions of the skeletal system Ⓦ

General functions of the skeletal system	Skeletal parts	Part functions

3. Muscular System

Muscles are tissues that can contract to shorten, then relax to lengthen. Fish move by contracting and relaxing their muscles. Like humans, fish have three types of muscles; skeletal muscles, smooth muscles, and heart muscles.

A. **Skeletal muscles** move the skeleton. They are composed of bundles of cells. When the cells are stimulated by nerves,

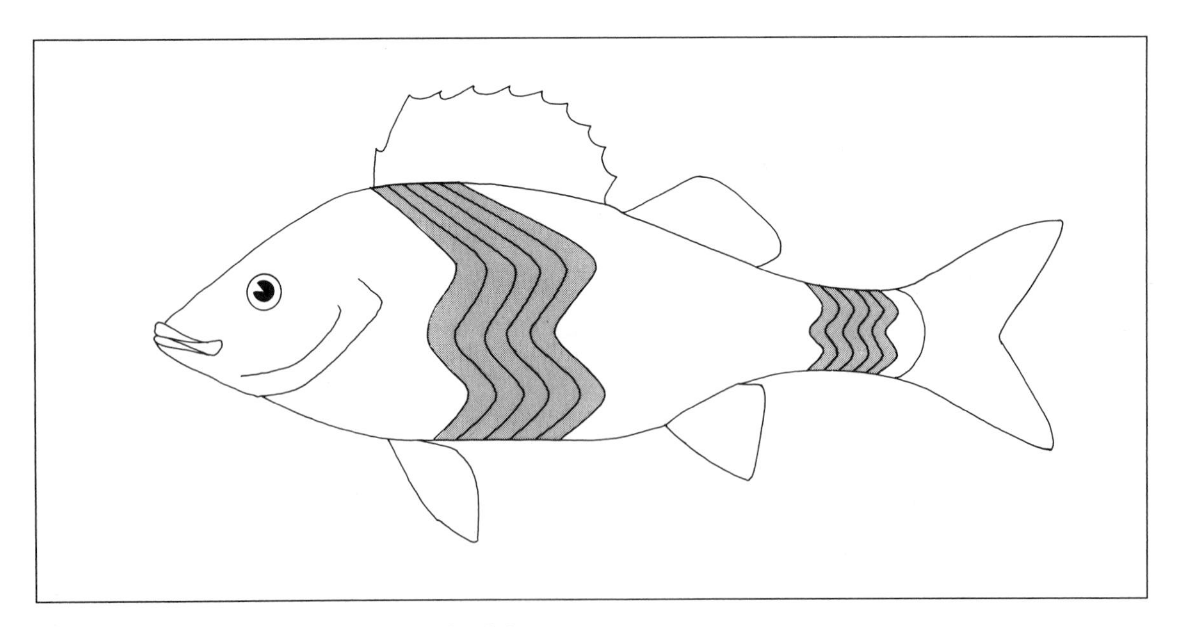

Fig. 7–5. Skeletal muscle pattern of a fish

they contract. When just a few cells are stimulated, the muscle shortens slightly. When more cells are stimulated, the muscle shortens more. Muscles are attached to bones by strong connective tissues called **tendons.** When muscles shorten, the pull on tendons moves bones.

Because skeletal muscles appear under a microscope as small cross-bands or striations, they are also called **striated muscles.** Skeletal muscles are **voluntary;** that is, they move only when the thinking part of the brain signals them to move. To swim, animals must learn to contract and relax their skeletal muscles, just as humans do when they learn to walk. Most of the body of the fish from the head to the tail is composed of layers of skeletal muscle. See Fig. 7–5. These layers are arranged in W-shaped bands attached to the skeleton and the skin. This interlocking network of muscles allows the fish to move the body back and forth in a smooth, undulating motion. Such motion would not be possible if the muscles ran along the length of the body.

A fish swims by alternately contracting muscles on either side of its body. See (A) in Fig. 7–6. Swimming begins when the muscles on one side of the body contract, pulling the caudal fin toward that side. The sideways movement of the caudal fin pushes the fish forward. Then the muscles on the opposite side of the

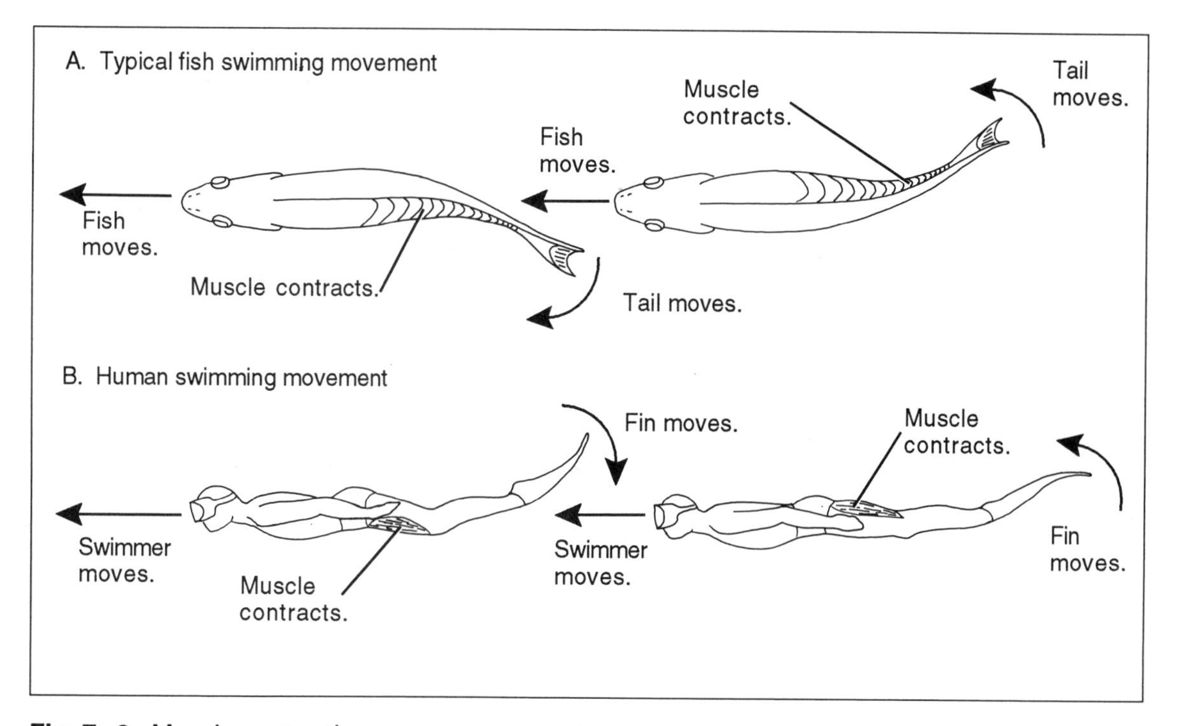

Fig. 7–6. Muscle contraction causes movement.

body contract and the caudal fin moves toward the other side of the body. Compare this movement with that of a swimmer using swim fins. Fish, including sharks, swim with a side-to-side motion; humans wearing fins swim with an up-and-down motion, like porpoises or whales. See (B) in Fig. 7–6.

Skeletal muscles are also attached to bones that move the other fins. Many fish swim (both forward and backward) by flapping their pectoral fins. Fast-swimming fish with long, thin pectoral fins use them for steering. Fish with wide pectoral fins use them for propulsion. Skeletal muscles also move dorsal fins. Faster-swimming fish reduce water drag by tucking in their dorsal fins; slower-swimming reef fish have larger dorsal fins, which they sometimes flare to protect themselves in encounters with other fish.

B. **Smooth muscles** move internal organs of the body and line tubes such as the intestinal tract and blood vessels. They are **involuntary;** that is, they move without signals from the thinking part of the brain. For example, smooth muscles automatically contract and relax in waves to push food through the digestive tract from the mouth to the anus. Other smooth muscles control the flow of blood and other body fluids, movement in the urogenital tract, and other automatic muscular processes. (These processes are explained in the next section.)

C. **Heart muscles** move blood. The heart muscles are also involuntary. By rhythmically contracting and relaxing, they pump blood through the blood vessels. Cross-striations in heart muscle are visible under a microscope; therefore they are not included in the category of smooth muscles.

QUESTIONS

12. Fill in Table 7–4 to show the functions of different kinds of muscles.

13. Muscles and their functions are described with terms that refer to location, microscopic appearance, and type of nerve control (voluntary or involuntary). Fill in Table 7–5 to organize these terms.

14. How is the swimming movement of a porpoise like that of a fish? How is the movement different?

15. Besides propulsion, what other movements can fins produce?

Table 7–4. Muscles and their functions Ⓦ

General function of the muscular system	Muscle kinds	Muscle functions

Table 7–5. Muscles, their appearance and control Ⓦ

Muscle kinds	Microscopic appearance	Nerve control
Skeletal		
Smooth		
Heart		

16. Besides swimming, what other movements of the fish's body might be controlled by skeletal muscles?

4. Digestive System

The function of the digestive system is to break food particles into molecules that can pass into the bloodstream, which carries them to the cells of the body. The **digestive system** is a long tube beginning at the mouth and ending at the anus. See Fig. 7–7. Specialized regions in the tube perform different functions. Glands attached to this tube produce chemicals that break food into nutrient molecules. Nutrient molecules are the building blocks and food source used in making and maintaining cells. The most common nutrients are fats, amino acids, sugars, minerals, water, and vitamins.

Food is pushed through the digestive tube by smooth muscles wrapped in rings around the entire tube. See (A) in Fig. 7–8. When the ring of smooth muscle contracts, the tube narrows, pushing food farther along the tube. **Peristalsis,** the contracting and relaxing of smooth muscles, creates a wavelike motion that pushes undigested food along the tube to the anus. See (B) in Fig. 7–8.

Three main groups of organs make up the digestive system: the mouth, the digestive tube, and the digestive glands.

A. Food and water enter the body through the **mouth,** where food is swallowed whole or chewed into small pieces. In swallowing, the tongue helps push food through the **pharynx** into the **esophagus,** which is a short, narrow tube between mouth and stomach. Gill rakers prevent food from escaping through the gill covers. See Fig. 7–9.

B. The **digestive tube** is the passageway from the esophagus to the anus. Food passes from the esophagus into the stomach, where it is partially digested before moving into the intestine. Chemicals in the intestine break the partially digested food into nutrient molecules. Only molecules can pass into the bloodstream. Undigested material collects in the posterior part of the intestine and passes out of the body through the anus in a periodic process called **defecation.** The solid material eliminated is called **feces.**

C. The **digestive glands** produce chemicals that break down food. Two such

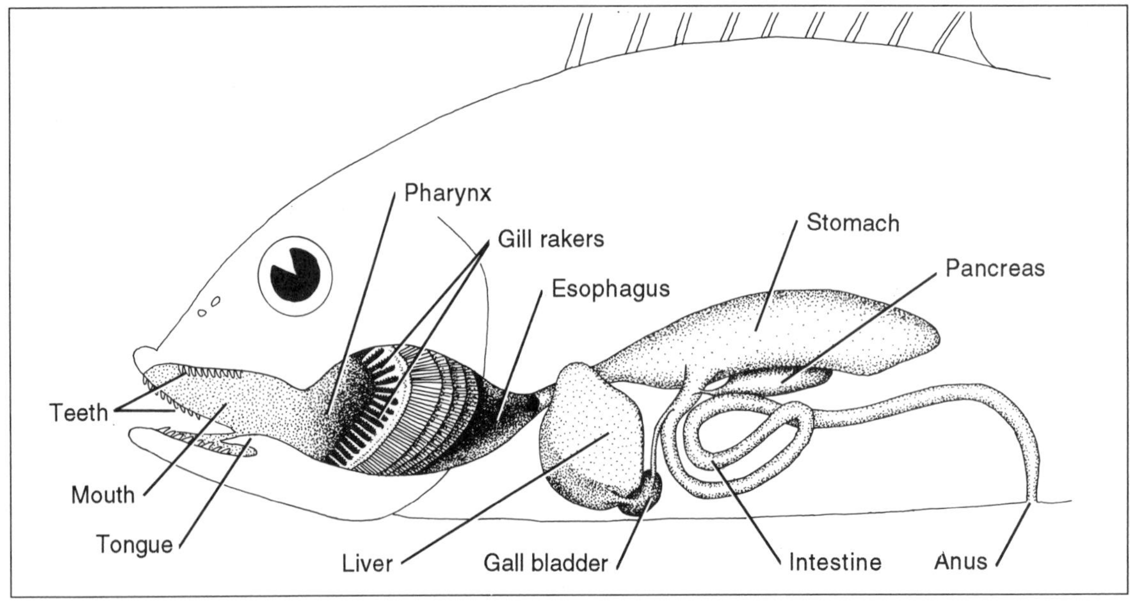

Fig. 7–7. The digestive system of a fish

glands are the **liver** and the **pancreas.** See Fig. 7–7. The liver produces **bile,** a substance that breaks fats and oils into smaller particles. Connected to the liver is a structure called the **gall bladder,** which stores the bile produced between meals. The pancreas lies next to the stomach. The pancreas

Table 7–6. Organs and functions of the digestive system

General function of the digestive system	Digestive organs	Organ functions

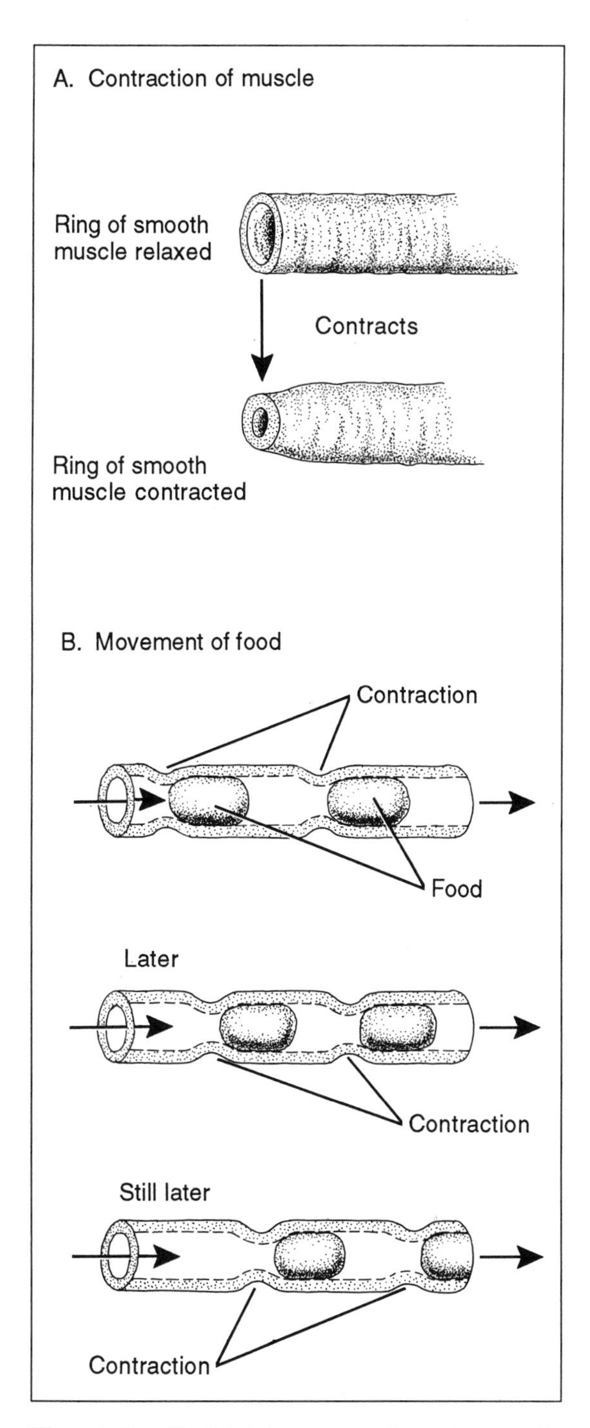

Fig. 7–8. Peristalsis, contraction of smooth muscles in the digestive tract

and other small digestive glands lining the intestines produce chemicals called **enzymes,** which travel from the glands into the intestine through small tubes called ducts.

QUESTIONS

17. What are the organs of the digestive system and their functions? See Table 7–1. Fill in Table 7–6 with information from this reading.

18. When a fish eats, in what sequence do organs break down the food? What process does each organ perform?

19. Peristalsis is the contraction of smooth muscles to push food along the intestine. Why is this term used? Look up the origin of the word for help. See Fig. 7–8.

20. What kinds of chemicals break food into molecules? Give examples of some food molecules.

21. Why must food be broken into molecules in the digestive process?

5. Respiratory System

The functions of the respiratory system are to take oxygen (O_2) into the body and pass carbon dioxide (CO_2) out of the body. The respiratory organs in fish are gills. Each gill has many gill filaments, which contain a vast network of tiny blood vessels called **capillaries**. See Fig. 7–9.

The gill rakers, which keep food in the mouth, are in the mouth cavity. The gill filaments are in the gill cavity. The **gill cover** (also called the **operculum**) is the body surface that covers the gills. See Fig. 7–10.

Water moves over the gills in a pumping action with two steps. In the first step, the mouth cavity opens, making it larger and drawing in water. See (A) in Fig. 7–10. In this step the gill covers are closed. In the second step, the mouth closes, making the mouth cavity smaller. Then the gill covers open and the water passes out through them. See (B) in Fig. 7–10. (When swimming fast, some fish, such as sharks and tunas, just open their mouths and gill openings, letting water pass continuously through their gills.)

As the water passes over the gills, blood in the capillaries of the gill filaments passes carbon dioxide into the water and picks up dissolved oxygen from the water. The blood then carries the oxygen to the body.

Oxygen (O_2) is essential in the body because it combines with food molecules to release energy for the body's needs. This chemical process breaks down nutrient molecules from digested food into water (H_2O) and carbon dioxide (CO_2) and releases energy. The oxidation of sugar, an example of this process, is shown in the equation at the bottom of this page.

Some fish have a **gas bladder**, a silvery sac lying below the kidneys, which are up against the vertrebrae. In some fish the bladder is part of the respiratory system. In many fish the gas bladder serves no respiratory function

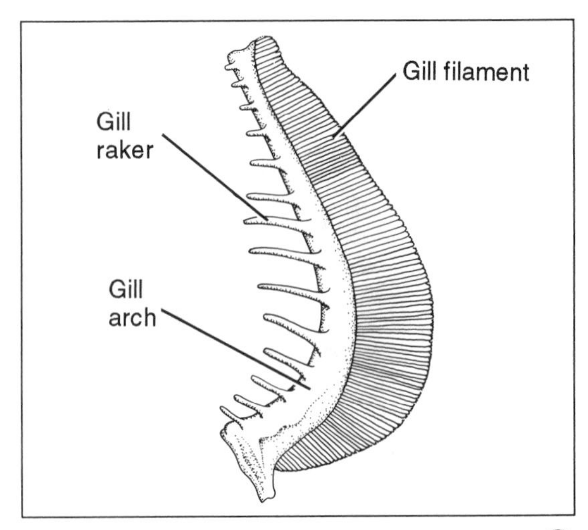

Fig. 7–9. A fish gill 

but regulates the fish's buoyancy instead. It does this by making the fish's density equal to the density of the surrounding water. For example, the density of average seawater is 1.026 g/mL, but the density of fish flesh and bones is 1.076 g/mL, making the fish denser than seawater. The fish sinks if its body density is greater than the density of water. The density of the gas bladder, filled mostly with oxygen and nitrogen gases, is only 0.007 g/mL. Acting like an inflatable balloon inside the fish, the gas bladder reduces the density of the fish's body until it is the same as the density of seawater. In this way, the fish does not sink or rise, but floats within the water column.

When the fish swims into shallow water,

$$6O_2 + C_6H_{12}O_6 \longrightarrow 6CO_2 + 6H_2O + \text{energy}$$

Oxygen + sugar ⟶ carbon dioxide + water + releases energy with enzymes

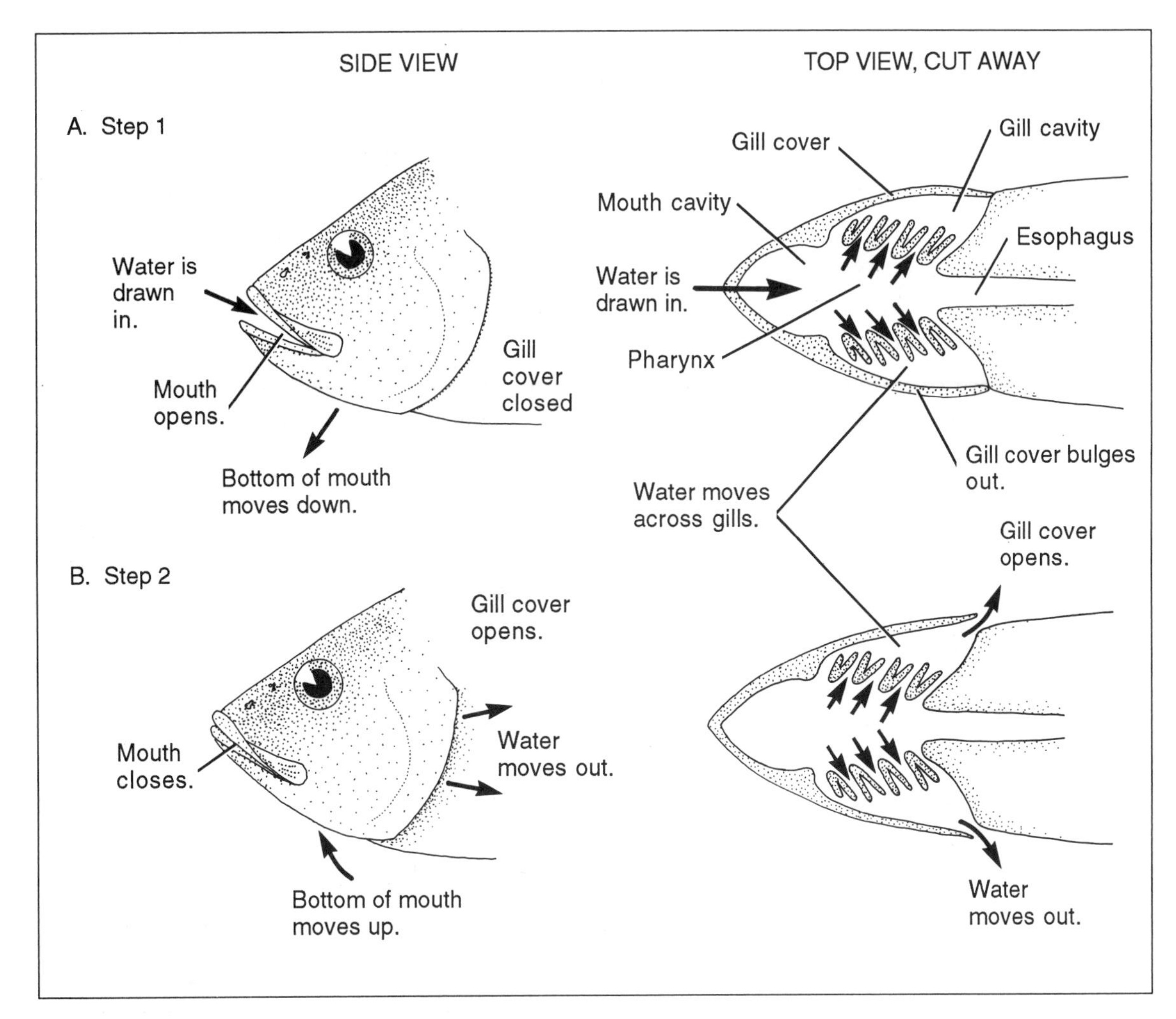

Fig. 7–10. Movement of water past the gills

its gas bladder expands because the pressure of water surrounding the fish is less. The fish compensates by absorbing some of the gas back into its body cells, bringing the gas bladder back to its original size. When the fish swims deeper, its gas bladder gets smaller because of the increase in water pressure. Then more gas enters the bladder, enlarging it again. In this way the fish remains neutrally buoyant—that is, equal in density to seawater.

Because gases move slowly in and out of the bladder, fish caught at great depths are often bloated when brought to the surface. The gas in the bladder expands rapidly when the fish moves from the high pressure of deep water to the lower atmospheric pressure at the surface. A fish pulled quickly to the surface cannot absorb the gases quickly enough, and sudden expansion of the bladder can injure it. Fish collectors must bring trapped fish to the surface slowly by stages to let the fish's body absorb the gases from the bladder.

Some fish (lungfish) use the gas bladder as an accessory respiratory organ or "lung" when they crawl on land. In many groups of fish (herring, pike, catfish, eels), an open tube connects the gas bladder to the digestive tract. These fish adjust gas content in their bladder by swallowing and expelling air through their mouth.

Still other fish, such as grunts and toadfish, use the gas bladder to produce sound. Muscles in the wall of the bladder contract rapidly, producing a low-frequency (low-pitch) sound that is resonated and amplified in the bladder.

Fish that have no gas bladder are always more dense than the surrounding water, so they sink if they stop swimming. Sharks, for example, must keep swimming to stay afloat. They use their tails and pectoral fins like airplane wings, adjusting the amount of lift to control the depth of their swimming.

QUESTIONS

22. What are the organs in the respiratory system and their functions? Fill in Table 7–7 with information from this reading. See Table 7–1.

23. Draw the head region of a fish. Use words and arrows to describe the movement of oxygen from the water into the fish, the fish's use of the oxygen, and the movement of carbon dioxide out of the fish.

Table 7–7. Organs and functions of the respiratory system 

General functions of the respiratory system	Respiratory organs	Organ functions

24. How does a submarine move from the surface into deep water? Compare this procedure to a fish with a gas bladder moving into deeper water.

6. Circulatory System

The circulatory system is a transportation system for body fluids that carry nutrients, oxygen, and hormones to cells and carbon dioxide and waste from cells. See Fig. 7–11. It is made up of the heart, the system of arteries, veins, and capillaries, the blood, and the lymph ducts.

A. The **heart** pumps blood to all parts of the body. In the fish it is a muscular organ of four chambers, two of which are also present in humans. Valves between the chambers allow the blood to flow in only one direction. When the heart muscle contracts, it forces blood into the arteries.

See Fig. 7–12 on page 78.

B. A network of tubes called **arteries, capillaries,** and **veins** connects the heart with all parts of the body. See Fig. 7–11. The arteries carry blood from the heart to the capillaries. The capillaries, microscopic in size and very numerous, have thin walls through which nutrient molecules can move. The molecules move through the walls of the capillaries and into the fluids around the tissues. The veins carry blood from the capillaries back to the heart.

C. **Blood** is a tissue that consists of plasma (the liquid part) and blood cells. Plasma contains water, carbon dioxide (CO_2), hormones, nutrients, wastes, and other molecules. Blood cells are of two main types, red and white. **Red blood cells** carry oxygen (O_2) from the gills to other cells in the body. In red cells, special molecules that combine chemically with oxygen can pick up and release oxygen, depending on the surrounding environment. These molecules, called hemoglobin, contain iron atoms. When hemoglobin combines with oxygen, it turns bright red. When hemoglobin releases its oxygen, it turns a very dark red. **White blood cells** fight disease. They often concentrate around infected wounds, killing bacteria and transporting wastes away from the wound. (Dead cells in a wound form pus.)

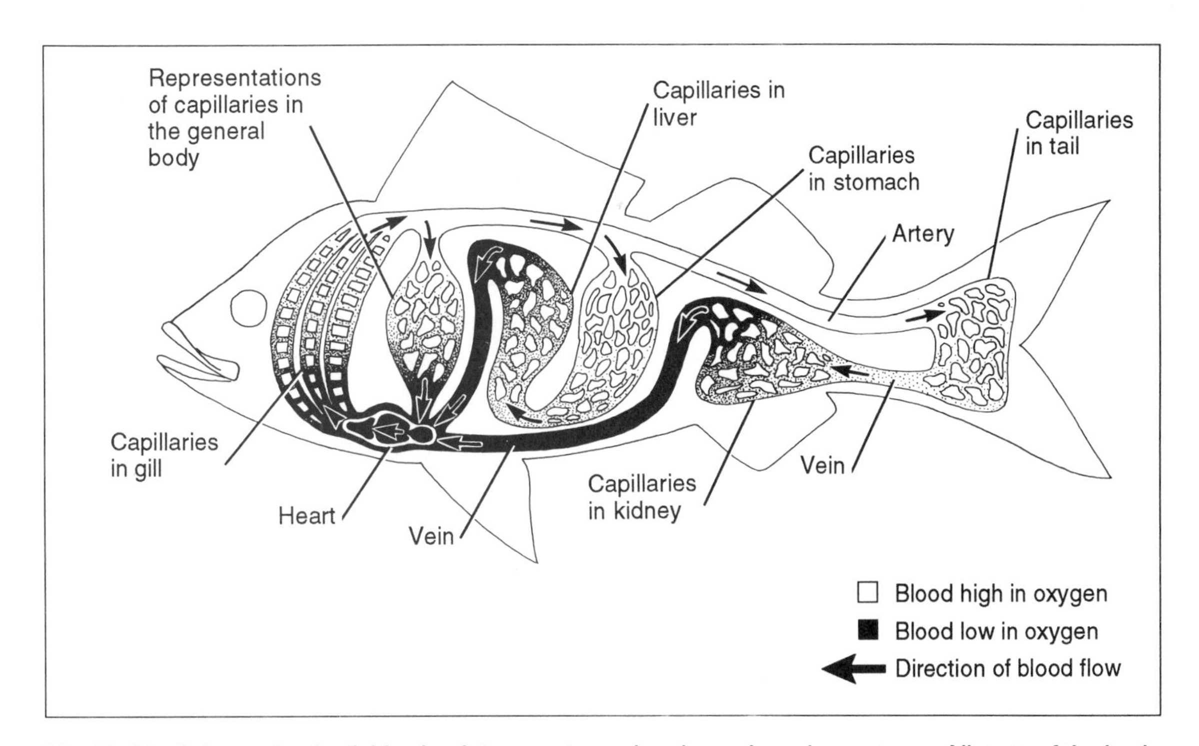

Fig. 7–11. Schematic of a fish's circulatory system, showing only major systems. All parts of the body are served by arteries and capillaries and veins. Ⓦ

Blood that is low in oxygen and high in carbon dioxide is pumped by the heart to the gills, where it releases its carbon dioxide and picks up more oxygen through capillaries in the gill filaments. From the gills the blood, now rich in oxygen, flows through branching arteries to the brain, digestive system, and other tissues and organs. From the digestive system the blood absorbs nutrients and distributes them through the body. In each tissue and organ, some of the blood

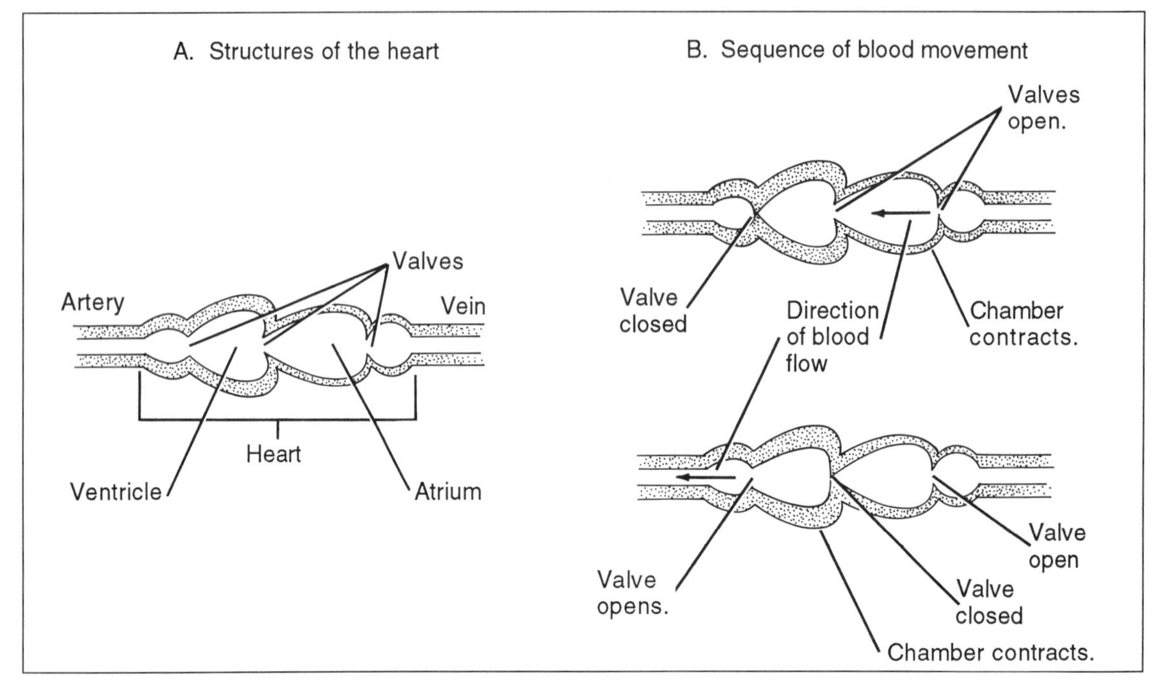

Fig. 7–12. Contraction of heart muscles moves blood through the system.

plasma passes through capillaries and flows around the cells. Oxygen and nutrient molecules move from the plasma into the cells. CO_2 and waste products move from the cells into the plasma. The plasma then passes back into the capillaries and carries wastes away. See Fig. 7–13.

D. Another network of tubes, called **lymph ducts,** picks up the liquid that passes out of the capillaries and collects in parts of the fish's body. The lymph ducts return this liquid (called **lymph**) to the veins.

The circulatory system works like a canal system. It carries the oxygen and building materials needed to grow, maintain, and repair the body, and it transports white blood cells to destroy disease invaders. It also carries wastes to the lungs, liver, and kidneys, which expel them.

Table 7–8. Organs and functions of the circulatory system Ⓦ

General function of the circulatory system	Circulatory organs	Organ functions

QUESTIONS

25. What are the organs in the circulatory system and their functions? Fill in Table 7–8 with information from this reading.

26. Explain why blood flows in only one direction in the blood vessels.

27. What part of the circulatory system performs each of the following processes?
    a. uptake of oxygen
    b. absorption of food molecules
    c. release of carbon dioxide
    d. distribution of food and oxygen to cells

28. What are the functional differences between red and white blood cells?

7. Excretory System

The **excretory system** removes many wastes produced by the body. Its chief organs are the **kidneys**, a pair of long, dark-red organs lying just under the vertebrae. In some fish, there may appear to be only one kidney. The kidneys filter small molecules from the blood. After filtering, usable materials such as sugars, salts, and water are absorbed back into the blood. The remaining waste products pass from the kidneys down the **urinary tubes** to

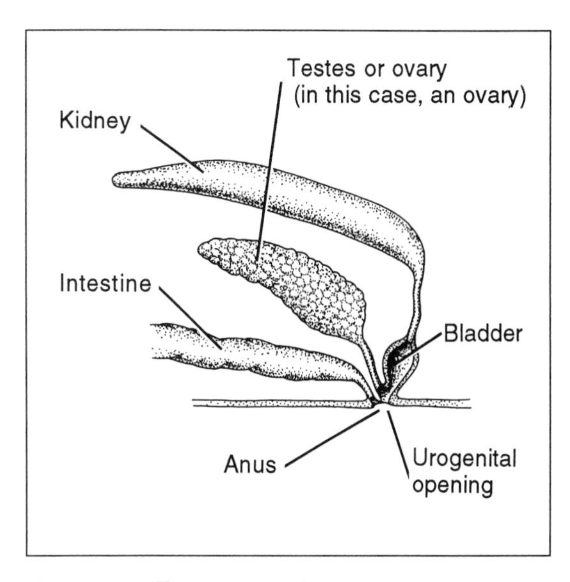

Fig. 7–13. Excretory and reproductive systems of a fish Ⓦ

Table 7–9. Organs and functions of the excretory system Ⓦ

General function of the excretory system	Excretory organs	Organ functions

the **bladder,** if present, and out through an opening behind the anus called the **urogenital opening.** This is the same opening through which pass materials from the urinary system and the reproductive system (eggs from the ovaries or sperm from the testes). See Fig. 7–13.

The blood also carries other waste products and excess salts to the gill filaments. CO_2 and ammonia are excreted by the gills, and so is salt if the fish lives in seawater. The gills, though usually considered part of the respiratory system, are also excretory organs.

The liver also removes wastes from the blood, but it is considered part of the digestive system, not the excretory system. The liver cleans blood after it has picked up digested products from the intestine. Wastes are converted into bile and stored in the gall bladder, where they wait to be poured back into the digestive tract to aid in digestion.

QUESTIONS

29. What are the organs in the excretory system and their functions? Fill in Table 7–9 with information from this reading.

30. Why is the kidney considered a selective excretory organ? What substances does it excrete? What substances does it not excrete?

31. Where in the body does the fish form the substances excreted by the kidney?

32. What organs remove waste products from the blood? What organ stores products from the kidney for later removal? Where do products from the kidneys leave the body?

8. Reproductive System

Reproduction is the process by which organisms produce offspring. Fish develop when eggs from the ovaries of a female are fertilized by sperm from the testes of a male. Both egg and sperm are single cells. Fertilized fish eggs develop into embryos, which use the yolk in the egg as food. After a period of development, the embryos become free-swimming fish.

Fish have many ways of **spawning,** that is, shedding eggs and sperm. In the ocean, most males and females shed their eggs and sperm into the water in the same place at the same time. Fertilization takes place externally. But some females lay eggs in nests, where males fertilize them. Other fish, including sharks and guppies, fertilize their eggs internally. Here too the embryos get their nutrients from yolk in the eggs. They hatch from the eggs inside the female's body and are born alive.

Several groups of fish can change their sex. One of the most interesting fish of this group is the Hawaiian cleaner wrasse. A male cleaner wrasse often has a harem, a group of females that stay with him. If a male disappears, the dominant female in the harem assumes the male role and, within several weeks, her ovaries become functional testes. Some fish that change sex also change color patterns and behavior.

The testis or ovary of a fish is connected to a genital duct through which eggs or sperm pass to the outside. See Fig. 7–13.

QUESTIONS

33. What are the organs in the reproductive system and their functions? Fill in Table 7–10. List both the testes and the ovaries.

34. Where are eggs and sperm produced in fish? How do these reproductive cells get outside the fish's body?

35. What might be the advantages of external spawning and fertilization? Of laying eggs in nests? Of internal fertilization?

36. Most behaviors of fish enhance the survival of their species. How would a change of sex in some groups of fish help them survive?

Table 7–10. Organs and functions of the reproductive system 

General function of the reproductive system	Reproductive organs	Organ functions

9. Nervous System

The **nervous system** is a complex group of tissues and organs that control most body processes. It operates like a telephone system, with a master computer in its central office and a complex of cables and lines linking the parts of the system. But the nervous system uses biochemical signals instead of electric current.

The nervous system has two major divisions: the central nervous system and the peripheral nervous system.

The **central nervous system** consists of the brain and the spinal cord. The **brain** receives information from sense organs that monitor conditions both within and around the fish. The brain interprets this information and sends response commands to the body. The brain, a soft and delicate organ, is surrounded and protected by the bones of the skull.

A. The **brain** of a fish is divided into six major parts, each with a different function. See Fig. 7–14.

1. Two **olfactory bulbs,** which control the organs of smell, sit side by side at the end of long stalks at the very front of the brain. From the nostrils they receive information about chemicals in the water. Olfactory nerves carry this information to the brain.
2. The **cerebrum** consists of two lobes behind the olfactory bulbs. The cerebrum controls the voluntary muscles. It also stores memories. Fish have a limited memory—enough to learn simple tasks and adapt to new environments. In higher animals, such as humans, the cerebrum is the thinking part of the brain.
3. Two **optic lobes** lying just behind the cerebrum control vision. Large nerves called **optic nerves** connect the optic lobes to the eyes.
4. The **cerebellum,** behind the optic lobes, is the control center for coordinating skeletal muscle once contraction and relaxation is initiated by the cerebrum. When the command goes out from the cerebrum to swimming muscles, for example, the cere-

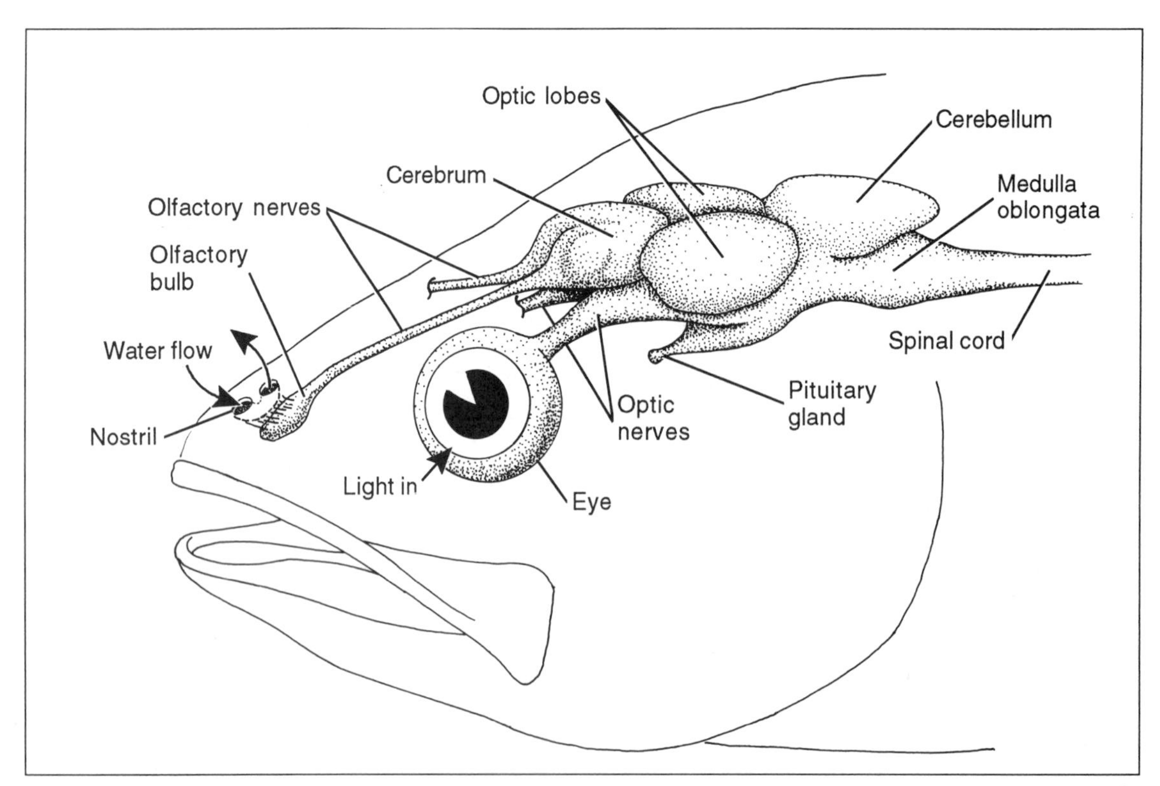

Fig. 7–14. Brain and sense organs of a fish

bellum takes over and ensures that the muscles work in proper rhythm and order.

5. The **medulla,** lying under the cerebellum, connects the brain to the spinal cord. One of its functions is to control the flow of hormones in the fish. It also controls the heart, the smooth muscles of the internal organs, and the rhythmic contraction of gill muscles in respiration.
6. The **pituitary gland,** beneath the optic lobes, is the master gland of the endocrine system of the body.

B. The **spinal cord,** which runs through holes in the vertebrae, acts like a telephone trunk line. Composed of long nerve fibers, it carries nerve impulses to sensory receptors in the brain and transmits nerve impulses from the brain to the muscles, glands, and other tissues.

The **peripheral nervous system** is the network of nerves that connect muscles and sensory organs to the central nervous system. There are two types of nerves, **sensory nerves,** which carry information from the sensory organs to the spinal cord or brain, and **motor nerves,** which send commands from the brain or spinal cord to the muscles and glands.

QUESTIONS

37. What are the parts of the nervous system and their functions? Fill in Table 7–11.

38. Imagine that a big predatory fish smells prey in the water nearby. It swims toward the source of the smell, sees the prey, and swims quickly to catch and eat it. The rapid movement raises the rate of water moving over the gills, and the fish gets more oxygen. Describe the sequence of nervous system structures and functions at work during this action.

C. The **sensory organs** send the information they receive to the central nervous system and the brain. Fish use their sense organs to detect changes in their bodies and in their environment. These organs include the eyes, the ears, the lateral lines, the nostrils, and the taste organs, all equipped with sensory nerve endings.

1. The **eyes** of fish resemble human eyes. See Fig. 7–15. At the front of

Table 7–11. Organs and functions of the nervous system Ⓦ

General function of the nervous system	Nervous system organs	Organ functions

each eye is a lens, held in place by a **suspensory ligament.** The lens focuses images of objects on the retina. To bring near and far objects into focus, the **lens retractor muscle** moves the lens back and forth. The **retina** is a light-sensitive membrane rich in nerves that connect to the optic lobes of the brain by **optic nerves.** When light shines on the nerves of the retina, the optic nerves send impulses to the optic lobes. Because fish have no eyelids, their eyes are always open.

2. Fish have two **inner ears** embedded in spaces in their skulls. The lower chambers, the sacculus and the lagena, detect sound vibrations. See Fig. 7–16. Small stonelike bones, called **otoliths,** float in the fluid that fills these chambers. These otoliths lightly touch hair cells that are sensitive to movement. Like the otoliths in our ears, they help the fish to keep its equilibrium. When the fish changes position, the otoliths bump the hair cells, which send nerve impulses to the brain. The otoliths also enable the fish to detect sound vibrations in the water. In some fish, vibration in the gas bladder, an organ that controls gases in a fish, is trans-

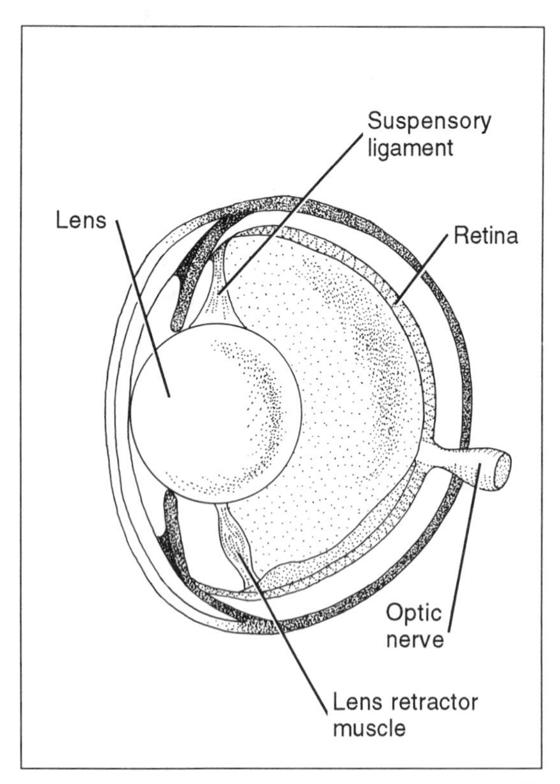

Fig. 7–15. Eye of a fish 

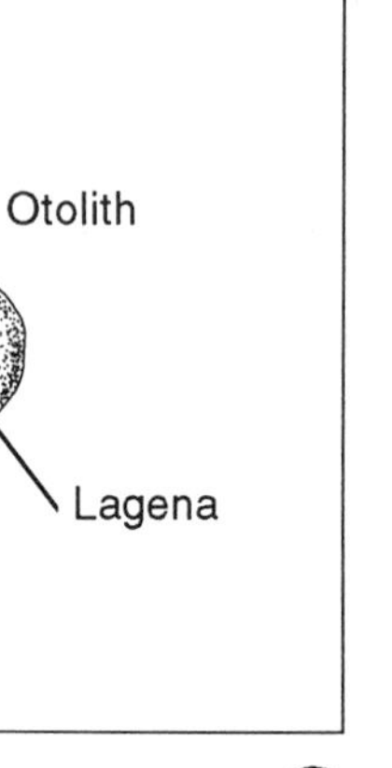

Fig. 7–16. Inner ear of a fish

mitted to the inner ear, aiding in sound reception.

The **semicircular canals** of the ears detect changes in position and movement. See Fig. 7–16. A small bulge at the end of each semicircular canal, called an **ampulla,** contains hair cells sensitive to movement. When the fish rolls right or left, tail up or tail down, the liquids and otoliths (ear stones) push against the hairlike nerve endings lining the canal, sending messages to the brain.

3. Running along each side of their bodies fish have a row of nerves that register changes in pressure. The nerve endings are in a system of tubes in specialized scales. This system of tubes and pressure-sensing nerve endings is called the **lateral line.** When water pressure changes or the fish enters a current or another fish swims by, water moves faster through the tubes, activating the nerve endings. As Fig. 7–17 shows, the lateral line runs the length of the fish, ending in pores on the head.
4. The sense of smell is well developed in some groups of fish. Water circulates through openings in the head called **nostrils.** See Fig. 7–14. A pit in the skull bone con-

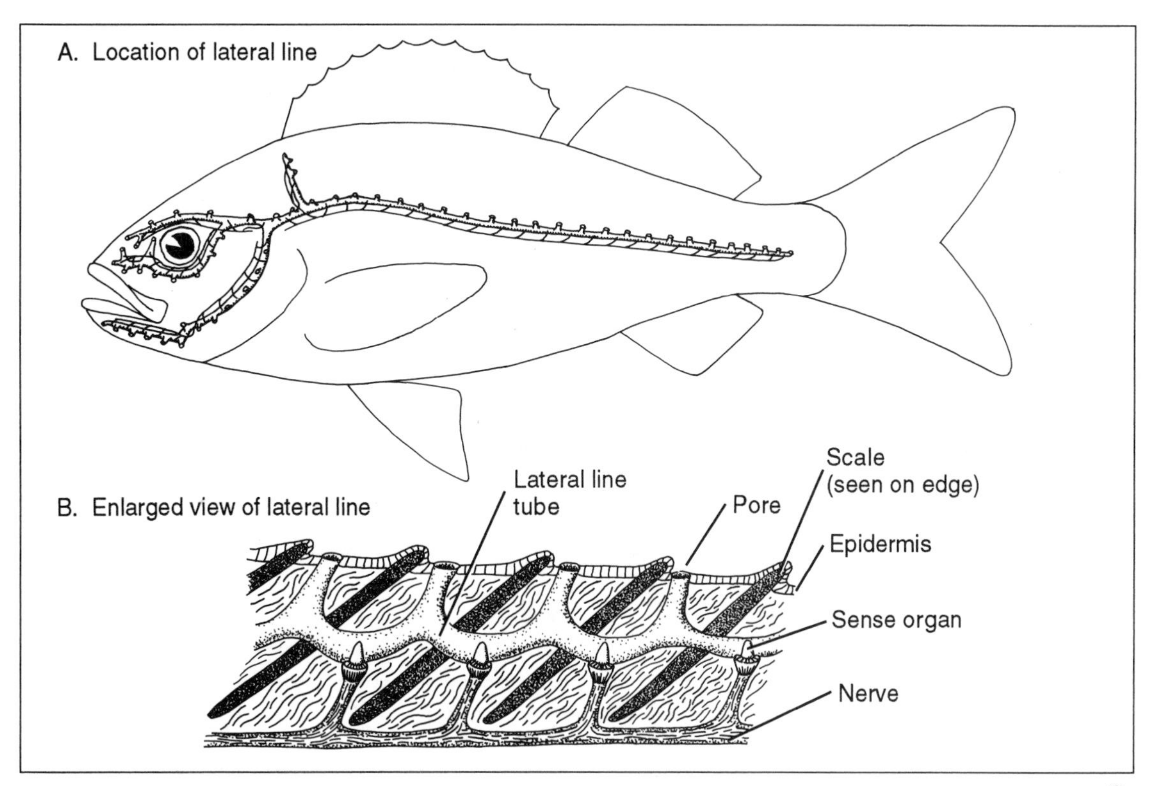

Fig. 7–17 . Lateral line of a fish

tains the olfactory organ, which is lined with cells that are sensitive to various molecules dissolved in the water. The sensory cells are clustered in the **olfactory bulbs** in the forebrain. When the cells are stimulated by these molecules, a nerve impulse travels to the brain, where the fish smells the substance in the water.

5. Receptors that detect touch and taste are found in many parts of the body. In most fish, **taste receptors** are in the mouth, but some fish have touch-and-taste receptors on their fins or other structures, such as the barbels of a goatfish.

QUESTIONS

39. What are the organs in the sensory system and their functions? Fill in Table 7–12 with information from this reading.

40. What is the function of eyelids? What advantages might there be in having no eyelids? Why do humans blink their eyelids?

41. Where are the sound detectors in fish? In humans?

42. What structures in a fish detect changes in water pressure and current? Do humans have any similar sensory structures?

43. What advantages might there be to fish in having taste receptors outside the mouth? Give examples of these receptors and tell where they are located.

44. How is the sense of smell similar in humans and fish? How is it different?

10. Endocrine System

The **endocrine system** uses chemicals called **hormones** to control important body processes. Hormones can slow body processes, speed them up, or start new ones. They can control processes such as (1) rate of growth, (2) development of sex characteristics, and (3) the capacity to respond to light and stress.

Table 7–12. Organs and functions of the sensory system Ⓦ

General function of the sensory system	Sensory organs	Organ functions

The nervous system sends electrochemical signals to and from the brain at a speed of several hundred miles per hour. By contrast, hormones act much more slowly than nerve impulses, but they can operate for long periods.

The endocrine glands feed their chemicals into the bloodstream through capillary walls instead of through tubes. A major endocrine gland is the pituitary, lying under the brain. See Fig. 7–14.

QUESTIONS

45. How does the endocrine system function?

46. Both the nervous system and the hormones of the endocrine system control processes in the body. What are the advantages of each kind of control?

FURTHER INVESTIGATIONS

1. How can studying fish help us understand human biology?

2. What techniques would an artist have to use to draw the organs of a fish in three dimensions? How could fish art be important in the education of scientific illustrators?

3. Use a microscope to study the growth rings on scales of several species of fish to determine their age.

8. Dissecting a Fish

In this activity you will examine the internal anatomy of a fish. See Topic 7, Anatomy and Function of Organ Systems in Fish, for information and drawings to guide you in dissecting your fish. First you will open the fish and observe and identify the organs in the body cavities. Then you will cook the fish and observe its muscular and bony structures.

ACTIVITY

Examine a fish internally to identify organs of the different systems.

MATERIALS

- copies of Workbook Tables 8–1 and 8–2
- newspapers or dissecting pan
- dissecting scissors
- fresh whole fish
- sudsy water
- paper towels
- three 8½ x 11-in sheets of plain paper
- teasing needle
- forceps
- dissecting microscope or hand lens
- pins
- blunt probe
- microscope slide and coverslip
- methylene blue in dropping bottle
- compound microscope
- centimeter ruler
- aluminum pie pan
- frying pan and lid
- heat source
- balance or spring scale
- two 8½ x 11-in sheets of cardboard
- glue
- calculator

PROCEDURE

1. Use Table 8–1 to help you organize your drawings, sketches, notes in your notebook, and other dissection activities in this topic. Follow your teacher's directions for turning in your completed work.

2. Spread clean newspaper over the lab table. Use a dissecting pan, if available. Use clean dissecting scissors.

3. Obtain a fish. Gently swish it through sudsy water. Rinse it and pat it dry with paper towels.

4. Put the fish on a clean, folded section of newspaper or a dissecting pan. Align the fish as shown in Fig. 8–1. If you do not know the name of the fish, find it in a reference book or identify its family by using the keys in Topic 4, Keying Bony Fish to Family.

Table 8–1. Fish dissection activities

Ⓦ

		Procedure
Drawings		
______	Drawing 1. External anatomy of a ______________ (Name of fish)	5
______	Drawing 2. Internal anatomy of a ______________ (Name of fish)	7
	______ General outline of the fish	5
	______ Gas bladder, if the fish has one	8
	______ Digestive system organs	8
	______ Heart, blood vessels	10
	______ Male or female reproductive organs	11
	______ Kidney, urogenital opening	12
	______ Eye muscles, optic nerves	13
Sketches		
______	Sketch 1. Teeth	5
______	Sketch 2. Jaw structure	8
______	Sketch 3. Fish gill	9
______	Sketch 4. Eggs or sperm	11
______	Sketch 5. Parts of the eye	13
______	Sketch 6. Parts of the brain (optional)	14
______	Sketch 7. Muscle pattern	16
Notebook records		
______	Stomach contents	8
______	Intestine length, ratio of intestine length to body length	9
______	Contents of ovaries or testes	11
Display		
______	Skeletal system	17

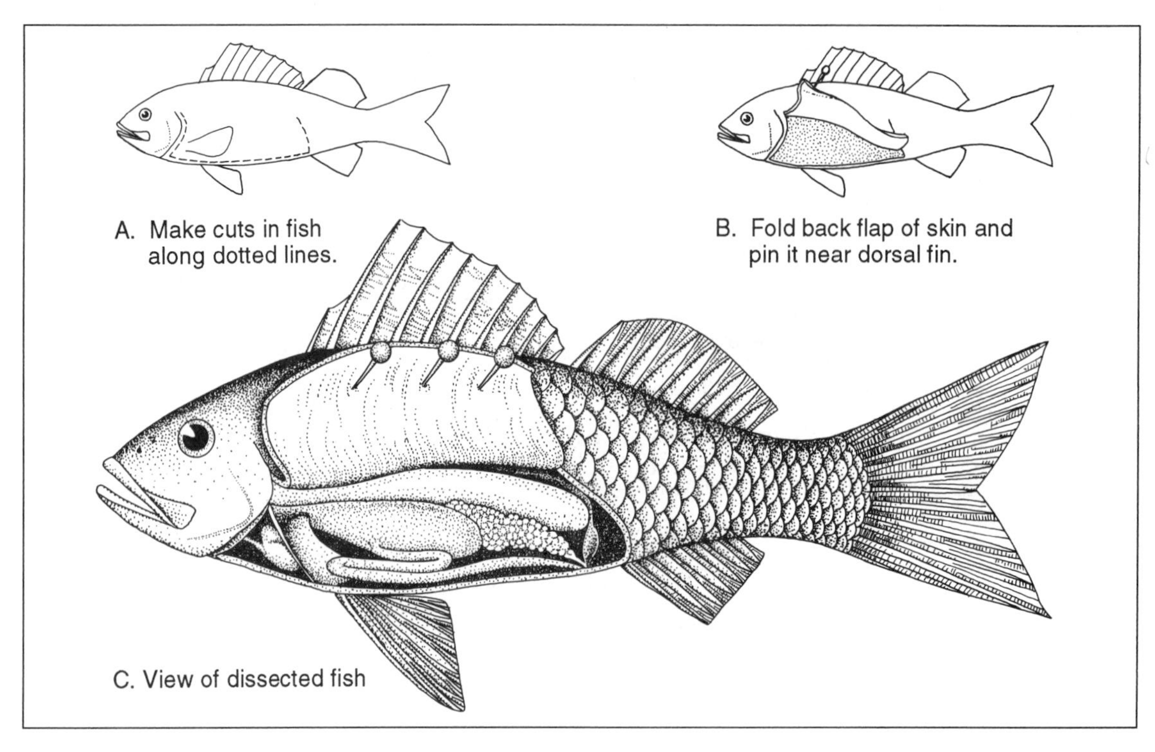

Fig. 8–1. Dissected fish showing internal anatomy

5. Make a pencil drawing of the fish showing its external features. Refer as needed to Fig. 2–1 in Topic 2, External Anatomy.
   a. On a plain sheet of 8 ½ x 11-in paper turned sideways, draw the outline of the fish big enough to fill most of the space.
   b. Find and identify each of your fish's external features, including all openings in its body. Draw and label what you observe.
   c. Examine your fish's teeth. If they are small, pull or cut one or two out of the jaw. View the teeth under a dissecting microscope or a hand lens. Sketch the teeth in your notebook. Label as "Sketch 1. Teeth."
   d. Above your fish drawing, center the title "Drawing 1. External anatomy of a [name of the fish]."

6. Open the fish to expose its organs. See Fig. 8–1.
   a. With the dissecting scissors, make a shallow cut through the skin of the fish's belly. Starting at the anus, cut forward (anteriorly) toward the throat along the ventral midline. To avoid cutting into organs, insert the scissors a short distance, then cut the flesh with short outward snips.

b. Expose the organs in the body cavity. Make an upward anterior cut through the skin and muscles along the edge of the gill plate and toward the dorsal fin. Make an upward posterior cut straight up the side of the fish. Fold the flap of skin and muscle dorsally and pin it out of the way.

7. Make a drawing of the fish showing its internal features. Record notes and sketches in your notebook.
   a. Follow Procedures 8–12 below, referring as needed to Topic 7, Anatomy and Function of Organ Systems in Fish. Draw the organs you observe in your own fish, not the ones in the examples in Topic 7. The organs of fishes vary in shape, size, and location.
   b. Title this drawing "Drawing 2. Internal anatomy of a [name of fish]."

8. Observe the digestive system. Find and identify the digestive organs. Draw and label them in Drawing 2. Refer as needed to Fig. 7–7.
   a. Note how the jaws move when the mouth is opened and closed. In your notebook, sketch the jaw in both open and closed positions. Label as "Sketch 2. Jaw structure."
   b. Look into the mouth and see how the gill rakers provide a channel for food to enter the esophagus.
   c. Cut open the stomach. If you find any food, put a small amount on a microscope slide, add a drop of water, and place a coverslip over it. Observe it under the dissecting microscope at 10X. Try to identify the contents. Are the remains from animals, plants, or both? Record your findings in your notebook.
   d. Carefully remove the entire intestine from the stomach to the anus. Lay it in a straight line without stretching it and measure its length. Record the data in your notebook.
   e. Measure the body length of your fish. Refer to Table 5–1, Fish Measurements. Calculate the ratio of intestine length to body length (intestine length ÷ body length). Record the data in your notebook.

9. Observe the respiratory system. Refer as needed to Fig. 7–9.
   a. Remove a gill arch with its attached gill filaments and gill rakers. Make a separate labeled sketch showing these features. Title it "Sketch 3. Fish gill."
   b. Compare the gill rakers of your fish with those of other types of fish. Record your observations in your notebook.
   c. Determine whether your fish has a gas bladder. If it has, draw and label it in Drawing 2.

10. Observe the circulatory system. Refer as needed to Fig. 7–11.
   a. Find the heart. It is full of dark-red blood. It may be located anteriorly, almost under the gills. Draw and label it in Drawing 2.

b. Find the large blood vessels that lead to the heart and those that lead from the heart to the gills. Draw and label these in Drawing 2.
c. Gently open the heart, wash out the blood, and look at the structure.

11. Observe the reproductive system. Refer as needed to Fig. 7–13 and to Topic 7, Section 8, Reproductive System.
    a. If your fish has well-developed ovaries, they will be full of tiny pinkish or yellowish eggs. If your fish has well-developed testes, they will contain white fluid. Draw and label either the male or female organs in Drawing 2.
    b. Find the opening where the eggs or sperm pass into the water. Draw and label it in Drawing 2.
    c. Remove a sample of the contents of the ovaries (eggs) or testes (sperm), place it on a microscope slide, add a drop of methylene blue, and observe it under a 10X dissecting microscope for eggs or a 100X to 400X compound microscope for sperm. Sketch your observations in your notebook. Title as "Sketch 4. Eggs or sperm."

12. Observe the excretory system. Refer as needed to Fig. 7–13.
    a. Tease the soft organs away from the fish's body cavity and locate the kidney.
    b. Draw and label it in Drawing 2.
    c. Find the opening through which excretory wastes leave the body. Draw and label it in Drawing 2.

13. Observe the eye. Refer as needed to Fig. 7–14.
    a. Carefully remove the skin around the eye socket. Find the muscles that attach the eyeball to the surrounding bones and move the eye. Draw and label them in Drawing 2.
    b. Find the optic nerve that carries sensory nerve impulses from the eye to the brain. Add these to Drawing 2.
    c. Cut the muscles and the optic nerve and remove the eyeball from the socket. Carefully cut the eyeball to observe its inner layers and the shape and position of the lens. In your notebook, sketch and label the parts of the eye. Title as "Sketch 5. Parts of the eye."

14. (Optional step for one team of students) Because this procedure damages the skeleton, making the fish unusable for study of the skeletal system in Procedure 17, use another fish. Share results with the class.
    a. Carefully cut away the top of the skull to expose the brain.
    b. Find the five regions of the brain. Use the title "Sketch 6. Parts of the brain."
    c. Find some of the nerves leading from the brain.

15. Steam the fish to make it easy to separate the skin, muscle tissue, and bones for Procedures 16 and 17.
    a. Punch holes in a thin aluminum pie pan. Place the pan upside down in a large frying pan. Add water to the

frying pan to a depth of about half an inch.

b. Lay the fish on the pie pan without letting the fish touch the water.

c. Cover with a lid that does not touch the fish. Put the frying pan on a heat source and steam the fish for about a half hour. Let the fish cool.

16. Observe the muscular and integumentary systems. Refer as needed to Sections 1 and 3 in Topic 7.

a. Lay the fish with the undissected side up. Carefully tease away the skin and scales from the muscles and skull over the entire side of the body.

b. Observe the muscles and tendons. Make a separate sketch of the muscle pattern of the fish. Title it "Sketch 7. Muscle pattern."

c. Carefully remove all the muscles from one side of the fish without disturbing the position of the skeletal bones. (A small amount of tissue will probably be left on the bones). As you proceed, note the arrangement of the muscles in relation to the skeleton. Lay a piece of cardboard over the fish, turn the fish over to expose the other side, and repeat the procedure.

17. Observe the skeletal system.

a. Examine the backbone and ribs.

b. Observe the bones that support the fins. Note the location of the dorsal fin support skeleton in relation to the vertebrae.

c. Examine the skull. In your notebook, record which parts are hard and which are flexible.

d. Without breaking the bones apart, carefully remove all soft tissues and organs from the skeleton of the skull, body, and fins.

e. (Optional) Lay the skeletal parts carefully on a piece of clean cardboard. Arrange the bones in their original positions in the fish body. When the bones dry, glue them in place on the cardboard. Use glue if necessary to reattach the bones to each other.

18. (Optional step for one team of students)

a. Follow Procedure 15 to steam another fish.

b. Lay the fish on a piece of paper toweling and gently pat the surface until the excess water has been removed. Take care not to damage the skin or scales.

c. Weigh the fish. Record the weight to tenths of a gram in Table 8–2.

d. Carefully tease away the skin and scales from the muscles, skull, and fins over the entire body. Weigh the skin and scales to the nearest tenth of a gram. Record it in Table 8–2.

e. Without disturbing the position of the skeletal bones, carefully remove all the muscles from one side of the fish. A small amount of tissue will probably be left on the bones. Put the removed muscles on a piece of paper. Lay a cardboard over the fish and turn the fish over to expose the other side. Repeat the procedure.

Table 8–2. Weight of parts of a fish and calculated percentage of total body weight Ⓦ

Part of fish	Weight	Percentage of total body weight
Entire fish, cooked		100%
Skin and scales		
Muscles		
Skeleton		
Other parts (eyes, gills, internal organs)		

f. Weigh the muscle to the nearest tenth of a gram and record the weight in Table 8–2.
g. Carefully remove the remaining parts of the fish from the skeleton, including the eyes, gills, and internal organs. Again, try not to disturb the position of the bones.
h. Weigh the organs to the nearest tenth of a gram and record the weight in Table 8–2.
i. Without breaking the bones apart, weigh the skeleton and record its weight in Table 8–2.
j. Calculate the percentage of total body weight made up by each part of the fish and record in Table 8–2.
k. Make a pie graph showing the percentages of the total body weight represented by the skin and scales, muscles, skeleton, and other parts of the fish.

19. Using Table 8–1 as a checklist, make sure you have completed all dissecting assignments. Assemble your work as directed by your teacher.

QUESTIONS

1. What do we mean when we say that an organism is made up of different systems?
2. Is your fish a herbivore (a plant eater) or a carnivore (an animal eater)? How did you find your answer?
3. From the class findings do you see a relationship between the type of food a fish eats and the length of its intestine? What is your evidence?
4. Was your fish a male or a female? How did you find your answer?
5. To which system do gill rakers belong? Explain your answer.
6. What is the function of gill filaments?
7. Why don't bottom-living fish need gas bladders?
8. When you eat a large fish, which system(s) do you eat?

9. Are the bones that support the fin attached to the backbone? What is your evidence?

10. What sense organs do fish have that humans do not have?

11. A fish's body is supported by water. Why then does it have a backbone? Why does the backbone have so many bones?

12. Which organs belong to two or more systems?

13. Which organ system makes up the largest bulk of the body of the fish? Why do you think this is so?

14. Compare the weight distribution percentages of several species of fish. Are they similar or different? Why?

FURTHER INVESTIGATIONS

1. Mount the skeletons of several species of fish.
   a. How do skeletons of fish from different environments differ, if at all?
   b. How do skeletons of slow-moving fish differ from those of fast, long-distance swimmers?

2. Compare the size and shape of various bones among fish species. Can the differences be related to feeding, swimming, or some other behavior of the living fish?

3. Trace the path of blood through the circulatory system.

4. Trace the path of food through the digestive system.

5. Make a list of fish with special kinds of sensory organs.

6. Dissect several types of fish and find the differences between them.

7. Make a collection of scale types, skulls, and teeth of local fish species.

8. Compare the fish's organs to human organs by looking at a labeled model of a human body. Report to the class on how a human skeleton supports and protects the body parts. Compare the functions of bones and muscles in movement in a fish and in a human.

9. Compare fish blood cells with human blood cells. Get prepared, stained slides from your teacher. Observe these with a compound microscope at 100X and 400X. Draw the red blood cells. At 400X find and draw white blood cells.

10. Why don't humans eat the digestive system of fish?

11. The fish-processing industry uses non-edible parts of fish for other products. Which parts do they use? What products do they make from them?

12. What evidence did you find of parasites in your fish? What precautions should humans take in eating fish?

9. Fish Behavior

Behavioral biologists often use sophisticated devices to study the actions of animals. One such device is the **event recorder,** which resembles a typewriter. Each time an animal does something, the observer presses a key and holds it down until the animal starts to do something else, thus making a record of how often and how long the animal performs each behavior. The observer also notes what outside object or action seems to stimulate the behavior. From the data the observer can calculate **frequency,** the number of times a behavior occurs within a specified period, and the **percentage of time** the animal spends in each behavior. See Table 9–1, a record of the time that four fish, two males and two females, spent in courting and fighting and unnamed other behaviors.

The table shows that Male 1 and Female 1 engaged in **courtship behavior** 30% of the time. Male 2 did not try to court the females, but he fought both Male 1 and Female 1. This aggression suggests that Male 1 and Female 1 have staked out a **territory**—a space they defend as theirs. When Male 2 entered the territory, there was aggression between them. Female 2 spent 100% of her time doing other things. From these observations, we infer that Male 1, Male 2, and Female 1 recognized each other. We also infer that Male 2 was recognized as a competitor. Female 2 may or may not have been recognized.

Table 9–1. Percentage of time spent in activities

Activity	Male 1	Male 2	Female 1	Female 2
Courtship				
Male 1	–	–	30%	–
Male 2	–	–	–	–
Female 1	30%	–	–	–
Female 2	–	–	–	–
Aggression				
Male 1	–	30%	–	–
Male 2	30%	–	12%	–
Female 1	–	12%	–	–
Female 2	–	–	–	–
Other behavior	40%	58%	58%	100%

In the following activities you will observe several kinds of fish. These fish react not only to other fish but also to their own **habitats**—types of living spaces, such as rocks, sand, plants, and volume of water. You will look for changes in both the actions and coloration of the fish.

The way an animal behaves is often caused by something in its environment. The cause is called a **stimulus** (the plural is *stimuli*); the behavior is called a **response.** See Table 9–2.

QUESTIONS

1. How did the researcher prepare for the experiment described here?

2. What controls were necessary during the experiment?

3. How could this experiment be carried out in a natural environment rather than in the simulated environment of a laboratory aquarium?

Table 9–2. Glossary of terms for describing fish behaviors

Advertising coloration. Use of colors to signal or warn. Examples are the bright coloration of poisonous fish and the different coloration of dangerous spines from the rest of a fish's body. Cleaner wrasses use advertising coloration to attract fish to clean.

Advertising behavior. Use of movement to signal wants. An example is a signal to a cleaner wrasse by a fish that wants to be cleaned.

Aggregation. Bunching or grouping together without orienting in the same direction or keeping equal spacing.

Aggression. Threatening or fighting others. To show aggression, most fish raise their dorsal fin spines, push out their gill covers, open their mouths, and approach other fish. Some fish also change color. In fighting, fish may bite, stab with spines or blades, or chase offenders away.

Camouflage and ***mimicry.*** Behaviors used by some fish to disguise their presence in the environment. A fish that uses changes in bodily appearance to blend with coral, rocks, or sand is camouflaging itself. A fish that behaves like seaweed is mimicking seaweed.

Courtship. Behaviors that occur before and during mating. These differ among species. Behaviors include changes in color, close contact between the mating fish, and abnormal swimming patterns such as wriggling and shuddering. The male usually takes the lead during courtship, the female during **spawning** (egg-laying).

Table 9–2 *continued.* Glossary of terms for describing fish behaviors

Food searching. Behaviors that occur before and during feeding. Among some fish, food searching looks like random hunting and pecking. Other fish lie in wait to dart out and snatch passing prey. Some fish feed alongside other species; others do not. Some feed in schools; others feed alone.

Fright. Behaviors in reaction to fear, such as moving away or changing color.

Habitat preference. Behaviors related to where a fish lives. Some fish are very specific about what they require. Some fish need substrates such as sand or rocks. Some either avoid or remain near, on, or under a specific object. Certain butterflyfish must have a particular coral to eat; otherwise they starve.

Learning. Behaviors that fish engage in to recognize objects and other animals in their habitat. Many fish can easily be trained to come to a specific place to receive food; some can learn to navigate mazes.

Movement. Behaviors such as swimming, hovering, perching, and lying on the bottom. Some fish swim all the time; others stay on the bottom most of the time. Some fish, such as shrimpfish, spend most of their time in a head-down position; others, such as sea horses, remain in a head-up position.

Pecking order. Organization among fish by levels of authority. One or more dominant individuals control the others. Usually the larger, stronger, more mature individuals (often males) dominate.

Schooling. Bunching or grouping of fish all orienting in one direction and keeping equal spacing.

Stress behaviors. Responses to disruptive, disturbing, or unfamiliar stimuli.

Territoriality. Defense of space required to live, find food, and reproduce.

ACTIVITY

Devise an experiment on fish behavior.

MATERIALS

See Options 1 through 4 below

PROCEDURE

1. Work in teams of two to four to design and perform an experiment investigating a specific problem related to fish behavior. Modify one of the four options that follow, or develop an experiment of your own. Use references to learn about the fish you choose to study.

2. Before selecting your topic or attempting any observations or experiments with your fish, learn how to set up and main-

tain a healthy aquarium habitat for the fish you plan to study.

3. With your team members, write a research plan. Ask your teacher for help in designing your plan. When you write your problem statement, name the behavior you want to observe. State the problem as a question about the relationship between a stimulus and the behavior.

4. Have your teacher approve your plan before you start the experiment.

5. Get the equipment you need—aquaria, pumps, filters, sand and gravel, heater, cover, water, and food for the fish. Be sure the rocks, coral, gravel, and sand are clean and safe to put into the aquarium.
   a. Study aquarium manuals to learn setup procedures.
   b. If you do not have an established aquarium, treat the water with a water conditioner before adding fish. Follow instructions in manuals.

6. Set up and arrange the aquarium for your experiment. If you are setting up a new aquarium, get some sand or gravel from an established aquarium and mix it in with the new sand and gravel for covering the subsand filter. Start the aquarium pump and wait at least one day. Doing this will speed the growth of beneficial microbes in the filter system. The microbes break down and recycle wastes.

7. Get the fish. Put them in the aquarium. Wait several days for them to acclimate before you begin your experiment.

8. Perform your experiment. For each observation, ask yourself, What is the fish responding to? How is it responding? Record your observations.

9. Make a written report of the results of your investigation. Ask your teacher for suggestions on organizing the sections of your report.

10. Present your findings to the class. Ask your teacher for suggestions on how to prepare and present an oral report.

OPTION 1. Tilapia Stress

Tilapia are cichlids (SIK lidz). Tilapia have the unusual habit of holding their young in their mouth during early development. They are hardy fish that can live in a wide variety of water conditions. They are important aquaculture fish, providing protein for people around the world. They grow to lengths of 15–18 cm and masses of 125–205 g within 12 to 24 months. Fig. 9–1 shows a common tilapia.

MATERIALS for Option 1

- 20-gal established freshwater aquarium
- six 4- to 6-cm long live tilapia
- copy of Workbook Table 9–3
- stopwatch
- 20-gal aquarium with fresh water only
- net

PROCEDURE for Option 1

1. Observe unstressed tilapia that have

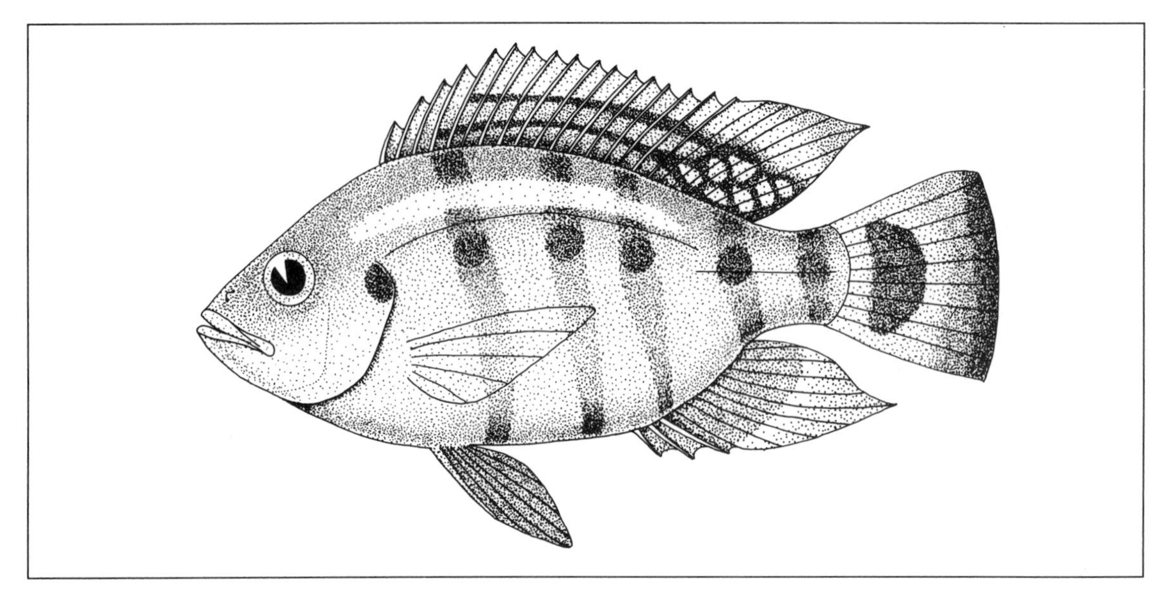

Fig. 9–1. The common tilapia, *Sartherodon mossambicus*

been living in an established aquarium for some time. Fill in Table 9–3 with such observations as these:

a. Respiration. Use a stopwatch to time the respiration rate, the number of times a minute the operculum (mouth) moves. Time for several minutes.
b. Coloration. Observe and sketch the color pattern(s) of your fish.
c. Dorsal fin position. Observe the number of seconds this fin is raised in 1 min. Wait 2 or 3 min, then repeat the observation. Calculate the average percentage of time the dorsal fin is raised.
d. Swimming. Time a fish for 1 min. Record how many seconds it engages in swimming. Repeat this several times at intervals of 2 or 3 min. Calculate the average percentage of time the fish engages in swimming.
e. Other behaviors. List other behaviors.

2. Set up another aquarium with only water in it. Remove a tilapia from its familiar aquarium and put it in this aquarium. Repeat Procedure 1, this time observing the behavior of tilapia in the unfamiliar aquarium. Record your observations in Table 9–3.

3. If time permits, add more tilapia to the unfamiliar aquarium. Observe their behaviors and record the data.

4. Return the tilapia to their established aquarium at the end of the experiment. A bare aquarium may not meet the tilapia's needs.

Table 9–3. Behavior and coloration of tilapia 

Behavioral observation	Established aquarium	Bare aquarium
Respiration rate		
Coloration		
Dorsal fin position		
Swimming		
Other behavior		

QUESTIONS for Option 1

1. How do the behavior and coloration of the tilapia differ in the familiar, established aquarium and the unfamiliar, bare aquarium?

2. What stimuli caused the behavioral change(s)?

3. How long does it take a tilapia to adjust to a new environment?

4. How long does it take a tilapia to adjust to the presence of a second tilapia?

5. What factors seem to make adjustment easier?

6. What factors seem to make adjustment harder?

7. What questions did you raise that need further study?

OPTION 2. Guppy Courtship Behavior

Guppies are live-bearing fish used in many countries to control mosquito larvae. They belong to the family Poeciliidae, the toothcarps. Females are larger than males (about 8 cm to the males' 6 cm), and their anal fin is broader. Males are more brightly colored than females. See Fig. 9–2. In this experiment you will observe their courtship and mating behavior.

Besides using event recorders, scientists also show behavioral interactions by using diagrams of sequences of actions displayed by fish. A typical diagram of a behavioral interaction is shown in Fig. 9–3.

Note that the example of courtship behavior in Fig. 9–3 on page 103 is for a different family of fish, the cichlids. Unlike guppies, cichlids build nests in gravel and lay their eggs in the nest. Cichlids also differ from guppies in that they show parental care. The diagram you will make to show guppy courtship behavior, therefore, will differ from the one in Fig. 9–3.

MATERIALS for Option 2

- 5- or 10-gal established freshwater aquarium
- 10 to 12 adult guppies
- net
- two temporary holding freshwater aquaria
- copies of Workbook Fig. 9–2 and Table 9–4
- colored pencils or crayons

PROCEDURE for Option 2

1. Remove all the guppies from the established aquarium, separating the males from the females. Put all the males in a temporary aquarium such as a quart or half-gallon mayonnaise jar filled with water. Put all the females in a second temporary aquarium. See Fig. 9–2 on distinguishing males and females.

2. Do not allow the males and females to see each other. Either put something between the two aquaria to block their view or set the two aquaria far apart. Keep them apart for 24 hr or more.

3. Observe a male. With colored pencils or crayons, show the color pattern in (A) in Fig. 9–2. Observe the females and note any differences among them. Record this information in (B) in Fig. 9–2.

4. Put four females and one male into an established aquarium with no other fish in it. Observe the male and female guppies and record your observations in Table 9–4. Include such observations as these:
   a. Color change. Does the color pattern change during courting? How?
   b. Fin action. Which fins move differently during courting and not court-

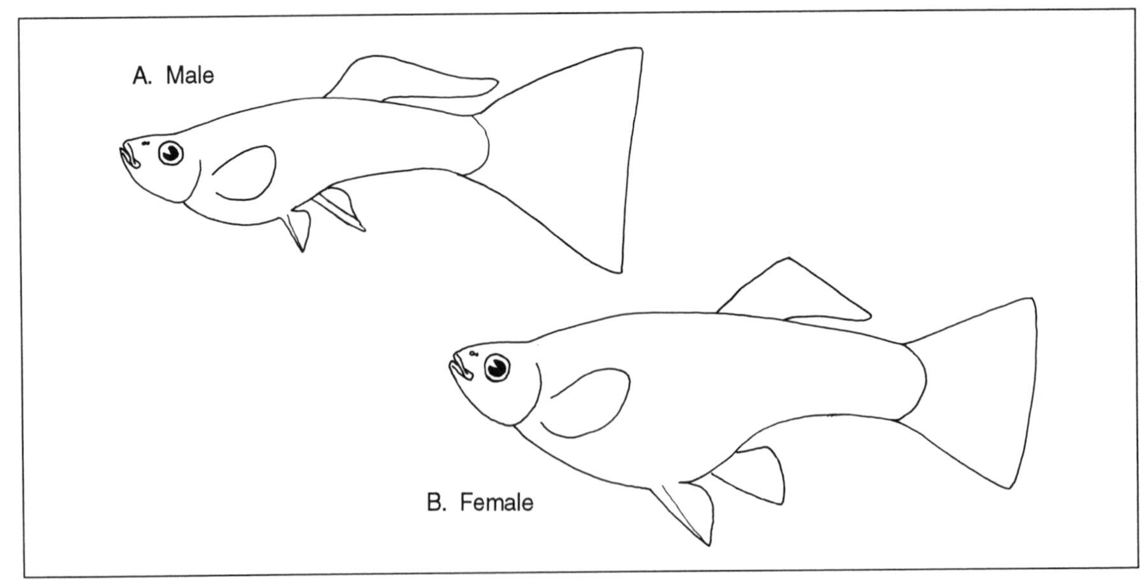

Fig. 9–2. Male and female guppies Ⓦ

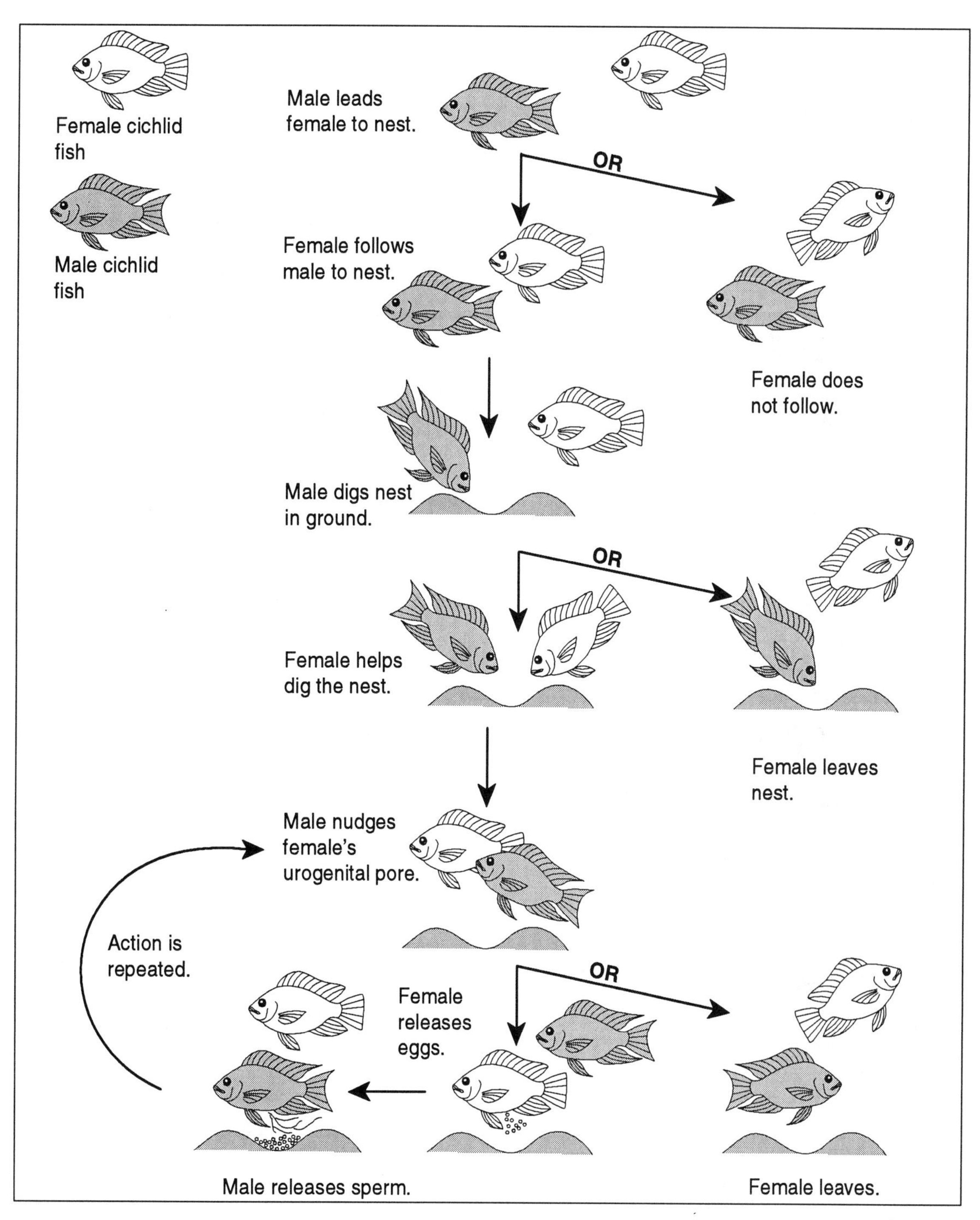

Fig. 9–3. A diagram showing courtship behavior of some cichlid fishes. (NOTE: These are not guppies.)

ing? What, if any, is the normal function of these fins?

c. Body action. How is the body held during courting? Is this position different from the normal swimming positions?

d. Position in relation to the opposite sex during courtship. Tell where the male guppy is when he is courting. Does he move randomly about the tank, or does he take a specific position in relation to the female? What is the position and movement of the female?

e. Preference of males for females. Tell whether the male singles out one female or courts all females. If the male shows a preference, what are the characteristics of the preferred female? Do females show any preference or rejection of the male?

f. Other observations.

5. Observe the sequence of events in guppy courtship and spawning. Look for answers to these questions:

a. Who initiates courtship?

b. What is the response of the female to the male?

c. What is the response of the male to the female?

6. Repeat the experiment if time permits. When you are through, return all the guppies to the established aquarium.

QUESTIONS for Option 2

8. Describe or draw the sequence of events in guppy courtship. Fig. 9–3 shows an example of courtship for another family of fish, the cichlids.

9. Does the male change color during courtship? What role might color change play in courtship?

10. Why were the females separated from the males for several days before you began observing courtship?

11. How would you determine whether the courtship you observed is universal among guppies?

12. What brought courtship to an end?

Table 9–4. Guppy behavior Ⓦ

Event	Observation notes	
	Male	Female
Color change		
Fin action		
Body action		
Position to other sex		
Preference for other sex		
Other observations		

13. What did the mated pair do after courtship ended?

14. What questions do you have for further study of courtship behavior?

OPTION 3. Training and Learned Behaviors

In this experiment look for evidence of learned behaviors. Use healthy, well-established fish such as goldfish or oscars. Before you begin, read references from a pet store or other sources to learn about their feeding behaviors.

MATERIALS for Option 3

- 2 or 3 small, easy-to-keep fishes of the same species
- 20-gal established aquarium
- net
- fish food

PROCEDURE for Option 3

1. Begin with an established aquarium with no fish in it. Put two or three small fish of the same species in the aquarium.

2. Train the fish to swim toward you to find food.
   a. Stand at one end of the aquarium. Call it End A. Put a small amount of food in the aquarium from that end. Remain standing there until the fish come and eat the food. Time how long it takes for the fish to come and eat the food at End A. Record the data. Repeat this daily for at least a week.
   b. Then switch the feeding routine to the other side of the tank. Approach the aquarium from End B, put food in the aquarium from that end, and wait until the fish eat. Time how long it takes for the fish to come and eat the food at End B. Repeat this daily for at least a week.
   c. Test to see whether the fish are now trained to swim to you to find food. Alternate where you stand (either End A or End B), but consistently feed the fish from the side where you are standing. Observe and record the results for at least a week.
   d. Graph the data that you gathered in Procedures 2.a. through 2.c. Design graphs to best illustrate the data. Label the graphs. You could design three separate graphs, one for each data set, or combine all three data sets in a single graph.

3. Now test to determine whether the fish can be retrained to swim away from you to find food.
   a. Stand at End A and put a small amount of food into the aquarium at End B. Remain standing at End A until the fish approach End B and eat the food. Time how long it takes for the fish to come to the food. Record the data. Repeat this daily until the fish swim directly toward End B, not toward you. Reinforce this training by continuing this feeding pattern for at least a week.
   b. Switch the routine. Stand at End B and put food at End A. Wait at End B until the fish approach End A and eat the food. Record the data. Note how

many days it takes for the fish to become trained to swim directly to End A.

c. Test to see whether the fish are now trained to swim away from you to find food. Alternate where you stand (either End A or End B), but consistently feed the fish from the opposite end. Observe and record results for at least a week.

d. Design, draw, and label graphs to illustrate the data collected in Procedures 3.a. through 3.c.

4. If time permits, repeat these experiments with two or three fish of a different species. Compare the learning behaviors of the two species.

QUESTIONS for Option 3

15. In the first training situation, when the fish swam toward you for food, what was the stimulus? What was the response? Describe the stimulus and the response for each training situation.

16. What do we mean by training? By retraining? By learning behaviors? By learning? Give examples from these activities.

17. How long did it take to train the fish? Compare the graphs. Under what circumstances did the fish learn fastest? Slowest? How might differences in training time be explained?

18. What evidence, if any, do you have from your observations that fish can learn?

    a. What did they learn? How do you know that learning took place? How, if at all, did you test the learning?

    b. What differences, if any, did you notice among the fish of the same species in their learning behaviors? What might explain these differences?

19. How does prior training appear to affect learning behaviors? Before you began these experiments, what prior training, if any, did these fish have? Where did they live and how were they fed? How might these circumstances have affected their observed behaviors?

OPTION 4. Damselfish Territoriality

Damselfish like the ones in Fig. 9–4 are small (typically from 9 to 15 cm) and aggressive. All damselfish are marine fish; that is, they live in the ocean, not in fresh water. In this experiment you will observe damselfish exploring an unfamiliar aquarium and establishing their territories.

MATERIALS for Option 4

- experimental aquarium with seawater and subsand filter
- 2 branching coral heads or rock formations that provide shelter for the fish
- 6 to 12 similar-sized small damselfish in a suitable holding aquarium
- net
- watch or clock

PROCEDURE for Option 4

1. Set up the experimental seawater aquarium with one coral head or rock forma-

tion. Put one damselfish in the aquarium. Record its behavior for 5 min.

2. The next day record its behavior for 5 min; then put another damselfish in the aquarium. Record what happens.

3. If the fish ignore each other, add a fish every 5 min until they interact. Record their behavior.

4. Add another coral head or rock formation to the aquarium. Record what happens.

5. Record where the damselfish are the next day.

6. Design your own behavioral experiments to observe the interactions of damselfish and their environment.

QUESTIONS for Option 4

20. What behaviors did you observe when a damselfish first explored the crevices in the coral head or rock formation? What might explain these behaviors?

21. How many fish had to be added to stimulate interaction among the fish when there was one coral head or rock formation in the aquarium?

22. What happened when you added the second coral head or rock formation?

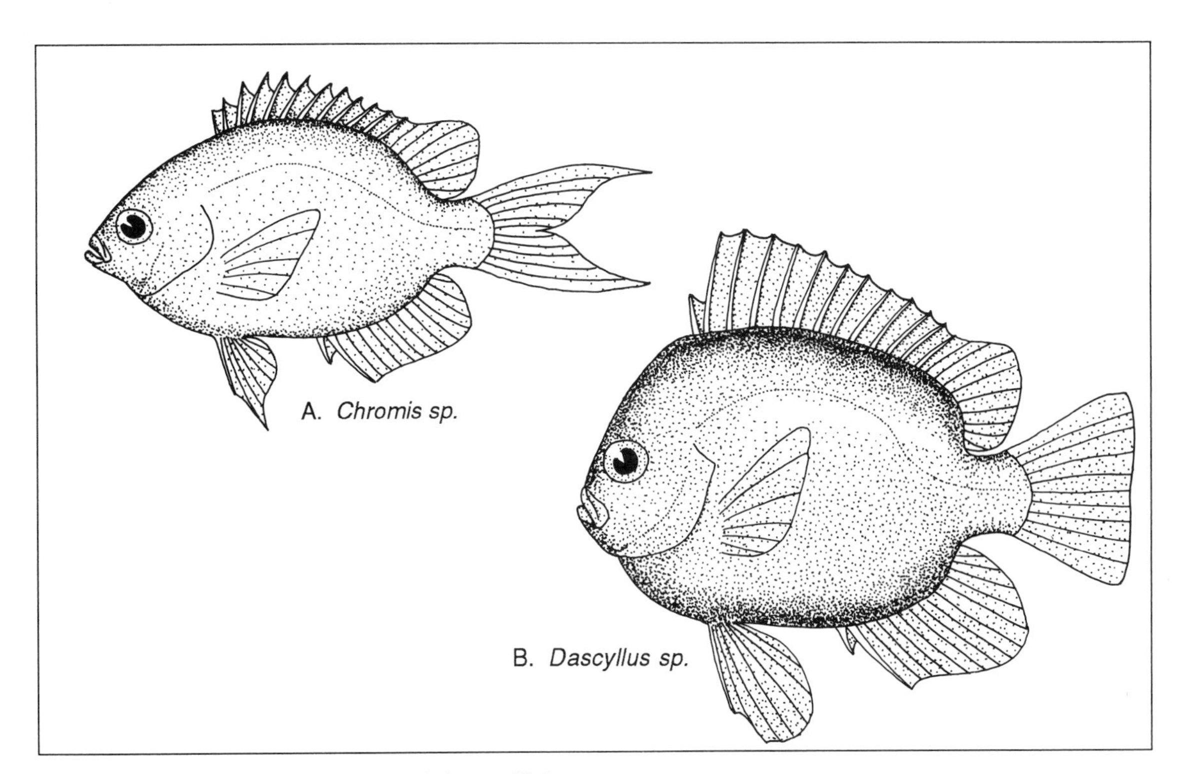

Fig. 9–4. Two common genera of damselfish

23. What hypothesis might explain the behavior of the damselfish? How would you test your hypothesis?

24. Do individual damselfish respond differently? If so, how? What hypothesis might explain these differences? How would you test your hypothesis?

25. What results did you find in your own experiments?

FURTHER INVESTIGATIONS

1. Observe gobies or fighting fish (*Betta splendens*) during spawning. Describe their behavior and record the stimuli that triggered it.

2. Observe fish at a local aquarium or while snorkeling or diving.
   a. How do male and female color patterns differ?
   b. Do males and females behave differently? If so, how?
   c. Do color patterns change during different behaviors? If so, how?
   d. Determine in detail how fins and other body parts are used in different swimming movements.

3. Study behaviors associated with territoriality. Determine the extent of a fish's territory. Experiment by changing the rocks and coral in the aquarium and observing how the fish changes its territorial behavior.

4. Experiment with different damselfish and such substrates as coral or rocks of different shape, size, and texture to determine the fish's preferences.

5. Observe damselfish in their natural habitat and determine the boundaries of their preferred habitat and territory.

6. Observe feeding behaviors of a number of species of fish.
   a. Describe in detail the fish's movements while hunting for food, biting, swallowing, and feeding.
   b. Are any differences in body structure related to feeding?
   c. What evidence, if any, did you observe of pecking order (dominance) among members of the same species during feeding? Among members of different species?

7. Design and carry out a learning experiment using a maze to determine whether carnivorous fish (meat eaters) are smarter than omnivorous fish (plant and animal eaters) or herbivorous fish (plant eaters). See Option 3 for help in designing a learning experiment.

8. Consult library references to learn about each of these science careers, what each specializes in, and how professionals in each area study behavior:
   a. behavioral biologist
   b. psychologist
   c. psychiatrist
   d. neurologist
   e. biological oceanographer

9. How might the design of fishing lures

relate to knowledge of fish behavior?

10. Talk to the owner of a pet shop or an aquarium supply store, or invite the owner to class, to learn about the business. Explore such questions as What special knowledge is needed? Where do the fish and other animals come from? What questions do customers most often ask?

11. Sometimes fishing operations accidentally hook or net porpoises, turtles, sharks, and other animals. Most of them are discarded at sea and die. How could knowledge of animal behavior prevent such accidents?

12. Read about new technologies that attract fish, such as aggregation devices and artificial reefs. What fish behaviors explain their effectiveness?

13. Fish ranching in the open ocean may be possible if fish fry (young) can be trained to swim to a food source when summoned by an underwater sound or other signal. Ask a librarian to help you find information on training fish and other wild animals.

10. Sharks

Sharks are the most feared fish in the ocean. Nearly everyone can form a mental image of how a shark looks and behaves. Most of us have seen photographs of sharks and watched movies or videos that portray sharks as vicious killers. Yet fewer than 30 of the more than 350 species of sharks are known to have attacked humans.

Sharks are an ancient class of vertebrates. The teeth and spines of sharks living today differ little from the fossilized remains of their ancestors that lived hundreds of millions of years ago. Knowing this, we can conclude that sharks are very well designed for living and reproducing in the ocean. We begin this topic by comparing sharks with the bony fish we have studied. Then we investigate shark behaviors, including attack patterns.

ACTIVITY 1

Compare sharks with bony fish.

MATERIALS

- copies of Workbook Table 10–1 and Fig. 2–1
- pencil or pen

PROCEDURE

1. Sharks are fish, but because their anatomical and functional features differ from those of the bony fish we have studied, they belong to a different class. Fig. 10–1 shows the external anatomy of a shark. Compare it with the exter-

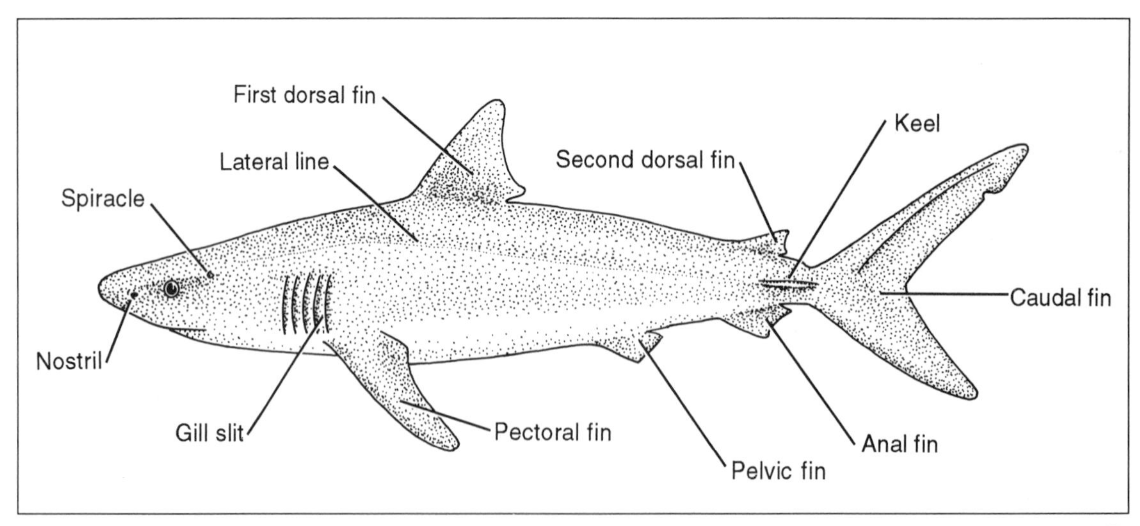

Fig. 10–1. Anatomy of a shark

nal anatomy of a bony fish in Fig. 2–1.

2. Complete Table 10–1, a comparison of bony fish and sharks.
   a. Study the information in the table on the structures and characteristics of sharks.
   b. Supply the information describing the structures and characteristics of bony fish. Refer as needed to Fig.

Table 10–1. Comparison of sharks with bony fish 

Structure or characteristic	Sharks	Bony fish
Skeleton	Cartilage; tough and flexible.	
Fins	No fin rays; fins are relatively inflexible; pectoral fins are used as "wings" to produce lift as shark swims. Caudal fin used to propel the shark forward.	
Scales	Toothlike placoid scales in dermis make skin rough and sandpapery. Refer to Topic 2, Fig. 2–3	
Spiracle	A small opening leading to the gill chamber through which water passes for respiration. Not all sharks have visible spiracles.	
Gill opening	Most species have five gill slits; some have six, some seven.	
Gas bladder	No gas bladder; most sharks must swim continuously to stay afloat.	
Respiration	Most species must swim continuously with mouth open to force water over the gills. A few species can pump water over the gills.	
Skin	Thick, tough, and durable; often used as leather.	
Teeth	Large, sharp, and serrated in most species; smaller in a few species. All sharks have several rows of teeth that constantly regenerate.	

2–1 and to the information in Topics 2, 6, and 7.

QUESTIONS

1. How do sharks compare with bony fish? What are the differences? What are the similarities?

2. In general, what advantages, if any, do bony fish have over sharks?

3. What advantages, if any, do sharks have over bony fish?

Types of Sharks

Some shark species are large, and some are dangerous, even deadly, to humans. More than half of all sharks, however, are less than 1 m (3 ft) long. The smallest is under 15 cm when fully grown. Fifteen sharks are described here, illustrating the great range of sizes and behaviors among sharks. See Table 10 – 2 and read about each species.

QUESTION

4. Why would a shark under 1 m (3 ft) hold little threat to humans?

ACTIVITY 2

Make a poster showing the habitats of sharks. Indicate which sharks are dangerous to humans.

MATERIALS

- copy of Workbook Fig. 10 – 2(A), Fig. 10 – 2(B), and Fig. 10 – 3
- scissors
- glue
- cardboard backing (optional)
- colored pencils or crayons

Table 10 – 2. Selected species of sharks

Basking shark. *Cetorhinus maximus.* This is the second-largest fish, reaching 11.7 m (35 ft) in length. It is an open-ocean plankton feeder considered harmless to humans. Its teeth are small. The mouth and gill slits are large to permit the passage of great quantities of water, which is filtered through long sievelike gill rakers.

Black-tipped reef shark. *Carcharhinus melanopterus.* This reef shark is often seen by swimmers and divers in the shallow waters of tropical oceans. It is curious about humans in the water, often lingering nearby to watch their activities. Although some people consider it harmless, it is on record as biting the ankles and legs of wading humans on sandy reef flats. It feeds on many species of small reef fish, squid, and octopus. It grows to 2 m (6 ft) in length.

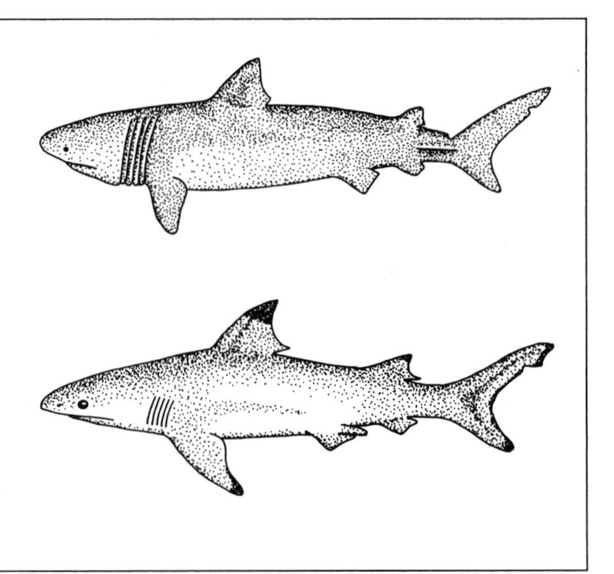

Table 10–2 *continued.* Selected species of sharks

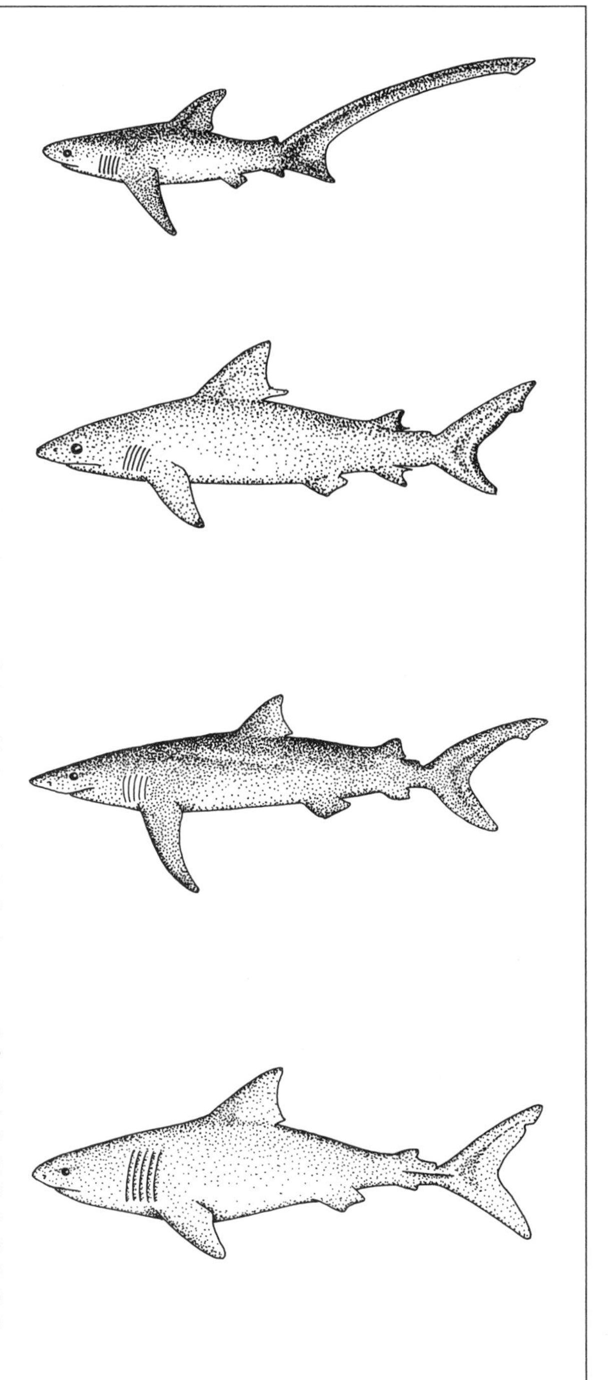

Common thresher shark. *Alopias vulpinus.* This open-ocean shark feeds on squid and small schooling fish. It is reported to use its extraordinarily long tail to stun the fish it preys upon, feeding on the outer members of the school. Thresher sharks are rarely seen near shore. They are considered harmless to humans. They grow to 6 m (18 ft) in length.

Gray reef shark. *Carcharhinus amblyrhynchus.* This shark lives in the deeper shoreline and reef regions of warmer ocean waters, feeding on many species of large and small reef and schooling fish, octopus, and squid. It has territorial instincts and aggressively defends a specific region of the reef. When confronted, it assumes a well-defined posture with its head arched back and its pectoral fins pointing strongly downward and performs an exaggerated back-and-forth swimming motion before attacking. It is considered very dangerous. It grows to 2.7 m (8 ft).

Great blue shark (blue whaler shark). *Prionace glauca.* This open-ocean shark feeds on a variety of foods, including fish, birds, squids, other sharks, and garbage. It is aggressive when feeding. It damages fishing nets and is very dangerous to humans. The upper body is a brilliant indigo blue shading to a light blue on the sides and to white on the belly. The name *whaler shark* was given by Australian whalers of the last century when the sharks attacked and ate parts of the whale carcasses the whalers were towing. It grows to a length of 5 m (15 ft).

Great white shark. *Carcharodon carcharias.* This is probably the most feared shark in the ocean, for good reason. It has been described as the world's most ferocious animal. It is normally an open-ocean fish but is often seen near shore, especially in Australia. It will eat almost anything, including large fish, birds, seals, porpoises, and turtles. It is aggressive, tough, and extremely dangerous to humans; it has even been known to attack large boats. It is responsible for more attacks on humans than any other shark species. The great white shark grows to a length of over 8.3 m (25 ft). This shark was the star in the *Jaws* films.

Table 10–2 *continued.* Selected species of sharks

Hammerhead shark. (Several species. A common hammerhead shark, *Sphyrna zygaena*, is shown here). Found both close to shore and in the open ocean, this shark feeds on a variety of surface- and bottom-dwelling fish, crabs, squid, and sting rays. In some regions it is very dangerous; in others it appears to be docile and more wary of humans. The adult female often goes into bays and harbors to give birth to her young. There is much disagreement on the function of the elaborate, flat, hammer-shaped head. It is probably used as a planing device in swimming, an aid to visual and olfactory perception, and a protection for the eyes when feeding on stingrays. It grows to a length of 4.3 m (13 ft).

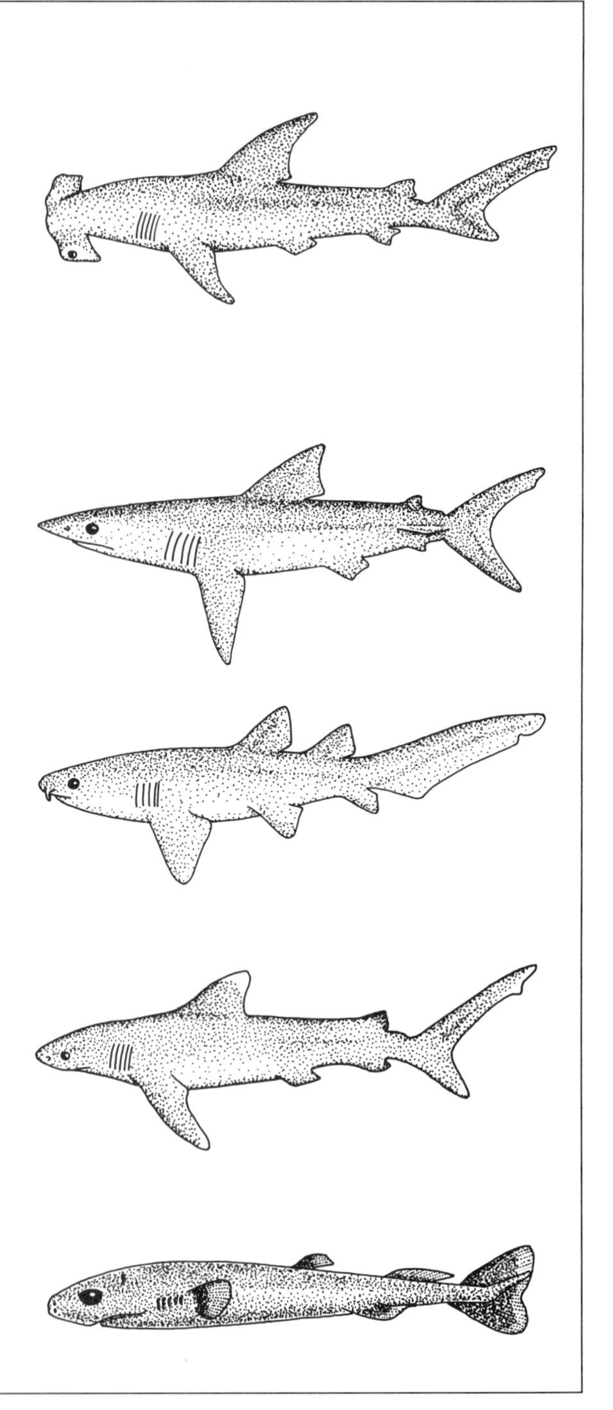

Mako Shark. (pronounced "may-co"). *Isurus oxyrinchus.* This shark is an open-ocean, active swimmer that is occasionally seen in shallow water. It is aggressive, strong, and very dangerous to humans. It feeds on swordfish and squid. It is much sought after by deep-sea sportfishers because of its speed, strength, and endurance. It grows to a length of 4 m (12 ft).

Nurse shark. *Ginglymostoma cirratum.* This is normally a very docile shark. It rests for long periods on the bottom of shallow-water reefs. It is often approached and even touched by scuba divers. It may, however, defend itself and attack when provoked. It has two long, fleshy barbels attached to its head near the nostrils. Its diet consists of lobsters, shrimp, squid, and small fish. It grows to a length of 4.3 m (13 ft).

Oceanic White-tipped Shark. *Carcharhinus (Pterolamiops) longimanus.* This is an open-ocean shark, rarely seen close to shore. It is an active, strong swimmer that feeds on a large variety of fish, squid, and birds. It often follows ships for long distances, claiming the garbage that is thrown overboard. It is considered extremely dangerous to humans if they ditch in open ocean. It grows to a length of 3.7 m (11 ft).

Pygmy shark. *Euprotomicrus bispinatus.* This is a very small shark that is rarely seen by humans. It lives in the open ocean ranging from the surface to the bottom at great depths. It feeds on small fish, squid, and crustaceans. Because of its small size and rare occurrence, it is harmless to humans. It grows to an average length of 20 cm (0.2 m, 8 in).

Table 10 –2 *continued.* Selected species of sharks

Spiny dogfish shark. *Squalus acanthias.* This small shark is common in cold, shallow shoreline waters, feeding on fish smaller than itself, squid, lobsters, crabs. It is considered harmless to humans. It is caught in large numbers on hook and line and in nets by fishers. It is valued as food. Biologists use dogfish sharks in research and as dissection specimens in college comparative anatomy classes. It grows to 1 m (3 ft).

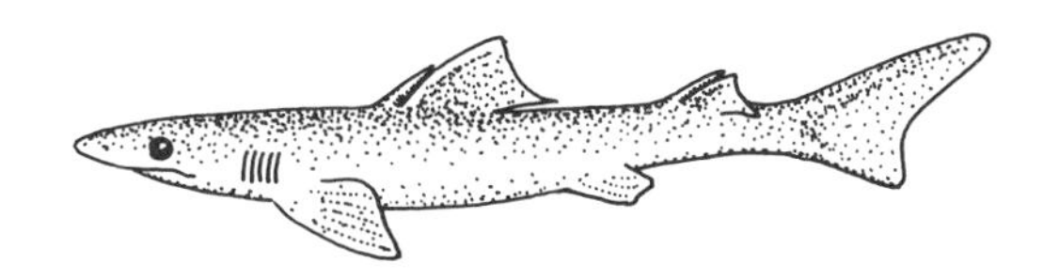

Tiger shark. *Galeocerdo cuvieri.* This shark is a notorious killer, second only to the white shark. It is found in the open ocean and close to shore. Its name comes from the vertical brown blotches and stripes on its back and sides, which fade as the animal ages. It eats almost anything. Fish, birds, seals, dogs, other sharks, parts of cows, canned goods, a sack of coal, and items of clothing have been found in the stomachs of these sharks. It grows to a length of 6 m (18 ft).

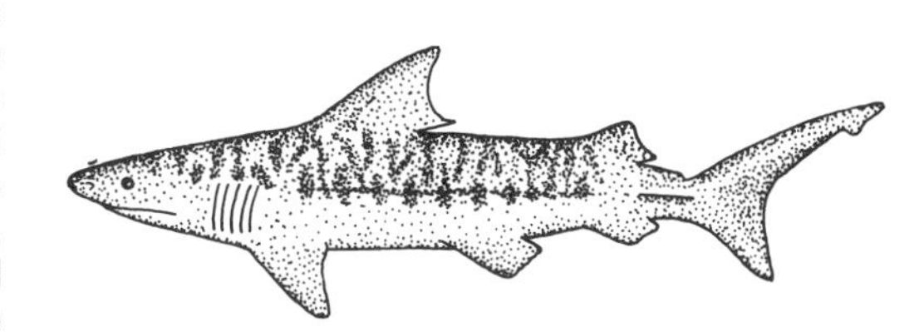

Whale shark. *Rhincodon typus.* The whale shark is the largest fish alive, reaching a length of over 20 m (65 ft). Because of its huge size, it is called a whale shark. It has a mouth with very small teeth at the front end of the body. It feeds on small fish, squid, and crustaceans. It is a slow swimmer of the open ocean, rarely encountered by humans. It is considered harmless.

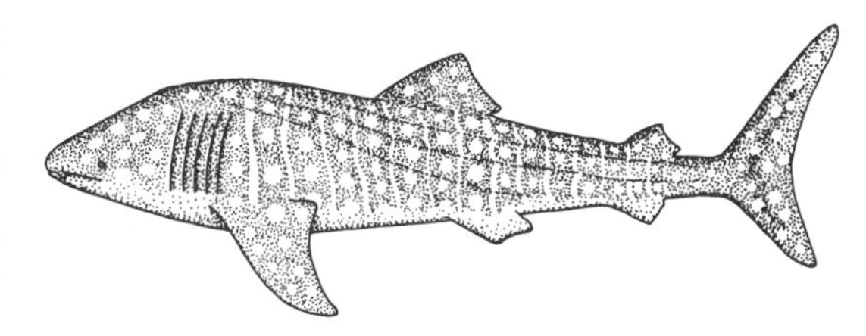

White-tipped reef shark. *Triaenodon obesus.* Common on shallow rocky and coral reefs, this shark is often found lying inactive on the bottom. It is one species that need not swim continuously to breathe. It can flex its gill covers voluntarily to move water over the gill surfaces. It is a docile shark during the daytime, generally considered non-aggressive. However, it attacks to defend itself when threatened or molested. At night it becomes aggressive, actively feeding on small reef fish, octopus, squid, crabs, lobsters, and rays. It grows to a length of 2.5 m (7 ft).

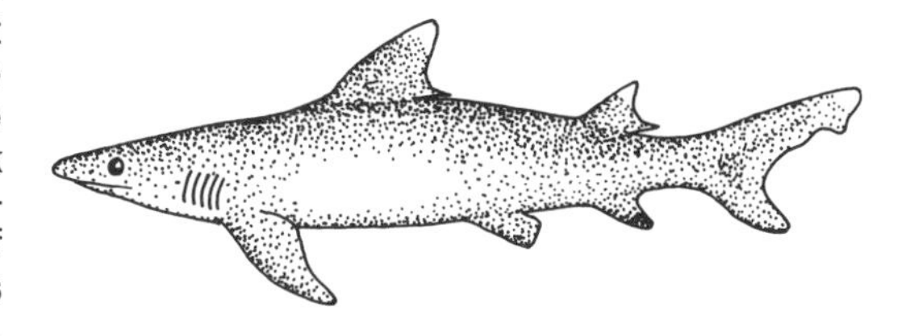

PROCEDURE

1. Make a poster showing the habitats of sharks by ocean zones. A **habitat** is the place where an organism lives, eats, and grows.
   a. Cut the edge off your copy of Fig. 10–2(B) along the dashed line.
   b. Glue or tape Fig. 10–2(A) along the dashed line in Fig. 10–2(B) to create a small poster of shark habitats.

2. Devise a color code for showing how dangerous each shark species is. Then color the sharks on your copy of Fig. 10–3. See Table 10–2 for descriptions of shark behaviors. Categorize the sharks as follows:

   Extremely dangerous: unusually aggressive behavior; considered a killer
   Very dangerous: aggressive, unpredictable behavior; known human fatalities
   Dangerous: known to bite people rarely or occasionally; attacks not fatal
   Harmless: not considered dangerous to humans

   Show your color code in the lower right-hand corner of your poster.

3. Position each species of shark in its probable habitat on your poster.
   a. Cut out the shark drawings from your copy of Fig. 10–3. Keep the name of each shark with its drawing.
   b. Using information from Table 10–2,

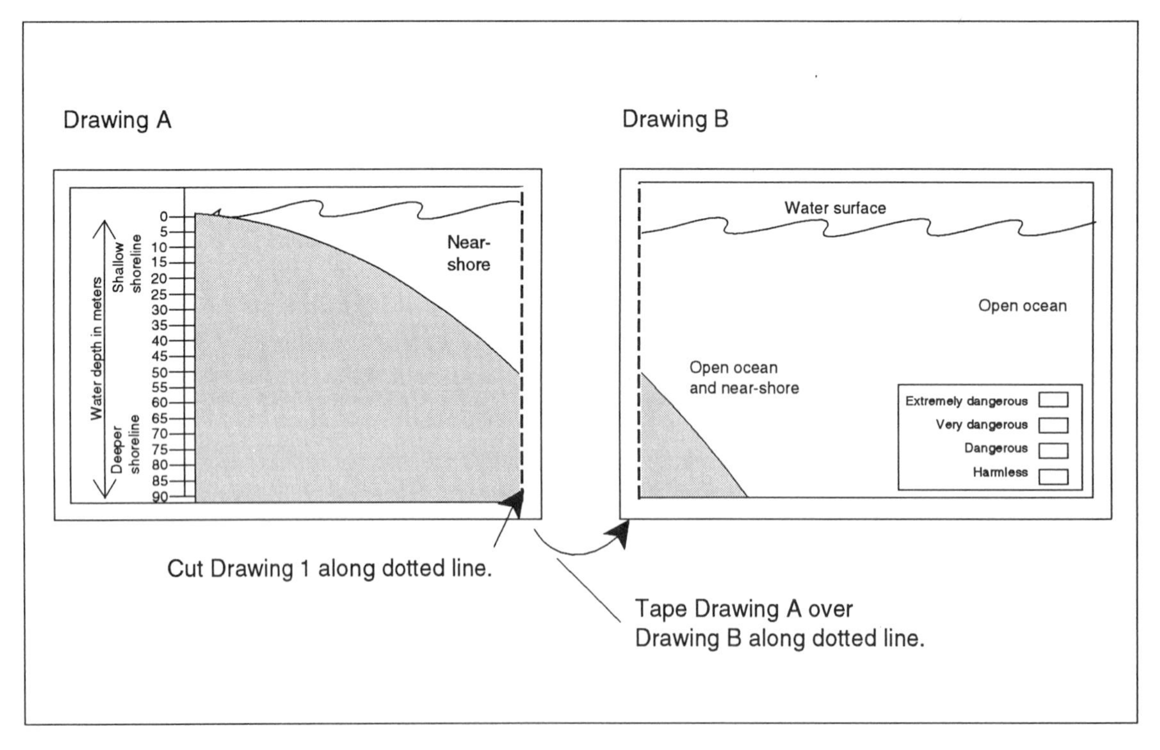

Fig. 10–2. Diagram of a shark habitat poster

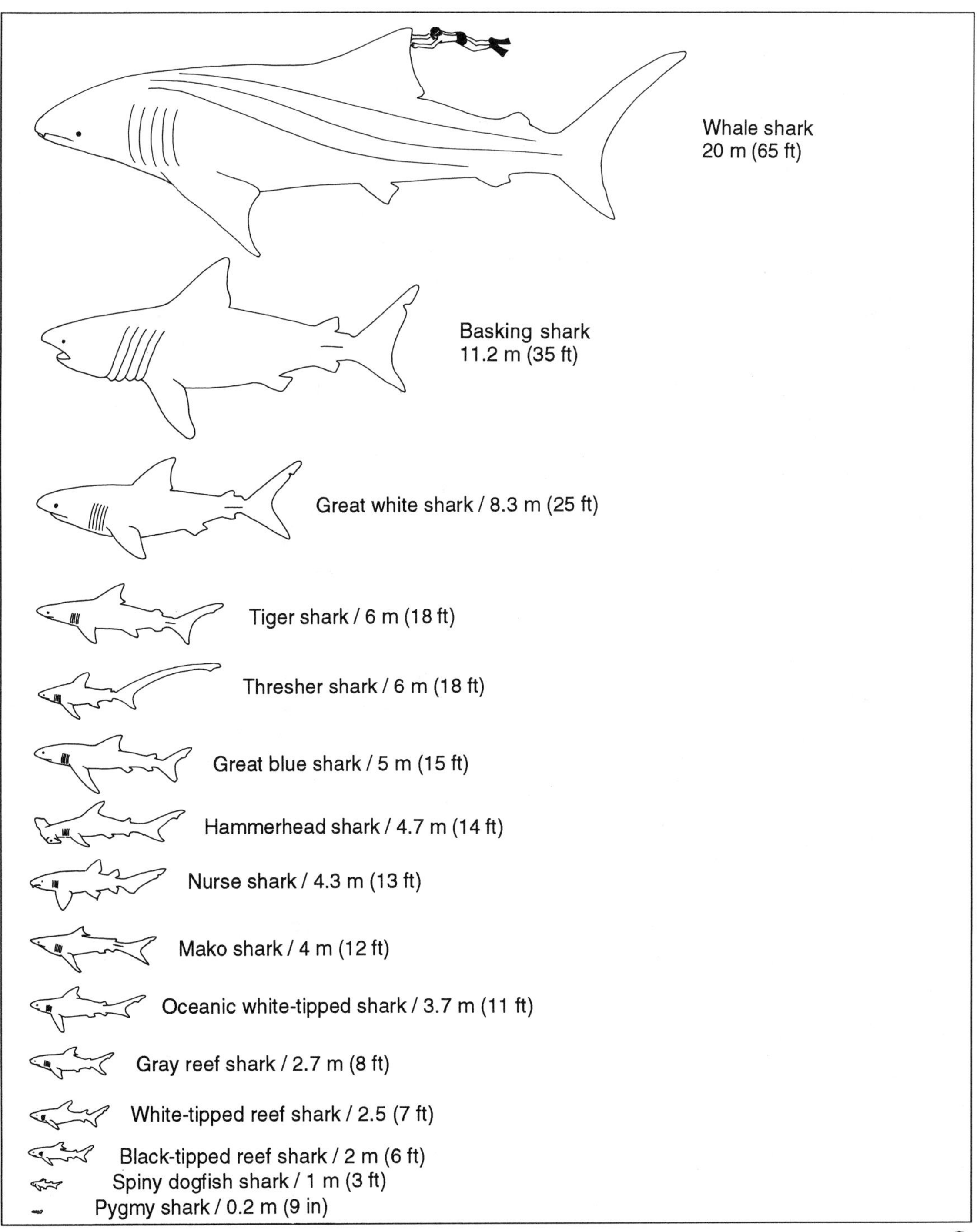

Fig. 10 – 3. Maximum sizes of various species of sharks scaled to relative size Ⓦ

decide where to place each shark on the poster—in near-shore waters, in open-ocean waters, or in both near-shore and open-ocean waters.

c. Using information from Table 10–2 again, arrange the sharks by what they eat. If the shark eats only surface-dwelling organisms, put it near the surface. If the shark eats bottom-dwelling organisms, put it near the seafloor.

d. Glue each shark drawing and its name to the poster.

4. (Optional) Add information to the poster telling what the sharks eat.

5. Compare your completed posters. Discuss similarities and differences among the posters.

QUESTIONS

5. What relationships, if any, are there between the size of a shark and
   a. the types of food it eats?
   b. its danger to humans?
   c. its ocean habitat?

6. How do variations in body form relate to a shark's method of food capture?

7. What advantage might its large gill slits give to a basking shark?

8. How might a shark swallow cans, coral, clothing, or chunks of wood without injuring itself?

9. Swimming beaches in Australia—but not in Hawaii—must be protected by shark nets. What hypothesis could explain why?

Naming Sharks

You learned in Topic 3 that scientists follow rules for naming species of organisms. The name, created by the scientist who first discovers or describes the species, uses Latin or Greek word parts describing distinctive features of the species.

Sometimes a species is named after its discoverer or a famous researcher. The person's last name becomes the species name, written in lowercase letters, often with an "i" added to the end. Two of the butterflyfish in Table 3–4, *C. tinkeri* and *C. kleini,* were named in this way.

Some shark species were named many years ago, when scientists knew very little about sharks. Translations of the scientific names often give clues to what scientists knew when they named the species.

ACTIVITY 3

Analyze the meanings of the scientific names of some species of sharks.

MATERIALS

- dictionary
- dictionary of word roots (optional)

PROCEDURE

1. Study the scientific names of the 14 shark species in Table 10–2.

2. Pick apart each name to identify its

Table 10–3. Glossary of Latin (L) and Greek (G) word parts

acanth, -a, -o (G). A spine, thorn
alope, -c, (G). A fox
aeno (G). Terrible
ambl, -y (G). Blunt
bi (L). Two, twice, double
carchar, -o (G). Jagged
cerd, -al (G). Cunning; a fox
cet, -a, -us (G). A whale
cirr, -us (L). A curl of hair
clope, -c, -x (G). A fox
cuvier. The name of a famous scientist
eu (G). Good, well
gale, -a, -i (G). A weasel; a cat
ginglym, -o, -us (G). A hinge
glauc, -o (G). Gray; bluish gray
is, -o (G). Equal
lamia (G). A vampirelike monster
long, -i (L). Long
man, -u (L). A hand
maxim (L). Largest, greatest
melan, -o (G). Black
micr, -o, -us (G). Small
obesus (L). To eat away; to devour
odon, -t, -to (G). A tooth
opsi, -o (G). Appearance, sight
oxy, -s (G). Sharp; acid
prion, -o (G). A saw
prot, -e, -o (G). First, original
pter, -o, -um (G). A wing; a feather; a fin
rhin, -o (G). A nose
rhina (G). A shark; a file or rasp
rhynch, -o, -us (G). A snout or beak
sphyr, -o (G). A hammer or mallet
spin, -a, -i (L). A spine, thorn
squal, -us (L). A dogfish
stom, -a, -ato, -o (G). A mouth
tri (L). Three
typ, -i, -o (G). A type
ur, -a, -o (G). The tail
vulp, -es, -i (L). A fox; cunning
zygaen, -a, (G). Hammerhead shark
-inus, -ina, -inum (L). Likeness; belonging to
-aceus, -acea, -aceum (L). Of; pertaining to

Latin or Greek parts. Refer to the glossary in Table 10–3.

3. Record your English translation of each scientific name.

4. Study a species of shark and list the features you think are important for describing it. Use a dictionary of word roots to create your own scientific name for that species. Refer to the rules in Topic 3 of this unit.

QUESTIONS

10. Does the scientific name always describe an obvious feature of the species?

11. Why do you think the scientist chose that name to describe the species?

12. What kinds of features, anatomical or behavioral, do the names refer to?

Shark Attack Patterns

Most sharks are not aggressive. Some are too small or have teeth too small to harm humans. But 27 species are known to have attacked humans. Most sharks are carnivores, meat-eating animals that consume smaller animals like turtles, seals, birds, and fish. Some sharks are predators that stalk and kill living prey; others are scavengers that find and eat the remains of dead animals.

Scientists are trying to understand what prompts sharks to attack humans and what humans can do to reduce their chances of being attacked. They have learned that the behavior patterns of sharks vary widely among species, so what is true of one species may not apply to others. (The same is true of the behavior patterns of lions, leopards, and house cats, all members of the cat family).

Because research on sharks in the open ocean is difficult and costly, scientists study reports of shark attacks to understand the conditions under which sharks attack humans. Unfortunately, there is no worldwide system for reporting shark attacks. Scientists do not even know the number of shark attacks each year. The U.S. Navy, concerned with shark attacks on shipwrecked sailors, and the oceanography departments of some American universities collect information, but it is often unreliable because it comes from victims or witnesses who are not trained observers. Nevertheless, from this information we can make many inferences about the behaviors of dangerous sharks and of the people who have been attacked.

As you work with the data in the next activity, keep in mind that the information is inconsistent because it comes from several sources. In this activity we are looking for trends, not exact values.

ACTIVITY 4

Determine the latitude, season, and time of day of most shark attacks worldwide.

MATERIALS

- copies of Workbook Figs. 10–4 and 10–5
- map or globe (optional)

PROCEDURE

1. Study the data in Table 10–4 showing the world distribution of shark attacks by month and the latitude of each attack.
   a. The numbers of attacks in each hemisphere are shown separately for tropic and temperate zones.
   b. Observe how the data from Table 10–4 on shark attacks during June are shown on the bar graph in Fig. 10–4.
   c. Using the data from Table 10–4, complete the bar graph in Fig. 10–4.

2. Show the relative numbers of shark attacks in a 24-hr day.
   a. See Table 10–5 for information on times of shark attacks.
   b. Show the number of attacks at a given time by placing dots on the clock in Fig. 10–5. (For example, the four dots above 11 A.M. show that four attacks occurred at that hour.)

QUESTIONS

13. Did most of the shark attacks occur
    a. in tropic zones (from 0° to 23°N or S) or in temperate zones (from 24° to 66°N or S)?
    b. in the northern hemisphere or in the southern hemisphere?
    c. in summer, fall, winter, or spring?

14. Which zone do you live in—a tropic zone, a temperate zone, or a polar zone?

15. At what time(s) of day did most shark attacks occur?

16. What does this information suggest
    a. about shark behavior?
    b. about human behavior?

Table 10–4. World distribution of shark attacks by month, hemisphere, and zone, 1941–1968

Month	Northern hemisphere		Southern hemisphere	
	Tropic zone 0°–23°N	Temperate zone 24°–66°N	Tropic zone 0°–23°S	Temperate zone 24°–66°S
June	5	10	7	0
July	9	26	4	1
August	5	9	4	1
September	1	7	4	0
October	1	5	5	2
November	1	0	12	9
December	1	2	6	25
January	3	0	11	44
February	3	2	11	20
March	4	0	7	18
April	3	4	11	7
May	3	7	10	2

Source: Clark 1975, 51

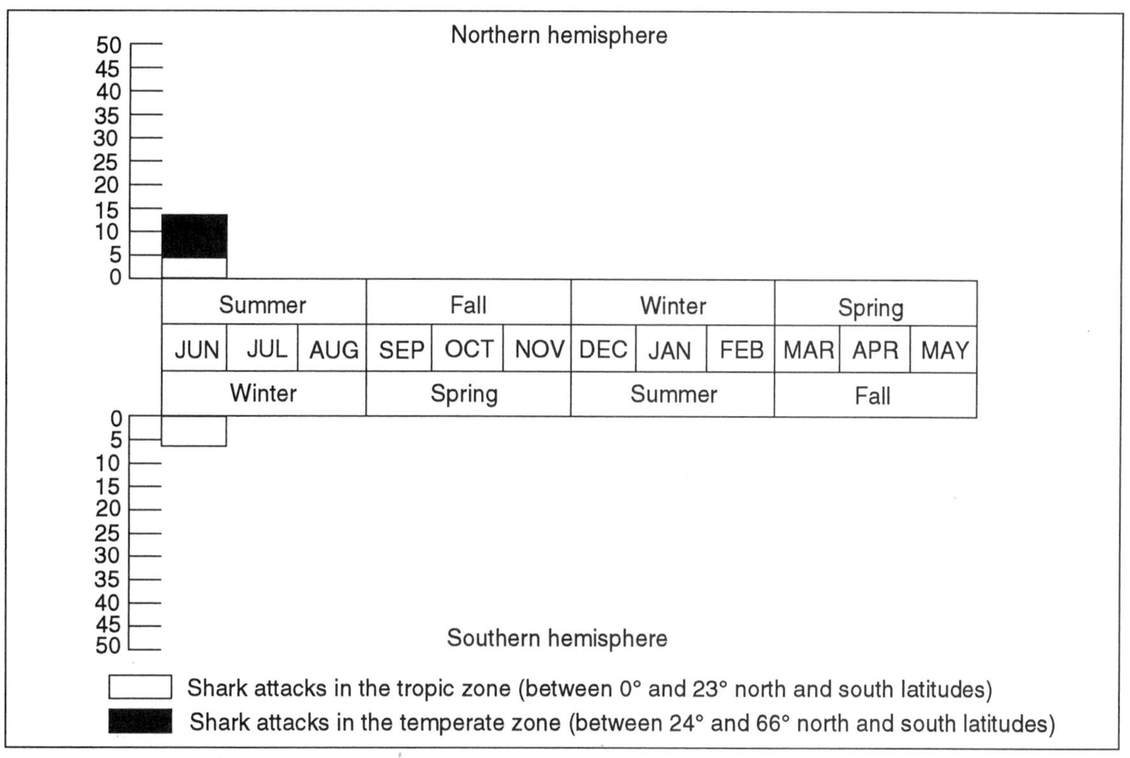

Fig. 10–4. Worldwide distribution of shark attacks

Ⓦ

Table 10 – 5. Worldwide shark attacks during 1971 by time of day

Time	Number of attacks
5:30 A.M.	1
7:30	1
9:00	1
9:30	2
10:00	1
10:30	1
11:00	4
11:30	2
12:00 noon	1
12:30 P.M.	3
1:00	1
1:30	1
2:00	2
3:00	8
3:30	5
4:00	8
4:30	4
5:00	4
5:30	6
6:00	5
7:00	1
8:00	1

Source: Clark 1975, 46

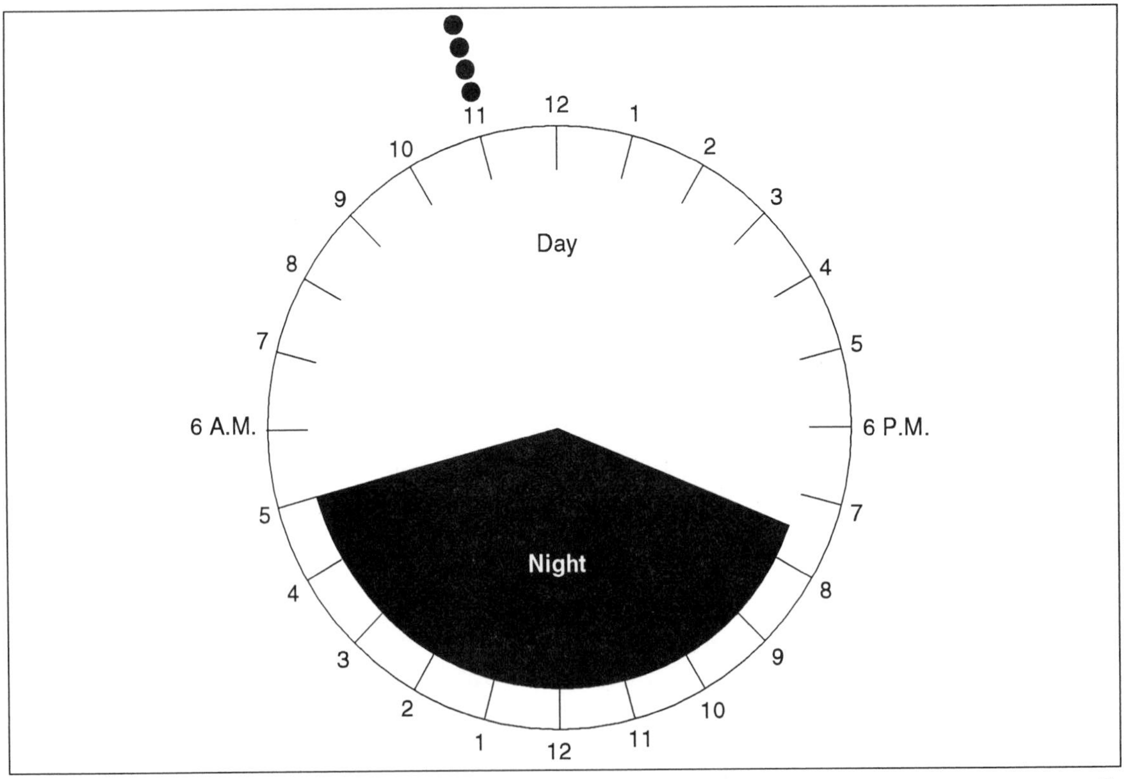

Fig. 10 – 5. Shark attacks by time of day

ACTIVITY 5

Describe the type of activity and location of victims attacked by sharks.

MATERIALS

- copies of Workbook Tables 10–6, 10–7, and 10–8
- copy of Workbook Fig. 10–6
- calculator (optional)

PROCEDURE

1. Complete Table 10–6. Calculate the percentage of attacks in each activity.
2. Using information in Table 10–6, draw bars on the graph in Fig. 10–6 to show the numbers of shark attacks by type of human activity.
3. Complete Table 10–7 showing the depth of victims at the time of attack. Calculate the percentage of victims who at the time of the attack
   a. were swimming on the surface.
   b. were submerged.
4. Complete Table 10–8 showing the envi-

Table 10–6. Activities of shark attack victims in Hawaii, 1886–1980 Ⓦ

Activity	Number of attacks	Percentage
Spear- or netfishing	23	
Swimming	9	
Surfing	8	
Scuba diving	2	
Other activities	3	
TOTAL	45	100%

Source: Balazs and Kam, 1982

Table 10–7. Worldwide data on depth of victims at time of attack, 1941–1968 Ⓦ

Depth of victim	Number of attacks	Percentage
Surface		
1–5 feet	797	
Submerged		
6–20 feet	59	
21–50 feet	22	
50+ feet	12	
TOTAL	890	100%

Source: Clark 1975, 47

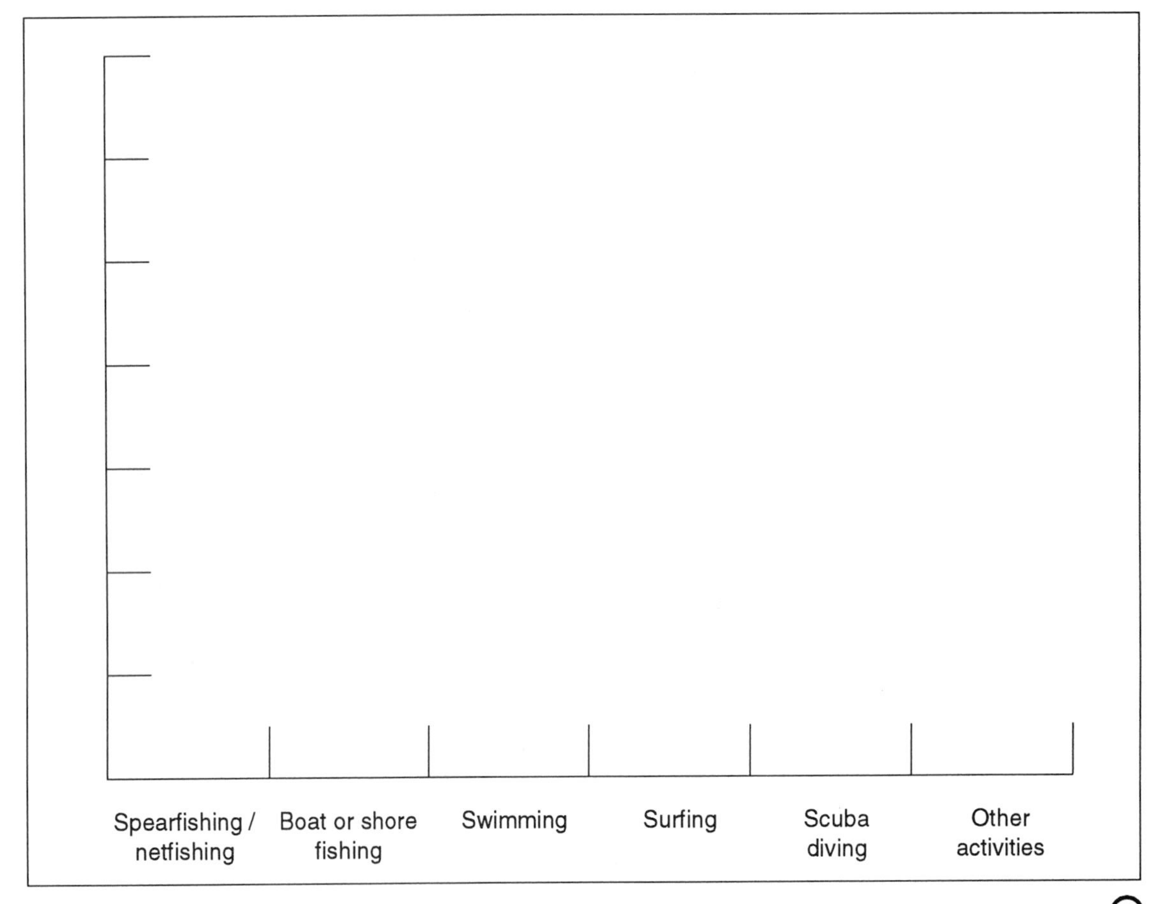

Fig. 10–6. Activities of shark attack victims

Table 10–8. Worldwide water environments where shark attacks occurred, 1941–1968

Environment	Number of attacks	Percentage
Beaches and inshore areas	435	
Sandbars, reefs, and banks	179	
Rivers and river mouths	95	
Harbors and bays	89	
Open sea	88	
Near breakwaters, piers, and jetties	41	
Outside breakers/surf zone	21	
TOTAL	948	100%

Source: Clark 1975, 48

ronments that victims were in at the time of the attacks. Calculate each percentage.

QUESTIONS

17. Under what conditions do most shark attacks occur by
    a. type of activity?
    b. submerged depth of the victim?
    c. type of environment?

18. What do your answers to Question 17 suggest about
    a. the shark habits that people should know to reduce their chance of being attacked?
    b. the behavior of people at the time of the shark's attack?

19. Using the data in Table 10–9, estimate what percentage of shark attack victims live to tell their experience.

20. Using the information in all the tables and figures referring to sharks, write a short essay telling when and where sharks have attacked humans.

FURTHER INVESTIGATIONS

1. Read about other species of sharks. Draw their outlines to scale and add them to your poster of sharks in the ocean. Include drawings of their teeth.

2. Construct an enlarged display of sharks drawn to scale as in Fig. 10–3. (One way is to make a transparency of the figure and project the shark outlines onto large sheets of paper taped to the wall or chalkboard.) Make the display similar to your shark poster and add detailed information. Use references.

3. Prepare an oral report on as many sharks as you can find that are harmless to

Table 10–9. Worldwide deaths related to shark attacks, 1941–1968

Descriptions	Number of cases	Percentages
No death (nonfatal)	744	64
Death resulting from shark attack	251	22
Death, no details	70	6
Assumed death by shark attack	49	4
Not known if death resulted from shark attack	21	2
Death probably not caused by shark attack	15	1
TOTAL	1,150	100%

Source: Clark 1975, 45

humans. Explain the details of their anatomy and behavior.

4. Using a dictionary of word roots, find the meanings of the names of the families of bony fish shown in Table 4–1.

5. Discuss whether the data on shark attacks justify the reputation of sharks as menacing killers lurking in the ocean for human victims. When you answer this, imagine how many people worldwide spend time in the ocean each year. What are the odds of being attacked?

6. Discuss the probability of a shark attack at a specific beach. To do this, you need to estimate each of the following:
   a. How many people enter the water?
   b. What kinds of activities do they engage in?
   c. How many shark attacks have occurred near that area in the past 10 to 100 years?

7. What tactics do you recommend to avoid attracting sharks and risking an attack? Go to the library to find studies on shark attacks. Report your findings to the class.

8. Using references, compare the anatomy and behavior of sharks with those of their close relatives, the rays and skates. Report your findings to the class.

9. Some environmentalists claim that humans are hunting and killing sharks at such a rate worldwide that sharks are becoming endangered. Using library references, gather information on shark hunting. Make a report to the class supporting or refuting the environmentalists' claims.

10. What is the economic and cultural value of sharks? What foods and other products are made from them? Why are sharks of interest in medicine? What roles have they played in various coastal and island societies?

11. In what ways do sharks help to keep the ocean environment healthy? What would happen if hunting vastly reduced the numbers of sharks?

12. On November 15, 1976, a strange-looking shark was caught off the island of Oahu in Hawaii. After examining it, scientists determined that it was a new species in a new family. Other specimens have been sighted and collected since then. The shark was first named "megamouth" for its peculiar jaw. Read references to learn about this species. Report your findings to the class.

11. Fish as a Food Resource

The oceans once offered a seemingly boundless supply of fish for food. But we now know this supply is limited. Many species have been overfished to satisfy consumers, and much fish biomass goes to waste in catching and preparing food for humans.

Fish protein concentrate (FPC), a nourishing powder made from ground fish and fish parts, is used as a food supplement for animals. Very little of the fish biomass goes to waste in making FPC. It is often added to chicken and pig feed, for example. But it is not widely used as a food additive for humans.

The most popular fish products in America are fish fillets or fish sticks. Most of the fish harvested from the ocean are labeled "undesirable" and not favored for making fish fillets or fish sticks. Often these undesirable fish are tossed overboard, and their biomass is wasted. There are ways of preparing fish that use these undesirable types of fish. In time, more Americans may be attracted to products such as fish cakes made from underused or unpopular fish species.

Fish cake and imitation crabmeat use a fish product called ***surimi*** (soo REE mee, Japanese). *Surimi* is a paste made from minced and blended fish considered undesirable or unpopular, like pollack. *Kamaboko* (kah mah BOH koh, Japanese) and *gefilte* fish (guh FIL tuh, Yiddish) are two types of fish-cake products. Fish cakes are made from blended fish mixed with sugar, salt, seasoning, and starch or eggs as a thickener or binder. They may be shaped into patties or sausages for pan frying, deep frying, boiling, broiling, baking, or steaming.

ACTIVITY

Make fish cake from underused fish species.

MATERIALS

- cleaning supplies
- copy of Workbook Table 11–1
- several 15-cm or larger fresh fish, to make 3 cups of meat (about 1 lb per cup)
- kitchen knife
- fork and spatula
- wax paper
- mixing bowl
- ingredients for one assigned recipe from Table 11–1
- blender (optional)
- flour, cornstarch, or bread crumbs
- measuring spoons and cups
- heat source
- frying pan
- pot holders
- 2 tablespoons cooking oil
- paper towels
- paper plates and forks
- 3 x 5-in index cards

Table 11–1. Fish cake recipes 

NOTE: c = cup; t = teaspoon; T = tablespoon

1. Onion fish cake
3 c diced fish
1 egg, beaten
1/2 t garlic salt
1 onion, diced

2. Pizza fish cake
3 c diced fish
1 egg, beaten
1/2 t oregano
1 T diced onion
1 t garlic salt
1 t cornstarch

3. Teriyaki fish cake
3 c diced fish
1/2 c soy sauce
1 egg, beaten
1/2 t sugar
1/2 t ginger
1 t cornstarch

4. Chive fish cake
3 c diced fish
1 egg, beaten
1/4 c chopped carrots
1/4 c minced chives
1 small clove garlic
1/2 t sugar
1 t cornstarch

5. Vegetable fish cake
3 c diced fish
1 egg, beaten
1/4 medium onion, diced
1/4 c diced carrot
2 t celery salt
2 t soy sauce
1 t cornstarch

6. Potato fish cake
3 c diced fish
1 egg, beaten
1/2 t garlic salt
1 T diced onion
1 c mashed potatoes
1/4 t pepper
1 t chopped parsley
1 t cornstarch

7. Mushroom fish cake
3 c diced fish
1/2 c diced onion
1/2 c diced carrot
1/2 c diced celery
1 large mushroom
1/2 t garlic salt
1/2 t salt
1 T chives
1/2 t sugar
1 t cornstarch

Preparation (all recipes)

1. Mix ingredients well. For a finer-textured product, put the diced flesh into a blender, add other ingredients, and blend to a smooth consistency.
2. Add cornstarch to thicken the mixture, beginning with a teaspoon. Add more a little at a time until the mixture thickens enough to hold a shape. Shape the mixture into small patties or sausages. Coat with flour, cornstarch, or bread crumbs. Place 2 tablespoons of the selected coating on waxed paper and roll one piece at a time in it.
3. Heat 2 to 4 tablespoons of oil in a frying pan. Fry the patties or sausages for 3 to 5 minutes on each side, adding oil as needed. Drain the patties or sausages on paper towels. Arrange them on a platter for serving.

PROCEDURE

1. Wash your hands. Work in a clean kitchen or a sanitary area of the laboratory. Thoroughly clean all cooking utensils. Keep your hands clean.

2. Wash the fish. Scale or skin them. (If you use bonefish, cut off the tail and squeeze the flesh out like toothpaste through the cut. Bonefish skin should not be filleted or washed.)

3. Fillet the fish the way your teacher shows you. Keep it clean by laying it on wax paper.

4. Dice the fish on each side.

5. Put the diced fish in a bowl, wash with tap water, and drain off the water.

6. Select a recipe from Table 11

Buying Fish

Supermarkets and seafood shops sell fish in a variety of forms. See Fig. 11. **Whole fish** is just that—fish as it comes from the water. **Drawn fish** (also called **cleaned fish**) is whole fish gutted and usually scaled. **Dressed fish** is cleaned fish with the head and fins removed.

Fish may be cut into steaks and fillets. **Steaks** are cross-sections of meat about 3/4-in thick, usually from a large fish. **Fillets** are sides of meat cut from the bone. Butterfly fillets are two sides of fish meat held together by the belly skin and flesh.

Fish sticks are pieces of fish meat cut into uniform size, breaded, and most often sold frozen.

Fresh Fish

To judge the freshness and quality of whole or drawn fish, rely on the condition of the eyes, as fishers do.

A fish in good condition has bright, clear protruding eyes. If the eyes are milky, cloudy, or sunken, the fish has probably been poorly stored or is at or near the end of its shelf life. Look at the gills. Bright red gills free of slime show that the fish is fresh. As a fish ages, its gills fade to pink, then to gray, finally to green. The skin of fish sold "fresh," or unfrozen, should be shiny, and the markings should look like the markings of a fish just caught. Fillets and steaks should look freshly cut and have no brown edges.

Smelling is another way to check the condition of fish. Most fresh fish have only a slight, wholesome smell. Oily fish, such as tuna, have a stronger smell.

The flesh should be firm and elastic, and when uncooked, it should not separate easily from the bones. To test the flesh, press it with a finger. If no dent remains, the texture is good and the fish is fresh.

Clean, gut, and wash whole fish before refrigerating to prevent spoilage caused by bacteria and enzymes,. Store fresh fish in airtight moisture-proof wrapping and refrigerate it below 40°F—preferably at 32°F (0°C).

Frozen Fish

To check the quality of frozen fish, make sure all the flesh is frozen hard and is not discolored. To prevent **freezer burn** (drying out), the wrapping should be airtight, moisture-proof, and undamaged. Ice or ice crystals show that the fish may have thawed and been refrozen. Because you cannot see fish sticks

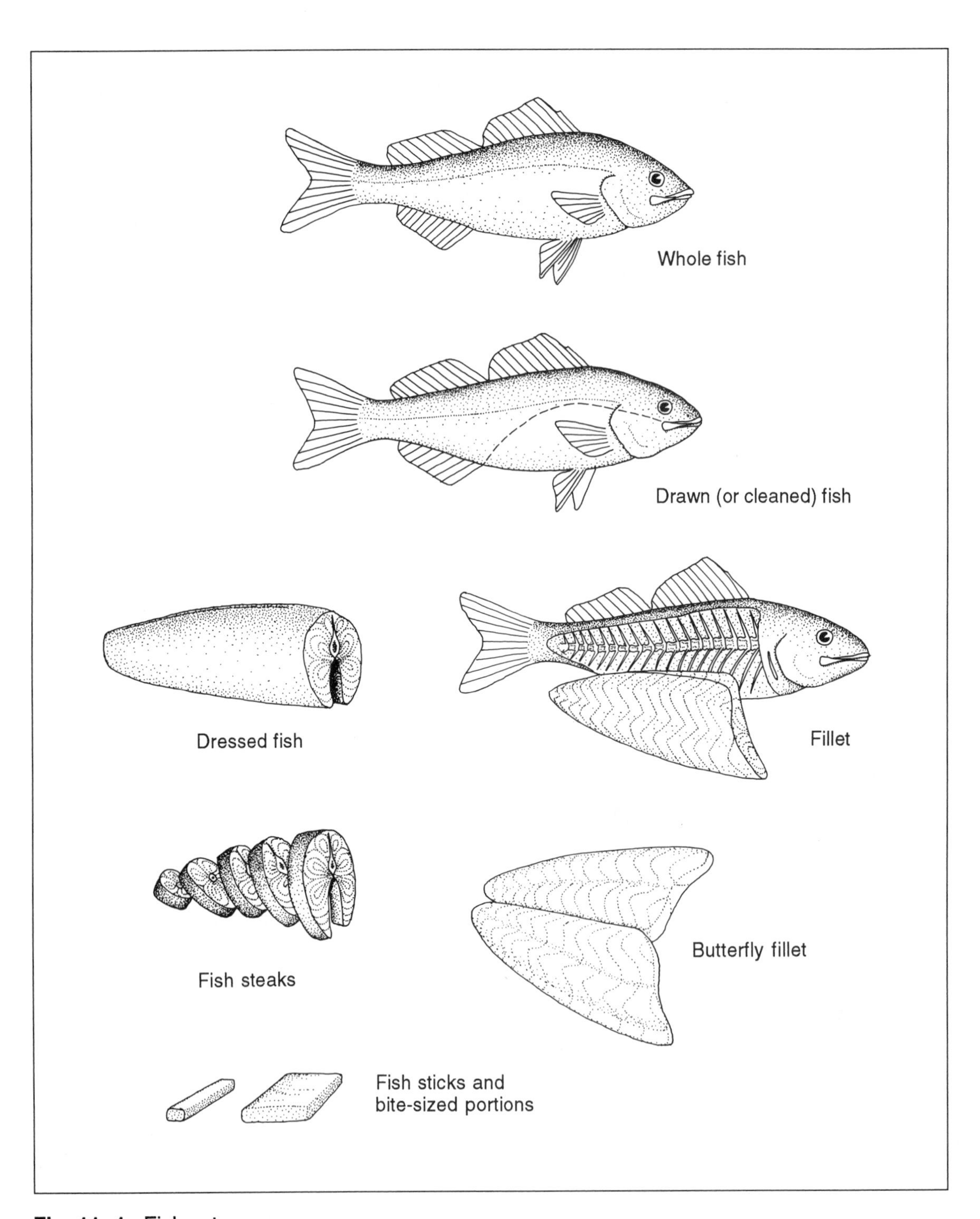

Fig. 11–1. Fish cuts

or frozen fish packaged in boxes, reject boxes that have ice on them.

To store fish for a long time, freeze it at 32°F (0°C) or lower in an airtight moisture-proof wrapping. Fish bought frozen can be glazed by dipping it in water. After a thin, glassy layer of ice forms on the fish, store it in the freezer. Wrapping or glazing prevents freezer burn.

Thawing Fish

To thaw frozen fish, let cold water run over it for 15 to 30 minutes. Keep steaks and fillets in their packaging to prevent damage during thawing.

Fish can be thawed overnight in the refrigerator at 40° to 45°F. In frost-free refrigerators, fish dries out quickly unless it is kept in airtight packaging.

Thawing fish at room temperature is more risky than other methods because thinner parts thaw faster than thicker parts. A package of fillets may take 3 to 4 hours to thaw—long enough for bacteria to multiply. It is better to cook fish before it thaws completely. Steaks, fillets, and fish sticks can even be cooked frozen if you allow a longer cooking time.

QUESTIONS

1. What are the advantages of fish cake over whole fish?
2. For what purpose is fish protein concentrate used?
3. Why might *kamaboko* not be a popular food in the United States?
4. Which local underused fish species would you suggest using in fish cake?
5. Which fish would you suggest not be used in fish cake? Why?

FURTHER INVESTIGATIONS

1. Visit a factory that processes fish or makes *surimi*. Study the process and find out what fish species are used.
2. Do a cultural-historical study of the use of fish by some national group—Chinese, Japanese, Indian, Swedish, French, or other.
3. Collect and try new fish recipes.
4. Have a *surimi*-cooking demonstration for your friends. Discuss the advantages of *surimi*. Compare the nutritional value of *surimi* and fresh or frozen fish.
5. Visit a fishmarket or the seafood section of a supermarket. Find out what's available in fresh, frozen, canned, and preserved fish. Where do the fish come from? Compare their costs.
6. Find information on common food fish consumed in the United States and other countries. Learn how many tons of each fish are caught each year. Prepare a chart ranking the catches from largest to smallest. Which species are being overfished? What, if anything, is being done to protect them?
7. Survey students in your class to find out how much fish they eat each year, what

kinds, and how they prepare it.

8. Compare the nutritional values of fish and other protein sources such as milk, cheese, beef, and chicken. How do their supermarket prices compare?

9. Find out why farmers feed fish supplements to livestock. What do the livestock normally eat? How does the fish supplement benefit the farmer?

10. Learn about career opportunities in the fish-food industry. Include catching the fish, processing them, and marketing the products.

UNIT 2
INVERTEBRATES

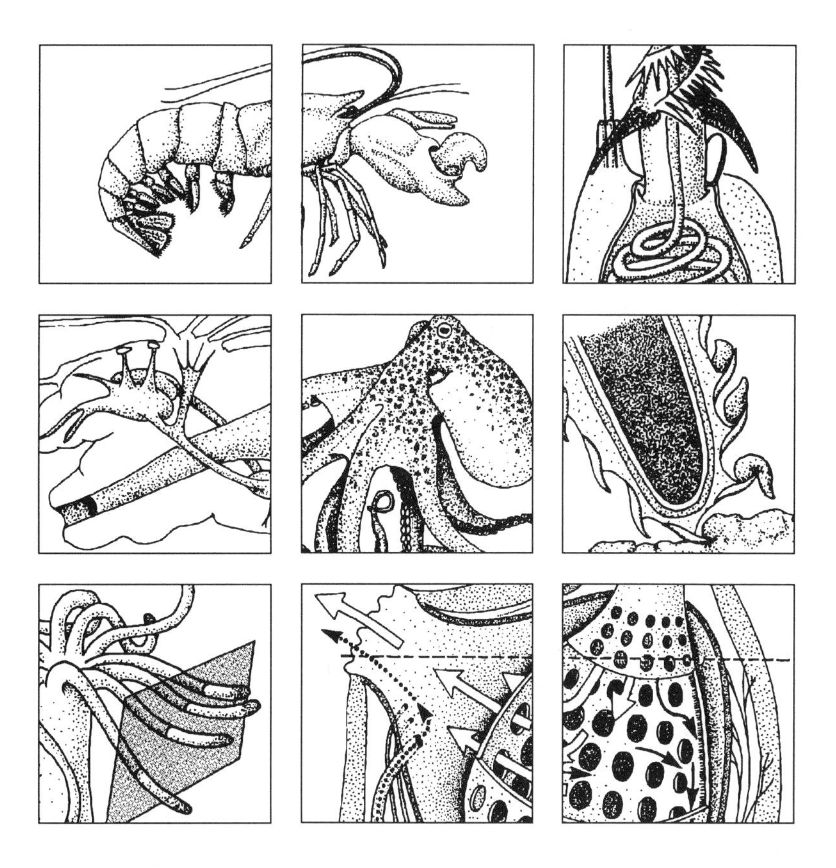

Framed by my mask, the reef is a vast seascape speckled with the bright colors of foraging fish. Mushroom-shaped corals jut outward into open spaces, and branching corals form a leafless stony forest. I see a giant clam that has lost its battle with encrusting coral and is forever trapped in a chalky casket. One tentacle of an octopus slides timidly out of a crevice, followed by another and another, until the bulbous body of the octopus emerges, eyes wide to possible danger. Like a rocket it launches itself toward another crevice and vanishes. The bright feather-duster gills of burrowing tube worms wave above the tiny feeding tentacles of a myriad of coral polyps. Sponges, sea urchins, and coralline algae squat in spaces ignored by other creatures. Snails, starfish, and spiny lobsters crawl through this vast community. Every moment the scene changes.

Coral reefs offer some of the richest and most varied collections of boneless creatures, but such creatures also live in almost every ocean environment. The most common visible inhabitants of the ocean, they supply much of the protein for fish, turtles, porpoises, and whales. To get a picture of their contribution to the dynamics of the living ocean, we now turn to a study of these fascinating animals without backbones.

Francis M. Pottenger III

1. Classification and Comparison of Invertebrates

Our planet is a remarkable place. It is the only place in our solar system and, as far as we know, in the universe, where life exists. Living creatures inhabit almost every part of our waters and land, and they exist in an astonishing variety of shapes and sizes. Over a million kinds of animals and plants are known, and probably millions more are yet to be discovered and described.

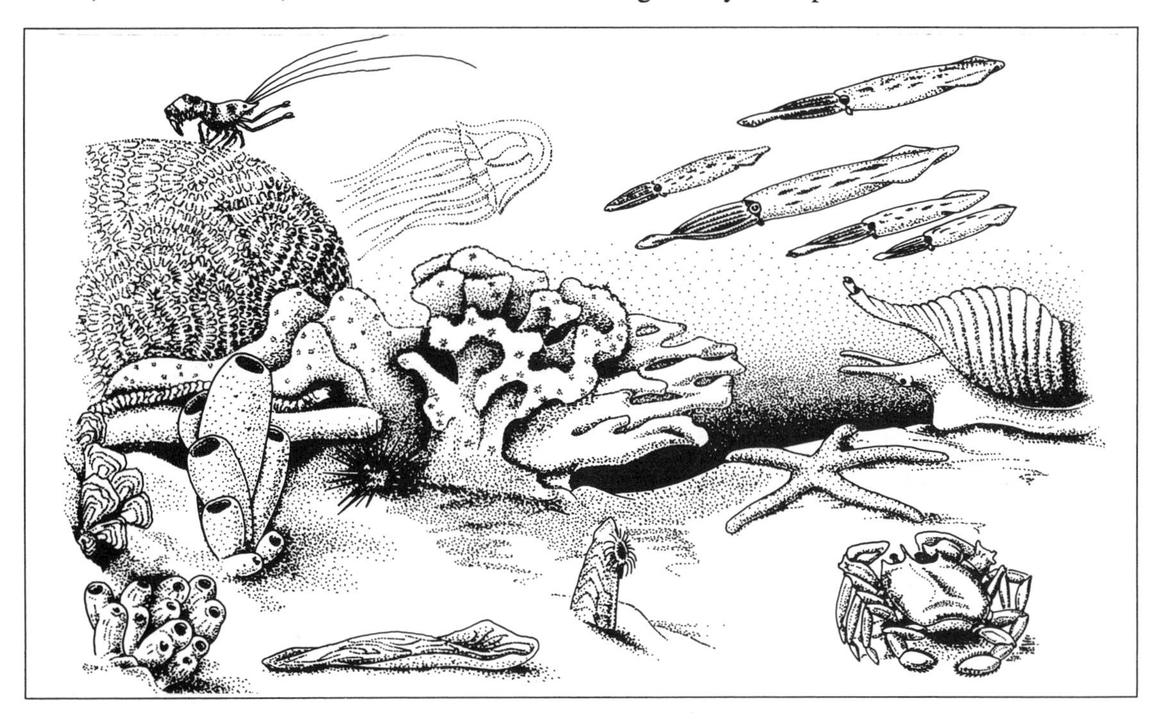

Fig. 1–1. Some invertebrate animals

To study this vast number of life forms, biologists classify organisms into groups and subgroups that have similar anatomy (body parts) and physiology (the workings of those parts). We know from Unit 1, Topic 3, Classification, Nomenclature, and Keys, that all animals are members of the animal kingdom. A kingdom is divided into smaller groups, the most inclusive being the phyla (the singular is *phylum*). A phylum is successively divided into classes, orders, families, genera (the singular is *genus),* and species. Each group may be further divided into subgroups, such as subphyla or subclasses. Using this classification system, we can study the characteristics of one kind of organism or compare the common characteristics of several groups.

Vertebrates and Invertebrates

In the phylum Chordata is a subphylum Vertebrata, which includes all animals with backbones. Among its members are animals such as fish, frogs, lizards, birds, and humans. They are all vertebrates. For discussion, animals are often divided into two groups, vertebrates and invertebrates. Although this division is convenient, it is confusing because invertebrates do not make up a formal scientific group.

Though the term **invertebrate** does not refer to a strictly defined scientific group, it is a handy term meaning "any animal without a backbone." All kinds of animals except vertebrates are invertebrates. Most of us are unfamiliar with invertebrates even though they are far more abundant in the ocean and on land than vertebrates are. See Fig. 1–1. Invertebrates include many phyla. In this unit we will investigate eight phyla of invertebrate animals that are common in the waters of the earth.

Scientific Names

Topic 1 begins the study of invertebrates by introducing terms biologists use to describe animals. We will use these terms in comparing the invertebrates we investigate in this unit.

Scientists have named groups of animals in terms that describe one or more of their unique features. These names most often use Latin or Greek word parts. As you become familiar with the word parts, terms that at first look foreign and difficult will become meaningful to you.

ACTIVITY 1

Translate the Latin and Greek word parts making up phylum names.

Find a major identifying feature of each phylum.

MATERIALS

- copy of Workbook Table 1–1

PROCEDURE

1. Study the scientific names of the invertebrate phyla listed in Table 1–1.
2. Translate each name from its Latin or Greek parts. Refer to the glossary of Latin (L) and Greek (G) word parts in Table 1–2.
   a. Word parts are in bold italics. An example is ***annel.***
   b. Alternative endings are in italics. An example is *-us.*
3. Record your translation of each phylum name in Table 1–1.
4. From your translations, tell what you think is the major feature of each phylum.

Table 1–1. Translation of scientific names of invertebrate phyla

Ⓦ

Phylum	Translation	Major feature
Porifera		
Cnidaria		
Platyhelminthes		
Annelida		
Mollusca		
Arthropoda		
Echinodermata		
Chordata		

Table 1–2. Latin and Greek word parts for phylum names

Word part and its meaning

annel, *-us* (L). A ring; a little ring

-arium, *-aria* (L). A place where something is kept

arthr, *-o, -um* (G). A joint (like the knee joint)

-atus, *-ata* (L). Having, possessing

chord, *-a* (G). A string

cnid, *-a, -o* (G). A nettle (a stinging or prickly plant)

coel, *-i, -o* (G). Hollow

derm, *-a, -ato, -o* (G). Skin

echin, *-o, -us* (G). A hedgehog; a sea urchin

enter, *-o, -um* (G). The intestine; gut

-fer (L). To bear; to carry

helmin, *-s, -th* (G). A worm

-id (L). A condition of

mollusc (L). Soft; a shellfish

not, *-a, -o, -um* (G). The back

plat, *-e, -i, -y* (G). Broad, flat

pod, *-o, -y* (G). A foot

por, *-i, -us* (L). A pore; small opening

QUESTIONS

1. Some books refer to phylum Cnidaria as phylum Coelenterata. What is the translation of this alternative name?

2. Why isn't English, German, Japanese, or some other language used to make scientific names? Suggest reasons why scientific names used by scientists in all countries are almost always made from Latin and Greek word parts.

3. What are the advantages to biologists of creating scientific names for groups of organisms?

4. In a scientific publication written in German or Japanese, how do we know which group of animals is being discussed?

5. Use a dictionary to show how Latin and Greek word parts make up many common nonscientific words. Give five or more examples of nonscientific words and show their Latin and Greek parts. For example:
   automobile: self + move
   suicide: self + kill
   microscope: small + view
   photograph: light + record

Comparing Animal Phyla

In this activity we begin learning terms that will be useful in our investigations of invertebrates. We also begin filling in a phylum comparison chart that we will use to summarize our studies.

ACTIVITY 2

Compare the features of some common invertebrate phyla.

MATERIALS

- copy of Workbook Table 1–3

PROCEDURE

1. Examine Table 1–3, Comparison of animal phyla by features. The name at the top of each column is the phylum name. For explanations of the terms in the left column, see the glossary in Table 1–4.

2. Keep Table 1–3 in your notebook where you can locate it readily. Each time you study a new phylum, record information in the table.
   a. You may have to use reference books to find some of the information you need.
   b. If you study other phyla, add columns to the table.
   c. (Optional) Add sketches of typical animals belonging to each phylum.

3. Use Table 1–3 to compare phyla and to review what you have studied. Follow your teacher's directions for completing and turning in the table, your drawings, and your notes.

Table 1–3. Comparison of animal phyla by features

Feature	Phylum							
	Porifera	Cnidaria	Platyhelminthes	Annelida	Mollusca	Arthropoda	Echinodermata	Chordata
Body symmetry								
Body segmentation								
Type of skeleton								
Type of digestive tract								
Type of nervous system								
Method of respiration								
Unique feature								
Economic importance								
Environmental niche								

Table 1–4. Glossary of terms used to describe phyla

1. ***Body symmetry*** refers to the arrangement of the parts of an organism. An organism has one of these symmetries: ***Asymmetry.*** Lacking regularity or pattern in the arrangement of body parts. ***Bilateral symmetry.*** Having similar body parts divided by an imaginary axis or line. The right side is similar to the left side, but the top is different from the bottom. ***Radial symmetry.*** Having similar parts radiating from the central axis of the body in a plane or cylinder. The top is different from the bottom.	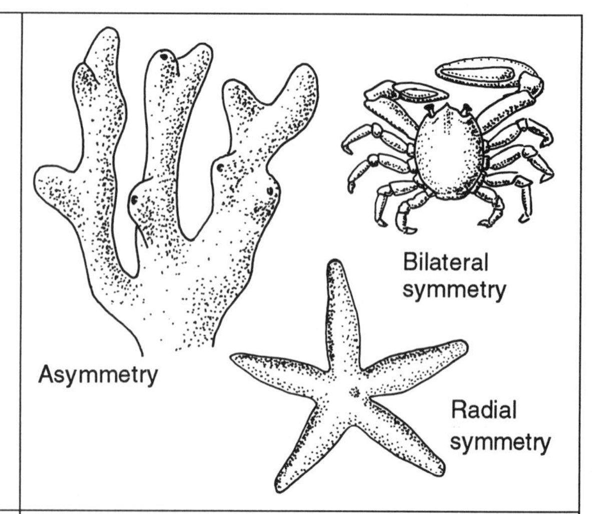
2. ***Body segmentation*** refers to the division of body parts into like units, not including legs. An animal is either segmented or nonsegmented. ***Segmented.*** Having a series of body parts, or segments, one following the other. Segments are often alike. ***Nonsegmented.*** Having no repetition of body parts.	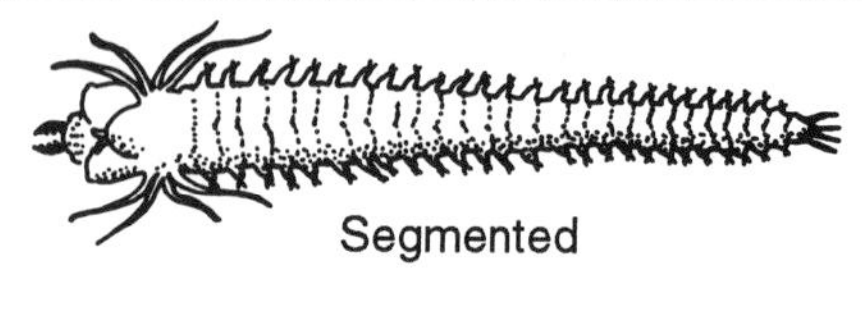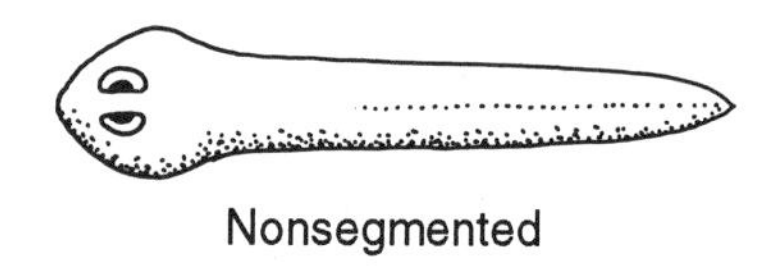
3. ***Body location*** refers to orientation of body features. Special location terms are used particularly with bilaterally symmetrical animals in much the same way that mapmakers use the terms north, south, east, and west. ***Anterior.*** Referring to the head end, usually containing sensory organs. ***Posterior.*** Referring to the hind end of an animal, often containing an excretory vent. ***Dorsal.*** Referring to the upper or back surface of an animal. ***Ventral.*** Referring to the lower or front surface covering most of the digestive organs. ***Lateral.*** Referring to the side of an animal.	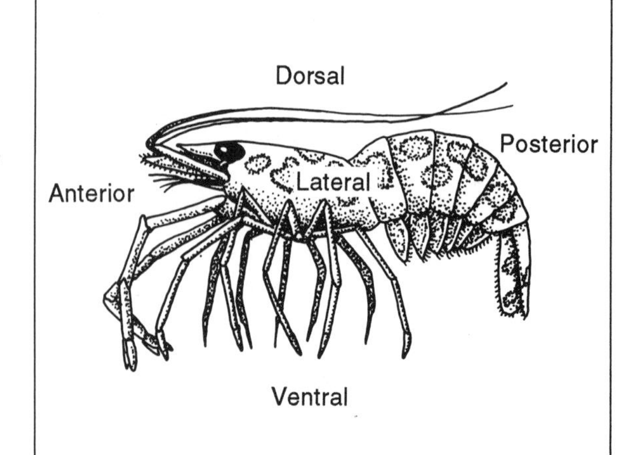

Table 1–4 *continued.* Glossary of terms used to describe phyla

4. ***Skeleton*** refers to the support structure that gives the body shape and a place for attaching the tissues and organs of the body.

   Exoskeleton. A hard shell outside the epidermis. Tissues and organs are attached to the inner surfaces of the shell.

   Endoskeleton. Hard plates or bones inside the epidermis with organs and tissues attached to the outer surfaces.

   Hydrostatic skeleton. Cavities inside the body which become rigid when filled with fluid under pressure.

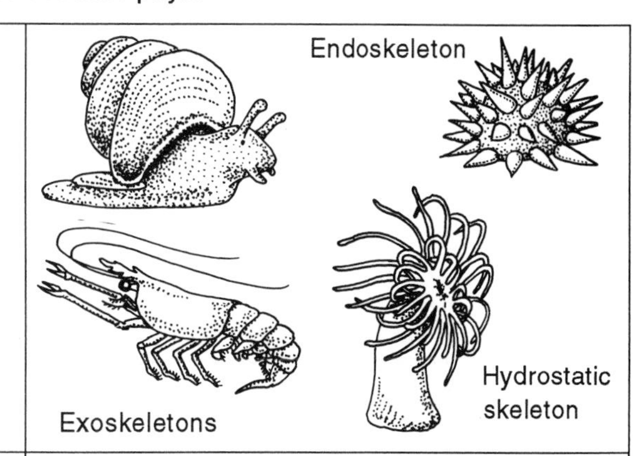

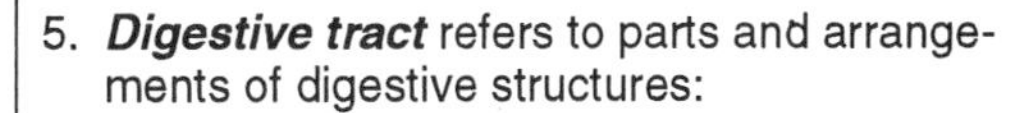

5. ***Digestive tract*** refers to parts and arrangements of digestive structures:

   No digestive tract. (See Topic 2, Sponges.)

   Saclike tract. Having a digestive pouch. The mouth and the anus are the same opening (like the opening in a balloon).

   Complete digestive tract. Having a mouth, a digestive tube, and an anus (like an earthworm's).

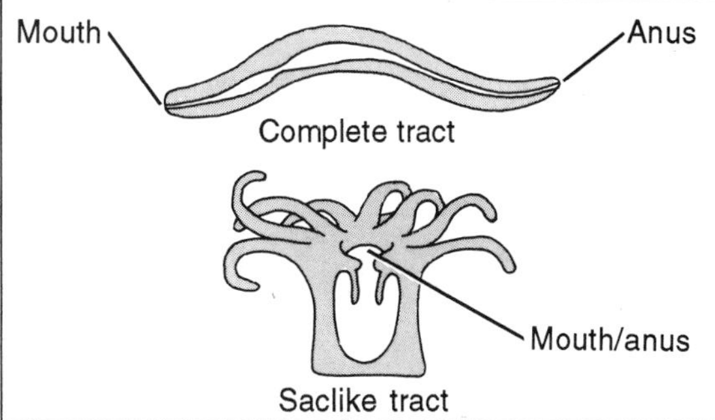

6. ***Nervous system*** refers to parts and arrangements of of nerve structures.

   Dorsal nerve cord runs along the "top" (dorsal side) of the animal above (dorsal to) the digestive tract.

   Ventral nerve cord runs along the "bottom" (ventral side) of the animal below (ventral to) the digestive tract.

   Nerve net runs throughout the animal (as in a three-dimensional spider web).

   Radial nerve cord fans out in rays from the center of the animal.

   Ganglion (the plural is *ganglia)* is a small swelling of the nerve cord, which may be anywhere on the cord. Not shown.

   Ladderlike nerve cord may form one row or branch into as many as three parts. Each main branch is controlled by ganglia.

   Brain is an enlarged anterior part of the nerve cord. Not shown.

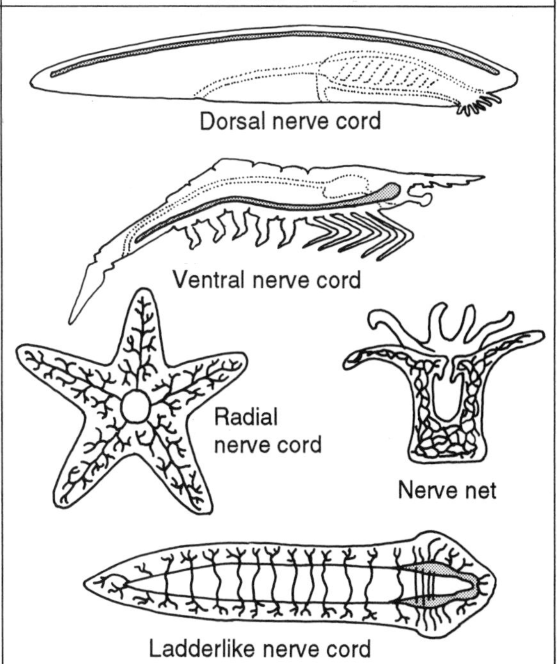

Table 1–4 *continued.* Glossary of terms used to describe phyla

7. ***Respiratory structure*** refers to types of body parts where respiration takes place. ***Skin*** or ***epidermis,*** the outermost layer of cells, allows oxygen to pass directly into the animal. There are no special organs for respiration in animals such as worms, sponges, or cnidarians. ***Gills*** are organs that remove dissolved oxygen from the water. They appear in fish, clams, lobsters, and other water-breathing animals. ***Lungs*** are organs that remove oxygen from the air. They appear in amphibians, reptiles, mammals, and other air-breathing animals.
8. ***Unique features*** are features in each phylum not found in any other. Often these features are indicated in the name of the phylum. For example, Echinodermata = spiny-skinned; Arthropoda = jointed feet.
9. ***Economic importance*** is value to humans. Value may refer to money or to attitudes of people and societies.
10. ***Environmental niche*** is the place of an organism in relation to other organisms in its environment, including its role in the **food chain** (what it eats and what eats it) and its **habitat** (where it lives).
11. Other terms used to describe organisms will come in later topics. Terms often used are these: ***Solitary.*** Living singly, not as part of a group or cluster. ***Colonial.*** Living in groups or clusters, often attached to each other. ***Sessile.*** Attached to the bottom, unable to move around. ***Motile.*** Able to move from place to place by crawling or swimming.

QUESTIONS

6. How many of the terms from the eleven categories in Table 1–4, can you use to describe the following organisms? Write your description.
   a. a human being
   b. a goldfish

7. What objects in the classroom have one of the symmetries shown in Table 1–4? Identify objects with their symmetry.

8. Select two items that you own. Describe their economic importance by their
   a. approximate cost when purchased new.
   b. nonmonetary value to you or to others.

FURTHER INVESTIGATIONS

1. Invent ten or more words from Greek or Latin word parts in Table 1–2. Also use word parts listed in Unit 1, Topic 3, Table 3–2, and Topic 10, Table 10–3. Define your words. Put a box around any words you invent that are like words listed in an unabridged dictionary.

2. Using a biology textbook, look up the scientific names of some of the subgroups of a few invertebrate phyla. For example, the common subgroups

(classes) in the phylum Mollusca are the Polyplacophora, Gastropoda, Scaphopoda, Cephalopoda, and Bivalvia (sometimes named Pelecypoda). See an unabridged dictionary or a dictionary of Latin and Greek word parts for translations of these terms. Report to the class on how accurately the names show the features of the groups.

3. Identify two or more animals in a local zoo or your neighborhood. From your knowledge of these animals, choose features that you think accurately describe them. Using a dictionary of Latin and Greek word parts, create a "scientific" name for each animal. Compare your names with the accepted scientific names for the animals.

4. Study body symmetry. Make a list of organisms that are radially symmetrical. How does this kind of symmetry help them survive?

5. Repeat Further Investigation 4, this time listing organisms that are bilaterally symmetrical.

6. Using library references, learn how economists, biologists, ecologists, and other people are trying to set economic and environmental values on
   a. food organisms, such as clams.
   b. endangered organisms, such as the humpback whale.
   c. beautiful organisms, such as seashells.

7. A respiratory tree that removes dissolved oxygen from the water is a special feature of one phylum. The organisms of which phylum have respiratory trees?

8. List scientific professions that study invertebrates. For example, a malacologist studies seashells (mollusks). Add careers that use invertebrates in some way. An example is a bait-shop owner.

9. List invertebrates that are threatened or endangered. Which are environmental pests? Which are considered economically important?

10. Suggest reasons why scientists might prefer using external physical features rather than physiological (body function) differences for naming groups of animals and plants.

2. Sponges

Sponges make up the phylum **Porifera.** They are common organisms living in the oceans, from the shallows to depths as great as 5 km. A few species live in freshwater lakes and streams. They are **sessile,** meaning they live permanently attached to rocks or other submerged objects. Some sponges grow in thin encrusting layers over rock surfaces; a few species can even bore into objects. Other species grow upright in simple vaselike or treelike forms. Some sponges are giants of the invertebrate world, reaching several meters in diameter. But most sponges are tiny organisms that often go unnoticed on the reef or seafloor because they don't look like animals and don't move noticeably. Many of the small sponges that hide under rocks or live on coral reefs are colored in vivid hues of yellow, orange, crimson, sky-blue, and ultramarine. See Fig. 2–1.

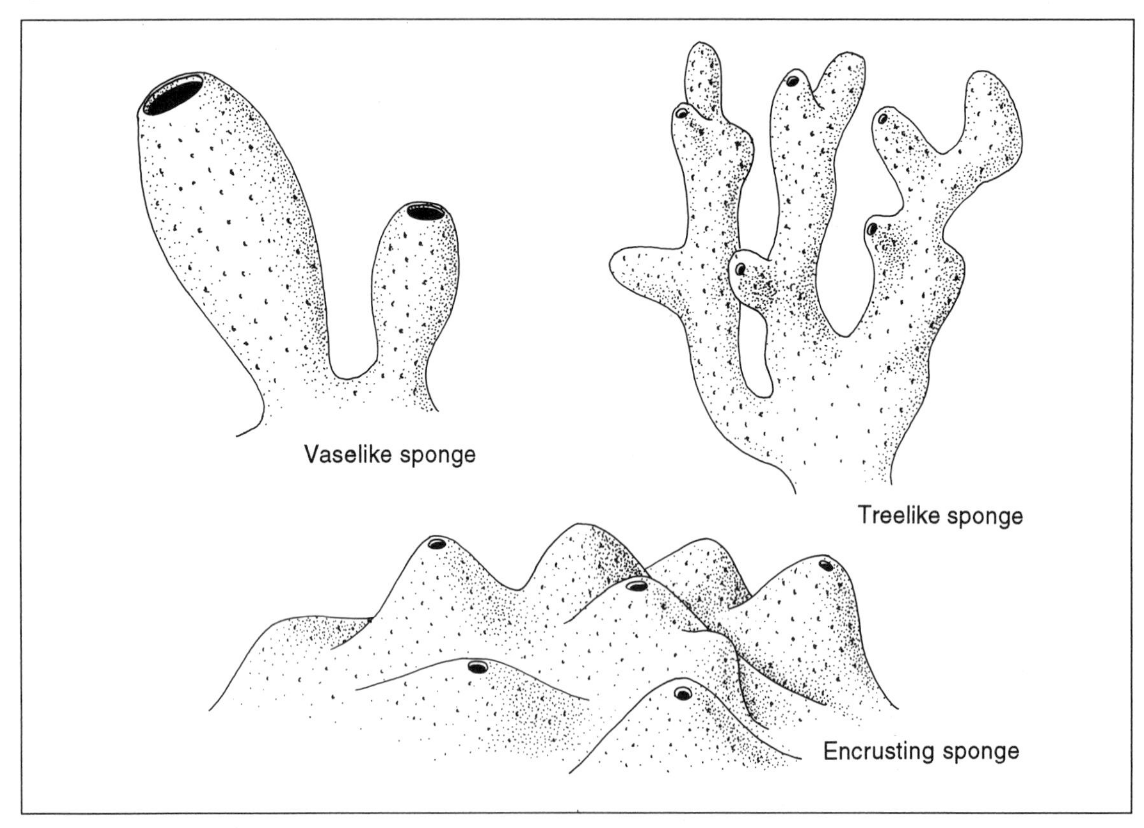

Fig. 2–1. Types of sponges

Skeleton

The texture of the skeletons of some sponges gave us the term "spongy." Many sponges feel soft and springy to the touch. They spring back into shape when you let go. These kinds of sponges have soft skeletons made of a flexible fibrous material called **spongin.** Other sponges have a stiff skeleton that feels prickly because it is made of hard, sliverlike **spicules.** There are even sponges that have both spicules and spongin; they feel both prickly and flexible. The skeletal structures of sponges lie between their inner and outer layers.

Many species of sponges can be identified by the shape and composition of their spicules. If spicules are made of silicon dioxide, the sponge is called **siliceous;** if the spicules are made of calcium carbonate, the

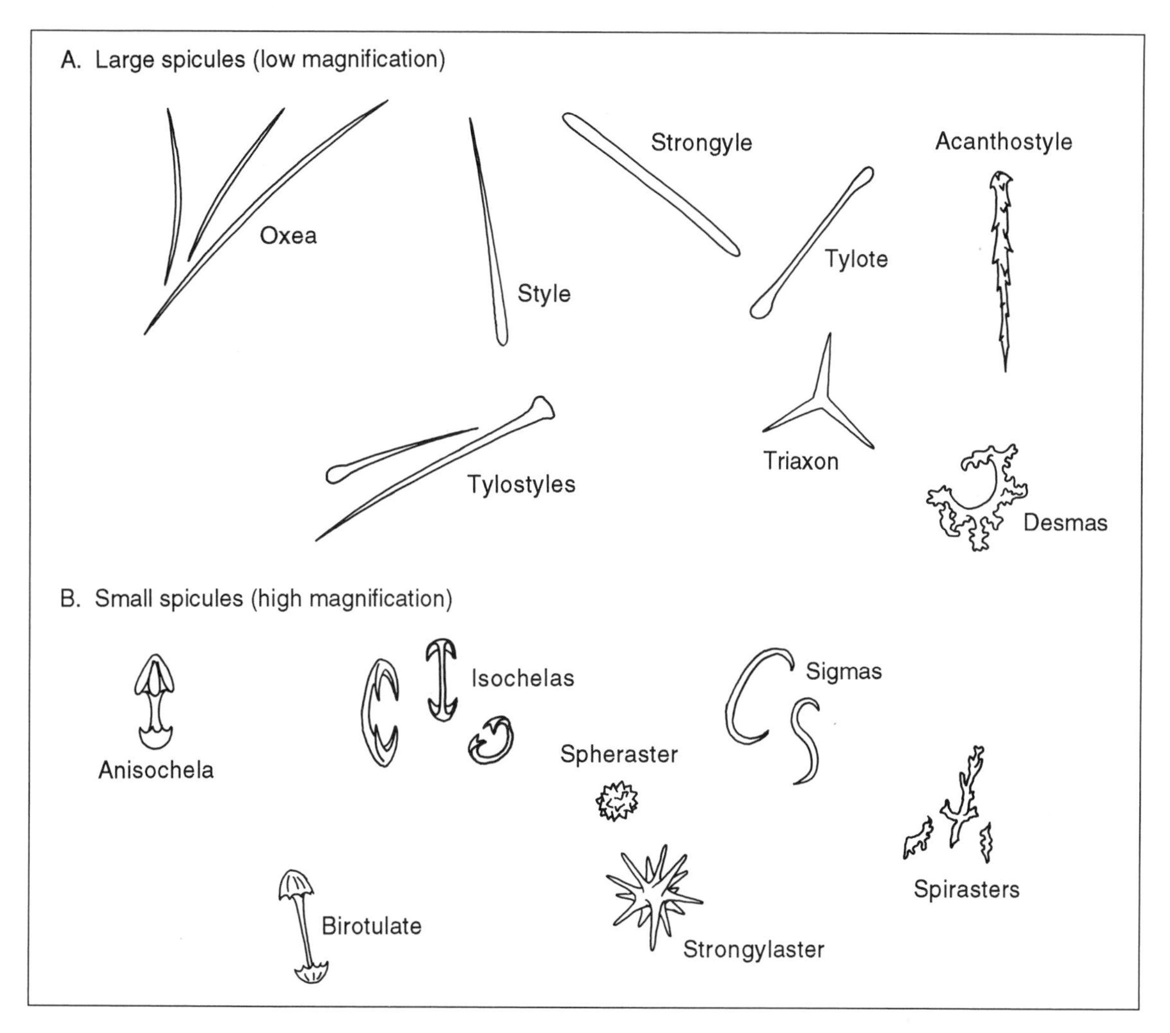

Fig. 2–2. Types of spicules

sponge is called **calcareous**. Spicules have many shapes and sizes. See Fig. 2–2. Some sponges have no spicules; others have so many that they look and feel like lacy skeletons of glass.

Sponge cells called **amoebocytes** work together to produce the spicules. Fig. 2–3 shows the gradual development of spicules by amoebocytes. Amoebocyte cells also produce spongin, the soft fiber that forms natural bath sponges.

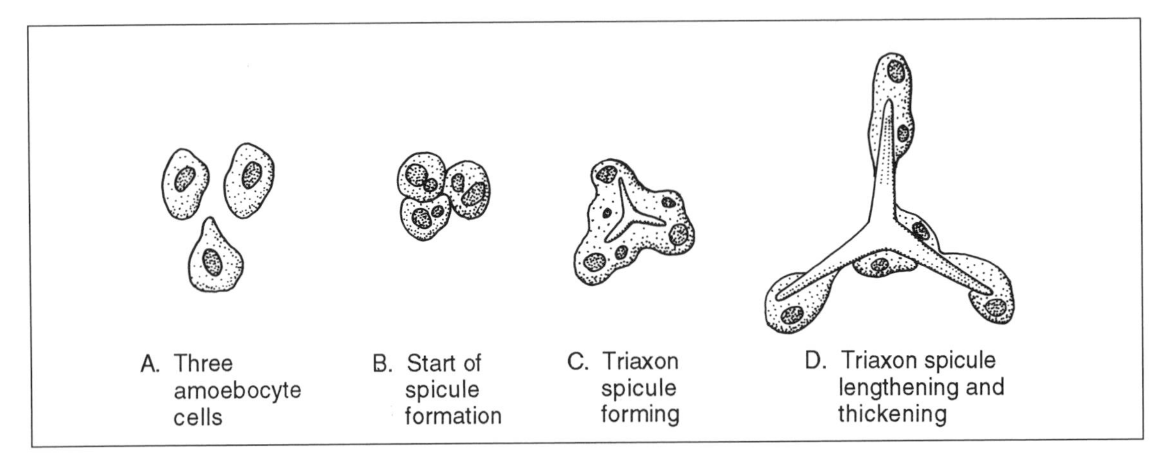

Fig. 2–3. Amoebocyte cells secreting a triaxon spicule

ACTIVITY 1

Observe and draw the skeletal structures of sponges.

Compare natural and synthetic sponges.

MATERIALS

- copies of Workbook Tables 2–1 and 2–2
- 3 natural sponge samples (dried, preserved, or live)
- 1 or more synthetic sponge samples
- tongs or rubber gloves
- microscope slides and coverslips
- forceps
- dissecting scissors
- dissecting microscope
- compound microscope
- clear-drying glue
- labels
- waterproof marker
- bleach
- eyedropper
- paper towels
- vinegar or other diluted acid in dropping bottle (optional)

PROCEDURE

1. Prepare a slide collection of natural and synthetic sponges. Compare their skeletal structures. Record your data in Table 2–1.

CAUTION: Handle live sponges only with tongs or rubber gloves. Some sponges have sharp spicules; others emit a mildly toxic chemical that can cause a rash or blisters.

Table 2–1. Comparison of sponge features Ⓦ

Sample	Description	Drawing at 20X	Drawing at 100X
A			
B			
C			
D			

a. Describe the general features of the intact sponge specimens. Record as much information as you can. For example, describe the color, texture, and shape of each one.
b. Prepare a specimen of each sample on a microscope slide. Read Procedures 2 through 4 for steps in preparing slides of each type of specimen. Label each slide.

2. For dried and synthetic specimens, prepare dry-mounted microscope slides.
   a. If the specimen has already been cleaned and dried, use forceps to place a piece of sponge measuring about 2 mm on a side on a slide. If the specimen is not clean, prepare it by following Procedures 4.a. through 4.c.
   b. Using a dissecting microscope, look first for large spicules or spongin at 20X. Draw what you see in Table 2–1.
   c. Using a compound microscope at 100X, look for small spicules or spongin. Draw what you see.
   d. Make a permanent slide as shown in Fig. 2–4. Place the specimen in the glue. Keep the slide flat until the

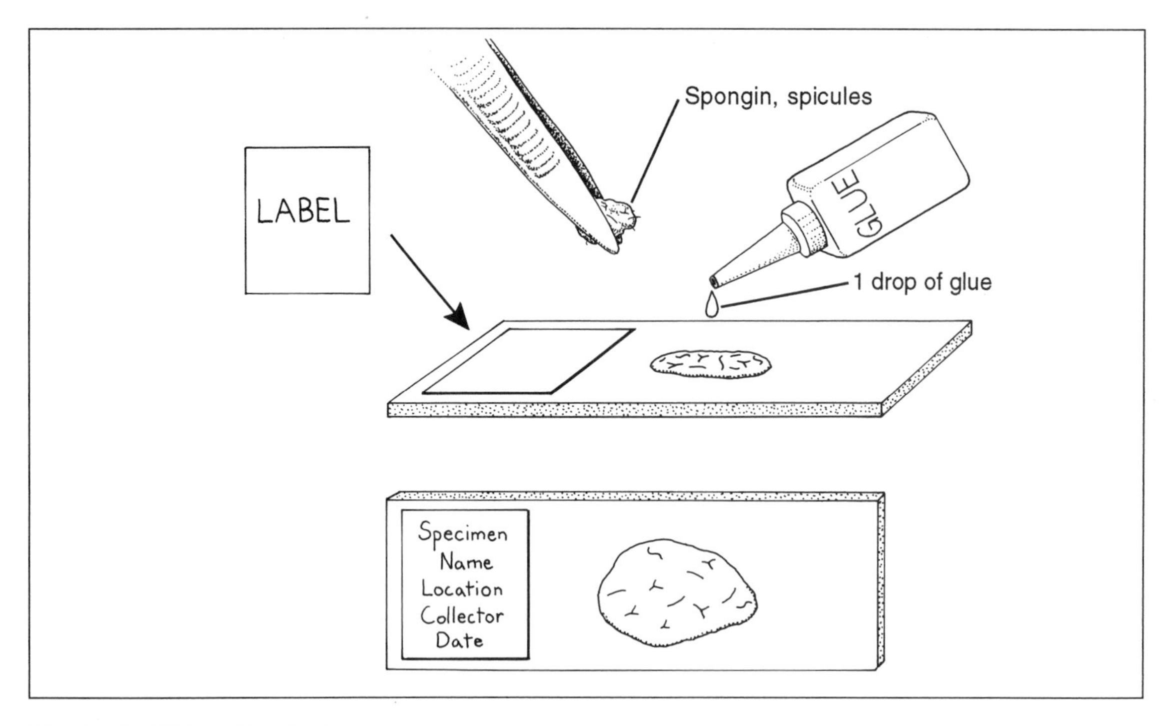

Fig. 2–4. Slide with spicules

glue dries. Protect the slide from drafts that could blow particles into the glue. Store the slide in the class slide-collection box.

e. Prepare a label for the slide. Write information on the label to identify the specimen. Consult your teacher for suggestions on the type of information to include, such as the name or number of the specimen, the location where it was collected, the collector's name, the date of collection, and the preparer's name or initials. See Fig. 2–4.

3. For sponges preserved with alcohol or other preservative, remove a piece of sponge measuring about 2 mm on a side with forceps or snip it off with scissors. Place the specimen on a microscope slide. Rinse it thoroughly with tap water. Let it air-dry for 24 hours or longer. Then follow Procedure 2.

4. For living sponges, prepare wet-mounted microscope slides. Refer to Fig. 2–5 as you carry out the following steps:
   a. Break off a piece of sponge measuring about 2 mm on a side with forceps or snip it off with scissors. Place the sample on a clean microscope slide. If it is wet, draw off excess water by touching it with the edge of a paper towel.

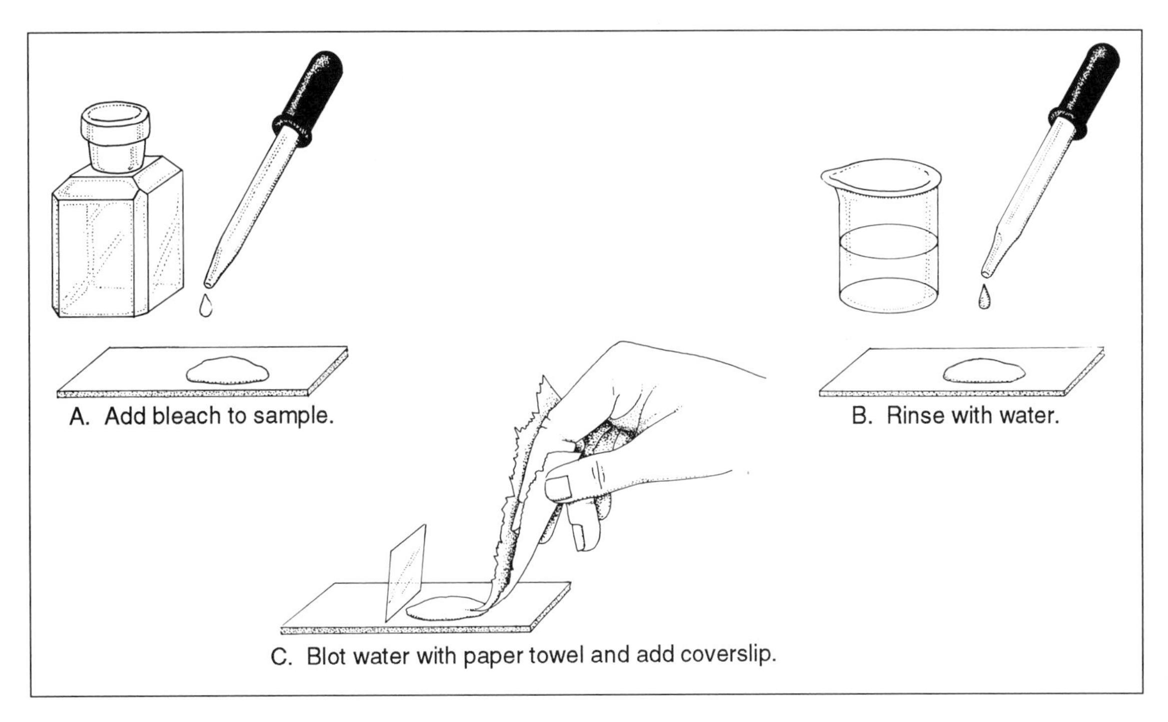

Fig. 2–5. Preparing a wet mount of a living sponge

b. With an eyedropper, cover the sample with bleach. Wait about 5 min while the bleach dissolves the flesh from the skeleton. See Fig. 2–5.

c. Using an eyedropper, carefully rinse the bleached skeleton twice with a few drops of tap water. Draw off the water from the specimen with a bit of paper towel.

d. Examine the bleached skeleton under a microscope at 20X. Add a coverslip and use a compound microscope to examine the specimen at 100X. Draw the skeletal structure in Table 2–1. Record whether you found spongin, spicules, or both.

e. After the specimen dries, glue it to the slide and label the slide as in Procedures 2.d. and 2.e.

5. (Optional) Test whether sponge spicules are made of calcium carbonate or silicon dioxide.
   a. Use a few loose sponge spicules. Do not use spicules glued to a microscope slide.
   b. Put a few drops of vinegar or other diluted acid on the spicules.
   c. Wait a few minutes. If the spicules are calcium carbonate, bubbles will form. If they are silicon dioxide, no bubbles will form.

6. Compare natural and synthetic sponges.
   a. List features that you think are desirable in a high-quality sponge.

Table 2–2. Comparison of natural and synthetic sponges 

Features of high-quality sponges	Natural sponge	Synthetic sponge

b. Devise and perform tests comparing natural and synthetic sponges on each of these features.

QUESTIONS

1. What are some possible functions of spicules and spongin? Use references for information you need to help answer this question. Make a sketch.

2. How do synthetic sponges compare with natural sponges in desirable qualities? Use data from Table 2–2 and make other additions.

3. What qualities should a sponge have for use in
   a. car washing?
   b. surgery?
   c. art work?

4. What are some other uses that humans have for sponges?

5. Excavating sponges bore holes into calcareous corals and shells. How do you think these sponges help to break down and recycle calcium materials?

Sponge Anatomy

One kind of sponge is shaped like a vase. Its walls are punched with tiny holes called **pores.** See Fig. 2–6. The pores give the phylum its name, Porifera. The outer surface of the sponge is a skinlike layer of **epithelial cells.** These cells protect and enclose the sponge; they can contract and shorten, moving the sponge body slightly. The tiny holes are the hollow insides of **porocyte cells,** a type of epithelial cell. Porocyte cells are narrow and elongated; they connect the outside of the sponge to the inside cavity, so that the sponge is like a sieve.

Simple vaselike sponges have a single large top opening, called the **osculum** (L. *oscul* = little mouth); compound sponges have many oscula. Epithelial cells around the osculum can contract enough to close the opening, but the process is slow, taking up to several minutes.

The inner surface of the sponge is lined

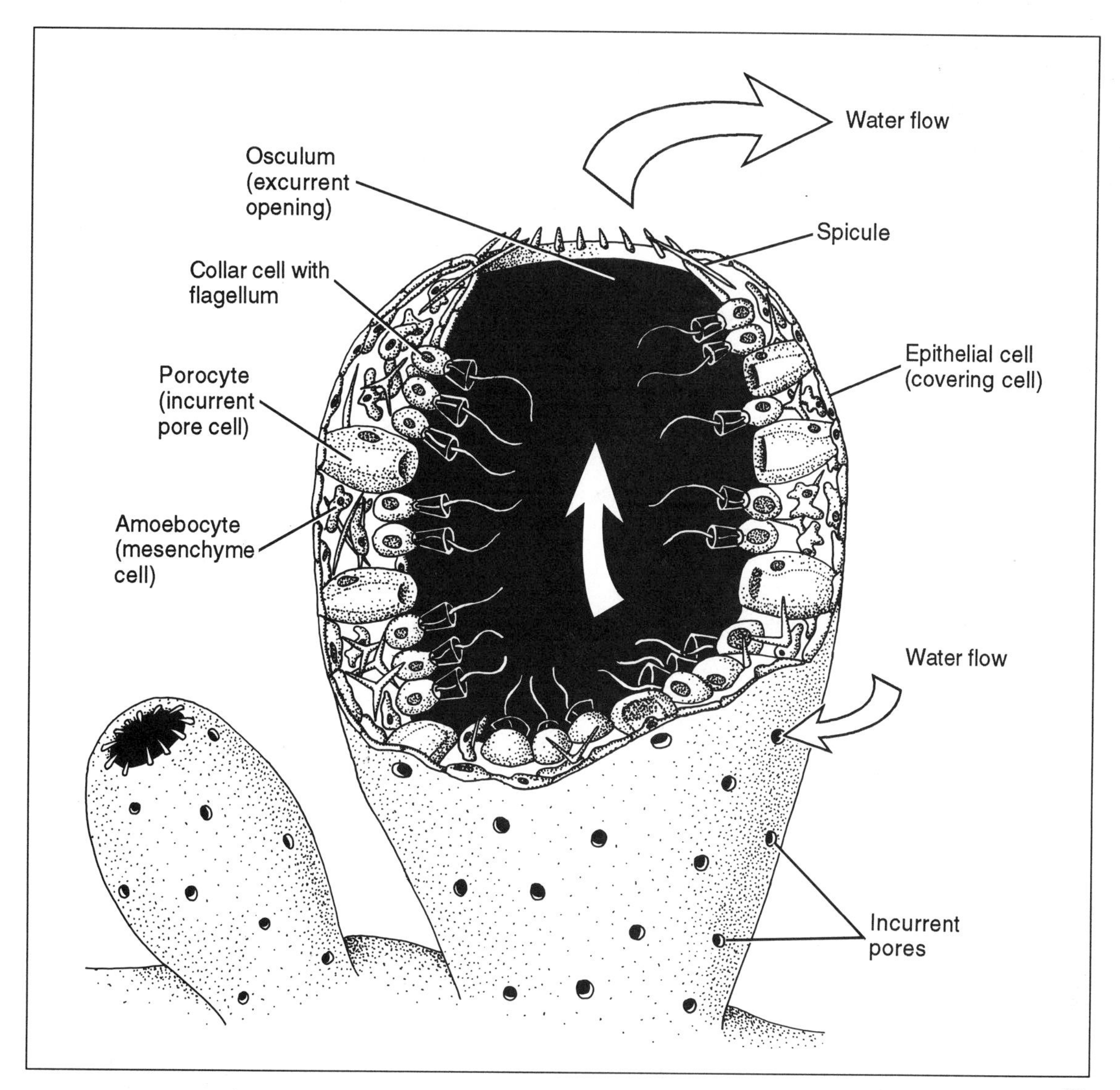

Fig. 2–6. Anatomy of a simple, vaselike sponge
Source: Modified from Buchsbaum 1976, 64

Ⓦ

with cells called **collar cells.** See Fig. 2–6. The collar is made of fine tubes surrounding a long whiplike thread called a **flagellum.** See Fig. 2–7. As flagella (the plural of *flagellum*) move back and forth, they create a current of water that moves through the many small porocyte cells and out the osculum. Several gallons of water can circulate through a fist-sized sponge in a single day.

Between the outer surface of epithelial cells and the inner surface of collar cells is a jellylike material. In this jelly are the spicules that support the sponge. There are also free-moving cells called **amoebocytes,** which look and act like the one-celled animal called an amoeba. Several kinds of amoebocytes each serve a special function such as producing the skeleton of spicules, digesting and transferring nutrients, or reproducing themselves.

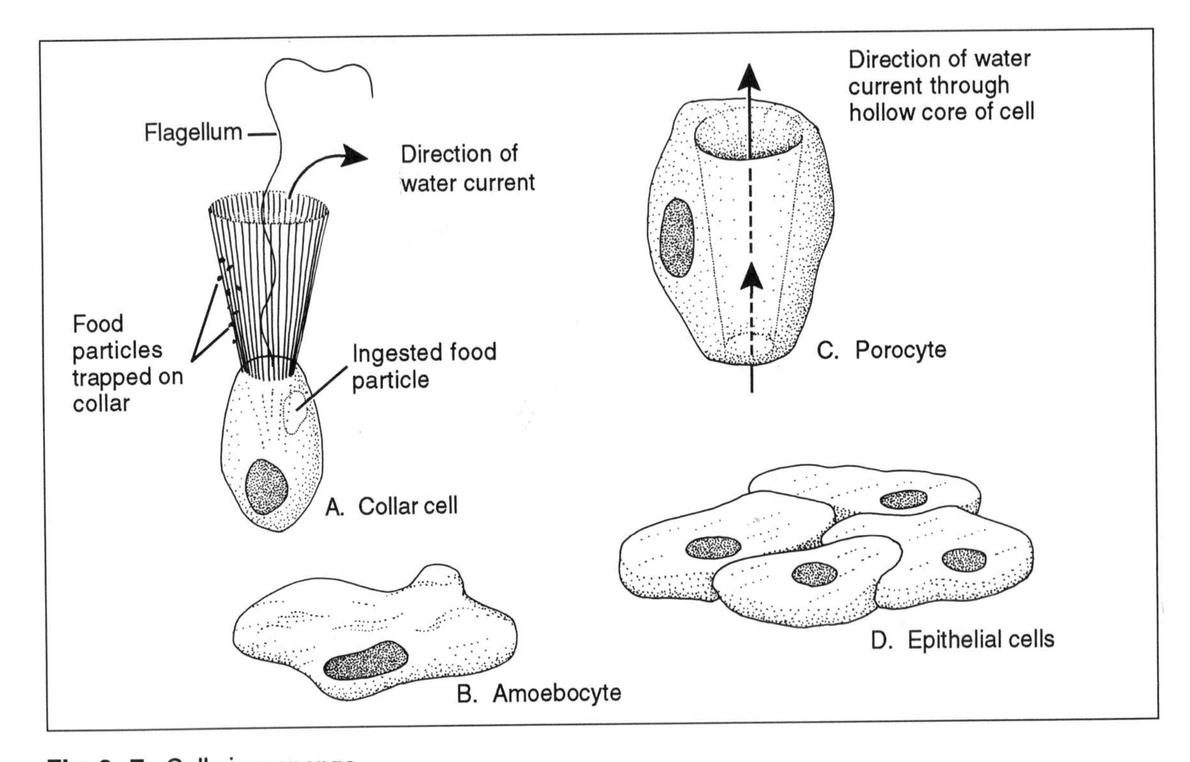

Fig. 2–7. Cells in a sponge

Feeding and Digestion

The beating flagella of the collar cells produce a water current that flows through the sponge cavities, bringing in tiny food particles such as suspended bacteria, bits of plant and animal matter called **detritus,** and tiny drifting organisms called plankton. For this reason sponges are described as detritus feeders. As the water circulates, fine tubes of the collar cells filter out the food particles and take them into the cells. So sponges can also be called filter feeders. See Fig. 2–6. Within the cells the food breaks down into nutrients, which are used for energy and building cell material. Some of the particles are passed on to amoebocytes, which carry them to other cells of the sponge.

Other Systems

All cells in a sponge are in contact with or near to seawater. Because each cell exchanges oxygen and carbon dioxide and discharges waste products into the seawater, a sponge has no respiratory, circulatory, or excretory system.

Living Together

Many species of plants and animals live on or in some other organism in a close association called **symbiosis,** which means "living together." Different kinds of symbiotic relationships go by different names. In **commensalism,** one species benefits without either harming or helping the other. For example, remora fish attach themselves to sharks for a free ride and perhaps a meal when the sharks feed. In **mutualism,** both partners benefit. An example is the sea anemone that lives on the back of a hermit crab. The sea anemone benefits by collecting scraps of food left floating from the hermit crab's messy feeding habits. The hermit crab benefits by using the anemone's stinging tentacles as a protective umbrella to ward off hermit crab predators. In **parasitism,** one organism harms another for its own benefit. Mosquitoes are parasites on humans because they suck blood and transmit diseases. In **predation,** one organism kills another for its own use—most often as food.

Symbiosis in Sponges

Large sponges have many small chambers where other organisms can live symbiotically. Although the sponges rarely benefit from this arrangement, their **symbionts,** the organisms that live in them, do. Therefore this level of symbiosis is commensalism. The kinds of symbionts a sponge may house can vary from a few to many animals.

ACTIVITY 2 (OPTIONAL)

Study the structure and function of a live sponge.
Look for symbionts living in the sponge.

MATERIALS

- live sponge
- tongs or rubber gloves
- small culture dish
- seawater
- blunt probe
- copy of Workbook Table 2–3
- dissecting microscope
- toothpicks
- carmine particles
- dissecting scissors or scalpel

PROCEDURE

1. Observe the external features and behavior of a living sponge. Use a dissecting microscope if necessary for your observations. Record your observations in Table 2–3.

   CAUTION: Handle live sponges only with tongs or rubber gloves. Some sponges have sharp spicules; others emit

Table 2–3. Sponge observations 

	Observations
Number of small openings (pores)	
Number of large openings (oscula)	
Texture of surface	
Response to touch	
Other features	
Path of water currents	
Internal structure	
Other organisms living in sponge	

a mildly toxic chemical that can cause a rash or blisters.

a. Submerge a live sponge in a culture dish of seawater.
b. Examine the external surface of the sponge. Note the texture of the external surface. Decide whether it is smooth or rough.
c. Note the number and location of small openings (pores) and large openings (oscula).
d. Gently touch the surface with a blunt probe and note any response.
e. Describe other features, such as color, shape, and branching.

2. Using a dissecting microscope, observe the flow of water through the sponge. Record your observations in Table 2–3.
   a. Using a toothpick, drop particles of carmine at a large opening (osculum) and watch for evidence of currents.
   b. Drop particles of carmine on the surface of the sponge between the

large openings and watch for evidence of currents.

3. Examine the inside of a sponge.
   a. Using a scalpel or dissecting scissors, carefully cut the sponge in half.
   b. Observe the inside of the sponge with the naked eye, then under a dissecting microscope.
   c. Draw the internal structure of the sponge in the allotted space in Table 2–3.

4. Look for symbiont organisms inside the sponge. Remove them and try to identify them. Record your notes in Table 2–3.

QUESTIONS

6. What seem to be the functions of the large and small holes in a sponge?

7. What do sponges filter from the water?

8. From the movement of carmine particles, describe the patterns of water flowing through the sponge. Where did the carmine particles go?

9. Because sponges live attached to rocks, they do not move around. How do they feed and respire?

10. Describe the sponge's response to touch. What does this response suggest about its sensitivity to its environment?

11. What evidence did you find of symbiont organisms living in or on the sponge?
    a. How many types of animals, if any, were living in the sponge?
    b. What advantages might there be for animals living in or on the sponge?
    c. How might these organisms harm or benefit the sponge?

12. Fill in phylum Porifera in Table 1–3, Comparison of animal phyla by features.

FURTHER INVESTIGATIONS

1. Use references to learn about the sponge industry, past, present, and future.
   a. For what purposes are sponges used? How have synthetic materials replaced natural sponges? What kinds of sponges are used in art, medicine, and cosmetics?
   b. How does the cost of a natural sponge compare with the cost of a synthetic sponge?
   c. How are sponges harvested? What environmental problems does harvesting of sponges cause?
   d. What technologies have been invented for harvesting sponges?

2. Examine other sponge species for spicules. Many spicules are visible only at high magnifications (100X to 400X). Use a compound microscope to observe small spicules. Consult references to find the names of the spicules. Make a key to the spicule samples.

3. If you live near a shoreline where sponges grow, find good collecting sites and mark them on a map. What patterns of sponge distribution do you find? How might these patterns relate

to features of the environment?

4. Conduct product tests. Get larger specimens of natural leathery (spongin) sponges and of synthetic sponges. Cut them into pieces of the same size. Test them to compare how well each holds water, how easily each can be squeezed out, how soft each feels, and how readily detergent can be rinsed out of each. Compare costs.

5. Glass sponges, members of the class Hexactinellida, form skeletons so beautiful that they seem like art works by a glass worker. In their living state they provide a private residence for a mated pair of shrimp. Use references to learn more about these sponges.

6. Some sponges play an important role as decomposers. By invading dead corals and seashells and boring tunnels in them, they break down and recycle the hard skeletal material. Find examples of the work of boring sponges in samples of coral and seashells.

7. Make a list of organisms that live together symbiotically. Choose examples that illustrate commensalism, mutualism, parasitism, and predation. In each case, describe how the relationship affects both organisms.

8. How are synthetic sponges made? What are they made of? What are some special uses of synthetic sponges that natural sponges aren't good for?

3. Cnidarians

Now we turn to another major group of animals slightly more complex than sponges, the animals of the phylum **Cnidaria** (G. *cnid* = nettle), pronounced "nuh DARE ee uh." This phylum includes corals, sea anemones, and jellyfish. Corals grow around most tropical islands. Sea anemones are widely distributed, from cold arctic waters to the equator, from shallow tide pools to the bottom of the deep ocean. Jellyfish float near the surface of the open oceans. There are even small anemone-like cnidarians (hydra) and a jellyfish living in freshwater lakes and streams. Cnidarians range in size from tiny animals no bigger than a pinhead to graceful giants with trailing tentacles several meters long.

The Cnidaria together with another phylum, now called the Ctenophora (tuh NOF er uh), used to be called phylum **Coelenterata** (G. *coel* = hollow; G. *enter* = gut, intestine). This name nicely described the bodies of cnidarians, which resemble two grocery bags, one inside the other, with jellylike material between them.

All cnidarians are carnivorous, capturing small drifting animals with their tentacles. Yet their bright colors and the graceful movement of their tentacles ringed around their mouth like petals have earned them the name "flowers of the animal kingdom." See Fig. 3–1.

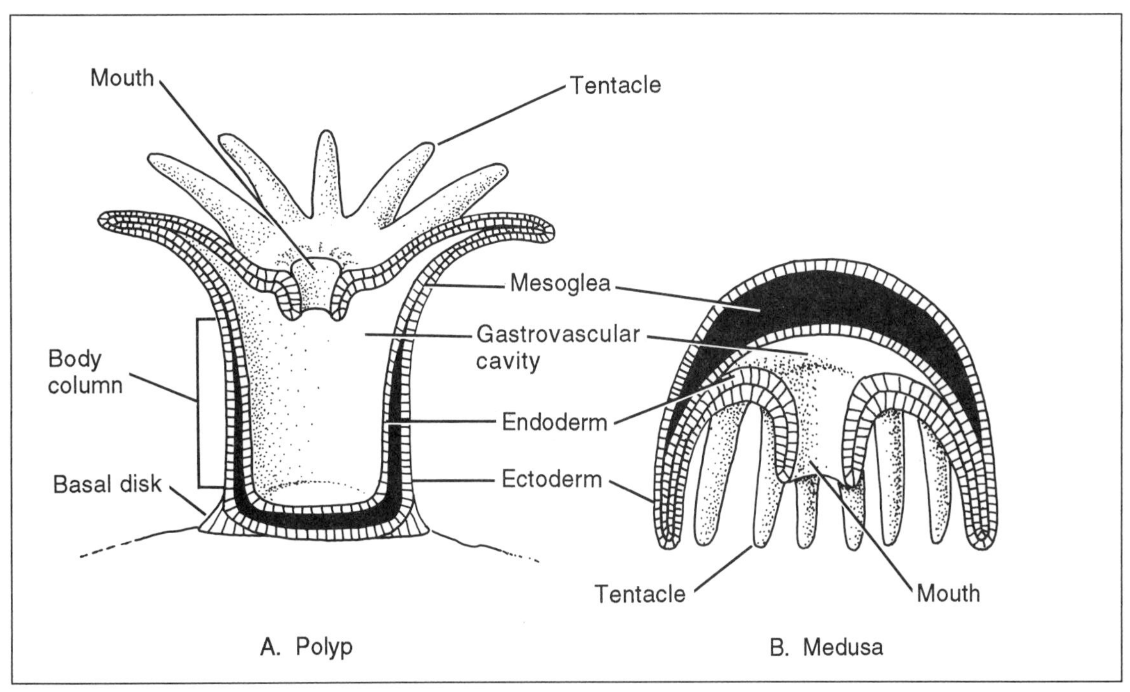

Fig. 3–1. Anatomy of the main cnidarian forms

Ⓦ

Body Structure

The outer layer, called the **ectoderm,** has cells that aid in capturing food and cells that secrete mucus. The inner layer, the **endoderm,** has cells that produce digestive enzymes and break up food particles. The jellylike material between the two layers is called the **mesoglea.** These body layers surround a central cavity called the **gastrovascular cavity,** which extends into the hollow tentacles. See Fig. 3–1. The gastrovascular cavity is also called the **coelenteron,** a word derived from the same Greek roots as the older phylum name Coelenterata.

Many cnidarians take two main forms during their life cycles:

1. a **polyp** form with the body shaped like a hollow cylinder or a bag that opens and closes at the top. Tentacles form a ring around a small mouth at the top of the bag. The mouth leads to a central body cavity, the gastrovascular cavity. See (A) in Fig. 3–1. Polyps attach to hard surfaces with their mouths up. Because they are sessile organisms, they can capture only food that touches their tentacles. Their mesoglea

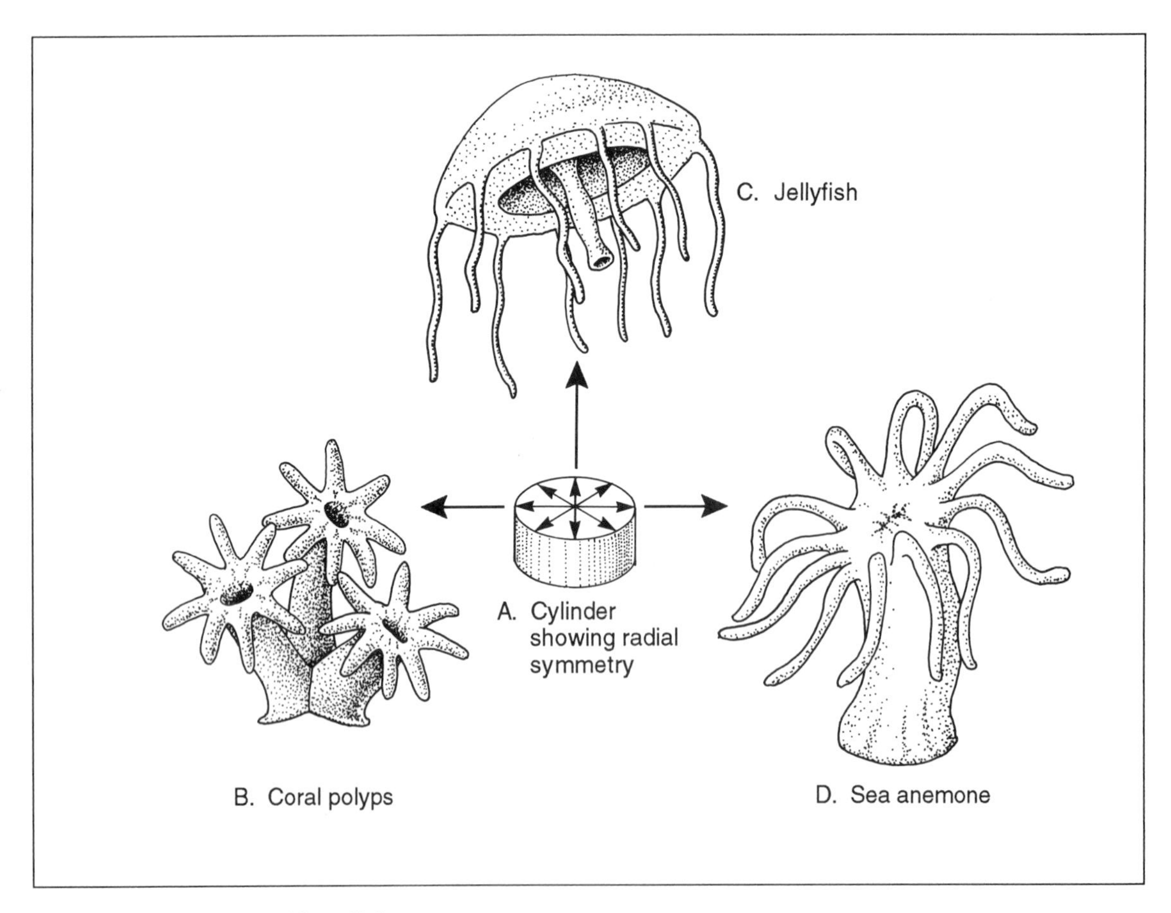

Fig. 3–2. Body plan with radial symmetry

layer is very thin. Corals and sea anemones are polyps. Most of these animals are small, but a few sea anemones can grow as large as 1 m (3 ft) in diameter.

2. a **medusa** form with the body shaped like an umbrella, the mouth and tentacles hanging down in the water. The mouth leads upward into the gastrovascular cavity. Medusae (the singular is *medusa*) are not sessile and usually swim freely in the open ocean. See (B) in Fig. 3–1. Their mesoglea is thick, making up most of their bulk. Jellyfish are medusae. Medusae come in many sizes, from a small, 2.5-cm (1-in) box medusa to a common species of *Cyania,* which has an umbrella over 2 m across.

Body Symmetry

The bodies of the Cnidaria extend out like a cylinder or an umbrella from a central axis, in **radial symmetry.** See (A) in Fig. 3–2. Because the tentacles of corals, jellyfish, and sea anemones have this radial structure, they can sting and capture food coming from any direction. Most sessile organisms, including plants, have radial symmetry.

Food Capture

Cnidarians have a unique feature: stinging cells called **cnidocytes** (NID uh sites). Each cnidocyte cell has a long, coiled, tubular harpoonlike structure, called a **nematocyst** (G. *nema* = thread; G. *cyst* = bag) turned in on itself like the finger of a glove pulled off inside out. When the nematocyst senses food, it fires outward, injecting venom through its tube into the prey. Each nematocyst can fire only once. New cnidocytes grow to replace used ones. See (A) in Fig. 3–3. Some tubes have sharp hooks, called barbs, along their surfaces.

Stings

All jellyfish sting to paralyze and capture prey for food. Even the sessile sea anemones, named for the flowers they resemble, are predatory organisms ready to sting prey, grasp it in their tentacles, and push it into their mouth.

The potency of the stinging venom varies among species. Some cnidarian venoms have little effect on humans; others are extremely poisonous. The venom of the Portuguese man-of-war is potent enough to inflict a painful sting, even after it is washed up on the beach. The venom of the sea wasp, a small jellyfish of Australia, has killed people. Some parts of the human body are more susceptible than others to stings. The many nerve endings in our face and lips make stings there more painful than they would be elsewhere.

Curiously, some marine organisms are immune to the sting of cnidarians. The clownfish, for example, lives among the stinging tentacles of a sea anemone, taking shelter and sharing bits of captured food. Another organism, the shell-less mollusk called *Glaucus,* is a predator of the man-of-war, ingesting unfired cnidocytes and using these stinging cells for its own defense. See Fig. 3–4. Turtles eat jellyfish with no apparent harm to themselves.

The cnidarian venom is a protein. The way to treat a sting is to break down the protein chemically with a "sting kill" medication or meat tenderizer. Because heat also helps to break down proteins, hot water can be used on a sting. Some people develop an allergic reac-

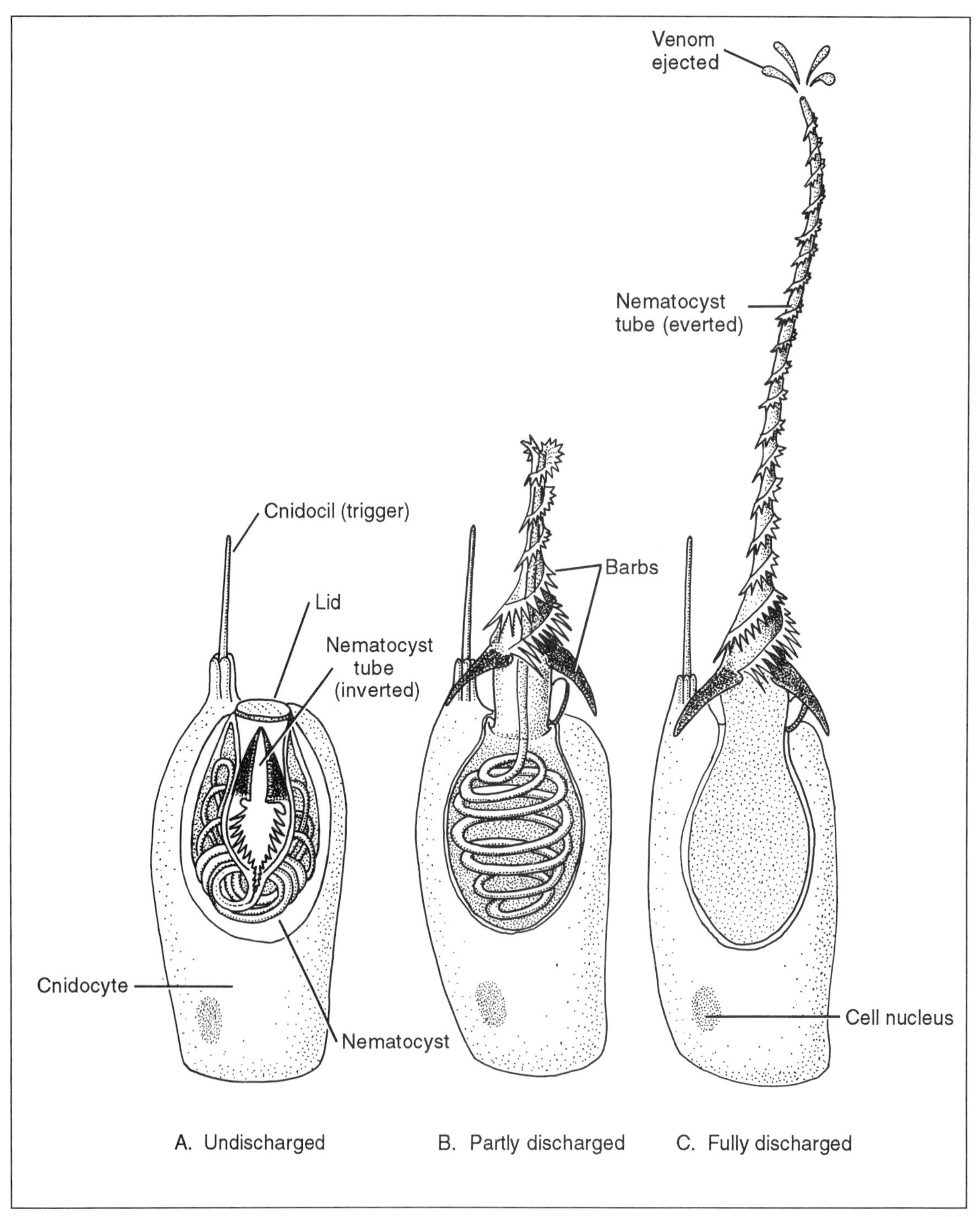

Fig. 3–3. A cnidocyte ejecting a nematocyst, very highly magnified

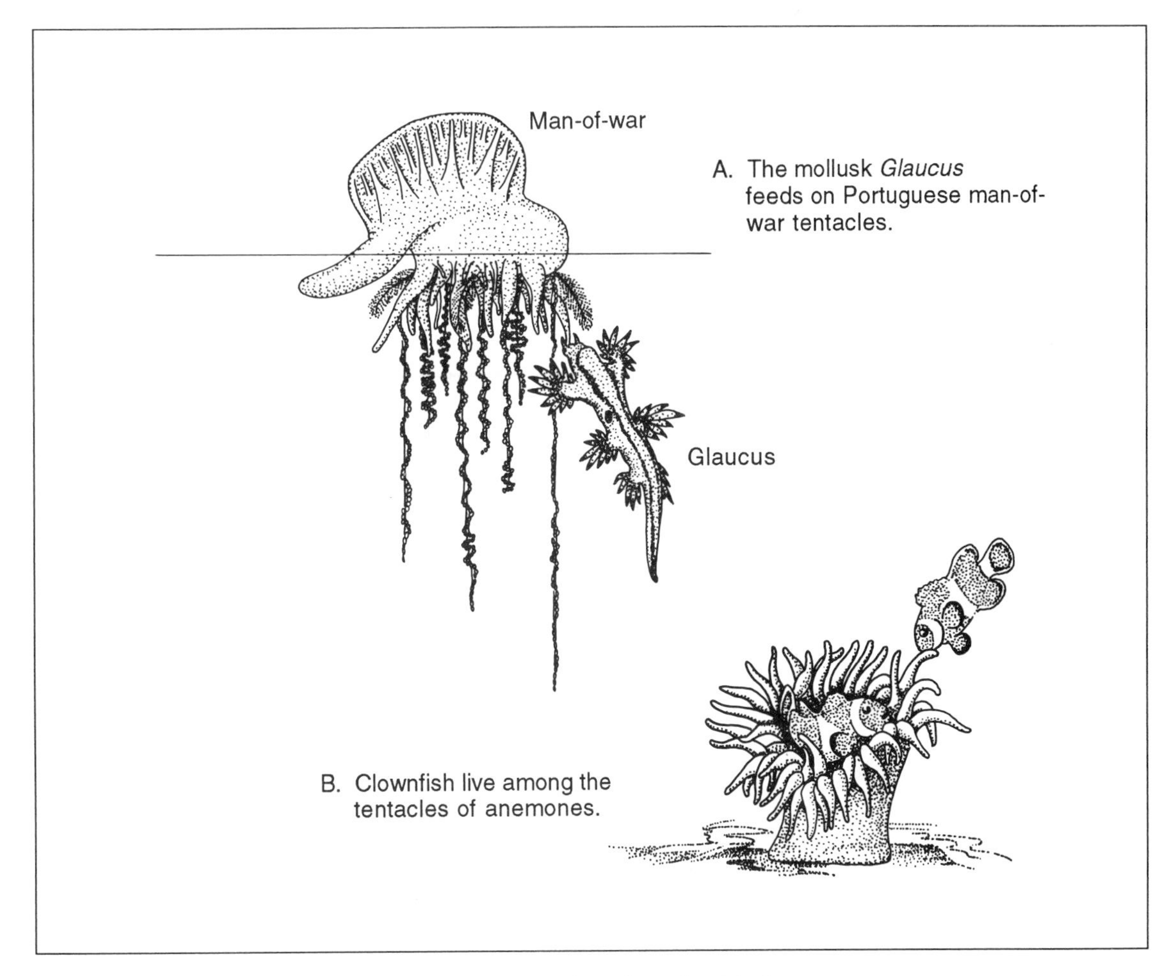

Fig. 3–4. Some organisms that are immune to the sting of cnidarians

tion to the venom after repeated stings. Seek medical help for anyone who faints or shows signs of unusual swelling or breathing distress after a cnidarian sting.

QUESTIONS

1. How might having cnidocytes (stinging cells) be advantageous
   a. to a jellyfish?
   b. to a sea anemone?
2. How does the body plan of a cnidarian (jellyfish, sea anemone) differ from that of a sponge?
3. Sea anemones were named because of their flowerlike appearance. How do sea anemones differ from flowers?
4. Using a dictionary, look up the meanings of the word parts for the following words:

ectoderm, endoderm, mesoglea, gastrovascular cavity, coelenteron, cnidocyte, nematocyst.

5. What kind of symbiotic relationship is represented by the clownfish and sea anemone, the Portuguese man-of-war and *Glaucus,* turtles and jellyfish? Refer to Topic 2, Sponges, for information on symbiosis.

ACTIVITY 1

View unfired and fired nematocysts under a microscope.

MATERIALS

- dissecting scissors
- sea anemone, live or frozen
- small culture dish
- seawater
- forceps
- dropper bottle of water
- microscope slides and coverslips
- compound microscope
- a hair from your head
- toothpicks

PROCEDURE

1. With scissors, snip off a 2-mm piece of a tentacle from a frozen or living sea anemone. Snipping a tentacle will not harm the sea anemone.

   CAUTION: Use forceps for handling sea anemones. Don't touch the tentacle with your hands.

2. Using forceps, place the piece of tentacle on a clean microscope slide. Add a drop of water and a coverslip.

3. Observing your specimen under a compound microscope at 100X, find unfired and fired nematocysts. Draw some of each.

4. Test the response of the nematocysts to a hair root.
   a. Pull out a head hair with a root.
   b. Insert the root of the hair under the coverslip, touching the tentacle tissue while your partner watches through the microscope.
   c. Pull the root slightly away from the tentacle.
   d. Observe how the nematocysts react to the hair root.

5. Test the response of the nematocysts to saliva.
   a. Place several drops of saliva on one end of a second glass slide.
   b. Get a fresh piece of tentacle and place it close to the saliva.
   c. Move the saliva onto the tentacle with a toothpick while your partner watches the tentacle through the microscope. After using the toothpick, break and discard it.
   d. Describe how the tentacle responds to the saliva.

QUESTIONS

6. Why do we use forceps when handling sea anemones in this activity? What does this fact suggest about handling sea

anemones or other cnidarians in the ocean or washed up on the beach?

7. In Procedures 4 and 5, which stimulant, hair or saliva, caused the firing of more nematocysts?

8. If a cnidarian has just finished feeding, predict whether it will discharge more nematocysts if the tentacles touch another piece of food. Explain your reasoning.

9. What might explain why some people get severe reactions to Portuguese man-of-war stings but others do not?

10. Use the following terms to describe a sea anemone, a Portuguese man-of-war, or another cnidarian:
    a. ectoderm
    b. nematocyst
    c. venom

Digestion

After a cnidarian stings and captures its prey, the tentacles work together to move it into the mouth. The prey is swallowed into the gastrovascular cavity and digested. Endoderm cells produce digestive chemicals called **enzymes,** which break the chunks of food into tiny particles. The cells then engulf the particles and further digest them into nutrient molecules. With this two-stage process, cnidarians can capture and digest animals ranging in size from small plankton to rather large organisms such as small reef fish. The cnidarian expels indigestible material through the mouth, which serves the gastrovascular cavity as both entrance and exit. See Fig. 3–1.

Hydrostatic Skeleton and Propulsion

Unlike sponges, which have skeletal structures made of spongin or spicules, sea anemones have no skeletal structure to support their soft tissues. Instead, they fill the gastrovascular cavity with water and close the mouth tight, putting the water under pressure as in a balloon filled with water. The water pressure supports the soft tissues. This feature is called a **hydrostatic skeleton.** See Fig. 3–5. If the sea anemone opens its mouth or contracts its body wall hard, the water flows out and the body collapses. It takes several minutes to pump water back into the cavity to expand the animal.

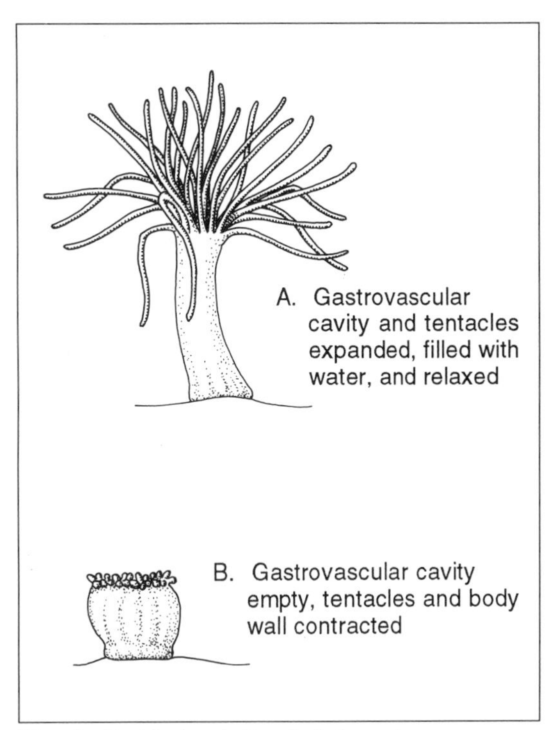

Fig. 3–5. Hydrostatic skeleton of a sea anemone

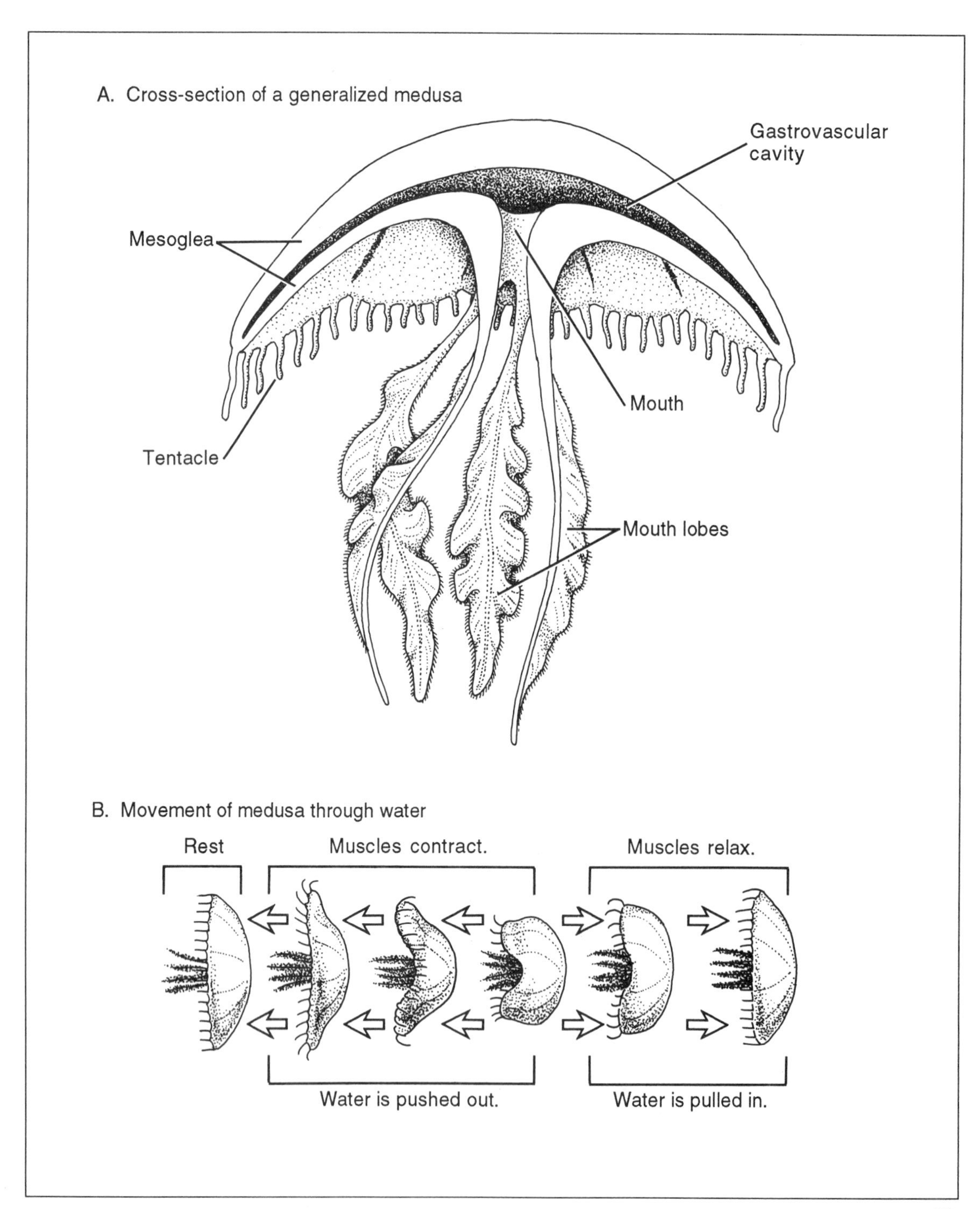

Fig. 3–6. Generalized body plan and swimming movements of a medusa

Some jellyfish are supported by a thick, elastic layer of mesoglea shaped like an umbrella. When a ring of muscles contracts, a jet of water is forced out from under the umbrella, moving the jellyfish forward. When the muscles relax, the stiff mesoglea springs back to its original shape, and the umbrella opens again. See Fig. 3–6. Alternating muscle contraction and relaxation create pulsating movements that propel the jellyfish through the water. Even so, jellyfish are such poor swimmers that they are classified as **plankton,** organisms that cannot swim against a current.

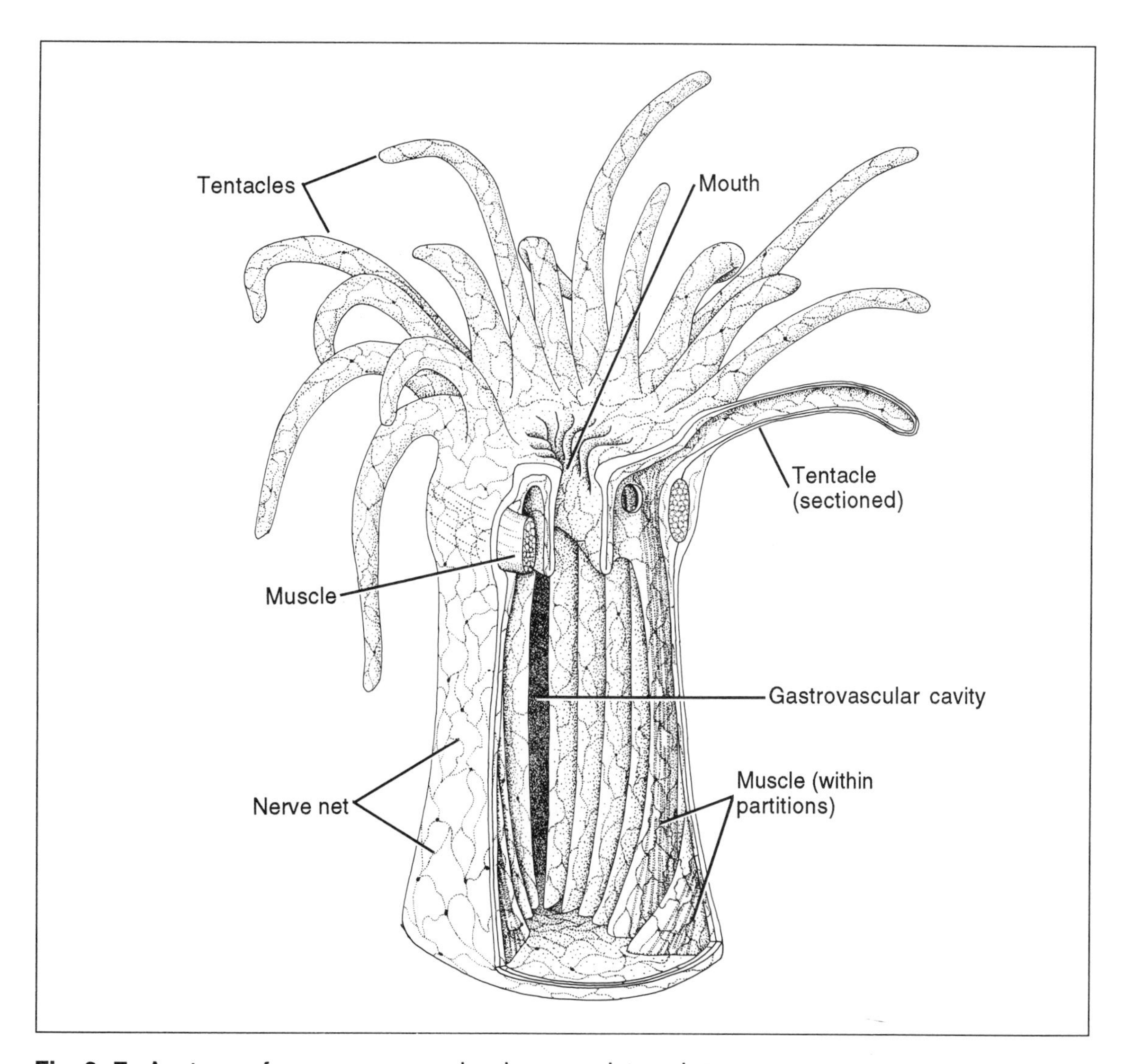

Fig. 3–7. Anatomy of a sea anemone showing some internal structures
Source: Modified from Wells 1968, 35

Respiration and Nutrient Absorption

Cnidarians have neither respiratory systems nor circulatory systems. Like cells in sponges, the cells in cnidarians get oxygen directly from the water surrounding them. Nutrients from digested food pass through the liquid between the cells to nourish all parts of the body, and wastes pass out by the same route.

Nervous and Muscular Systems

The nervous system of cnidarians consists of cells with long, thin fibers that respond to mechanical or chemical stimuli. The fibers connect, forming a network called a **nerve net.** See Fig. 3–7. The nerves send impulses to **muscle cells,** which respond by contracting.

In the sea anemone the muscular system consists of muscle cells lying in bands up and down the body wall and in a circle around the mouth cavity. See Fig. 3–7. The body shortens when the vertical bands contract. If muscles on only one side contract, the body bends in that direction. The mouth closes when the circular muscle contracts. See Fig. 3–5.

The ability to respond to a stimulus of touch or pressure is called **mechanoreception.** When something touches the surface of the sea anemone, the nerve cells send impulses to the muscle cells in the body wall and the muscle cells contract, causing the sea anemone to move.

The ability to respond to chemical stimuli is called **chemoreception.** Humans detect chemicals by taste and smell. Chemoreception is crucial to finding and testing foods, detecting harmful substances, and, in some organisms, selecting and attracting mates and finding suitable places to live. The ability to respond to changes in light intensity is called **photoreception.**

Most animals respond to mechanical and chemical stimuli by moving toward the stimulus (positive response) or away from it (negative response). Sometimes a stimulus triggers a complicated series of responses.

QUESTIONS

11. What might explain the large numbers of jellyfish that occasionally wash up on a beach?

12. Sea anemones are sessile (attached) animals. What do biologists mean when they say that a sea anemone moves?

13. Jellyfish propel themselves with rhythmic pulsations of their body, yet they are described as plankton (drifting organisms). How might this be explained?

14. What are some examples of mechanoreception, chemoreception, and photoreception in humans? Give specific examples.

ACTIVITY 2

Determine how a sea anemone responds to chemical, mechanical, and light stimuli.

MATERIALS

- small culture dish
- seawater
- live sea anemone
- copies of Workbook Tables 3–1 and 3–2
- forceps

Table 3–1. Sea anemone responses to mechanical stimulation

Ⓦ

Stimulus	Type of response			
	No response	Tentacles move	Sea anemone contracts	Other observations
Touching forceps to tentacle				
Touching forceps to body				
Tapping on container				
Agitating water				
Exposing to sudden direct light				
Exposing to sudden shade or shadow				

- 10 disks punched out of filter paper
- food substances listed in Table 3–2
- paper towels

PROCEDURE

1. Use a culture dish deep enough to hold a fully expanded sea anemone.

2. Fill the dish with seawater and put a sea anemone in it. Wait until the sea anemone relaxes with tentacles erect as shown in (A) in Fig. 3–5.

3. Observe the sea anemone's mechanoreception ability. Record your observations in Table 3–2.
   a. Test the response of the animal to each stimulus listed in the table. Do not cut the tissue of the animal.
   b. Look for these responses:
      No response. Animal does not react.
      Tentacles move. Animal moves at least one tentacle. Observe how many tentacles move and whether they move toward or away from the stimulus.
      Animal contracts. Animal withdraws tentacles and shortens body.
      Injury. Animal emits threadlike material.
   c. Let the animal rest between tests. If it contracts, wait until it relaxes.

4. Test the sea anemone's response to food substances. Record your data in Table 3–2.

a. If not already prepared, make small filter paper disks. Use a paper punch to make 10 small disks from filter paper. Handle the disks with forceps; do not touch them with your fingers. Soak one disk in each type of food substance listed in Table 3–2. If necessary, squeeze the food to get juice.

b. Using forceps, pass the first soaked disk quickly near the sea anemone's tentacles without touching them.

c. Decide which of these terms best describes the anemone's response to each chemical stimulus:

No response (0). Sea anemone does not move tentacles either toward or away from the disk.

Positive response (+). Tentacles move toward the disk, touch it, and

Table 3–2. Sea anemone responses to chemicals in food substances 

Examples of food substances	Actual food substances	Type of response (0, +, –)
Proteins Fish juice (non-oily) Shrimp juice Clam juice Fish-food solution		
Oils and fats Tuna oil Corn oil Butter		
Starch Bread Cornstarch Rice (cooked)		
Sugar Refined sugar Apple juice		
Acid Vinegar Lemon juice		
Other foods Seaweed juice Land-plant juice		

remain in place for 2 min or longer. **Negative response (–).** Tentacles move away from the disk; sea anemone may contract.

d. After each trial, wash the forceps and dry them with a clean paper towel.

NOTE: After cleaning the forceps, place the tips among the sea anemone's tentacles. If the sea anemone shows a positive response, the forceps are still dirty. Rewash them. Use clean forceps to remove any disks rejected by the sea anemone.

e. Wait until the sea anemone relaxes before starting a new trial.

f. Repeat Procedures 3.a. through 3.f. with each of the paper disks.

g. Using a plain unsoaked disk and clean forceps, periodically test the seawater for contamination. If the animal responds positively or negatively, replace the seawater.

QUESTIONS

15. What kinds of mechanical stimuli did the sea anemone respond to? How did it respond?

16. How did the sea anemone's responses to mechanical stimuli compare with its responses to food stimuli?

17. What steps did you take to make sure the organism was responding solely to a specific food, not to some other stimulus?

18. How might a sea anemone behave if it weren't hungry? How could you know that it wasn't hungry? How might a sea anemone's hunger affect your findings?

19. In this experiment, how might it be possible to get a positive response to a plain disk?

20. Which food or food substance did the sea anemone prefer? Which food did it seem to like least? What foods is a sea anemone likely to find in its natural environment?

21. In its natural environment, how might pollutants in the water affect a sea anemone's feeding responses?

22. Fill in the features of cnidarians in Table 1–3, Comparison of animal phyla by features. Use information from Topic 3, your teacher's explanations, and reference books.

Reproduction

Cnidarians reproduce themselves both sexually and asexually.

Sexual reproduction begins with the production of cells called **eggs** and **sperm.** See Fig. 3–8. The eggs are produced in female organs called **ovaries,** the sperm in male organs called **testes.** In many species, the same sea anemone produces both eggs and sperm.

Fertilization—the beginning of a new organism—occurs when an egg and a sperm unite. Some species release both eggs and sperm into the ocean, and fertilization happens in the water. In other species the male releases sperm into the water, sperm enter the

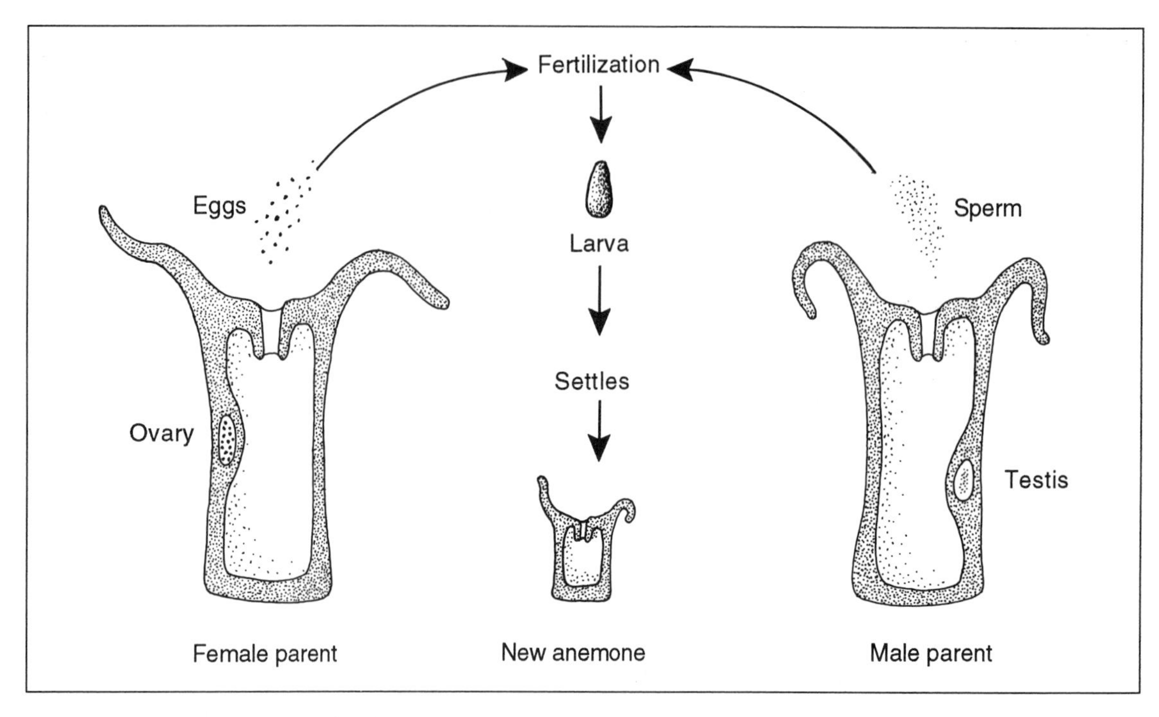

Fig. 3–8. Sexual reproduction in sea anemones and corals

ovary, and fertilization happens inside the female.

The new organism grows rapidly into a **larva** (the plural is *larvae*). A larva swims weakly by means of **cilia**—small hairlike structures that move it along by beating back and forth. Because larvae cannot swim against currents, they are classified as plankton, organisms that drift.

The larval stage is important in dispersing the species. Larvae can stay afloat for a long time, drifting hundreds of miles from the parent. Often, however, a larva settles out within minutes or hours, attaches to a hard surface, and grows into a sessile adult.

Reproduction without eggs and sperm is called **asexual reproduction.** This form is also common in cnidarians. One type is **budding,** like growing a new branch on a tree. Cells on the side or base of the parent begin to bulge out and form a new organism. The buds may remain attached to the parent. If many attached buds are produced, they form a large colony. In some organisms a bud detaches and settles down nearby to form a separate organism.

Regeneration

Cnidarians can also replace lost or damaged parts by **regeneration.** A small chunk of detached tissue may even regenerate into an entire new organism. Sea anemones can also regenerate lost parts. In the next activity we will see which parts can regenerate.

ACTIVITY 3

Observe regeneration in sea anemones. Determine conditions for regeneration.

MATERIALS

- six 250-mL beakers or jars
- seawater
- waterproof marker
- 3 sea anemones
- net
- microscope slide
- scalpel
- wax paper or aluminum foil
- copy of Workbook Table 3–3

PROCEDURE

1. Label the beakers from 1 to 6 and fill them with seawater.

2. Observe a sea anemone in an aquarium. Without disturbing it, note its size and number of tentacles. Record in your notebook.

3. Gently scrape a sea anemone from the aquarium.

4. Place the sea anemone on a microscope slide. Using a scalpel, slice through the

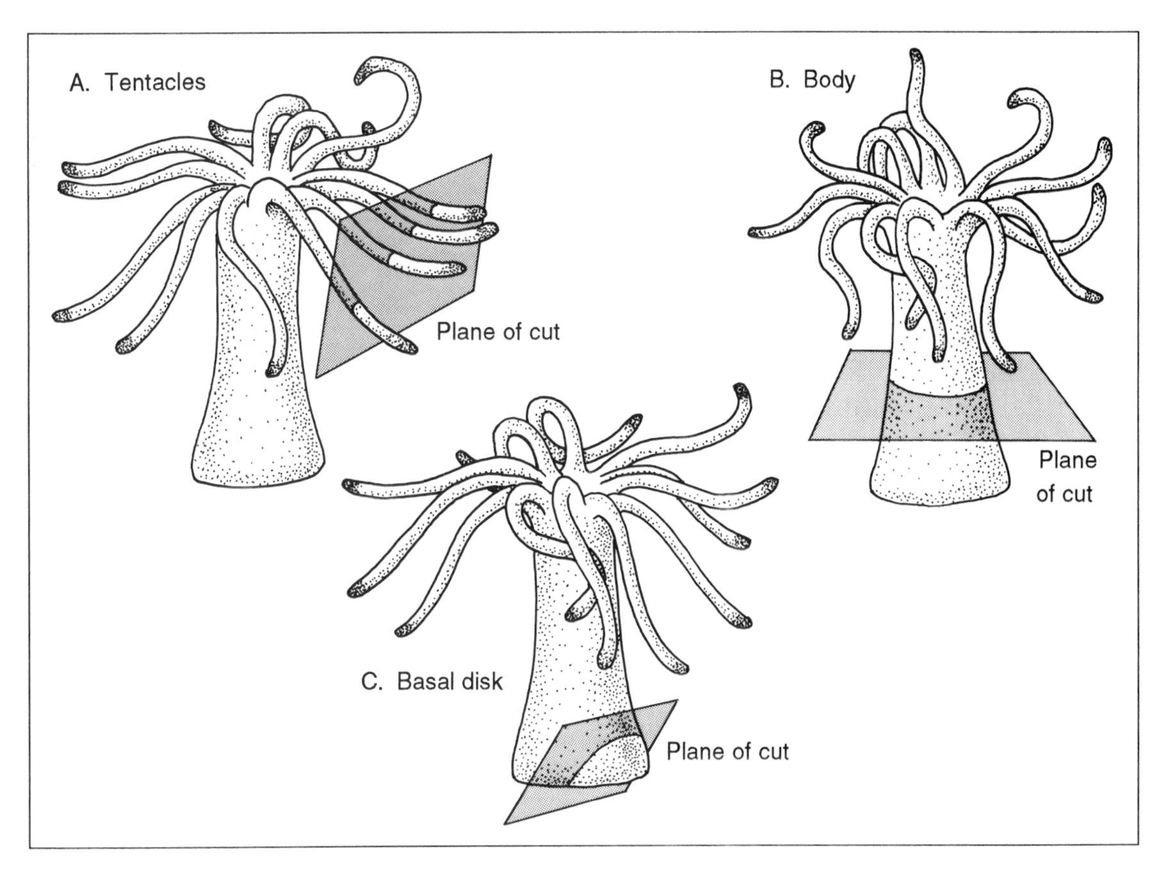

Fig. 3–9. Cutting sea anemones to observe regeneration

Table 3–3. Sea anemone regeneration Ⓦ

Date	Cut A		Cut B		Cut C	
	Beaker 1	Beaker 2	Beaker 3	Beaker 4	Beaker 5	Beaker 6
	Base	Tentacles	Top of body	Bottom of body	Small piece of body	Large piece of body

tissue as shown in (A) in Fig. 3–9. (Sea anemones often lose large parts of their bodies to predators and accidents.)

5. Place the tentacles in beaker 1 and the remainder of the anemone in beaker 2.

6. Draw pictures of the pieces in your notebook.

7. Cover the beakers loosely with wax paper or aluminum foil to reduce evaporation but allow for exchange of oxygen between the air and the water. Put the beakers in a cool, clean place.

8. Repeat Procedures 1 to 7 for two more sea anemones.
   a. Make the tissue cuts shown in (B) and (C) in Fig. 3–9.
   b. Put the parts of one sea anemone in beakers 3 and 4, the parts of the other anemone in beakers 5 and 6. See Table 3–3.
   c. Put beakers 3, 4, 5, and 6 near beakers 1 and 2.

9. Observe the sea anemones and sketch the regenerating animals every three days. If the water starts to turn cloudy or smell bad, replace it with clean seawater. Arrange your sketches in Table 3–3.

QUESTIONS

23. When the original sea anemone in beaker 1 heals, does it have more, fewer, or the same number of tentacles as it had before? What happened to the pieces of tentacles?

24. Which cut (A, B, or C) would you use to increase the anemone population of your aquarium the fastest?

25. Which cuts, if any, did not regenerate?

26. How is being able to regenerate an advantage to sea anemones? What might happen to a population of sea anemones if
    a. a boat propeller sliced through them?
    b. a fish ate part of the anemone?

FURTHER INVESTIGATIONS

1. How is it possible for animals like the clownfish and the *Glaucus* to be immune to the stings of cnidarians? Use library references to learn more about these organisms.

2. Set up other experimental situations to learn more about sea anemones.
   a. Determine whether seawater from different places affects the feeding response of a sea anemone.
   b. Determine the feeding preferences of other sea anemones. How might biologists study the food preferences of sea anemones in their natural environment?
   c. Simulate the effects of pollution on sea anemones. Make dilutions of such household products as detergents and leftover foods. Observe their effects on your sea anemone. (Start with a very low concentration, such as one drop of detergent in 1 L of seawater.) Explain how you made your dilutions.

d. Observe budding (asexual reproduction) from a sea anemone's basal disk. (Some species are better for observation than others.) Note the number of buds forming per unit of time, the rate of growth, and the change in growth rate with changes in the aquarium's temperature and salinity.

e. Cut several sea anemones at different column levels and see which ones regenerate the fastest. Repeat the experiment but put the beakers with severed pieces in a dark closet. Do these regenerate as well as the ones exposed to light? Explain. Test how the cut organisms respond to feeding.

3. Study cnidarians to learn which types of nematocysts each species contains. Draw the different nematocysts in each species.

4. Devise experiments to determine what happens when the tentacles of one sea anemone touch the tentacles of another sea anemone. First see what happens when the tentacles from two organisms of the same species touch each other. Then see what happens when the tentacles from two different species touch each other. Use this information to develop hypotheses about competition between organisms of different species (interspecies competition) and between organisms of the same species (intraspecies competition).

5. Study movements in sea anemones. When the anemones attach themselves to the walls of an aquarium, mark the spot. If they move, look for evidence of pedal laceration—tearing of the base—which might lead to asexual reproduction.

6. Ask a librarian to help you find examples of a medusa in ancient mythology. Look for modern examples as well.

7. Learn more about the venomous jellyfish such as the cubomedusa, lion's mane, and Portuguese man-of-war. What are the symptoms of a bad sting? How should a victim be treated? How dangerous are these animals to humans? Are jellyfish that have washed ashore as dangerous as ones in the water? How should they be handled?

8. Early observers noted that sea anemones had a flowerlike appearance. Look for pictures in books or videotapes that show the flowerlike appearance of sea anemones. Report to the class.

9. What animals eat sea anemones? Jellyfish? Use references to check your ideas. Are any cnidarians eaten by humans?

10. Investigate freshwater cnidarians, the hydra. If possible, collect specimens and bring them to class. Find out what they eat and how they reproduce. Are they dangerous to humans?

4. Corals and Coral Reefs

On land, trees form the forest, a structure that many plants and animals rely on for food, protection, and housing. In the ocean, corals form coral reefs, a structure that fish, invertebrates and algae rely on for feeding and protection. Coral reefs are sometimes called the forests of the sea. In tropical regions, coral reefs protect the coastline and beaches from wave and current erosion, and they form bays and lagoons that are safe havens for ships. Their special environmental and economic importance draws us to this study of corals.

Corals are members of the phylum Cnidaria. They have only a polyp stage. They look like small sea anemones, with tentacles and a soft body column supported by a hydrostatic skeleton. See Fig. 3–4 in Topic 3. Unlike anemones, hard coral polyps produce external skeletons of calcium carbonate.

How a Coral Grows

A new coral begins as a tiny planktonic (drifting) larva that settles on a hard object in a warm, shallow spot and grows into a coral polyp. See (A) in Fig. 4–1. The layer of the polyp's cells touching the surface secretes a skeleton that grows outward at the base. Since the skeleton lies outside the body of the polyp, it is called an **exoskeleton** (G. *exo* = outer). The part of the skeleton directly under the polyp is a cup-shaped depression called a **calyx** (L. *calix* = cup). A polyp can retract into its calyx for protection.

The bright-colored corals—yellow, green, orange, and purple—that a snorkeler sees in a reef are living corals. Usually only the soft, delicate polyp tissue is colored. Beneath the polyp lies the stony (calcareous) skeleton it secreted. The skeletons of most reef-building corals are chalky white. Careless divers can easily damage soft coral polyp tissues by grabbing or standing on corals. The soft polyps attract fish that feed on them.

A few species of corals spend their entire lives as a single polyp. They are called **solitary corals.** See (B) in Fig. 4–1. A single polyp that keeps secreting a skeleton produces a vertical tubular structure. Others, like the oval-shaped mushroom coral, grow outward, sometimes as large as a human's foot.

Most species of corals are **colonial corals,** often described as "coral heads." Like solitary corals, a colonial coral begins as a single polyp settling on a hard surface to grow. Unlike a solitary coral, a colonial coral grows by **budding,** a process of asexual reproduction in which new polyps form a ring around the original polyp. See (C) in Fig. 4–1. In colonial corals, all the polyps are joined by a thin layer of often-colorful surface tissue. All these polyps secrete skeletal matter, adding to the thickness, the diameter, and the mass of the coral skeleton. As successive polyps add more layers of skeletal matter, a coral head can become quite large.

Some colonial corals produce buds at the tips of small branches and grow into a complex branching shape. See (D) in Fig. 4–1.

Others bud only at the edges, forming a crust over the substrate. See (E) in Fig. 4–1. Colonial corals are therefore subdivided into **branching corals** and **encrusting corals.**

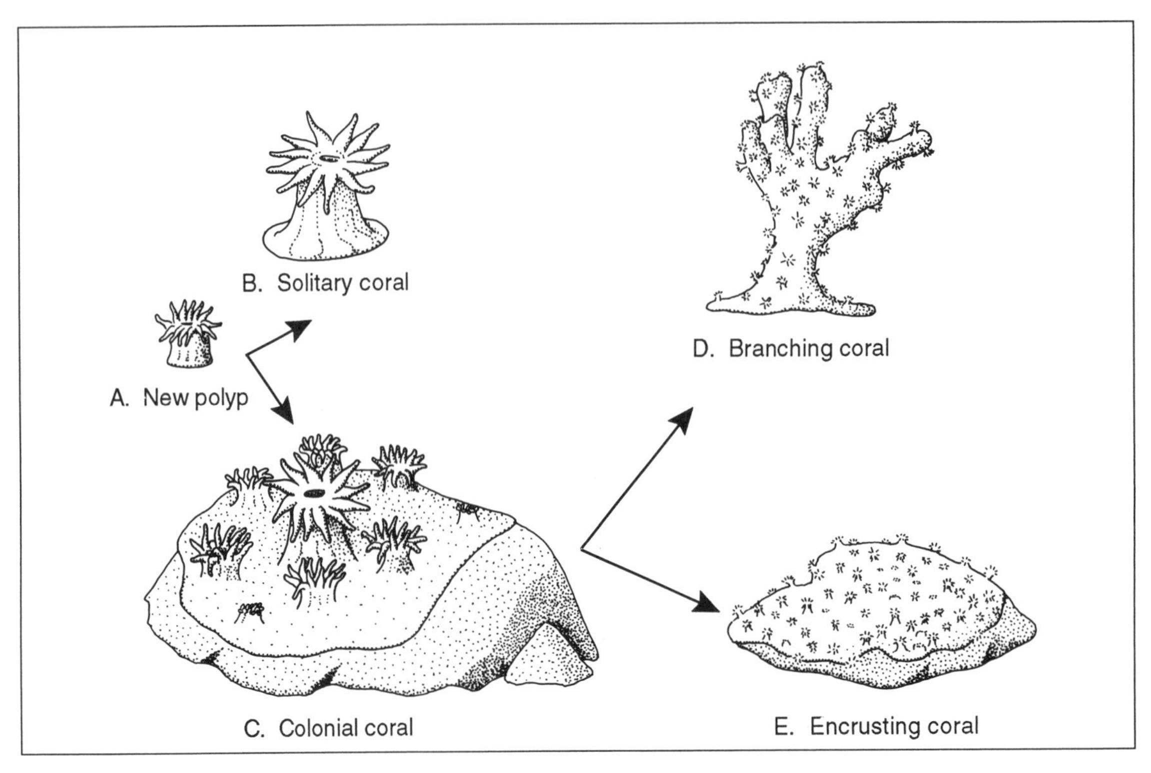

Fig. 4–1. Growth of solitary and colonial corals

Symbiosis

Many cnidarians, including most corals, have single-celled algae (plants) called **zooxanthellae** (G. *zoo* = animal; G. *xanth* = yellow; L. *ella* = small) living in cells in their tissues. This is an unusual example of a plant species living within an animal species. This symbiotic relationship is called **mutualism** because it benefits both species. Some mollusks, sponges, and tunicates also have algal cells living in their tissues.

Here is how mutualism works between a zooxanthella (algal) cell and a coral (animal) cell:

1. A zooxanthella (plant) cell exposed to sunlight begins **photosynthesis,** the process of taking in carbon dioxide and producing oxygen.
2. The coral (animal) cell uses the oxygen for respiration and produces carbon dioxide and other waste products.
3. The zooxanthella cell uses the carbon dioxide from the coral cell for photosyn-

thesis. It also uses the coral's other waste products as nutrients for itself. In its turn, it produces nutrients that the coral uses as food. In this exchange of materials, both cells benefit.

4. The zooxanthellae also stimulate skeletal secretion in many species of coral. Corals whose zooxanthellae are exposed to sunlight secrete skeleton up to ten times faster than corals in the dark.

So this symbiotic relationship between corals and zooxanthellae is very important in the growth of a coral reef. Reef-building corals live only in places where there is enough light for zooxanthellae to photosynthesize.

Identifying Coral Species

To a person unfamiliar with corals, most corals look alike. But the details of their skeletal structure distinguish one type from another. In Activity 1 you will learn how to identify different corals.

A distinguishing feature of coral is its calyx (the plural is *calyces*), or cup. The diameter of each calyx is one of the first features to note when examining a coral skeleton. Fig. 4–2

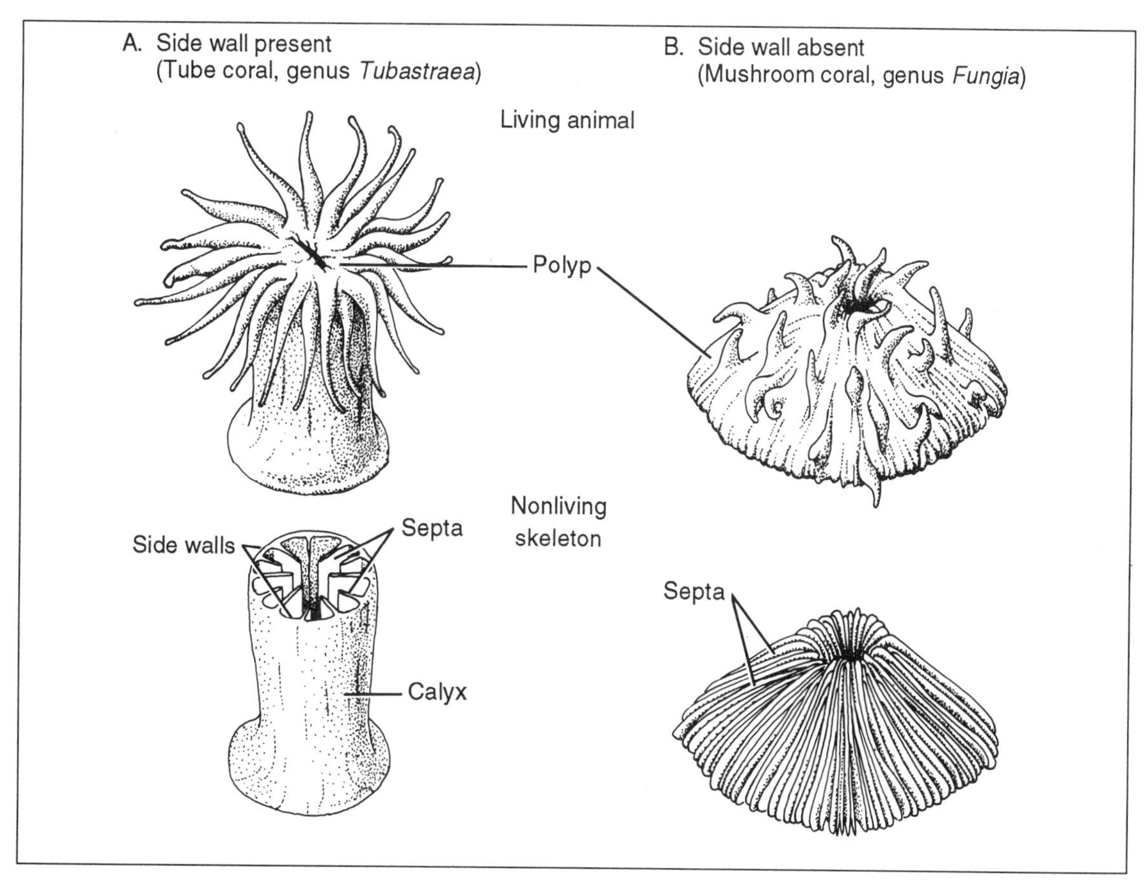

Fig. 4–2. Solitary coral calyx

shows living coral polyps and empty calyces with the coral tissue removed. The partitions radiating inward are called **septa** (L. *septum* = fence). In some solitary corals the calyx has side walls; in others it does not. See Fig. 4–2.

In colonial corals the calyces may be separated, leaving gaps, or not separated and touching. In some, parts of their side walls are missing. See Fig. 4–3. The edges of the calyx may be even with the coral surface or

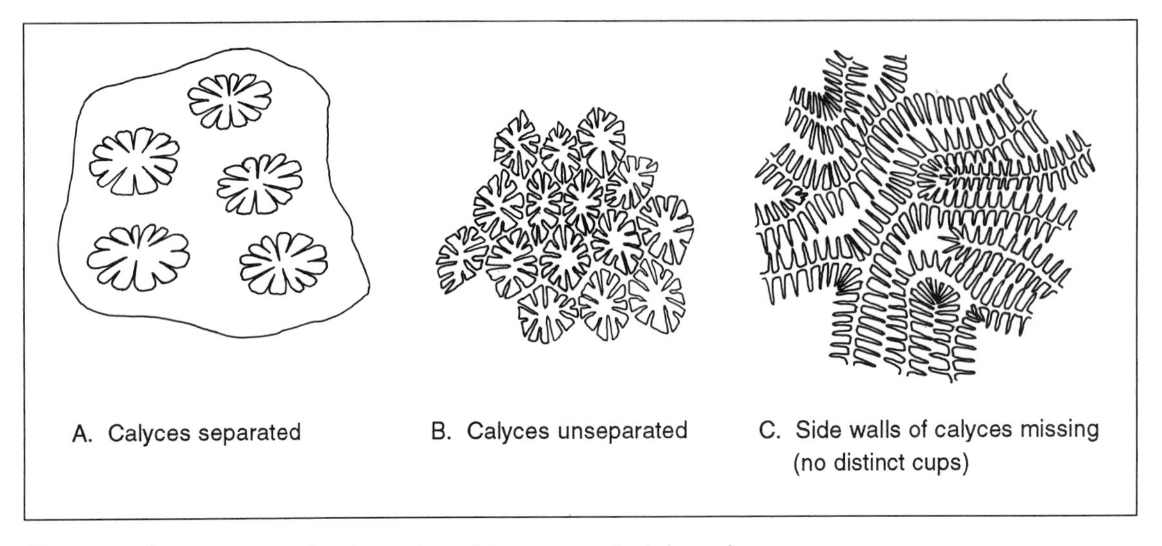

Fig. 4–3. Arrangement of calyces (cups) in some colonial corals

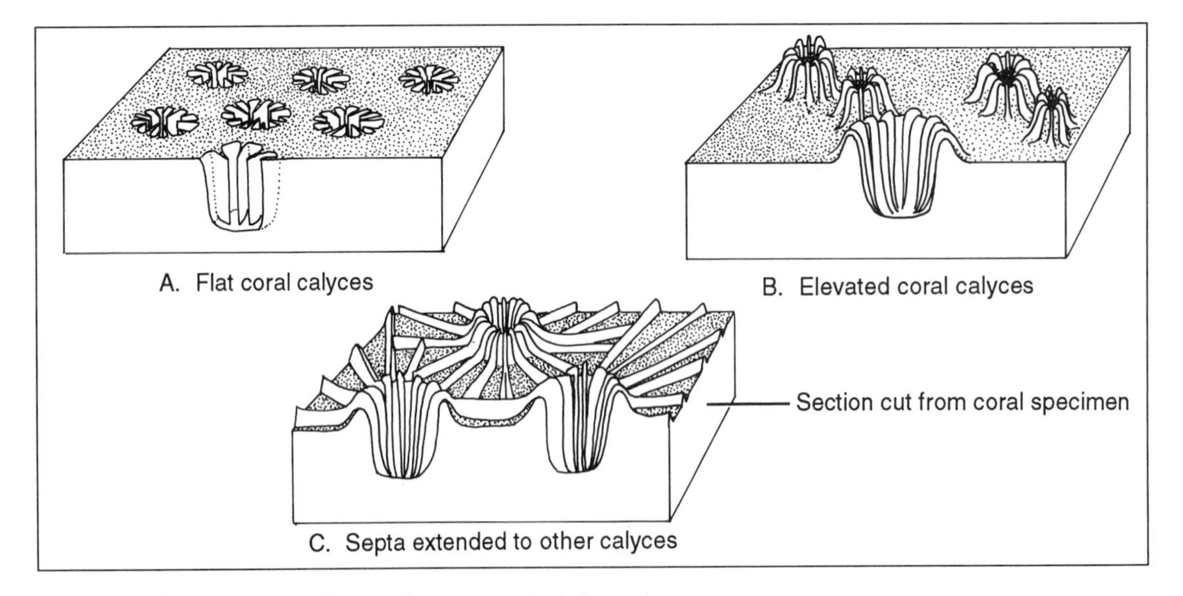

Fig. 4–4. Arrangement of septa in some colonial corals

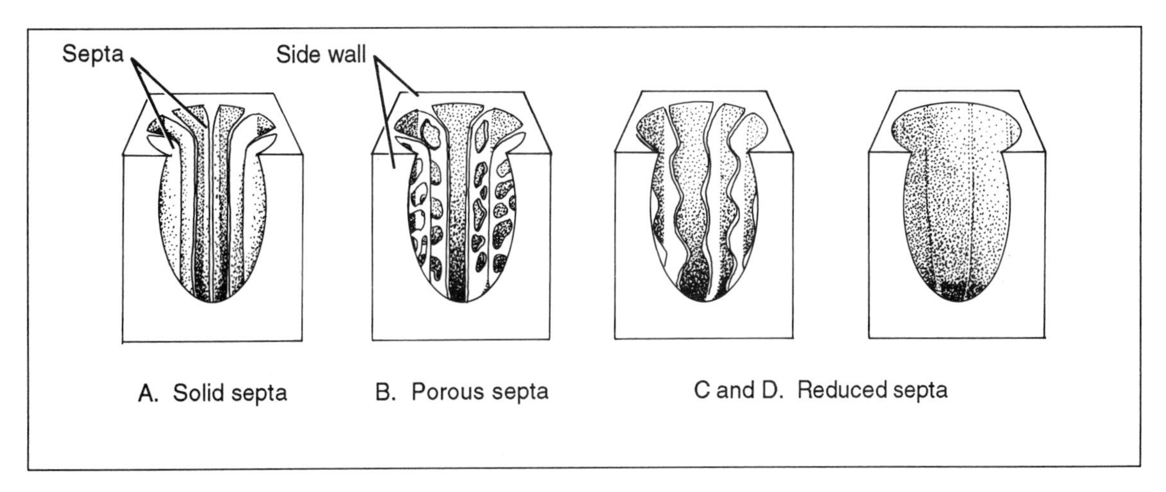

Fig. 4–5. Septa variations in colonial corals (shown with part of side walls removed)

raised above it. In some species the septa may extend outside the calyx and join with the septa of nearby calyces. See Fig. 4–4. The septa may be solid, porous, or reduced in size. See Fig. 4–5.

ACTIVITY 1
Examine five coral specimens and record their features.

MATERIALS

- 5 different reef-building coral skeletons
- dissecting microscope or hand lens
- copy of Workbook Table 4–1
- centimeter ruler
- coral key references (optional)

PROCEDURE

1. Place each sample on the dissecting microscope stage. Adjust the lighting to show contrasts. Because coral skeletons are white, they may reflect light and be difficult to see. Try to produce shadows.

2. Describe the features of the coral cups in Table 4–1. Refer to Figs. 4–2 through 4–5 as needed.

3. If a coral key is available, identify the corals by their scientific names.

QUESTIONS

1. How do the cup features of the colonial coral specimens differ? Which differed most?
   a. Do different specimens have distinctive cup features? Describe or draw them.
   b. If your samples came from beach gravel, how might you positively identify the coral type? Explain.

2. Which coral cup parts are lacking in a solitary coral like *Fungia?* See Fig. 4–2.

Table 4–1. Skeletal features of five corals

Description and measurements	Drawing of coral
Calyx description Calyx diameter___mm Gaps between calyces? yes___no___ Calyx elevated? yes___no___ Septa description Number of septa per calyx___ Entire___Porous___Reduced___ Join other calyces? yes___no___	
Calyx description Calyx diameter___mm Gaps between calyces? yes___no___ Calyx elevated? yes___no___ Septa description Number of septa per calyx___ Entire___Porous___Reduced___ Join other calyces? yes___no___	
Calyx description Calyx diameter___mm Gaps between calyces? yes___no___ Calyx elevated? yes___no___ Septa description Number of septa per calyx___ Entire___Porous___Reduced___ Join other calyces? yes___no___	
Calyx description Calyx diameter___mm Gaps between calyces? yes___no___ Calyx elevated? yes___no___ Septa description Number of septa per calyx___ Entire___Porous___Reduced___ Join other calyces? yes___no___	
Calyx description Calyx diameter___mm Gaps between calyces? yes___no___ Calyx elevated? yes___no___ Septa description Number of septa per calyx___ Entire___Porous___Reduced___ Join other calyces? yes___no___	

3. How does a colonial coral seem to grow? Explain by making sketches.

4. Which of the species you observed would probably break during a storm? What skeletal features make one coral more fragile than another?

5. Define the following terms:
   a. polyp
   b. colonial
   c. elevated cup
   d. septa

6. Some coral polyps are as small as the little "o" in words in this text. How can these small animals create coral heads? Massive coral reefs?

Coral Reef Formation

A coral reef begins when coral larvae settle on a hard substrate in warm, clear shallow water and begin secreting skeletons. Colonial corals bud and grow over many years. Their polyps deposit a mound of skeleton, one layer at a time, under the thin surface of their living tissue. Hundreds, thousands, or millions of coral colonies growing together on a rocky bottom eventually form a **coral reef**—a massive deposit of coral skeletons.

The shallow waters of tropical volcanic islands foster the growth of coral reefs. Coral polyps settle on the hard volcanic substrate and build their skeletons into coral heads and then into a reef. The corals keep growing as long as they get enough sunlight (for their symbiotic zooxanthellae), nutrients, and other necessities. If they grow upward too fast, their fragile polyps will die of exposure during very low tides.

Coral reef skeletons can become massive. On the coral islands of Bikini and Enewetak in the Pacific, scientists drilled through more than 2 km of skeletal material before hitting the volcanic rock that first formed the island. Knowing that coral polyps produce skeleton at a rate of only a few millimeters per year, we can appreciate what a feat it is for these tiny coral polyps to build a reef.

Parts of a Reef

The flat upper surface of a reef is called a **reef flat;** its outer seaward surface is called a **reef face.** See Fig. 4–6. Coral grows fastest on the reef face, where currents carry food particles to the living polyps. As coral colonies grow on the reef face, the reef extends seaward, the reef flat slowly becomes wider, and the reef face moves farther offshore.

The reef flat is so near the surface that most of it is exposed to the air during low tides. Tides limit the height to which coral can grow. If the upper tips of the coral are exposed to air too long, they die, producing the reef flat. Daily, the tide rises and falls, alternately covering and exposing the reef flat. When the tide falls, it leaves small pools of seawater. Sunlight heating these isolated pools reduces the oxygen content and evaporates some of the water, increasing its salinity. But rainfall dilutes the water in the pools, greatly decreasing its salinity. Only the hardiest animals can survive such severe changes. For these reasons few corals live on the flat of a reef.

Corals on the shallower part of the outer reef face take the most punishment from high wave energy and the abrasive force of moving sand particles. Hence only a few very hardy species of coral and coralline algae grow here. **Coralline algae** are marine algae (plants) that produce large amounts of calcium carbonate to form strong, robust skeletons. Of the two, coralline algae have adapted better to wave action than coral has. They make up as much as 90% of the calcium-producing organisms on the shallow outer reef face. This part of a reef could therefore be called an **algal reef** instead of a coral reef. When these algae die, they leave white skeletons that are often mistaken for coral. But a close look shows that their skeletons do not have calyces (cups) as coral skeletons do. These encrusting coralline algae cement parts of the reef together, making it very resistant to heavy wave action.

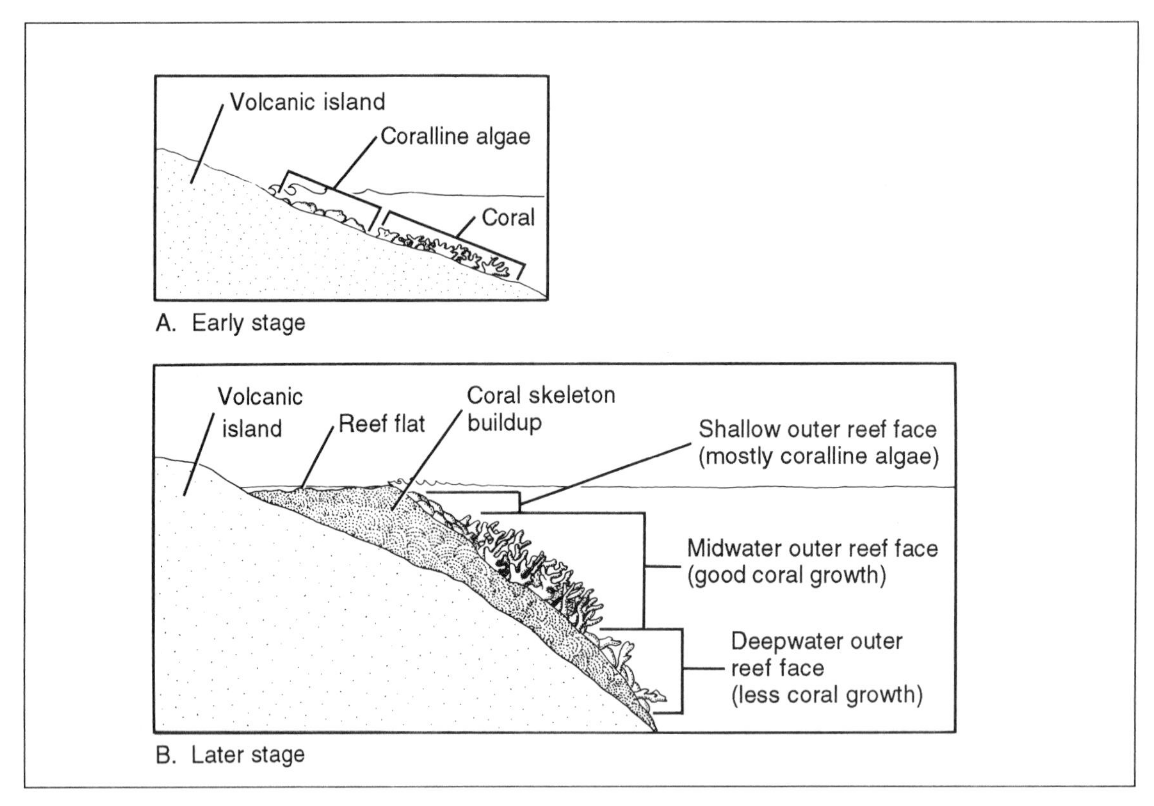

Fig. 4–6. Profile of a coral reef

Corals grow in luxurious abundance on the deeper part of the outer reef face, where they are exposed to less wave energy. Some coral reefs have as many as two hundred species of coral, all competing for space on the reef. Some faster-growing corals may overtake and grow on top of slower-growing corals, killing them.

Still deeper on the outer reef face (greater

than 30 m) the lack of light limits the growth of the common reef-building corals because the symbiotic algae (zooxanthellae) do not receive enough light to photosynthesize and stimulate the coral to produce skeleton.

Different coral species can tolerate different amounts of wave action, tidal exposure, and silting. Species become distributed in the reef in regions where they can tolerate the environmental stresses. Together, the corals of the reef offer a complex and colorful environment for the hundreds of other organisms that find food and shelter there—sponges, fish, mollusks, echinoderms, and many other marine organisms.

Coral Reef Evolution

Coral reefs form and change in predictable ways over long periods. Many begin on volcanic islands. Then, as the volcanic substrate changes, the corals respond. A volcanic island is so heavy that it gradually sinks into the crust of the earth below the ocean. This gradual sinking of the island is called **subsidence.** See Fig. 4–7. Erosion from wind and water also wears away the island. Over millions of years, an island gets smaller from erosion and subsidence while the surrounding coral reef grows larger. In this way an island and its attached coral reef slowly change in relative size.

In its early stages, when a reef is small and close to shore, it is called a **fringing reef.** See (A) in Fig. 4–7. As a reef grows in extent, it becomes a **barrier reef.** See (B) in Fig. 4–7. A region of shallow seawater called a **lagoon** often forms between the barrier reef and the island.

The island continues to subside and erode, and the ocean eventually covers it. The coral grows over the submerged surface of the island. Then all that can be seen at the surface is a circle of coral islands called a **coral atoll.** Coral grows faster at the open ocean edge than anywhere else, so that in the sunken island's place a large lagoon forms where less coral grows. See (C) in Fig. 4–7.

Along the reef, mounds of coral rubble pile up, forming small islets called **motus** (the singular is *motu*). Motus form when violent storms break large chunks off the outer reef face and throw them onto the reef flat. The motu, no more than a few feet above sea level, is all that appears above the water's surface. As a few species of plants are introduced onto the motu, by nature or by humans, vegetation covers it, anchoring the rubble in place.

In some places the island subsides faster than the coral grows. Then the whole atoll and the reef slowly sink. When the reef falls below the depth that sunlight reaches, it stops growing and dies because the zooxanthellae (the cells that corals depend on for food and oxygen) cannot photosynthesize. When reef growth no longer keeps up with subsidence, the island stops growing and gradually sinks to several hundred feet below sea level. This submerged atoll is called a **guyot** (GEE yoh).

Geologists have discovered that sea level has changed several times during the geologic past as ice caps formed and melted around the north and south poles. Reefs died when falling sea levels exposed the corals or when rising sea levels submerged them beyond the reach of sunlight.

Fossil coral reefs are often found far inland on tropical islands, or even in the middle of continents. Shifts of the earth's surface plates have moved ancient coral reefs to the tops of mountains. There are fossil coral reefs in Minnesota and Michigan, left from a time long ago when a shallow sea covered the middle of North America. Small pieces of these fossil corals in Michigan are called "Petoskey stones" for the town near which they are found.

QUESTIONS

7. In what ways do coral animals depend on plants?

8. What might be ideal conditions for coral reef growth? What conditions might inhibit reef growth? Make predictions.

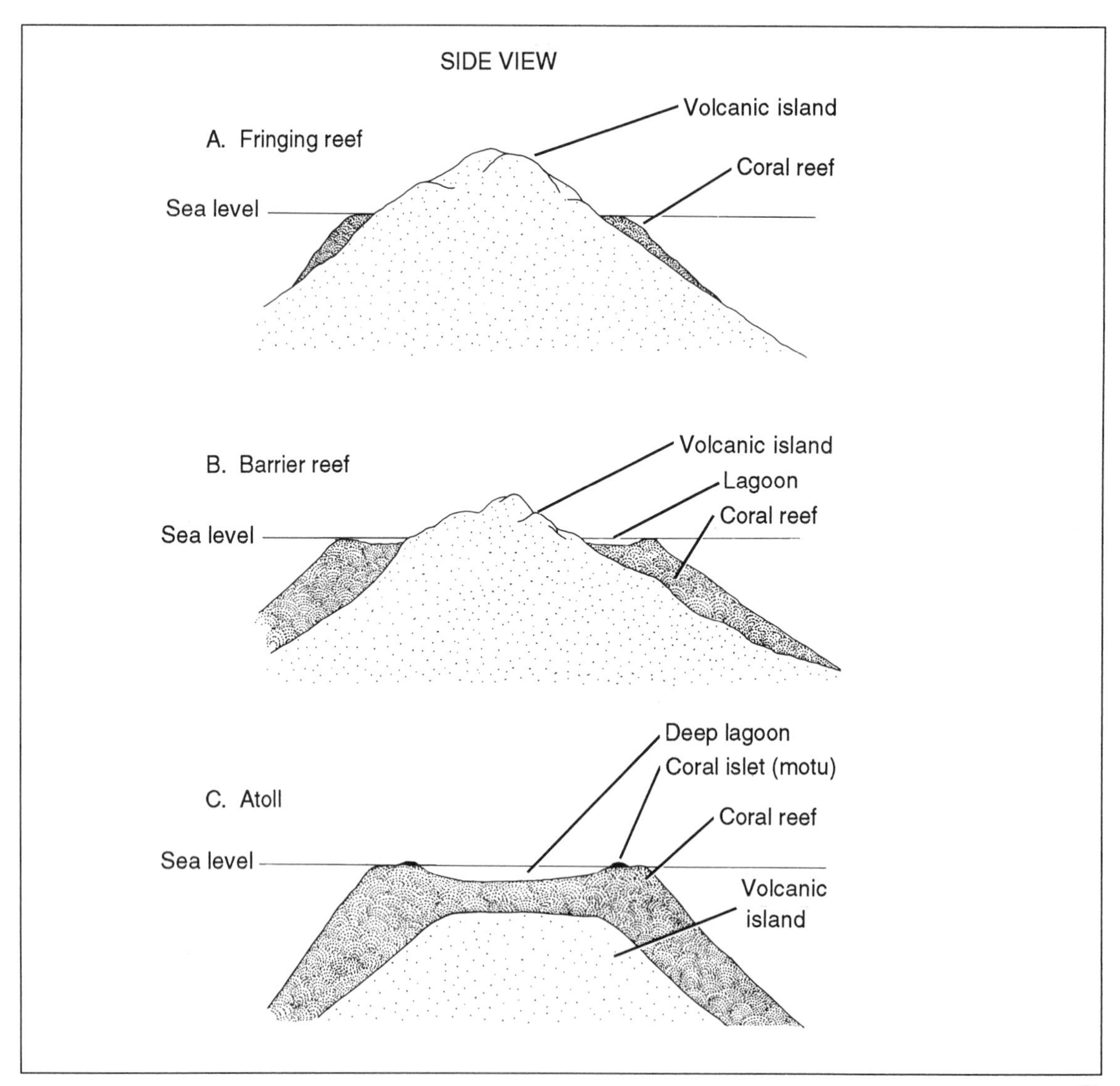

Fig. 4–7. Evolution of a coral reef

9. What would the fossils in a fossil coral reef look like? How would you recognize a coral fossil?

10. How might coral reefs be used to study the geological history of the earth?

Biological and Physical Agents of Change on a Coral Reef

A reef is made of coral and coralline algae that form a structure used by other organisms as a dwelling place. A coral reef, like a forest, is a complex community of many associated plants and animals. Organisms act as agents of change to cause the reef to grow or be destroyed. Physical conditions also determine the growth or destruction of the reef.

Biological agents of change include all the plants and animals that build up and destroy reefs. See Table 4–2. **Reef-building agents** are organisms that secrete the calcium carbonate skeletons that form the reef. **Crack-filling agents** are organisms that produce sediment or live in the cracks and crevices of the reef. **Passive agents** use the structure of the reef to live and hide in. They do not affect the reef structure but may eat other reef organisms or be eaten by them. **Destructive agents** erode the reef by grinding, chewing, or boring into it.

Physical agents of change—waves, currents, pollution, moving sand, silt deposits, fresh water, and severe shifts in temperature—kill corals and wear away the reef. See Table 4–2.

Table 4–2. Agents of change affecting the growth of a coral reef

Agents of change	Examples
Constructive agents–reef builders	Calcareous corals Encrusting coralline algae
Crack fillers	Encrusting coralline algae Fragments of corals *Foraminifera* (one-celled animals that make shells–for example, paper shells) Mollusks Echinoderms
Passive agents	Anemones Crustaceans Many fish Worms Red, green, and brown algae Octopuses Many mollusks

Table 4–2 *continued.* Agents of change affecting the growth of a coral reef

Agents of change	Examples
Destructive biological agents (organisms that destroy by chewing, eroding, blanketing, or producing acid)	Boring sponges Coral-eating fish (parrotfish) Worms Sea urchins and sea stars Boring mollusks Rapid-growing algae
Constructive physical agents (builders)	Calm water Adequate sunlight Optimum salinity Clear water Solid substrate Adequate nutrients
Destructive physical agents	Pounding waves Moving sand Smothering sediments (silt) Freshwater rain Very low tides Rising seafloor Sinking seafloor Rising or falling water temperature Runoff from land Excessive nutrients in water Pollution

ACTIVITY 2

Compare the agents of change on a coral reef and in a forest.

MATERIALS

- copy of Workbook Table 4–3

PROCEDURE

1. Fill in Table 4–3 with examples of specific agents that affect the structure of a forest.

2. Compare Table 4–3 with Table 4–2 and

discuss the similarities and differences between the agents of change on a coral reef and in a forest.

QUESTIONS

11. What do we mean by the "structure" of a forest? Of a reef? Describe the structure of the reef.

12. In what ways are corals in a reef like trees in a forest? How are they different?

13. What happens to the trees when they die? To the corals?

14. What are the differences between the growth of a tree and the growth of a forest? What are the differences between the growth of a single coral colony and the growth of a coral reef?

15. Compare the biological and physical agents that damage a forest and a coral reef. How are they similar? How are they different?

16. How does the amount of sunlight affect the growth of a coral reef? A forest?

Table 4–3. Agents affecting the growth of a forest

Agents and conditons of change	Examples
Forest builders	
Forest floor organisms	
Passive residents	
Destructive organisms	
Constructive physical agents	
Destructive physical agents	

Table 4–4. Physical agents affecting the growth of a coral reef

Turbidity and light. Turbidity is cloudiness of water from suspended particles of silt, clay, and plankton—microscopic plants and animals. The particles block light. Turbidity rises where plankton flourish or runoff carries silt and clay from rivers. Turbidity drops when silt and clay particles settle or when plankton die and their skeletal remains sink. Healthy, living coral polyps can remove moderate amounts of sediments that fall on them, but heavy deposits can smother and kill them.

Nutrient concentration and algal growth. Where light and nutrients are sufficient, algae that grow attached to a substrate (benthic algae) flourish. Like all green plants, these algae photosynthesize to produce the chemicals they need for growth. Algae are an important food source for many animals on the reef, but if the algae grow faster than the coral, they can cover and smother the coral polyps.

Water depth and light. The quantity of light that reaches the symbiotic zooxanthellae living in coral tissue is crucial to the growth of coral. In clear equatorial waters of the open ocean, reefs do not grow below 40 m. See Fig. 4–8.

Temperature. Water temperature is a crucial factor in forming coral reefs. Reef-building corals grow best between 25°C and 31°C. Some have survived temperatures as low as 18°C and as high as 35°C, but corals do not grow vigorously at such extremes.

Latitude and season. Because sunlight, called radiant energy, is more intense at the equator than at the poles, water in the equatorial zone between 23°N and 23°S is warmer than it is at higher latitudes. See Fig. 4–9. Less sunlight strikes the earth's surface on short winter days, and winter temperatures are lower than those of summer.

Cloud cover. Clouds block sunlight. Latitude, season, and cloud cover together control the amount of light striking the earth. (The units of radiant energy in Fig. 4–13 are shown in kcal / cm^2/month. One kcal equals 1,000 cal or 1,000 gm of water raised 1°C.)

Salinity. Coral grows best where salinity—the saltiness of seawater—is between 34‰ and 37‰. Most corals die in salinities below 25‰ and above 40‰. (Oceanographers express salinity with the symbol ‰, which means parts per thousand. Average seawater contains 35‰ of dissolved salts, which equals 3.5 %).

River runoff. All the oceans and marginal seas have salinities suitable for coral reef growth. But at some river mouths freshwater runoff can greatly reduce salinity. As you can see from Table 4–5, the Amazon is "King River" for runoff. (Major tropical rivers are shown in Fig. 4–14.) River runoff can reduce light penetration in the ocean by adding suspended silt and clay to the water. In addition, sediment deposited on the ocean bottom forms a soft substrate where coral reefs cannot grow. Large volumes of water are not always responsible for large amounts of sediment, as can be seen where the Mekong flows from Vietnam into the South China Sea.

Physical Agents Affecting the Growth of Coral Reefs

Coral reefs form only in certain parts of the world. As Table 4–3 shows, many physical agents affect the growth of the reef, both positively and negatively. Table 4–4 lists and explains these physical agents. Activity 3 investigates how some of these physical agents determine the worldwide distribution of coral reefs.

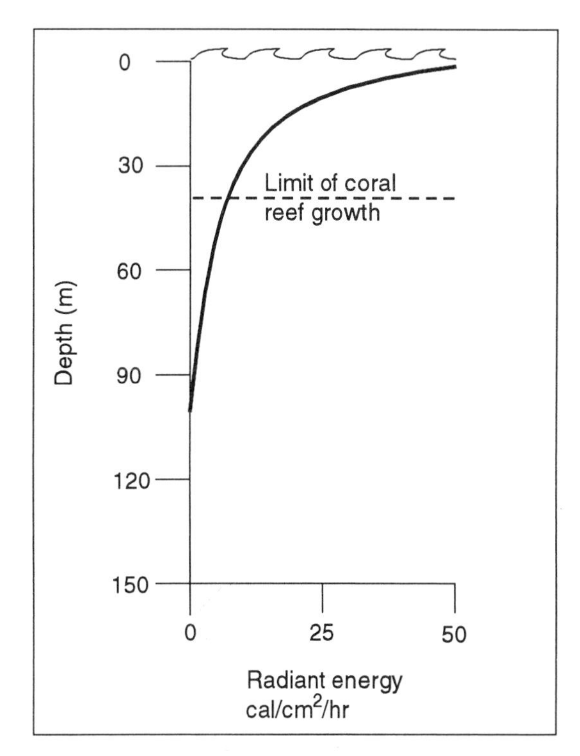

Fig. 4–8. Radiant energy, coral growth, and water depths at Bikini Atoll, location 11°N, 165°E

ACTIVITY 3

Generate and test a hypothesis about the global distribution of coral reefs.

MATERIALS

- copies of Workbook Figs. 4–10, 4–11, 4–12, 4–13, and 4–14
- colored pencils or crayons
- overhead projector and transparency film (optional)

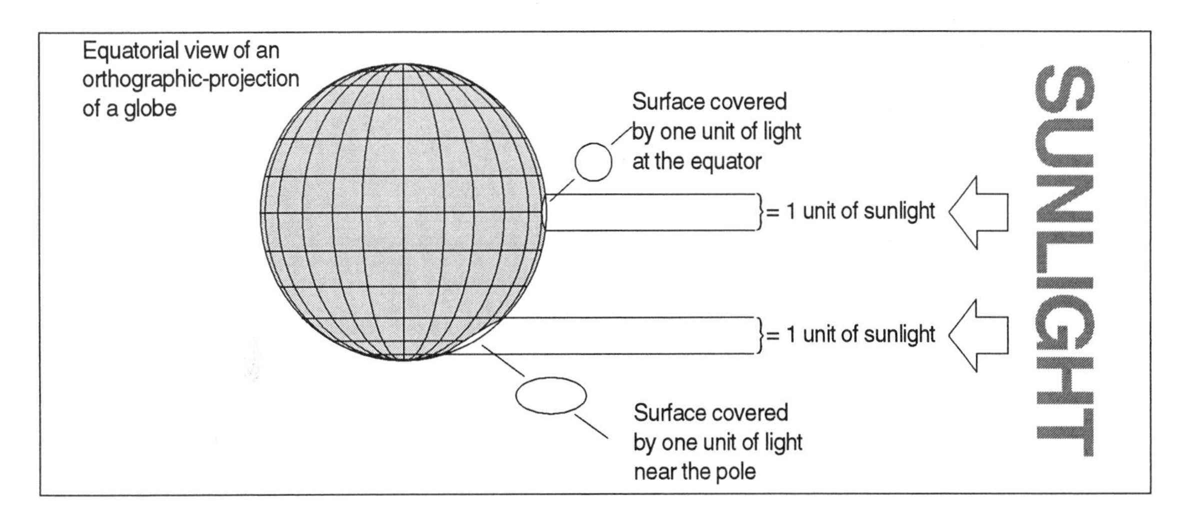

Fig. 4–9. Comparison of the surface area covered by one unit of sunlight at the equator and one unit near the pole showing that the amount of sunlight per square centimeter is greater at the equator than at the pole

Table 4–5. Water discharge and sediment transport of major tropical rivers

River	Location	Water discharge (km^3/yr)	Sediment transport (million ton/yr)
A. Amazon	Eastern South America	5,680	1,600
B. Zaire (Congo)	Southwestern Africa	728	480
C. Ganges	Western India	382	400
D. Indus	Eastern India	683	190
E. Mekong	Southeastern Asia	346	90

PROCEDURE

1. Examine Fig. 4–10, a map showing the distribution of coral reefs in the oceans.
   a. Find the regions of coral reefs. Color-code these regions light purple.
   b. In your notebook, identify and describe these regions.
   c. Write one or more hypotheses to explain the regional distribution of corals.

2. Color-code Fig. 4–11, a map showing ocean surface temperatures for February—winter in the northern hemisphere. Use blue for the coldest area (less than 20°C), red for the warmest area (greater than 25°C) and green for the area between them (20–25°C). Show the colors you use in the color code.

3. Using the same scheme, color-code Fig. 4–12, a map showing ocean surface temperatures in August—winter in the southern hemisphere.

4. Color-code Fig. 4–13, a composite map showing the minimum winter radiant energy in kilocalories (kcal) per square centimeter (cm^2) each month for both the northern and southern hemispheres. Use colors ranging from yellow to orange to green (or devise your own color scheme) to show amounts of solar radiation. Show your colors in the color code.

5. In Fig. 4–14 find the major rivers. At the mouth of each river draw concentric semicircles for each 100 million tons of sediment transport per year. For each 100 million tons of sediment, increase the radius of the semicircle 1 mm. Color-code the map. Show your colors in the code.

6. Compare the information in all the maps. One at a time, lay each map on top of Fig. 4–10, the map showing the distribution of coral reefs. Look for relationships between changes in the environment and the presence of corals. If possible, view the maps held together against a window or some other light source. Record your observations in your notebook.

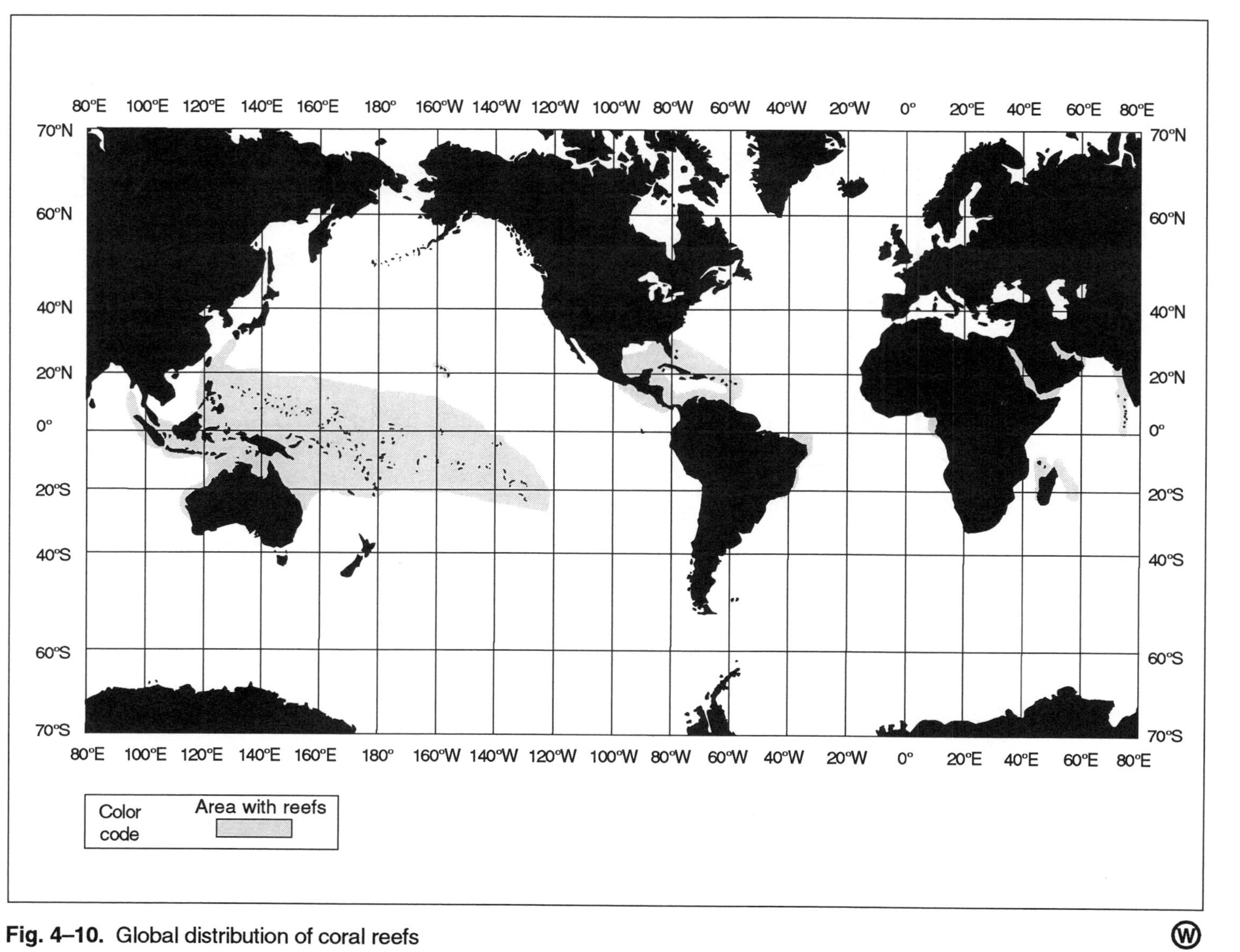

Fig. 4–10. Global distribution of coral reefs

Ⓦ

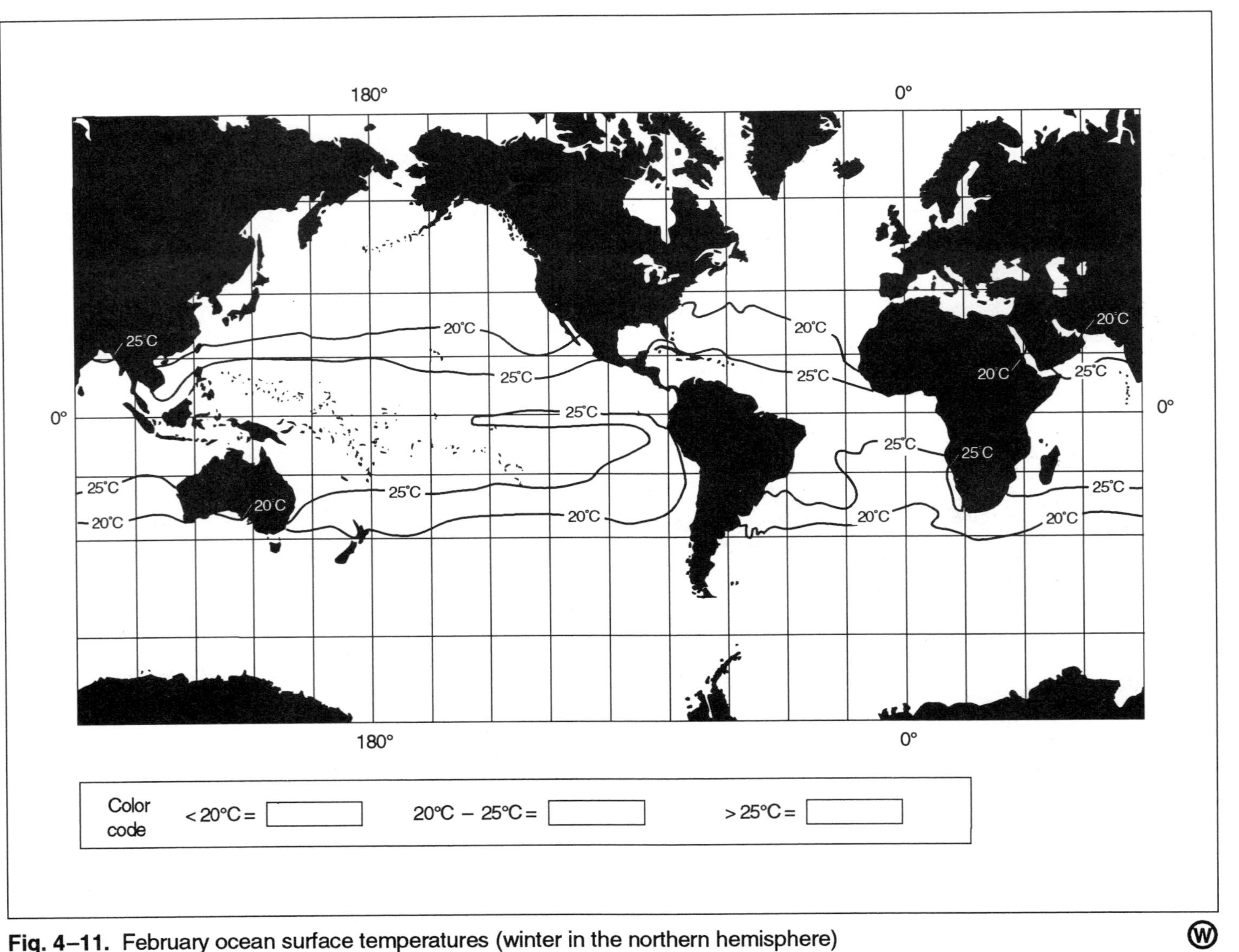

Fig. 4–11. February ocean surface temperatures (winter in the northern hemisphere)

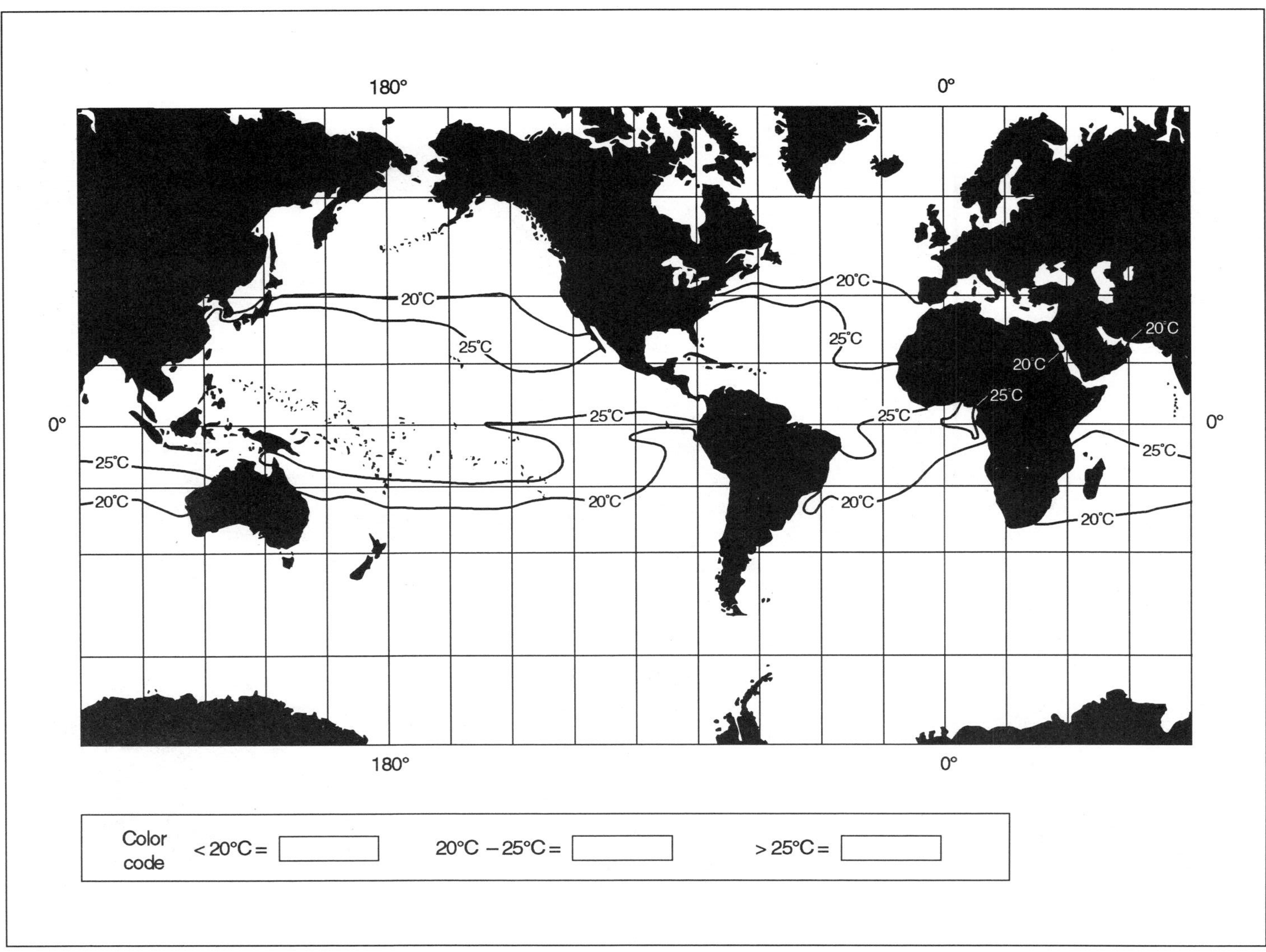

Fig. 4–12. August surface temperatures (winter in the southern hemisphere)

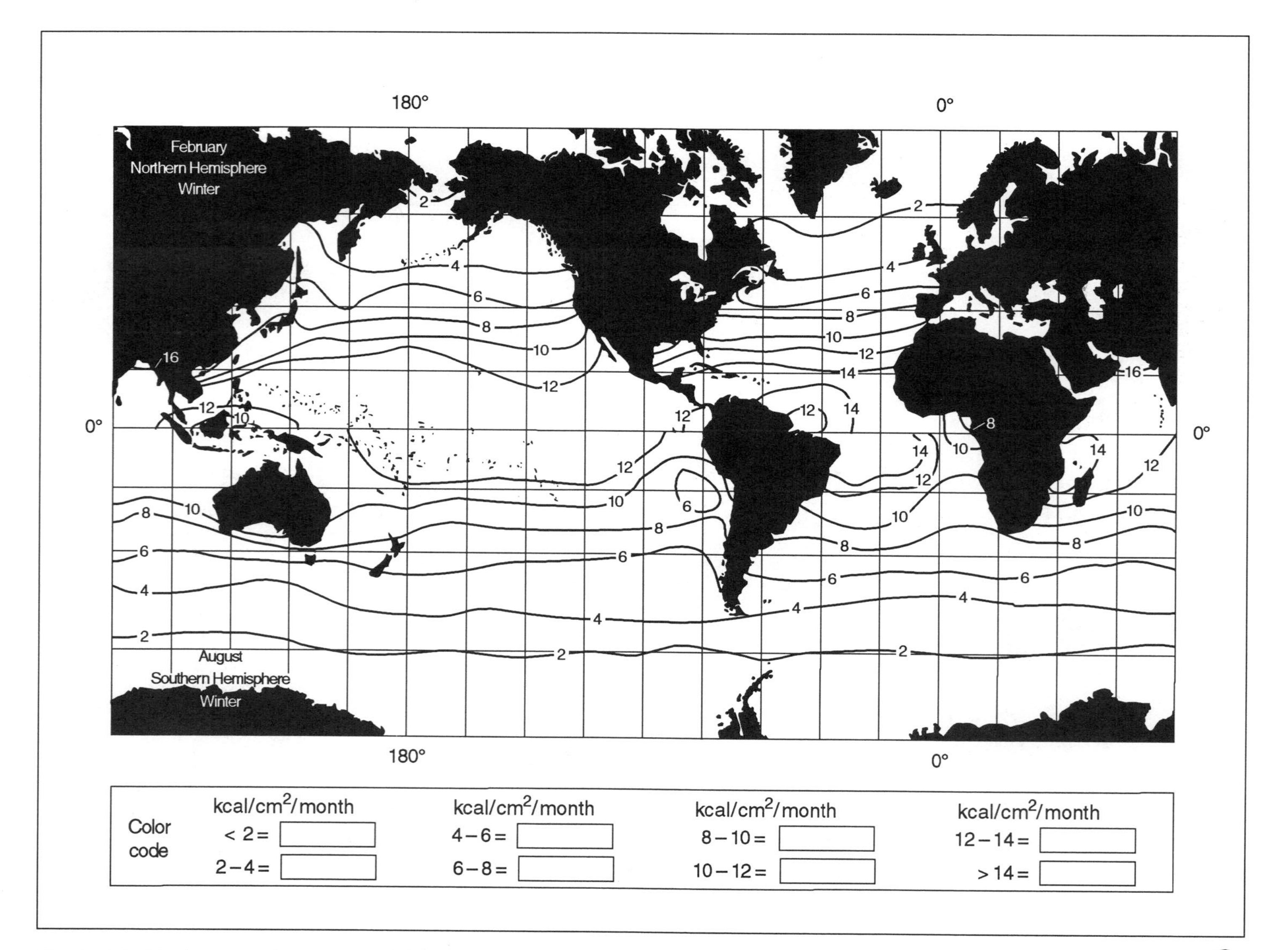

Fig. 4–13. Minimum radiant energy (This composite map shows winter values for northern and southern hemispheres.) Ⓦ

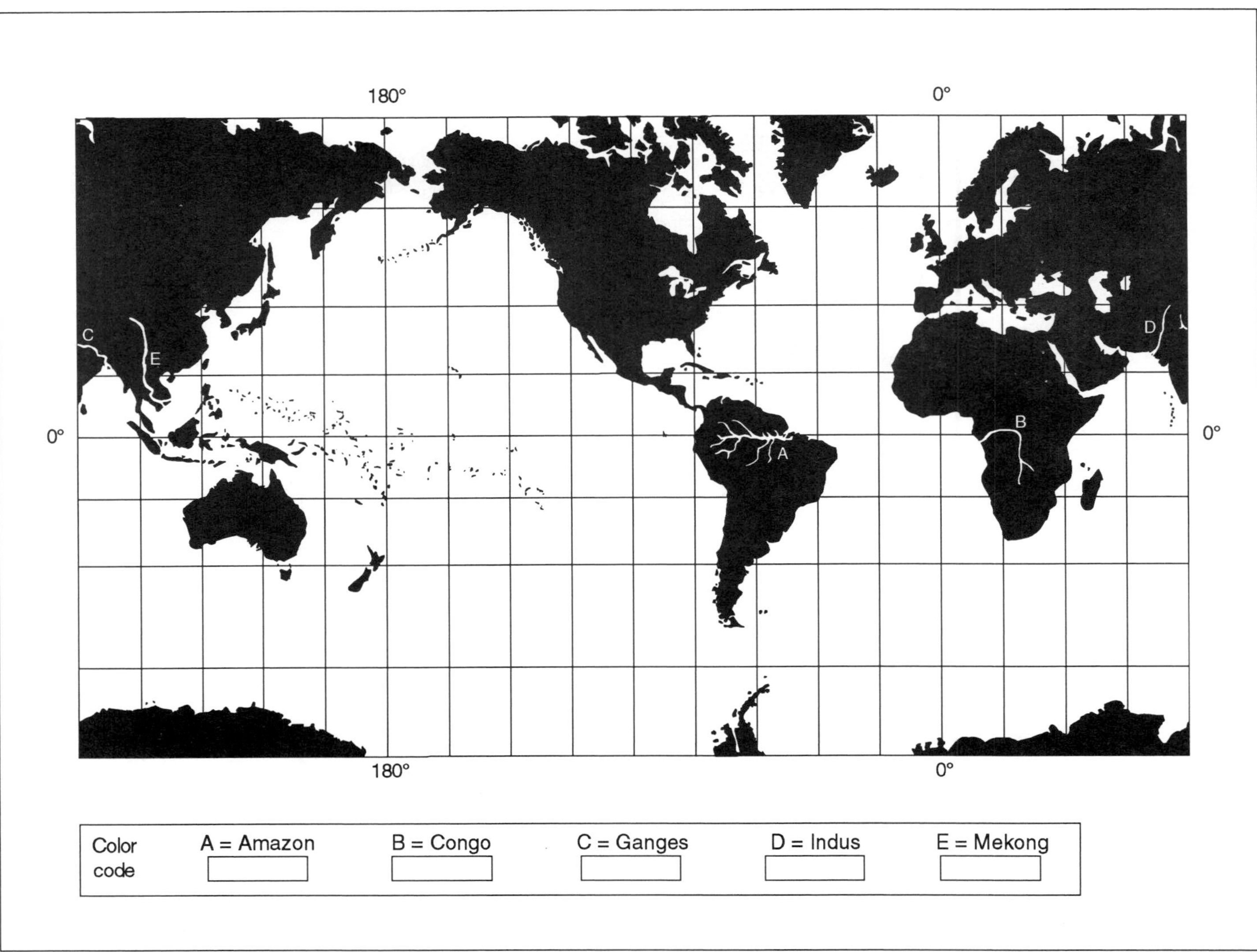

Fig. 4–14. Major tropical rivers of the world

QUESTIONS

17. How is solar energy (sunlight) related to
    a. ocean surface temperature?
    b. salinity?

18. What is the maximum depth at which coral reefs can grow? What is the main factor that limits coral growth below this depth?

19. What might account for the absence of coral reefs off
    a. West Africa?
    b. Northwest India?
    c. Northeast India?
    d. Northeast South America?
    e. Eastern Central Pacific?
    f. Northern Mexico and California?

20. Under what conditions do coral reefs grow best?

21. What environmental conditions limit the distribution of corals?

22. Why were average minimum temperatures of winter shown in Figs. 4–11 and 4–12? Why was the radiant energy expressed as the average minimum winter value? Would using the minimum values for temperature and radiant energy in summer have produced conclusions similar to yours?

FURTHER INVESTIGATIONS

1. Coral reefs are severely threatened in many parts of the world. Some environmentalists claim that coral reefs are being destroyed faster than the rain forests are.
    a. How could coastal erosion, use of fertilizers, coral collecting, and numbers of people visiting the reefs be affecting the reefs? Which of these conditions may be most threatening?
    b. What are the predicted effects of global warming and sea-level fluctuation on coral reefs? Which may be the most threatening?
    c. Learn about coral bleaching, where it occurs, what its causes are, and what actions can be taken to halt the destruction of reefs.
    d. Learn about marine sanctuary programs and marine parks established in efforts to protect coral reefs.
    e. What can snorkelers and scuba divers do to minimize harm to the reefs? List specific actions.
    f. What can you do to help protect living coral reefs?

2. Report on the economic importance of coral. Find out about new uses of coral—for example, in replacing human bone. What restrictions, if any, do you think should be placed on coral collecting?

3. Learn about animals that eat coral. What adaptations have these animals made that fit them for eating coral? How much damage can they do to a coral reef? What controls the population of the coral eaters?

4. Find out about the black, red, pink, and gold corals used in jewelry. How do they

differ in structure from the stony corals studied here? Where are they found? How are they harvested? What are the environmental concerns and economic issues related to their harvesting?

5. Make clay models of the stages of coral reef formation from a fringing reef to a coral atoll. Place the models in a container of water to show the position of the sea on the coral reef. Lower the water level and predict what would happen to the reef. Raise the water level to submerge the reef. Again predict the changes in the reef.

6. Many people live on coral atolls. Read about those people. How do they get food and water? What crops do they grow? What materials do they use for buildings? How do they travel between islands?

7. Use references to learn more about the formation and location of guyots in the Atlantic, Pacific, and Indian oceans. Report your findings to the class.

8. Charles Darwin, in *The Structure and Distribution of Coral Reefs,* proposed a theory for the evolution of coral reefs. Read his explanation of reef formation. Compare it with explanations in modern oceanography texts.

9. Create a dichotomous key for the five corals you used in Activity 1. Use the features shown in Figs. 4–1 to 4–5.

10. How might differences in an environment affect the physical shape of coral colonies? How might water depth and light penetration affect the growth of corals?

5. Worms

Many people think of worms as slimy, crawly creatures good only for loosening garden soil or baiting fishhooks. Theirs is a very limited view of worms. Biologists find worms interesting because they display a great range in size, efficiency, complexity, and body structure. Many phyla of animals fit the category called worms—long, thin creatures that get around efficiently without legs. Different phyla of worms have different degrees of complexity. Some worms, such as flatworms, are simple animals barely more complex than a cnidarian. The complexity of other worms rivals that of more advanced mollusks—snails and oysters, for example. A study of worms, therefore, can show us a possible history of how some organ systems and body features evolved.

We will study worms starting with the least complex, the flatworms, and end with a study of the very complex members of the annelid phylum. We determine the degree of complexity by the number of different body features and systems an animal has. A more complex animal has more features and systems than a less complex animal.

Worms are the first invertebrate animals with **bilateral symmetry** that we study. See Fig. 5–1. Like fish, they have definite front and rear ends. Because organs for sensing light, touch, and smell are in their heads, worms can detect the kinds of environment they encounter. The front of the worm is called the **anterior** end; the rear is the **posterior** end. The under part is the **ventral** surface; the upper part is the **dorsal** surface. The sides of the body are called the **lateral** surfaces.

We will examine six features and systems that reveal an evolving complexity in the body structure of worms:

1. a **mesoderm,** an intermediate body layer that forms muscle tissue
2. a **central nervous system** guided by a "brain"
3. an **excretory system** to eliminate some kinds of waste products
4. a **complete digestive system,** from an anterior mouth to a posterior anus
5. a **coelom,** a body cavity between the digestive tube and the external body wall
6. a **circulatory system** consisting of a series of tubes (vessels) filled with fluid (blood) to transport dissolved nutrients, oxygen, and waste products around the body rapidly and efficiently

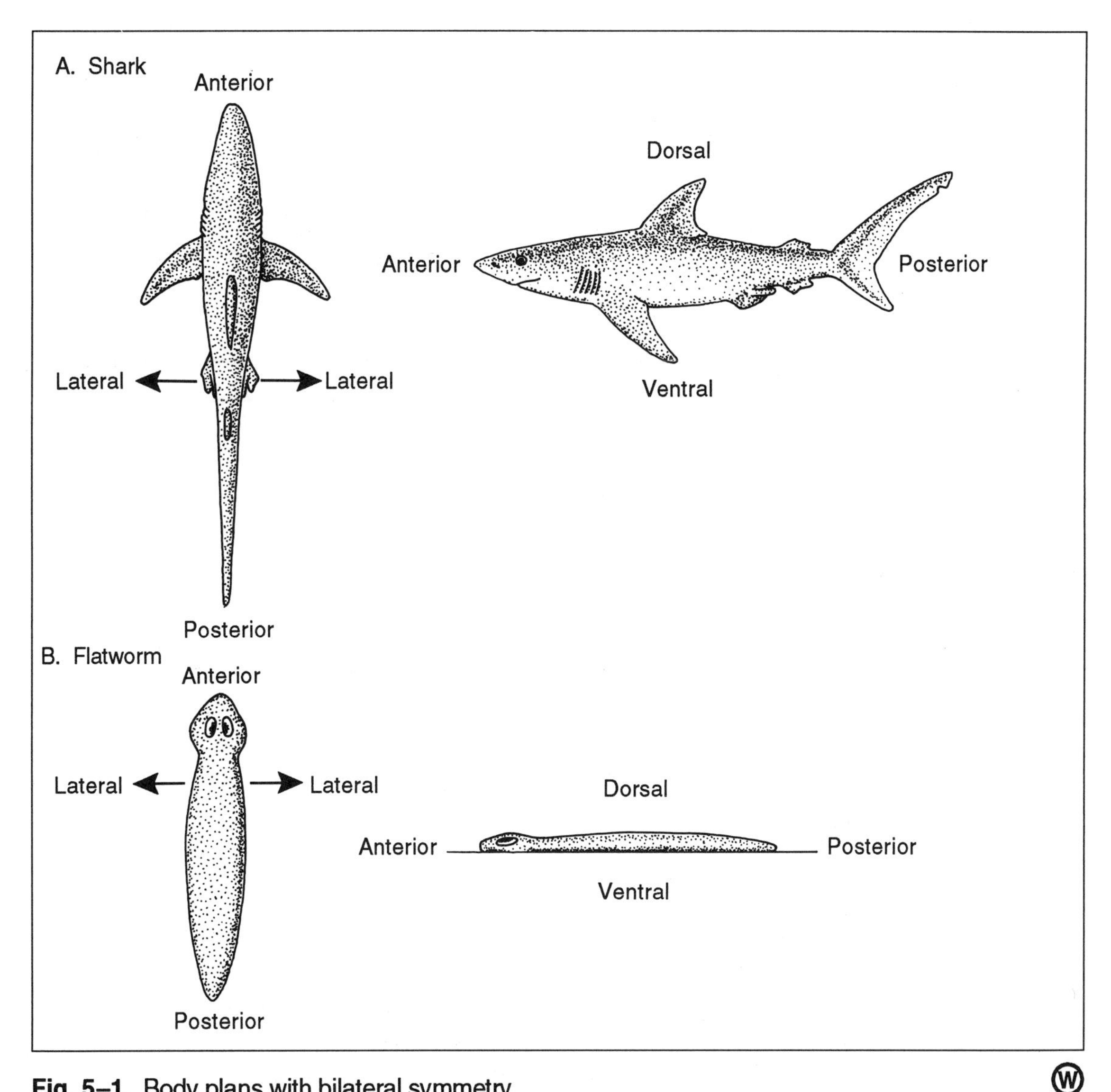

Fig. 5–1. Body plans with bilateral symmetry

Simple Worms: The Flatworms

The least complicated of the worm groups are the flatworms of the phylum **Platyhelminthes** (G. *platy* = flat; G. *helminth* = worm), pronounced "plat ee hel MIN theze." See (A) in Fig. 5–2. Flatworms live on land, in fresh water, in the ocean, and in or on other animals as symbiotic parasites (tapeworms, for example). Worms that live as parasites in or on other animals, including humans, can make them sick or kill them. Marine flatworms, usually just a few centimeters long, live in the sand or under rocks in shallow water and feed on smaller animals. Some live symbiotically with crabs, clams, oysters, shrimp, and barnacles. Some marine flatworms are brilliantly colored; others are drab and blend into the environment.

A Three-Layered Body with No Coelom

Flatworms are more complex than cnidarians. Cnidarians have two layers of cells, the ectoderm and the endoderm; flatworms have a middle layer called the **mesoderm** between the other two layers. See (B) in Fig. 5–2. This extra layer is important because its cells specialize into a muscular system that enables an animal to move around.

Beginning with the flatworms, all the animals we will study have a mesoderm and a muscular system. The cells of the ectoderm and endoderm are also more organized than similar cells of cnidarians. Groups of tissues evolved to form organs, such as the ones in the digestive, nervous, and excretory systems.

Like the cnidarians, flatworms have a digestive system with only a single opening into the digestive cavity, but the flatworm's cavity branches into all parts of the its body. See (B) in Fig. 5–2. This feature is the source of the name for some marine flatworms, **Polycladida** (G. *poly* = many; G. *cladus* = branch). These flatworms feed through a long, tubular **pharynx,** which extends from the body, sur-

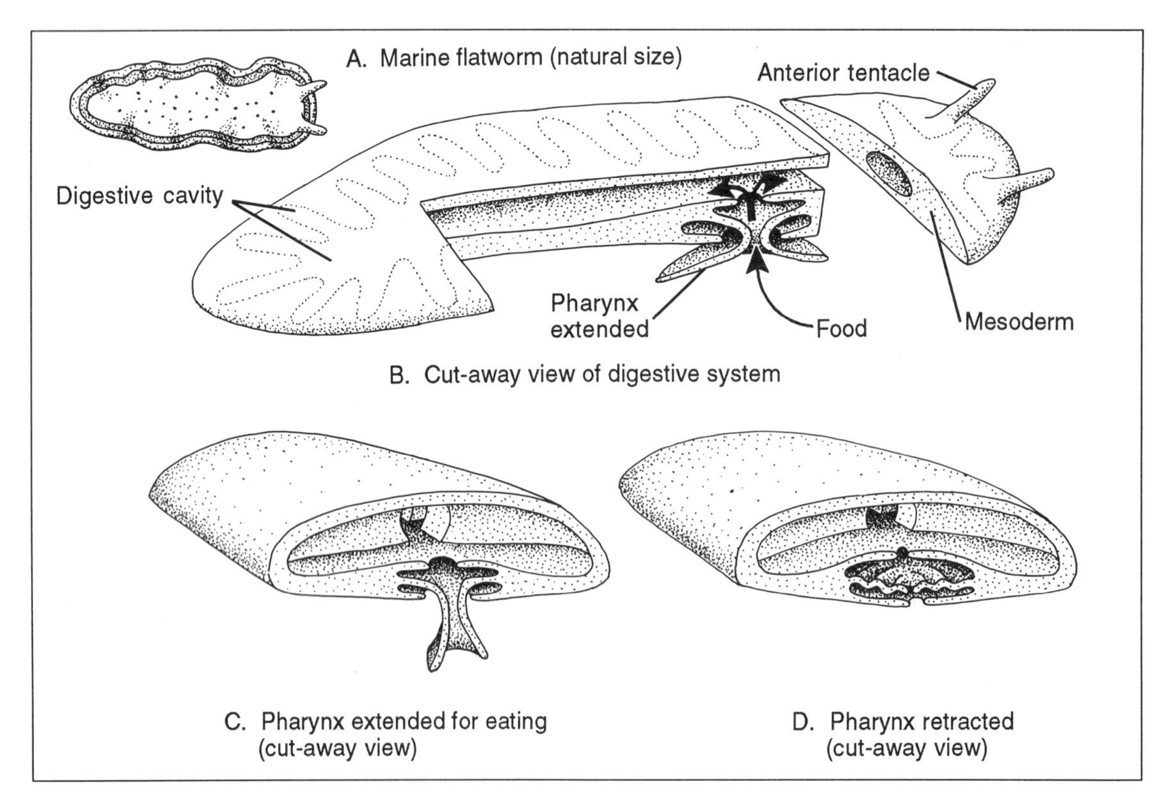

Fig. 5–2. Marine flatworm

rounds the food, and tears it into very fine pieces. See (C) and (D) in Fig. 5–2. Cells lining the digestive cavity finish digesting the food. Then the dissolved nutrients move to other cells of the body. Undigested food passes out through the mouth, as in the cnidarians.

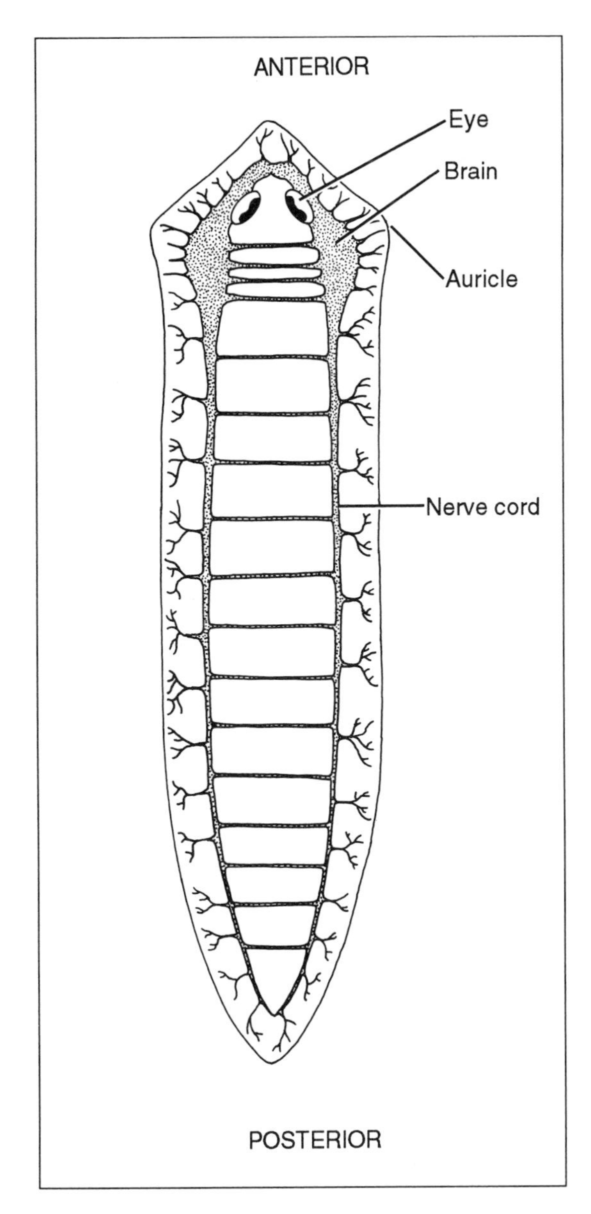

Fig. 5–3. Nervous system of a flatworm

Like most self-propelling animals, flatworms have a **central nervous system.** A central nervous system consists of a mass of nerve cells, called a **brain,** in the anterior part of the body, and a **nerve cord** extending from the brain toward the posterior end of the body. See Fig. 5–3. Sensory cells in the head detect changes in the environment. Sensory cells that respond to light are clustered in two eyes in the head. Sensory cells that detect water currents, solid objects, and chemicals are in two flaplike projections on the head called **auricles.** In self-propelling animals, these sensory organs in the head are the first part of the animal that encounters new surroundings. The brain receives information from the sensory structures and sends signals to other parts of the body along two strands of nerve cells running toward the tail. Because the nerve strands are connected by cross-strands in the shape of a stepladder, this kind of nervous system is often called a "nerve ladder."

The excretory system removes waste products and excess water from tissues of flatworms. Flatworms have a surprisingly elaborate system to rid the body of wastes. See Fig. 5–4. This network runs the length of the animal on each side and opens to the outside through small pores in the posterior region of the body. Connected to the tubes are tiny cells that move wastes and water from the tissues into the tubes. These cells have hairlike threads called **flagella** (L. *flagellum* = whip) that beat back and forth, creating a current of fluid that constantly moves toward the excretory pores. Because this movement looks like a flickering fire, the structure is

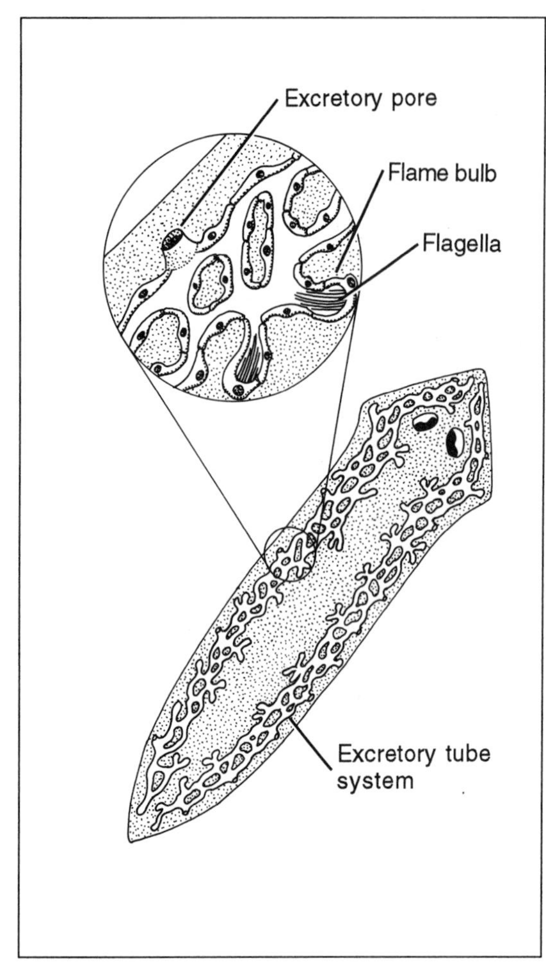

Fig. 5–4. Excretory system of a flatworm

called a **flame bulb.**

QUESTION

1. How do body structures and functions of a flatworm compare with those of a cnidarian for
   a. sensory responses to the environment?
   b. arrangement of the nervous system?
   c. obtaining food?
   d. movement?
   e. excretion of body wastes?

ACTIVITY 1

Observe the behavior of a freshwater flatworm.

MATERIALS

- live freshwater flatworms (planarians, *Dugesia tigrina*)
- Petri dish
- fresh water from an aquarium
- dissecting microscope or hand lens
- eyedropper
- small probe, such as a brush bristle
- various small pebbles
- black construction paper
- raw beef liver or hard-boiled egg yolk

PROCEDURE

1. Put a live freshwater flatworm in a Petri dish containing fresh water from an aquarium.

   NOTE: Do not use untreated tap water. If it is chlorinated, it could kill the animal. Chemicals are available at pet stores to dechlorinate and condition tap water for aquarium use. Otherwise, boil tap water to drive off the chlorine. Let the water cool. Then vigorously shake or stir the water in a jar to oxygenate it before putting the animal in it.

2. Observe the shape and structure of your animal. If you can't see details clearly, use a dissecting microscope or a hand lens. Draw dorsal, ventral, and lateral

views. Label the head and tail. Draw other structures you see, and try to determine their function.

3. Observe the animal's method of movement and describe it in your notebook.

4. Test the animal's response to water currents from different directions.
   a. Fill an eyedropper with water. Gently direct a slow, continuous current of water at the head of the planarian from its left. Observe its response. Repeat the procedure several times on the same animal and on different animals. Record your observations in your notebook.
   b. Repeat the procedure, directing the water current from different directions. Observe how different parts of the body respond to the water flow.

5. Test the animal's sensitivity to touch (mechanoreception).
   a. Touch the animal at several points along its body with a small probe such as a bristle from a brush. Note its response to the stimulus at different body points. Record your observations.
   b. Put objects in the path of movement and observe the responses to the stimuli.

6. Test the animal's response to light (photoreception).
   a. Cover half of the Petri dish with black construction paper. Start the test with the animal in the lighted part of the dish.
   b. Observe its movements for several minutes. Determine whether the worm is responding to light or to some other stimulus. Repeat the experiment several times. Record your data.

7. (Optional) Observe the feeding behavior of the worm.
   a. Review the information on the structures and mechanisms of feeding to guide your observations.
   b. Put a tiny piece of raw liver or hard-boiled egg yolk in the dish. Wait until the animal begins to feed. Record your observations of how it feeds.
   c. Devise an experiment to determine the worm's food preference. Try sugar, starch, and protein foods. See Table 3–2 in Topic 3, Cnidarians, for a list of foods containing these substances.

QUESTIONS

2. What is the flatworm's shape? What type of symmetry does it have?

3. How does the flatworm move? How does its shape relate to its method of moving? What structures are necessary for this type of movement?

4. Did the planarian move toward or away from water currents? Which parts of its body are most sensitive to water currents? What function do these responses serve in the natural environment?

5. Which body parts are most sensitive to touch? Which are least sensitive? How does the animal respond to objects in its path?

6. Does the planarian move toward or away from the light? What function do these responses serve in its natural environment?

7. How does a planarian feed? Would you describe planarians as carnivores, herbivores, or omnivores?

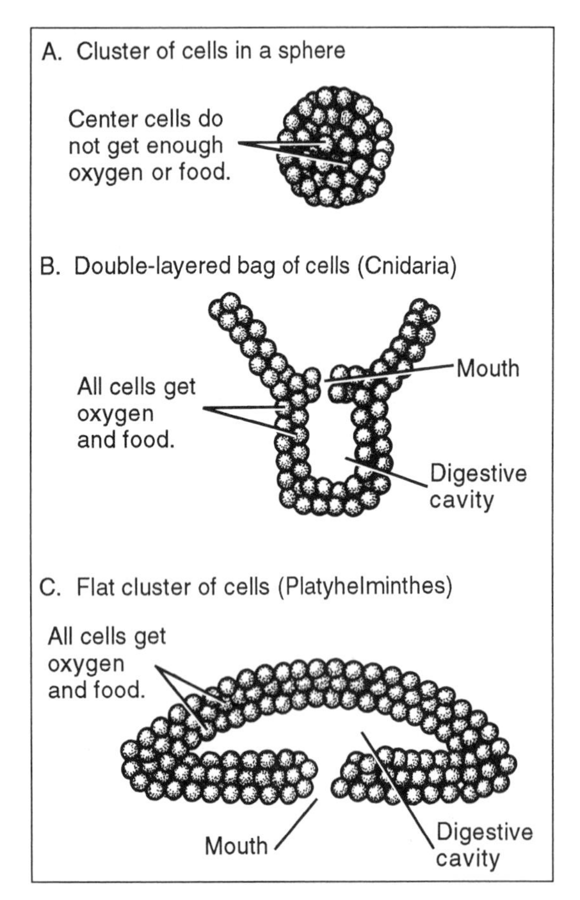

Fig. 5–5. Arrangements of cell clusters

Living Without a Circulatory System

Flatworms have no circulatory system. Animals without a circulatory system have limited ability to deliver oxygen and nutrients to their body cells because of the way that molecules of a substance behave. As molecules spread through water in a movement called **diffusion,** they become less concentrated as they move away from their source. Thus a ball-shaped marine animal would not get adequate oxygen and nutrients to its innermost cells because the cells are too far from the body's surface for molecules to move (diffuse) to them. See (A) in Fig. 5–5. But cnidarians have no problem with diffusion because most cells of their bag-shaped bodies are in direct contact with the water, making the exchange of oxygen and nutrients easy. See (B) in Fig. 5–5. Flatworms, bag-shaped but flattened, also get oxygen and nutrients to their body cells easily because all their cells are either close to their outer surface or their digestive cavity. See (C) in Fig. 5–5.

ACTIVITY 2

Measure diffusion in solids of different shapes. Determine how surface area and volume affect diffusion.

MATERIALS

- blocks of 3% agar-phenolphthalein in four sizes:
  - 0.5 cm x 0.5 cm x 0.5 cm
  - 1 cm x 1 cm x 1 cm
  - 2 cm x 2 cm x 2 cm
  - 0.5 cm x 4 cm x 4 cm
- centimeter ruler
- copy of Workbook Table 5–1

- stopwatch or clock
- white vinegar
- small culture dish

PROCEDURE

1. Your teacher will give you four blocks of agar of different sizes and shapes.
   a. Measure the length, width, and height of each block.
   b. Sketch each block.
   c. Calculate the volume and surface area of each block. Record data in Table 5–1.

2. Pour vinegar into the culture dish to a depth of at least 3 cm.

Table 5–1. Efficiency of clearing in agar blocks of different shapes 

Size of block	Sketch of block	Volume (cm^3)	Surface area (cm^2)	Time to turn clear (min)	Surface area/ volume ratio
0.5 cm x 0.5 cm x 0.5 cm					
1 cm x 1 cm x 1 cm					
2 cm x 2 cm x 2 cm					
0.5 cm x 4 cm x 4 cm					

3. Put all four agar blocks into the vinegar at the same time. Record the starting time. As the vinegar diffuses into the agar, the blocks will change color. Record the exact time that each block turns clear.

4. Calculate the ratio of surface area to volume (divide the surface area by the volume). Record the ratio in Table 5–1.

QUESTIONS

8. Which block has the greatest volume? The greatest surface area? Describe the shape of each block. How do the shapes differ?

9. Which block cleared the fastest? Which one cleared slowest?

10. Compare the surface area/volume ratio of the blocks. Which block cleared fastest? Why?

11. The change of color in this experiment is similar to the movement of oxygen and nutrients through an organism's tissues.

From your observations and analysis, what body shape do you think would be best for moving oxygen to an animal's tissues?

12. Suggest a shape with the same volume that would be even more efficient than the most efficient one in this activity. What would be its dimensions? Make a sketch. Calculate the surface area and the surface area/volume ratio.

13. Suggest reasons why a sea anemone is shaped like a grocery bag with the mouth up but a flatworm is shaped like a flat plastic bag with the mouth down.

14. What possible advantages and disadvantages does its flat shape give to Platyhelminthes?

15. Fill in phylum Platyhelminthes in Table 1–3, Comparison of animal phyla by features, in Topic 1.

Complex Worms: The Annelids

The worms in the phylum **Annelida** (L. *annelus* = ring) typically have segmented bodies. See Fig. 5–6. The body is divided into repeating sections called segments with many internal organs repeated in each segment. Earthworms are familiar terrestrial members of this phylum. See (A) in Fig. 5–6. Polychaetes are marine members. See (B) and (C) in Fig. 5–6.

Some annelid worms, such as earthworms,

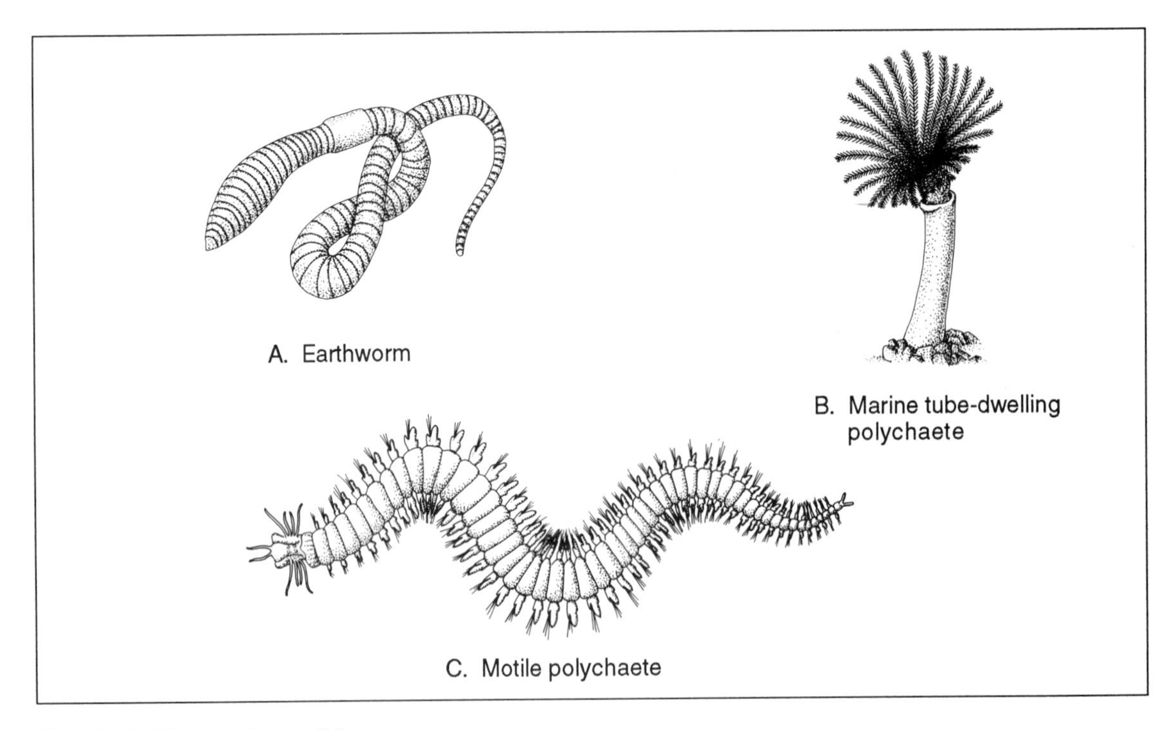

Fig. 5–6. Types of annelid worms

are important as fishing bait. The body of earthworms is largely protein; some people eat them. In parts of the Pacific, *palolo* worms (a kind of polychaete) are considered a delicacy. Some people in the United States are experimenting with ways to fry or bake earthworms or make them into a protein substitute for meat.

Most marine annelid worms are polychaetes (G. *poly* = many; G. *chaeta* = bristle) of the class Polychaeta. **Polychaete** worms are so named because most of their segments have muscular flaps called **parapodia** (G. *para* = near; G. *podia* = feet) on their sides. See (C) in Fig. 5–6. The free-moving (not sessile) polychaetes have stiff bristles called **setae** on their parapodia. Setae may dig into the sand for locomotion. Fireworms have earned their name from stinging bristles on each parapodium. These bristles can easily penetrate a person's skin, causing pain and swelling.

Some of these worms have a **proboscis** that can extend from their mouths to catch prey. This is a feeding organ that is often armed with small teeth or jaws on its tip. With their active lifestyle and good defenses, free-moving polychaetes can make their living in a variety of habitats such as mud, sand, sponges, live corals, and algae.

Tubeworms are sessile polychaetes that live in tubes that they secrete. The tubes, attached to rocks, may be leathery, calcareous, or sand-covered. See (B) in Fig. 5–6. These worms feed by extending feathery tentacles from the tube. Bits of food (detritus) move along grooves in the tentacles to the mouth. Some tubeworms retract their tentacles when food lands on them. Tubeworms use their parapodia to create currents of water that flow through the tubes to aid in respiration and help clean the tubes.

Segmented Worms with a Coelom

Annelid worms have evolved body features not found in flatworms. These features appear in some form in all larger, more complex animals:

1. a **complete digestive system,** from an anterior mouth to a posterior anus
2. a **coelom,** a body cavity between the digestive tube and the external body wall
3. a **circulatory system** consisting of a series of tubes (vessels) filled with fluid (blood) to transport dissolved nutrients, oxygen, and waste products rapidly and efficiently

Like flatworms, annelids have a mesoderm with muscle, a central nervous system, and an excretory system. Each of these systems is more advanced in the annelid than in the flatworm.

An animal with a **complete digestive system** has a mouth at one end, a long tube with specialized parts in the middle, and an anus at the other end. Such a system offers many advantages over the flatworm's method of digestion. With a complete digestive system an animal can eat while its previous meal digests. Parts of the digestive system can specialize to do different jobs, digesting food in stages. See Fig. 5–7. As the food moves along, it is broken into molecules and absorbed by the cells lining the tube. Muscles surrounding the tube contract, squeezing the food and pushing it along in a process called **peristalsis.** See Fig. 5–8. (Also see Fig. 7–8 in Unit 1, where peristalsis is described in fish.) Indigestible wastes pass out through the anus.

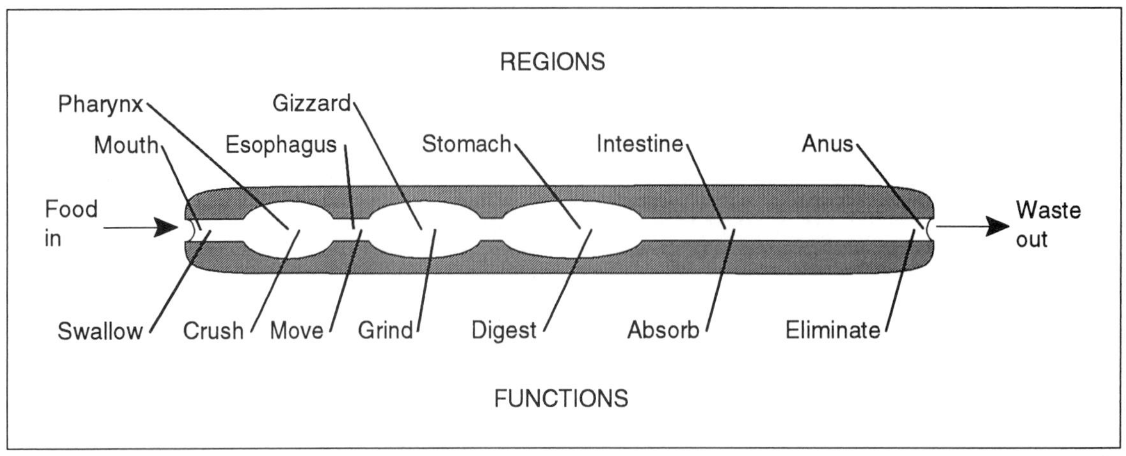

Fig. 5–7. Typical regions of specialization in a complete digestive system 

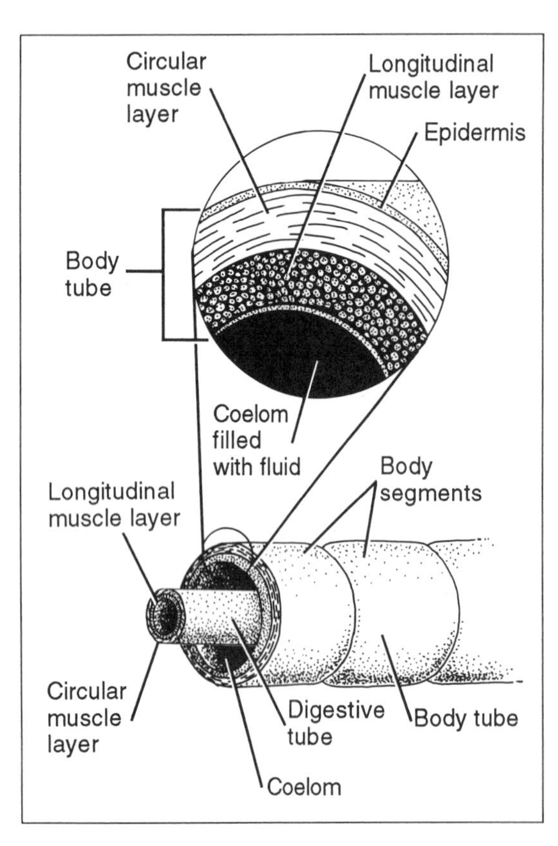

Fig. 5–8. Tube-within-a-tube construction

The **coelom** is a fluid-filled cavity lying between the digestive tube and the outer body tube. It is surrounded by mesoderm. The digestive tube lies inside the outer body tube. This arrangement is called "tube-within-a-tube construction." See Fig. 5–8. The fluid in the coelom supports the soft tissues of the body wall much as it does in the hydrostatic skeleton of cnidarians. This fluid contains nutrients as well as body wastes.

Muscles in the wall of the body tube and digestive tube can put pressure on the fluid to aid in movement. The muscles come from mesoderm tissue. In the body wall are two types of muscles, circular and longitudinal. When the circular muscles contract, the segment gets longer and narrower. When the longitudinal muscles contract, the segment gets shorter and fatter. See Fig. 5–9. These contractions produce the crawling movement of worms. The setae along the body stick in the substrate, holding parts of the worm in place while other parts move forward.

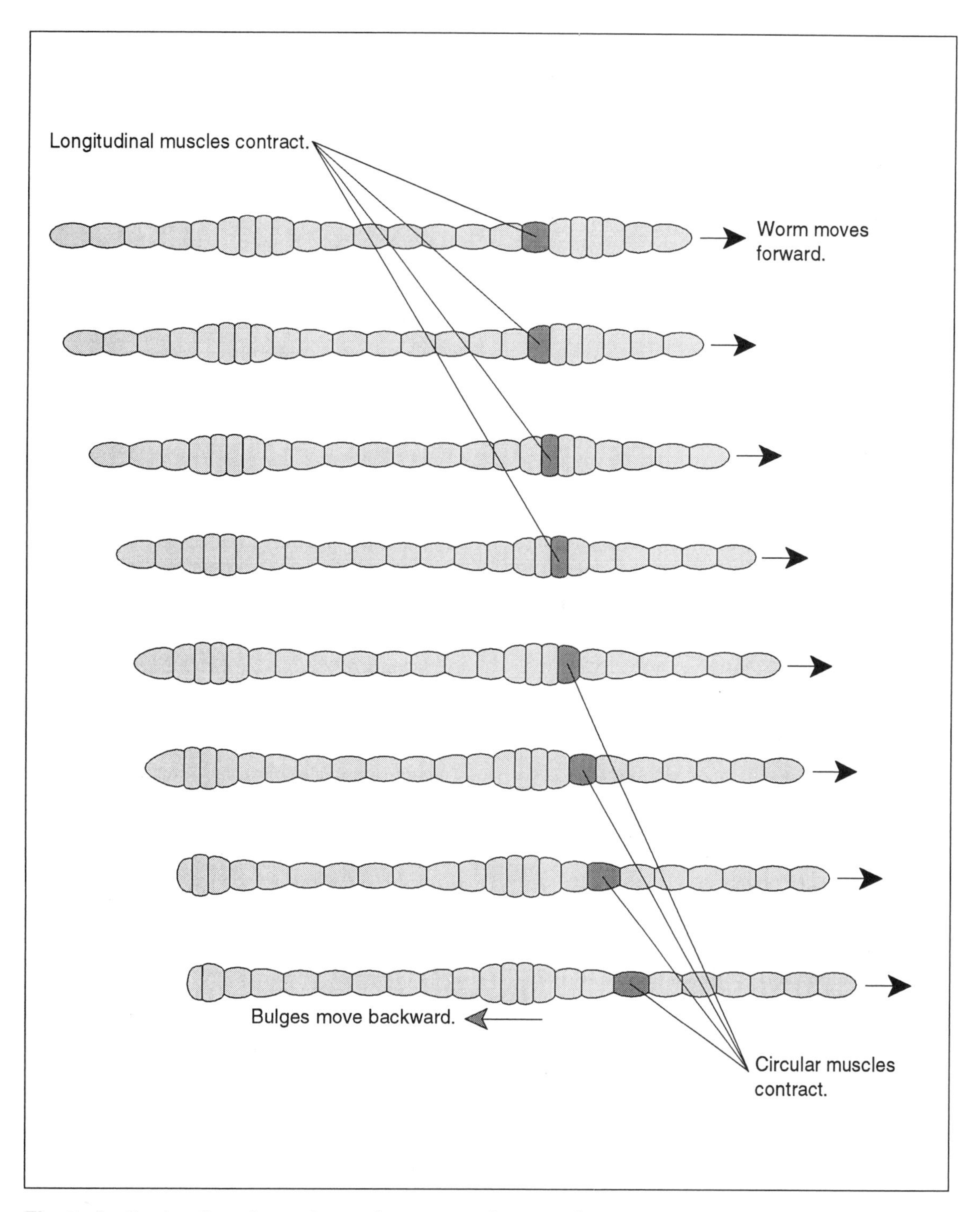

Fig. 5–9. Contraction of muscles and movement in an earthworm

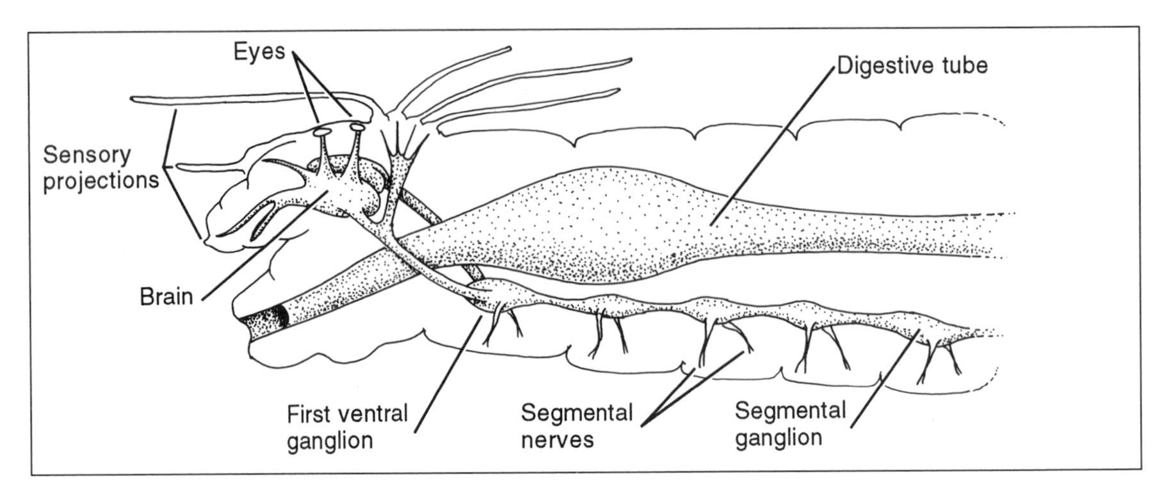

Fig. 5–10. Nervous system of a polychaete worm

Another system more advanced in annelids than in flatworms is the nervous system. In the anterior end of the annelid, above (dorsal to) the digestive tube, lies a pair of nerve clusters called a brain—far more primitive than a human brain but more advanced than a flatworm's. See Fig. 5–10. Nerves link the brain to sense organs in the head that detect whatever lies in front of it. Earthworms are eyeless, but polychaetes have eyes that can distinguish between light and dark. In a few worms the eyes can even detect shapes. Nerves also extend from the brain around the digestive tube and along the ventral surface. A cluster of nerve cells called a **ganglion** operates the organs in each segment.

The excretory system of annelid worms consists of a pair of small tubes in each segment. These tubes, called **nephridia** (G. *nephrus*=kidney; the singular is *nephridium*), are open at both ends. They filter coelomic fluid, which contains useful nutrient molecules along with waste molecules. As the fluid moves through the tube, useful molecules return to the coelom, and waste molecules pass into the water. Although this system appears less complex than a flatworm's, nephridia are actually a more advanced method of handling waste products because they filter fluid, keeping useful molecules inside the body. See Fig. 5–11.

Annelids have a **closed circulatory system** in which blood is pumped along by muscles in blood vessels. See Fig. 5–12. Blood flows through the microscopic capillaries, picking up food molecules from the digestive tract and oxygen from the skin, and sometimes the gills, and transporting them to the cells of the body. The **parapodia,** the flaps on the sides of the segments, increase the surface area of the skin for respiration. In an efficient circulatory system like this, an animal's internal tissues need not be close to its digestive and respiratory organs because the blood delivers nutrients and oxygen. Such a system lets animals grow quite large, unlike flatworms.

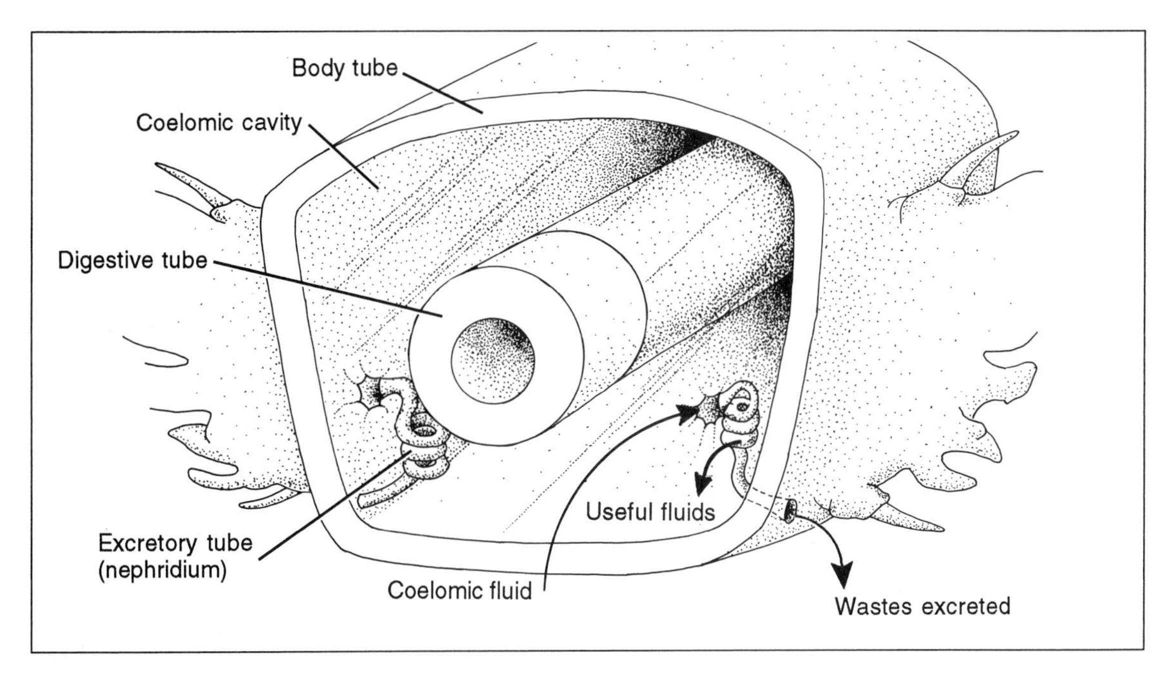

Fig. 5–11. Excretory system of a polychaete worm

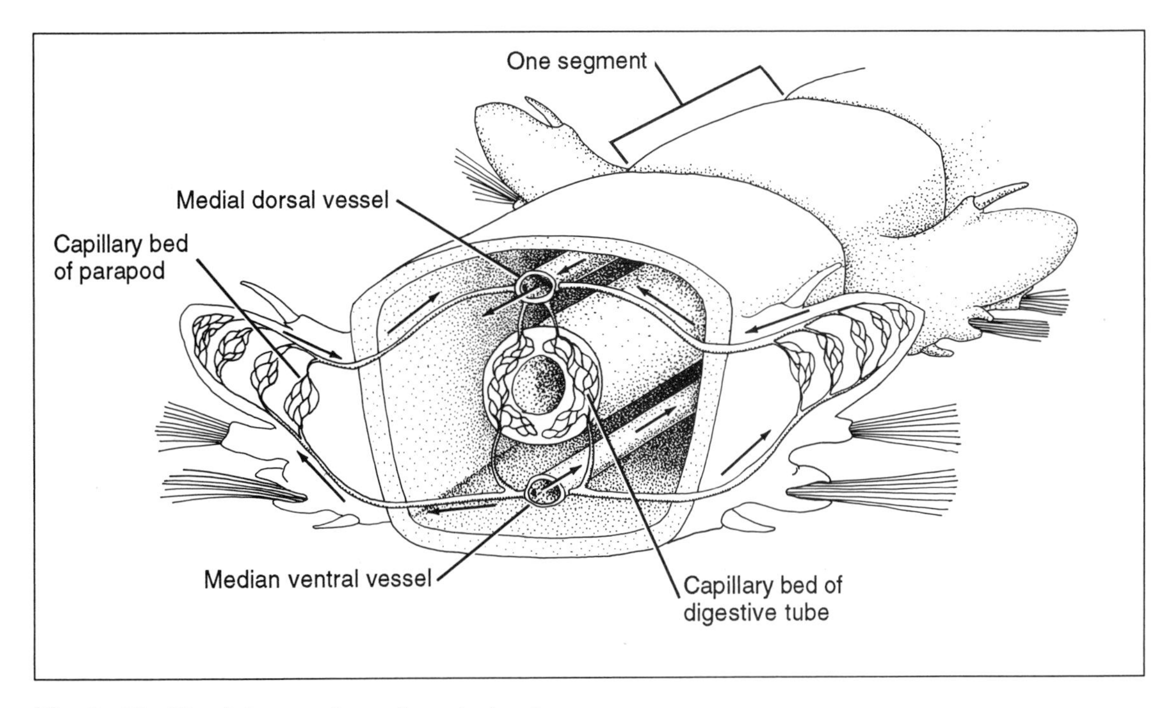

Fig. 5–12. Circulatory system of a polychaete worm

QUESTIONS

16. How does an annelid's digestive system differ from a flatworm's? In what ways is the digestive system of an annelid worm more efficient than a flatworm's?

17. Compare the excretory systems of a flatworm and an annelid worm. How are they similar? How are they different?

18. What is a coelom? What advantages does an animal with a coelom have over an animal, such as a flatworm, that has no coelom?

19. Fill in Table 5–2 comparing the body structures of a sea anemone, a flatworm, an annelid worm, and a fish. Are flatworms more like cnidarians or annelids? Are annelids more like flatworms or fish? Give evidence that supports your answer.

Table 5–2. Comparison of body structures of four groups of animals Ⓦ

Body structure	Sea anemone	Flatworm	Annelid worm	Fish
Mesoderm				
Digestive system				
Circulatory system				
Coelom				

In the next activity we will study the polychaete *Nereis,* a free-moving marine carnivore that lives in holes in the sandy or muddy bottom. Because some of these worms live in clam shells, they are commonly called clamworms.

ACTIVITY 3

Study a marine worm to identify the structures of its main systems.

MATERIALS

- clamworm (*Nereis*)

- newspapers or dissecting pan
- 8 ½ x 11-in sheet of plain paper
- scalpel
- microscope slide with coverslip
- compound microscope
- Petri dish
- dissecting microscope or hand lens

PROCEDURE

1. Lay a clamworm in your dissecting pan and draw it. Label its dorsal, ventral, anterior, and posterior surfaces and its segments, parapodia, and setae.

2. Study the head of the worm.

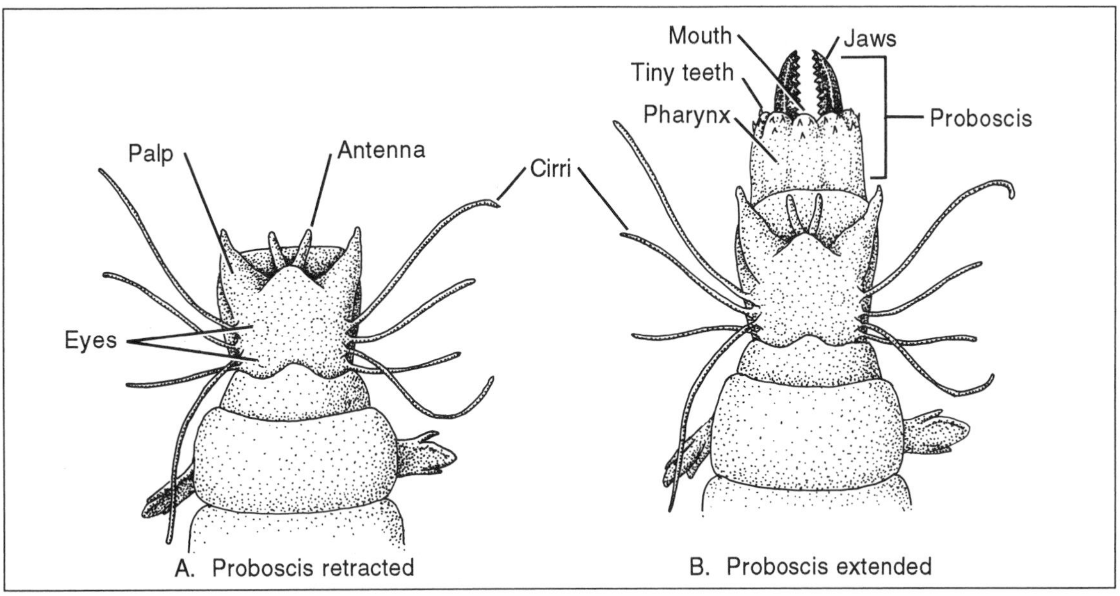

Fig. 5–13. Dorsal view of the head of a clamworm, *Nereis*

   a. Using Fig. 5–13 as a reference, find as many of the worm's head structures as you can. Because the proboscis of the clamworm is retractable, you may not be able to see it. See the heads of other clamworms to find one that is extended.
   b. Draw the head of a specimen with the proboscis contracted and one with the proboscis extended. Label the structures.

3. Study a parapodium. See Fig. 5–14.
   a. Using a scalpel, cut off a single parapodium and mount it on a microscope slide with a coverslip.
   b. Observe the structure under the compound microscope at low power (40X).
   c. Draw the parapodium and its attached setae.

4. Study a cross-section of the clamworm

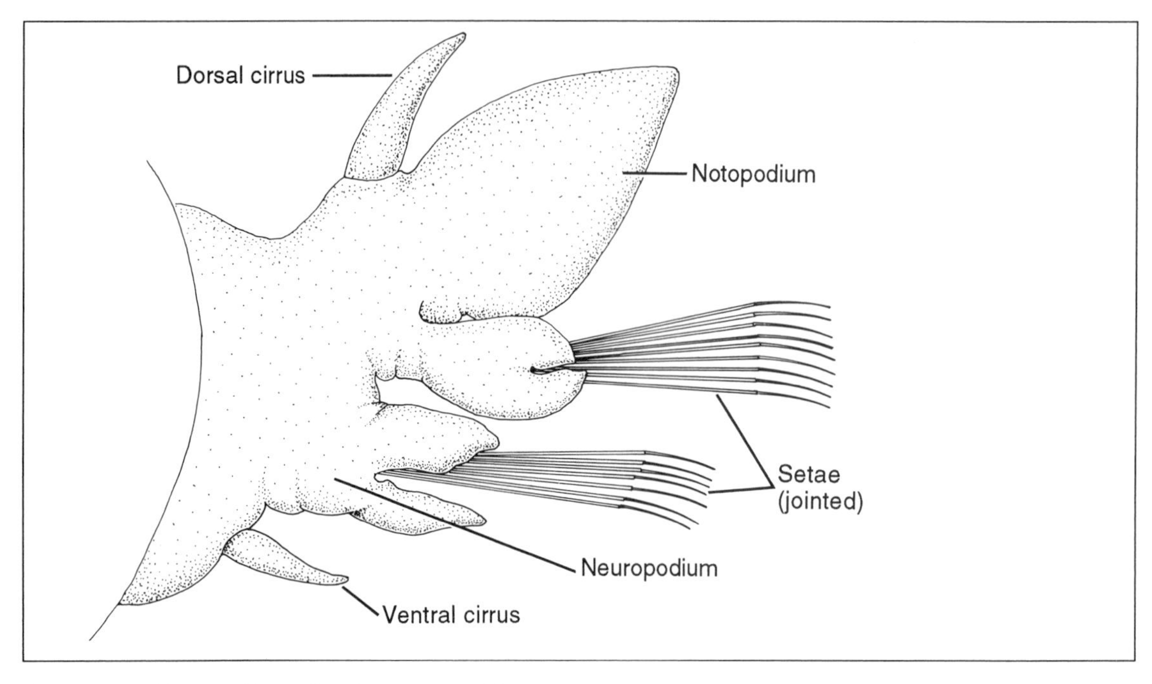

Fig. 5–14. Parapodium of a clamworm with setae

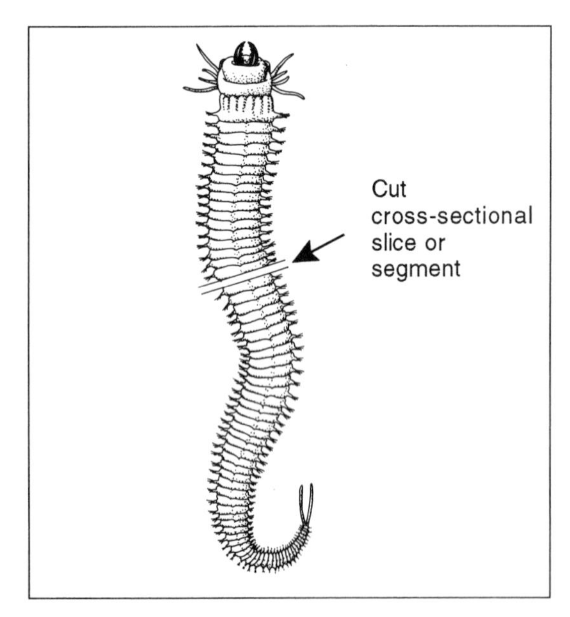

Fig. 5–15. Cutting a cross-sectional slice or segment of a clamworm

to find its internal organs. See Fig. 5–15.

a. Using a scalpel, cut a cross-sectional slice from a segment.
b. Place the section in a Petri dish or shallow container with enough water to cover it. Observe the section under a dissecting microscope or a hand lens.
c. Using Fig. 5–16 as a reference, identify the parts of the internal organs.
d. Draw your cross-section in as much detail as you can see. Label your drawing.

QUESTIONS

20. What might be the functions of the clamworm's proboscis and jaws? What kinds of food might a clamworm eat?

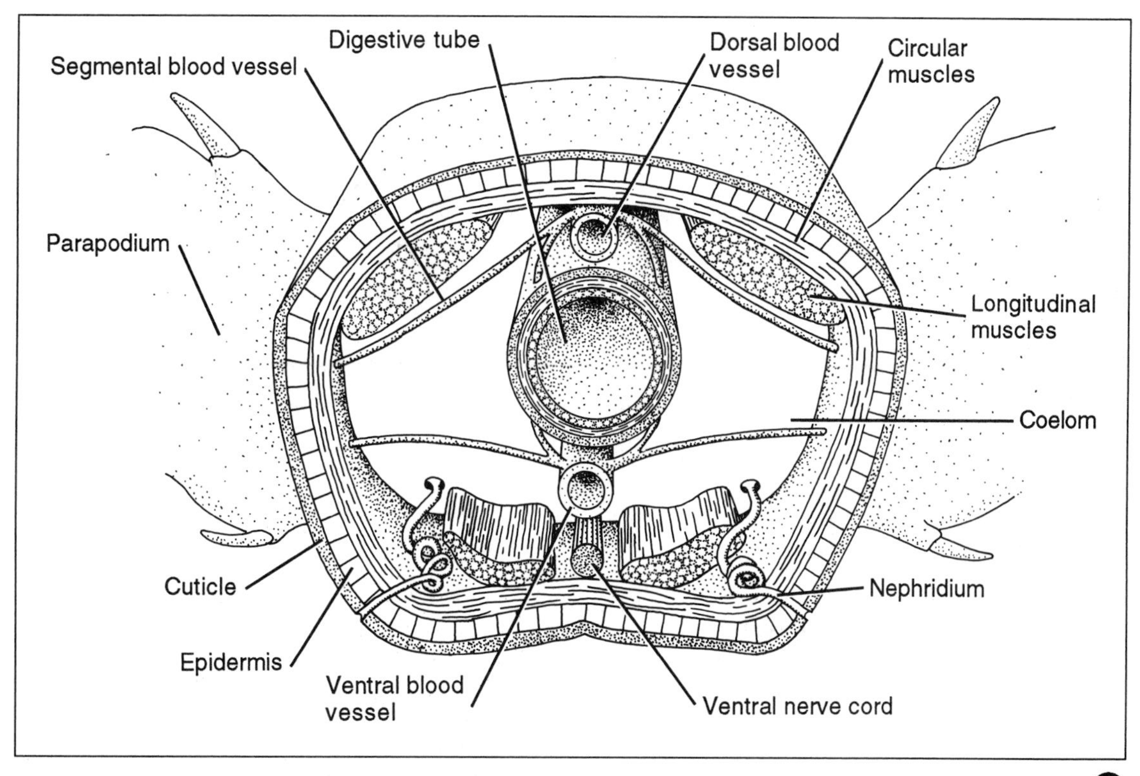

Fig. 5–16. Cross-sectional segment of a clamworm showing internal organs

21. In Fig. 5–13 several structures on the first (anterior) segment are labeled. Which ones might help a clamworm sense its prey?

22. What advantage might a segmented body give the polychaete?

23. A clamworm moves by crawling along the bottom and by swimming. What might be the functions of the parapodia and setae?

24. What advantages does a closed circulatory system give an organism?

25. Fill in phylum Annelida in Table 1–3, Comparison of animal phyla by features, in Topic 1, Classification and Comparison of Invertebrates.

FURTHER INVESTIGATIONS

1. Like the sea anemones you studied in Topic 3, Activity 3, planarian flatworms can regenerate. Use references to learn about planarian regeneration. If possible, carry out your own investigations. Report to the class.

2. Maintain one or several marine polychaete worms in a seawater aquarium.

Study their behavior, their feeding habits, and their food preferences.

3. Find a piece of glass tubing with an inside diameter about equal to the diameter of the tube of a tubeworm. Keeping your hands and the animal under water, carefully remove a tubeworm from its tube. Delicately, without damaging the worm, try to insert it into the glass tube. Observe the movements of its parts through the glass. Note any coordination of movements. Put bits of food in the tube and see if the worm feeds. Put a bit of food coloring at the opening of the tube and watch the currents of water as they carry the coloring through the tube.

4. How do the mouth parts of polychaete tubeworms differ from those of a clamworm? Why do they differ?

5. Marine tubeworms called "feather duster" worms are easy to maintain in an aquarium. If you can get some of these worms, observe their sensitivity to light and to touch. Sprinkle very fine bits of food on the tentacles and watch how the particles move toward the mouth.

6. Look for worms in the sandy substrate of an established aquarium with an undergravel filtration system. Use a spoon to dig into and scoop out a small sample of sand. Put it in water in a Petri dish and examine it under a dissecting microscope or a hand lens.

7. Other phyla of marine worms have interesting structural and behavioral characteristics. Use references to learn about the phylum Nemertea, phylum Echiura, phylum Sipuncula, and other phyla. Report to the class.

8. Many groups of worms are parasitic in humans and other animals and plants. They can damage organs, cause sickness, and even kill. These groups include the tapeworms (class Cestoda in the phylum Platyhelminthes), the threadworms and pinworms (phylum Nematoda), and the leeches (class Hirudinea in the phylum Annelida). Use references to learn more about these worms, their life cycles, and their importance to humans. Report to the class.

9. What roles do worms play in the environment? Earthworms, for example, aid in conditioning the soil. Learn more about where these animals live, what they eat, which animals prey on them, and what role they play in recycling plant material and refining inorganic soil particles.

6. Mollusks

The phylum **Mollusca,** with over 100,000 species, is the second-largest animal phylum. Among mollusks are many familiar members—chitons, clams, snails, slugs, and squids. The marine mollusks are probably the best known and easily recognized members of the phylum. Some of the shells are highly valued by collectors. From seashell collections we have learned much of what we know about this group. See Fig. 6–1.

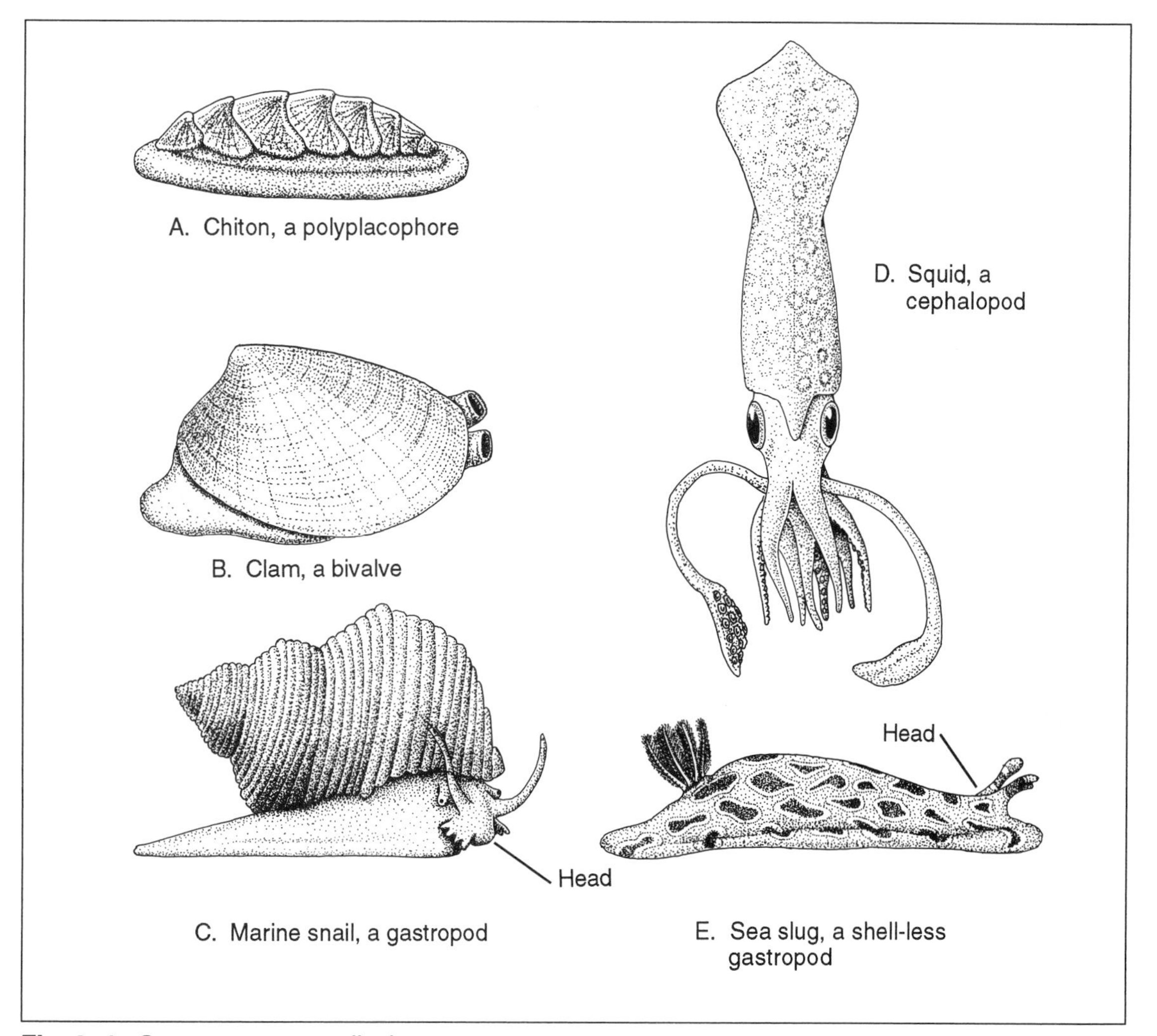

Fig. 6–1. Some common mollusks

A slug, a snail, a clam, and a squid do not look alike, but they are all mollusks. Three features are so common in mollusks that they are used to distinguish them from organisms in other phyla. The common mollusk features are

1. a specialized **foot** used in digging, grasping, or creeping.
2. a **mantle** that covers the soft body, encloses the internal organs, and, in many species, produces a shell. Not all mollusks produce a shell.
3. a **radula** (L. *radul* = scraper), which in most species is a rasplike scraping organ used in feeding. See Fig. 6–2. Not all mollusks have a radula, but nothing like it is found in any other group of organisms.

Foot

The **foot** is a muscular organ, shaped and used differently by different species. A clam uses its hatchet-shaped foot for digging. See (B) in Fig. 6–1. Clams and oysters belong to the class **Pelecypoda** (G. *pelec* = hatchet; G. *poda* = foot), though more recently the class has been called **Bivalvia** (L. *bi* = two; L. *valv* = folding door). A snail has a flat foot it uses for crawling. See (C) in Fig. 6–1. Because its stomach is in its foot, it is named **Gastropoda,** "stomach foot" (G. *gastro* = stomach). The foot in octopus and squids is modified into many tentacles that are attached to the animal's head. See (D) in Fig. 6–1. That feature gave the class its name **Cephalopoda** (G. *cephal* = head), or the "head-foot" mollusks. Octopus and squids use their tentacles for moving and for grasping and holding the prey they capture for food.

Mantle and Shell

In most mollusks the **mantle** produces the shell. The mantle also creates patterns of color on a shell. A chiton's mantle produces eight shell-like plates that cover the body. Joints between the plates allow the chiton to curl up in a ball and to move flexibly. See (A) in Fig. 6–1. Bivalves (clams, oysters, etc.) produce two shells that are hinged at the top. See (B) in Fig. 6–1. The mantle of snails (gastropods) produces a single shell in a spiral shape. See (C) in Fig. 6–1. The mantle itself cannot be seen because it is on the inner surface of the shell. In some gastropods such as the cowries, the mantle extends over the shell, keeping the shell shiny and new in appearance. In other gastropods, like the sea hares, and in some cephalopods, like the squid and the octopus, the shell is very small and the mantle covers the shell completely. See (D) in Fig. 6–1. The nudibranchs or sea slugs (L. *nude* = nude; G. *branch* = gill) are gastropods that don't produce a shell, so these animals are all soft-bodied. See (E) in Fig. 6–1. The shell is an exoskeleton, even though it is completely surrounded by soft tissue in some mollusks. Because the shell is continually produced, it grows with the animal.

Radula

The mouth structures of many mollusks include a specially adapted rasplike tongue called a **radula.** Herbivorous (plant-eating) snails have a mouth with radula containing many rows, each row with five to seven complex teeth. The snail uses its radula like a file, scraping off small bits of food. See (B), (C), and (D) in Fig. 6–2. Snails favored for freshwater aquariums are herbivores. Watch how they eat as they glide about on the glass. You can see them using their radulas.

Snails called cone shells are carnivorous (meat-eating) hunters that produce venom in glands near the mouth. Their radulas are shaped into long, hollow teeth, which they thrust one at a time into their prey like harpoons. See Fig. 6–3. A barbed radular tooth fires through the

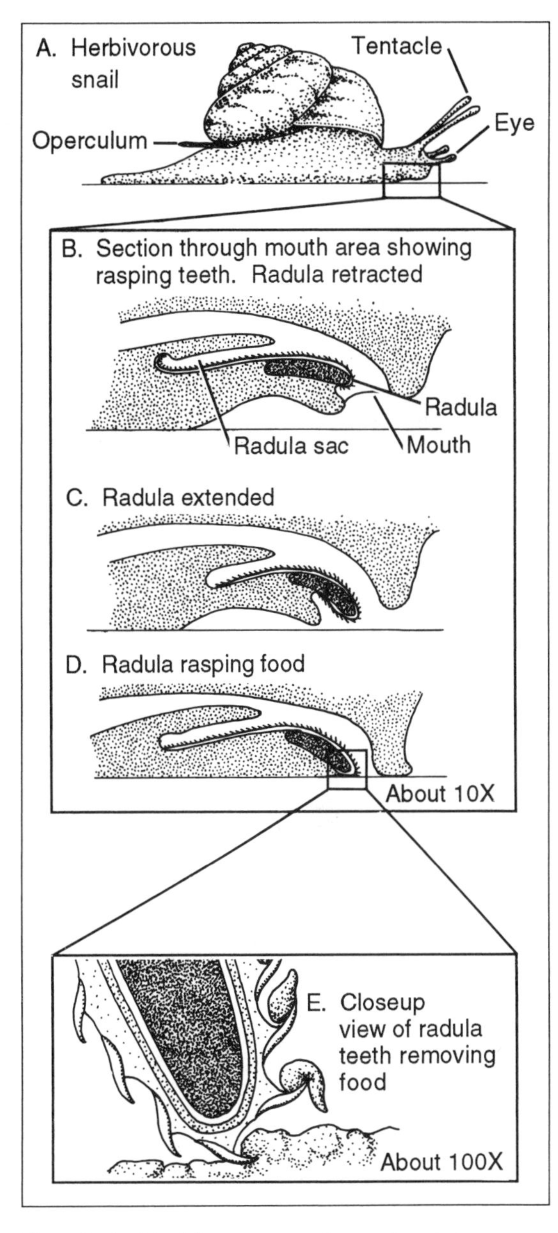

Fig. 6–2. Herbivorous gastropod radula

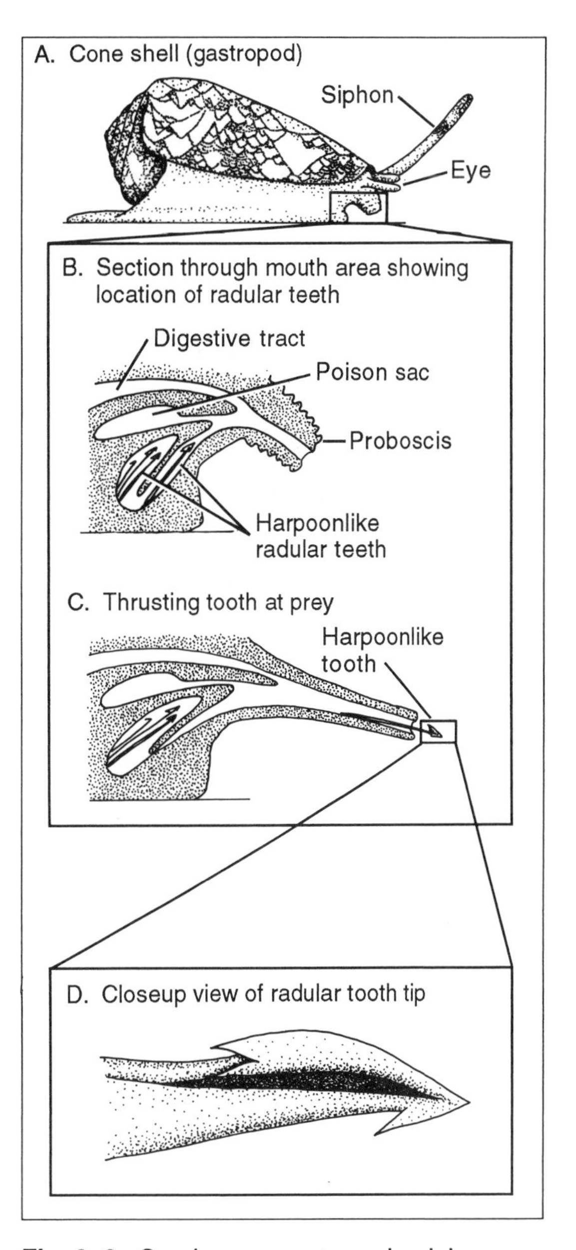

Fig. 6–3. Carnivorous gastropod radula

proboscis, an extension of the mouth. It pierces the prey, paralyzing it with venom and preventing its escape. The cone shell "swallows" the prey by engulfing it with its proboscis. In this way cones stalk and capture worms, mollusks, and even fish. Some cones produce a poison strong enough to kill humans who handle them carelessly. Their poison is a neurotoxin, one that attacks and destroys nerves.

Marine Bivalve Anatomy

The class of mollusks called **Bivalvia** includes clams, oysters, mussels, and scallops. They get their name from the two doorlike valves or shells that make up their exoskeleton. Foot size varies among marine bivalves. See Fig. 6–4. Clams have a big hatchet-shaped foot for moving about and for burrowing in mud or sand. See Fig. 6–5. By contrast, an oyster's or a mussel's foot is small because

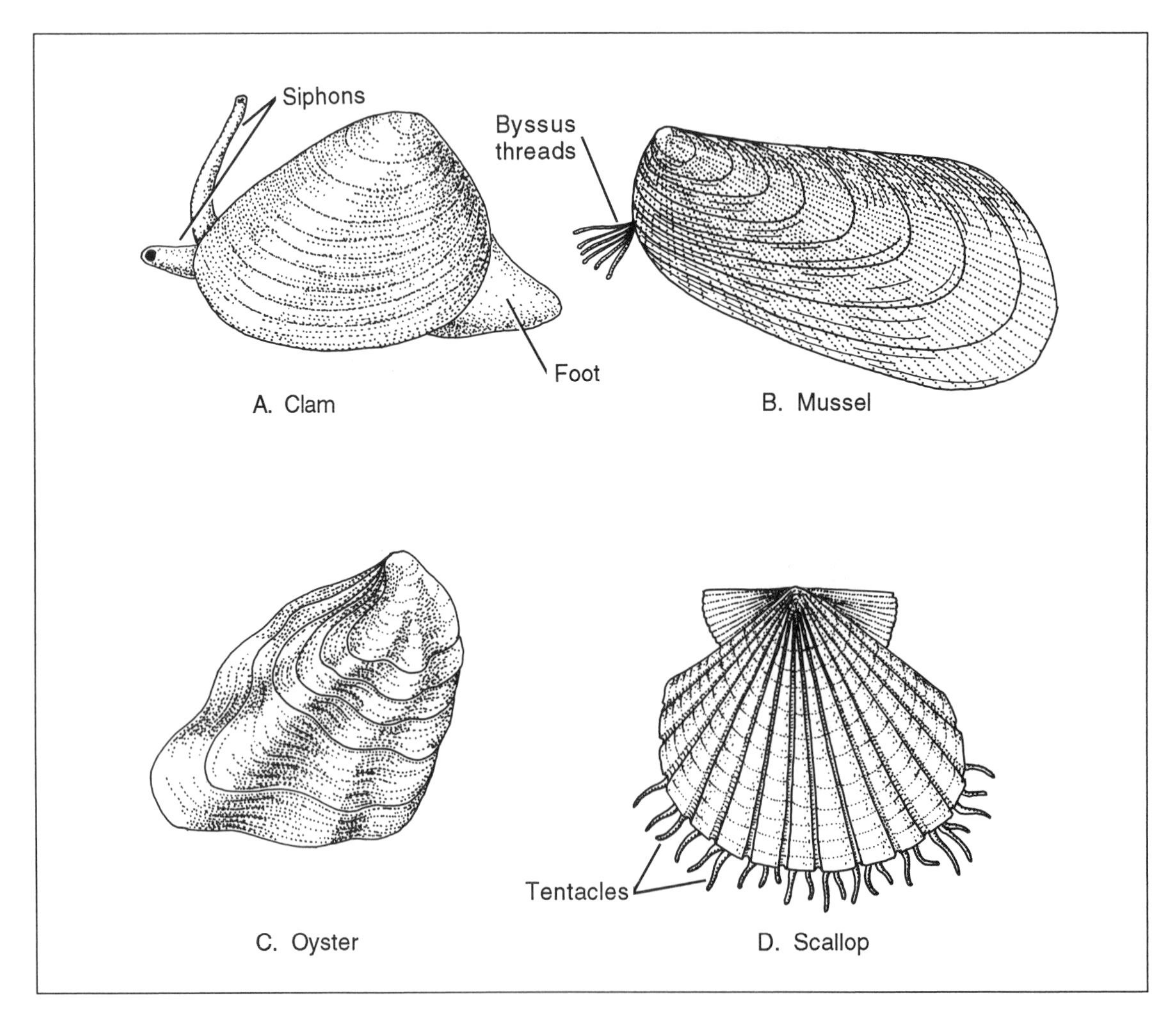

Fig. 6–4. Some types of bivalves

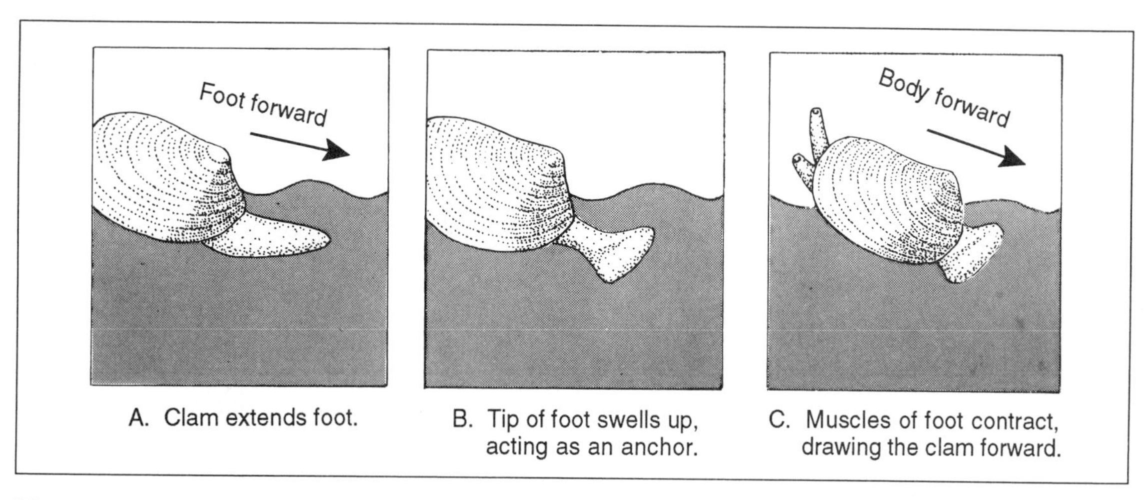

Fig. 6–5. A clam using its foot to move about
Source: Modified from Pearse and Buchsbaum 1982, 350

these animals attach themselves to hard objects early in life and do not move around. Scallops don't use their small foot to move around either. They swim by jet propulsion, clapping their shells together and forcing water out the rim.

Water enters and leaves a bivalve by way of two tubes called **siphons.** One siphon takes in water while the other expels water and wastes. Water taken in contains oxygen and food particles consisting of detritus and plankton. As the water flows across the gills, oxygen and carbon dioxide are exchanged. Mucus on the gills traps microscopic food particles, and tiny hairlike **cilia** on the gills move the food-laden mucus toward the mouth. Liplike structures called **palps** help sort the food and direct it into the mouth. Bivalves do not have a radula. See Fig. 6–8. The food suspended in mucus moves through the digestive organs, which break it down and absorb it.

In some bivalves, such as oysters, mantle tissue secretes **nacre** (NAY ker), a pearly substance that coats any irritating particles—bits of gravel, for example—that lodge between the mantle and the shell. As coats of nacre build up, a pearl forms. **Cultured pearls** used in jewelry are products of oysters raised on aquaculture farms, where oysters are purposely seeded with particles to stimulate the production of pearls. The cost of pearls varies with size, color, and luster. Before plastic came into use, the shells of bivalves were commonly used to make buttons.

Bivalves such as clams, oysters, and scallops are valuable as food; in fact, they make up a major share of the marine invertebrate cash crop. Except for the shell, bivalves can be eaten whole. But when water in which they grow becomes polluted with chemicals or disease organisms, bivalves should not be eaten. At certain times of year, for example, microscopic organisms called dinoflagellates multiply rapidly in the enclosed waters of bays and estuaries. When they grow so thick that the pigment in their bodies makes the water look red, the phenomenon is called a **red tide.** Toxic substances produced by dinoflagellates can concentrate in the clams and oysters that use them as food. Although the bivalves are not harmed, the toxin attacks the nervous system of humans who eat the clams and oysters. This "paralytic shellfish poisoning" can be fatal to humans.

ACTIVITY 1

Observe the external and internal features of a bivalve.

Trace the flow of water, nutrients, and wastes through a bivalve.

MATERIALS

- heat source
- 1,000-mL beaker
- tongs
- fresh clam
- newspapers or dissecting pan
- paper towels
- scalpel
- blunt probe
- copy of Workbook Fig. 6–9
- colored pencils or crayons
- large culture dish (optional)
- seawater (optional)
- eyedropper (optional)
- carmine dye solution (optional)
- dissecting pan with wax bottom (optional)
- pins (optional)
- copy of Workbook Fig. 6–10

PROCEDURE

1. If the shells of the clam are closed tight, steam the clam in hot water until it opens. Lift it from the hot water with tongs. Drain the excess water out of the clam. Throughout the following procedures, refer to Table 6–1 as needed for definitions of terms.

2. Cut the clam open.
   a. Lay the clam on newspapers or a dissecting pan with the umbo to the left. Insert a scalpel between the valves and move the blade dorsally along the valve margin to cut the adductor muscles at positions (A) and (B) in Fig. 6–6.
   b. Carefully slit the hinge ligament at the umbo.

3. Hold the clam so that its anterior end faces you and its umbo faces up. See Fig. 6–7.
   a. Find the mantle and the gills on both sides of the soft body cavity.
   b. Observe, sketch, and identify the structures shown in Fig. 6–7.
   c. Turn the clam around and look at it from the posterior end. Observe, draw, and identify the structures.
   d. Observe, draw, and identify the structures from the ventral side.
   e. Expose the clam's interior anatomy by gently separating the mantle from the upper valve with a blunt probe and then lifting the upper valve.

4. Reposition the clam with its umbo to the left as shown in Fig. 6–8. Lift and fold the top mantle to expose the gills and body cavity. Find the body structures

Table 6–1. Glossary of parts of bivalves

Adductor muscles. Muscles that close the valves and hold them shut.

Bivalve anterior end. The end of a bivalve with the mouth and main sense organs.

Bivalve posterior end. The end of a bivalve where the siphons and anus are.

Bivalve dorsal side. The hinged side of a bivalve.

Bivalve ventral side. The open end of the clam from which the foot protrudes.

Excurrent siphon. A tube that pumps out filtered water and waste materials. It is dorsal to the incurrent siphon and opens to the posterior end of the bivalve.

Foot. The large muscle on the ventral or anterior part of the body, used for locomotion.

Gills. Respiratory organs, the site of O_2 and CO_2 exchange and food particle entrapment.

Hinge ligament. A tough, elastic ligament that connects the valves like a door hinge.

Hinge teeth. Interlocking projections on the dorsal surface or top of both shells that keep the shells aligned and prevent them from slipping out of position.

Incurrent siphon. A tube that pumps in nutrients and oxygen-rich water. It is ventral to the excurrent siphon at the posterior end of the bivalve.

Lines of growth. Major concentric ridges that show the shape of the animal at previous stages of development.

Mantle. Tissue that lines and produces the shell and encloses the soft body parts.

Mouth. The external opening to the digestive system. It is at the anterior end of the bivalve inside a groove between the palps.

Muscle scars. Circular indentations on the inner valve lining where the adductor muscles attach to the valve.

Nacre. The shell's interior wall produced by the mantle; commonly known as mother-of-pearl.

Pallial line. The line on the interior of the valve showing where the mantle stopped secreting the nacre (pearly substance).

Palps. Liplike structures that sort out material collected by the gills and transfer edible food to the mouth. They are at the anterior end of the bivalve.

Pearl. A secretion produced by the mantle in response to an irritating foreign particle. Found in only a few bivalves.

Umbo. The smallest and oldest part of the bivalve shell, located near the hinge. It lies off-center, protrudes slightly, and is outlined by the smallest *line of growth* (see above).

Valve. The exoskeleton, which protects the soft body and provides for muscle attachments. Commonly called a shell. Because clams have two shells, they are called bivalves.

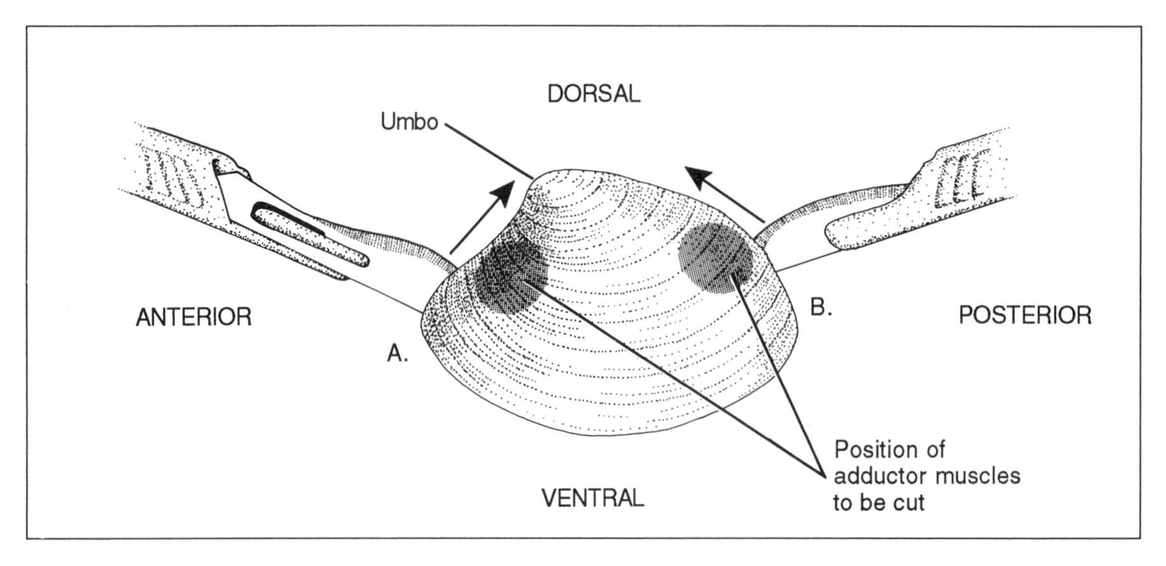

Fig. 6–6. Cutting a clam open

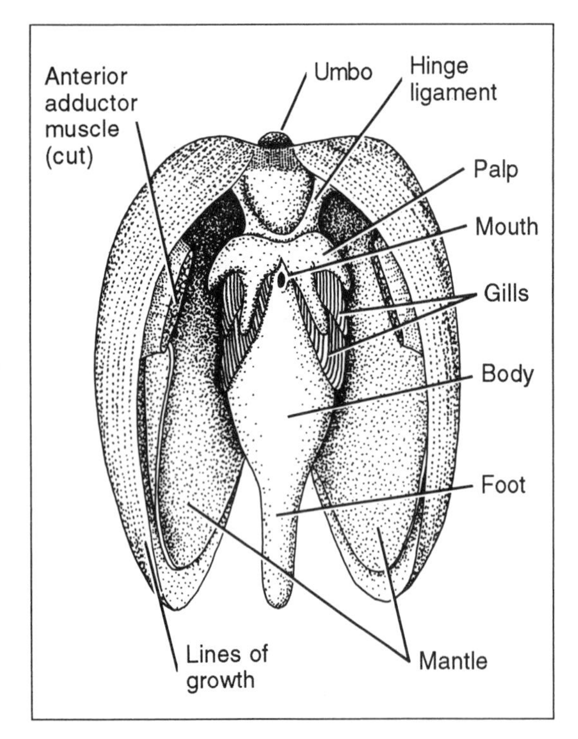

Fig. 6–7. View of partly opened clam from umbo (anterior) end 

listed below. Draw and label the internal parts of your clam. See Table 6–1 for definitions of the parts.

a. gills	g. adductor muscles
b. palp	h. incurrent siphon
c. foot	i. excurrent siphon
d. body	j. hinge ligament
e. mantle	k. hinge teeth
f. mouth	l. umbo

5. Using different-colored pencils or crayons, sketch arrows to show the pathway of food and water into and out of the clam's body. See Fig. 6–9.

6. (Optional) If you have a live, unsteamed clam, take these steps:
   a. Remove one valve and roll back the mantle. Put the clam in a bowl of seawater. Using an eyedropper, slowly add a carmine solution to the

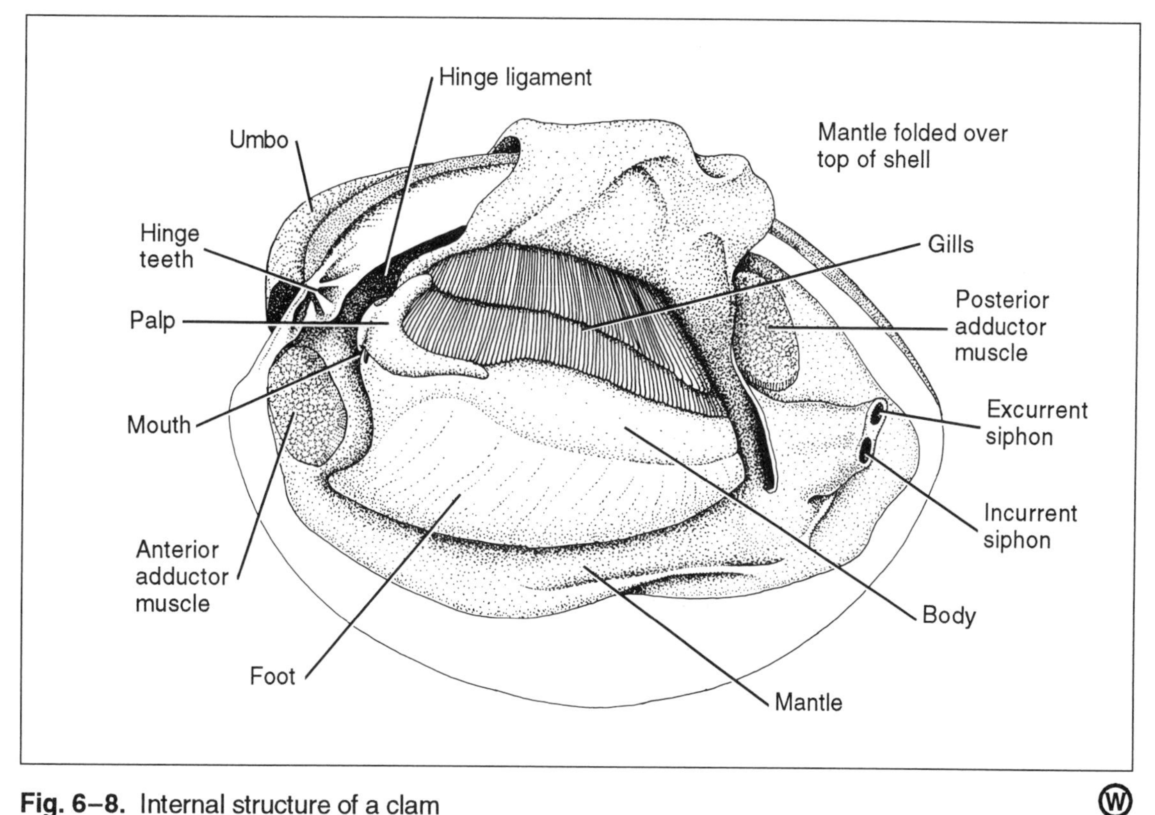

Fig. 6–8. Internal structure of a clam Ⓦ

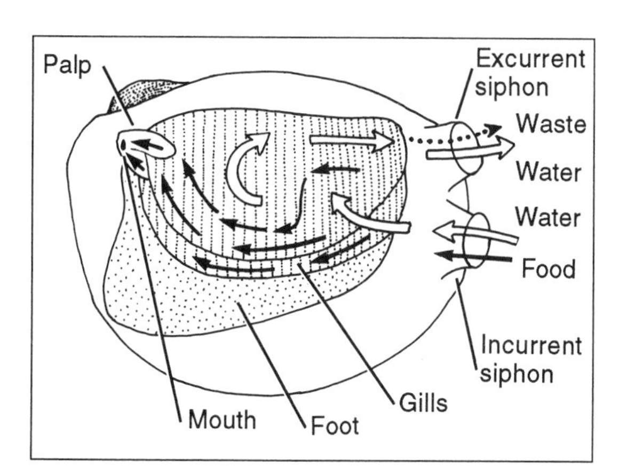

Fig. 6–9. Movement of food and water over the gills of a clam

posterior region of the gill. Observe the flow of particles. Record your observations.

b. Remove a 3-cm x 3-cm piece of gill from your live clam. Spread it out and pin it in a dissecting pan with a waxed bottom. Cover the gill with seawater. Add carmine solution and watch the flow pattern under a dissecting microscope. Modify by adding water of varying temperatures and salinities. Record your observations.

7. Draw the interior features of the valve.
   a. Cut away and remove all soft body materials. Rinse the valve.
   b. Position the clam with its umbo to the left as shown in Fig. 6–6. Sketch its outline.
   c. Find the hinge teeth, the hinge ligament, the muscle scars, the pallial line, and the nacre. Draw and label them in the outline.

8. Turn the valve over and trace another outline. Draw and label the exterior features of the valve. Find and examine its umbo, lines of growth, and anterior and posterior ends.

QUESTIONS

1. What are the features that differentiate mollusks from other phyla? Record your answers in Table 1–3, Comparison of animal phyla by features, in Topic 1 of this unit.

2. How does a bivalve filter-feed? What does it eat? What should humans keep in mind when eating bivalves?

3. The bivalve exoskeleton consists of two hard valves (shells).
   a. What are the advantages to these organisms of having such an exoskeleton? What are some possible disadvantages?
   b. As a bivalve grows larger, what happens to its exoskeleton?

4. What is the function of hinge teeth on the bivalve shell?

5. What holds the two valves of a bivalve together? How do bivalves open and close their valves?

Identifying Gastropod Shells

Gastropods are the largest group of mollusks. The ones we usually think of are snails and slugs. Most gastropods have a calcareous shell protecting the soft-bodied animal inside. Some gastropods, such as sea slugs, sea hares, and garden slugs, lack a shell or have a reduced shell buried in the folds of their mantle. Most creep about on a flattened foot, but some swim, using extended folds of their mantle as fins.

Most snails are herbivorous. They use a radula (a ribbon of modified teeth in the throat) to scrape algae from surfaces. See Fig. 6–2. Some gastropods are carnivores, stalking other snails, worms, and fish for food. See Fig. 6–3. Other gastropods use the radula (plus acidic secretions) to bore holes in shells and prey on other mollusks.

In this activity we examine gastropod shells and describe their shapes. We will see a wide range of shapes, many of which do not match the ones in Fig. 6–10. Malacologists (scientists who study mollusks) use many features of shell structure to classify species of shells. To learn the names of gastropod shells, use a shell identification book.

ACTIVITY 2

Describe differences among gastropod shells. Construct a key using shell features.

MATERIALS

- four different gastropod shells

- copies of Workbook Tables 6–3, 6–4, and 6–5
- centimeter ruler

PROCEDURE

1. Use four numbered shells.

2. Using Table 6–2 as a guide, identify the features of each shell. Some shells will not have all the structures shown; others will have structures that vary from them.

3. Using Fig. 6–10 as a guide, examine each gastropod shell for the features in Table 6–3. Make checks in the boxes for features the animal has. Leave the other boxes blank.
   a. Position the shells with the apex up. Decide which shape in Fig. 6–10 best fits each shell.
   b. Measure and record the length (in centimeters) of the entire shell, the aperture, the spiral, and the body whorl. If the shell does not match any of the shapes in Fig. 6–10, sketch it and invent a descriptive name for the shape.
   c. Look at the margins of the aperture. Check the phrase that best describes the presence or absence of teeth on the columella lip and outer lip.
   d. Look for a lip canal, notch, varices, and operculum. Check those you find. Notice whether the aperture opens to the left or to the right.
   e. Examine the sculpturing for such features as ridges, knobs, spines, and grooves.
   f. Describe the colors and patterns. Sketch them or use words like *spotted* or *striped.*
   g. Record other visible features, including erosion, scar marks, drilled or bored holes, and encrusting by other marine life.
   h. Record other observations.

4. In Table 6–4, make careful pencil drawings of each gastropod shell with its apex up and its aperture facing you. Fill most of the space in the table, even if the shell is small.

5. Reposition the gastropod shells so that you are looking down on the apex.
   a. Sketch the spiral shape, sutures, and shoulders in Table 6–5.
   b. Observe and describe the direction of the spire as clockwise or counterclockwise.
   c. Estimate and record the greatest width of the shell in centimeters.
   d. Count and record the number of whorls.
   e. Sketch or describe differences among the whorls. Note colors, patterns, and sculpture.

6. Using the terms in Fig. 6–10 and Tables 6–2 and 6–3, make a dichotomous key of five gastropods. Refer as needed to Topic 3 in Unit 1, Fish, to review dichotomous keys.

7. (Optional) Examine the coloration of several individuals of the same species. Observe and record how they vary in color, pattern, teeth, and sculpturing.

Table 6–2. Features of two gastropod shells

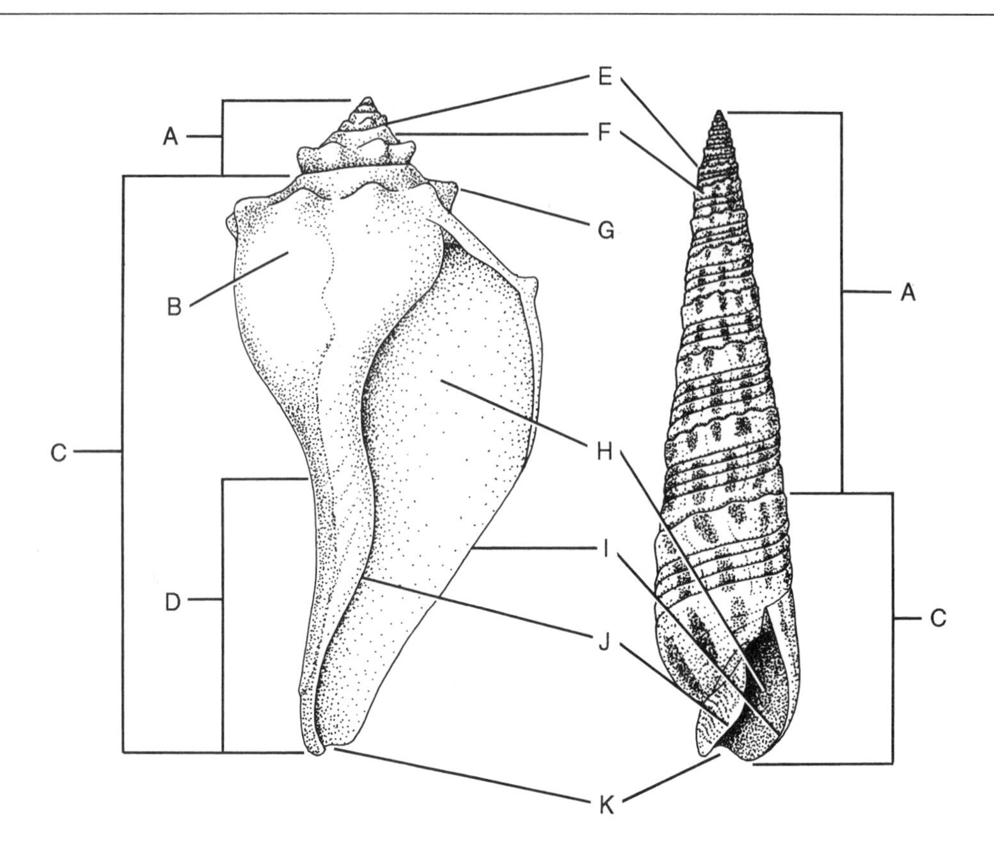

A. ***Spire.*** Part of the shell from its tip (apex) to the body whorl.
B. ***Shoulder.*** The top of the body whorl.
C. ***Body whorl.*** The part of the shell the animal lives in.
D. ***Canal.*** A tubular extension of the body whorl.
E. ***Suture.*** Spiral grooves where one whorl overlaps another.
F. ***Whorl.*** Each "wrap" of the shell as it grows.
G. ***Shell ornamentation.*** The knobs, spines, and colors on the outside of the shell.
H. ***Aperture.*** The opening into the shell interior.
I. ***Lip.*** The outer and newest edge of the aperture.
J. ***Columella lip.*** The rounded inner lip of the aperture.
K. ***Notch.*** An indentation at the bottom of the shell beside the tip of the canal.
L. ***Varices.*** Raised ribs, usually running vertically, caused by periodic thickening of the outer lip during shell growth (not shown in drawing).
M. ***Operculum.*** A plate that seals the aperture in many shells (not shown in drawing).

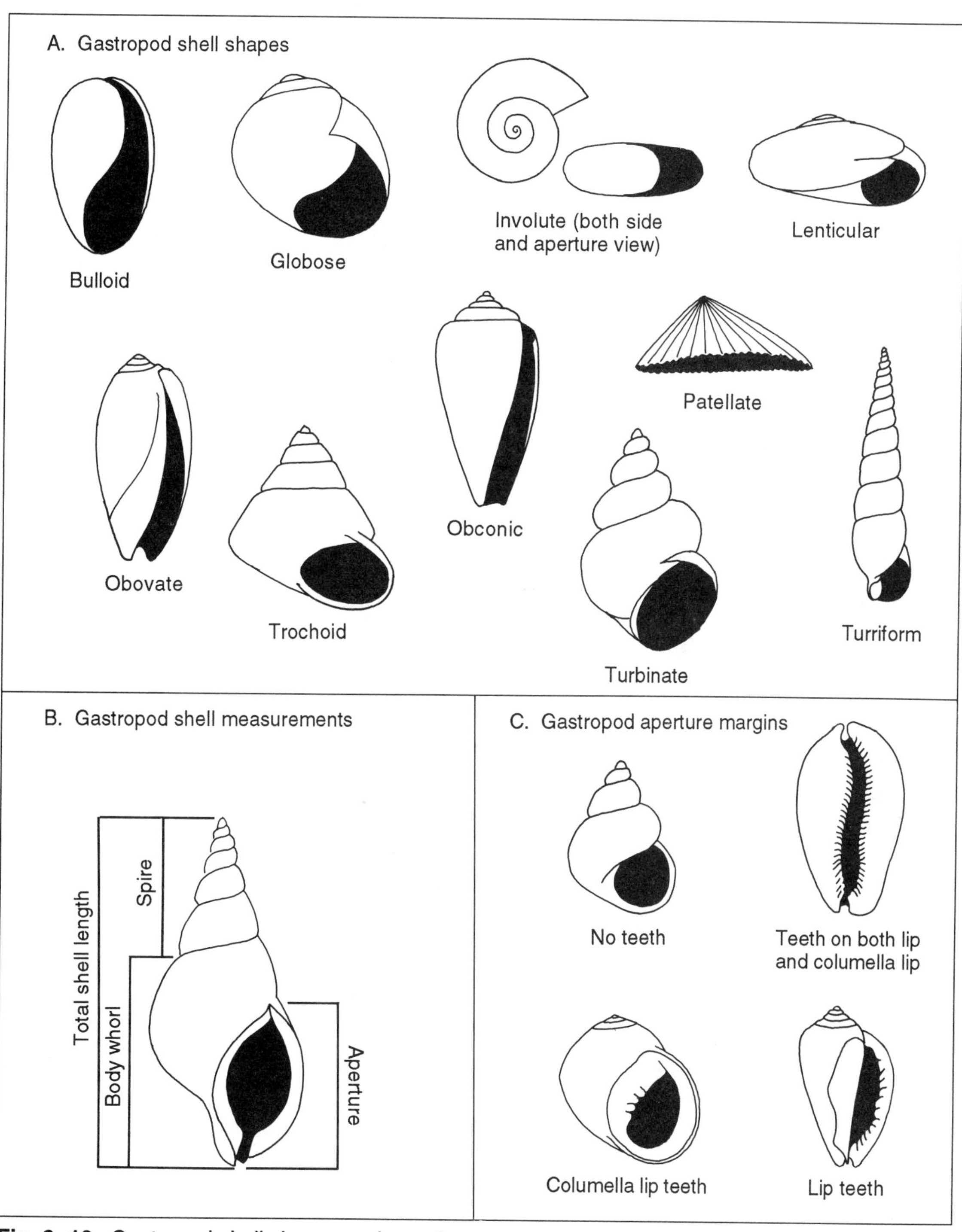

Fig. 6–10. Gastropod shell shapes and margins

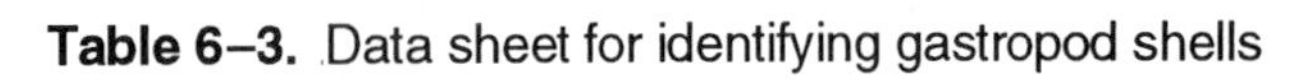

Table 6–3. Data sheet for identifying gastropod shells

Shell	1.	2.	3.	4.
A. Shell shape				
Bulloid				
Globose				
Involute				
Lenticular				
Obovate				
Obconic				
Patellate				
Trochoid				
Turbinate				
Turriform				
Other				
B. Shell measurements				
Total shell length				
Aperture length				
Spire length				
Body whorl length				
C. Aperture margin				
No teeth				
Lip teeth				
Columella lip teeth				
Both columella and lip teeth				
D. Aperture features				
Canal				
Notch				
Varices				
Operculum				
Opens right				
Opens left				

Table 6–3 *continued.* Data sheet for identifying gastropod shells Ⓦ

Shell	1.	2.	3.	4.
E. Sculpturing				
Ridges				
Knobs				
Spines				
Grooves				
Other				
F. Color and pattern				
G. Visible features (Scars, encrustations, drilled/bored holes, erosion)				
H. Other notes				

Table 6–4. Drawings of gastropod shells Ⓦ

1.	2.
3.	4.

Table 6–5. Apex view of gastropod shells

Ⓦ

Shell	1	2	3	4
Top-down sketch (spiral shape, sutures, shoulders)				
Direction of spiral (clockwise or counterclockwise)				
Estimated greatest width (in cm)				
Number of whorls				
Differences among whorls (colors, patterns, sculptures)				

QUESTIONS

6. Gastropod shells are exoskeletons.
   a. What is the function of the shell in these organisms?
   b. What are some of the advantages and disadvantages of having an exoskeleton?

7. What general statements, if any, can be made about
   a. the location of the aperture of gastropod shells?
   b. the direction in which the shells coil?
   c. the colors of the shells?
   d. the patterns of the shells?

8. How do gastropods grow larger? How does their growth differ from the growth of bivalves?

9. What features of gastropod shells
   a. vary among individuals of the same species?
   b. do not vary among individuals of the same species?

10. Suggest how shell shapes may reveal adaptations to their environment. Give

reasons for each suggestion. What shell shapes might be an advantage for gastropods that

a. live clamped to wave-pounded rocks?
b. move through sand or mud?

ACTIVITY 3
Observe a live aquatic snail.

MATERIALS

- 5- or 10-gal established aquarium (seawater or freshwater)
- live snail (seawater or freshwater)
- references on aquarium snails (optional)

PROCEDURE

1. Observe a live snail in an aquarium.
   a. Carefully draw the snail and label its body parts. See Fig. 6–1. Look for the foot, mantle, operculum (if present), tentacles, siphon, eyes, and radula. Because snail body plans vary, you may need to use references.
   b. Describe the snail's sensory structures, including the tentacles and eyes (if present). Include these in your drawings. Observe and record how the snail appears to use its sensory structures. Determine what mechanical and chemical stimuli the snail responds to, such as food, touch, change in light intensity, or the presence of other organisms.
   c. Observe the snail feeding. Determine how it uses its mouth and radula to get food. Design and perform experiments to find out what the snail prefers to eat.
   d. Observe the undersurface of the snail's foot as it crawls along the glass surface of the aquarium. Look for muscle contractions that could explain how it moves.

2. Track the movements of one snail. Determine whether the snail has a set pattern of movement and whether it goes consistently to the same place (habitat). If possible, observe snail behavior at night or under simulated nighttime conditions. Determine whether the snail is most active during the day or night and under what conditions it withdraws into its shell.

3. Observe two or more snails.
   a. Look for evidence that the animal may be defending a territory. Describe any encounters between snails.
   b. Table 9–1 in Unit 1 describes some fish behaviors. Decide which, if any, of these behaviors the snails also exhibit. Record your data.

QUESTIONS

11. What are the advantages and disadvantages of keeping snails with other organisms in a freshwater aquarium? What role, if any, do they serve in maintaining a healthy aquarium?

12. How does a snail move? When is it most active? When does it pull into its shell?

13. How does a snail use its mouth and

radula when it eats? Describe in detail how they move when a snail feeds.

14. Compare the movements and behaviors of an aquatic snail with those of a slug or a land snail. How are they similar? Different?

Head–Foot Mollusks

The cephalopods include squid, octopus, cuttlefish, and nautilus. The class name Cephalopoda, meaning "head-foot," aptly describes this group. The foot in this group has specialized by dividing into arms, which are attached to the head.

Most cephalopods do not have external shells. The nautilus is the only living exception, having a complete, well-developed shell separated into geometrically precise chambers. See (A) in Fig. 6–11. These chambers contain gas that the animal produces to regulate changes in buoyancy when it moves to shallower or deeper water. The amount of gas in the chamber changes, so that the nautilus rests, rises, or sinks.

The squid has an internal remnant of a

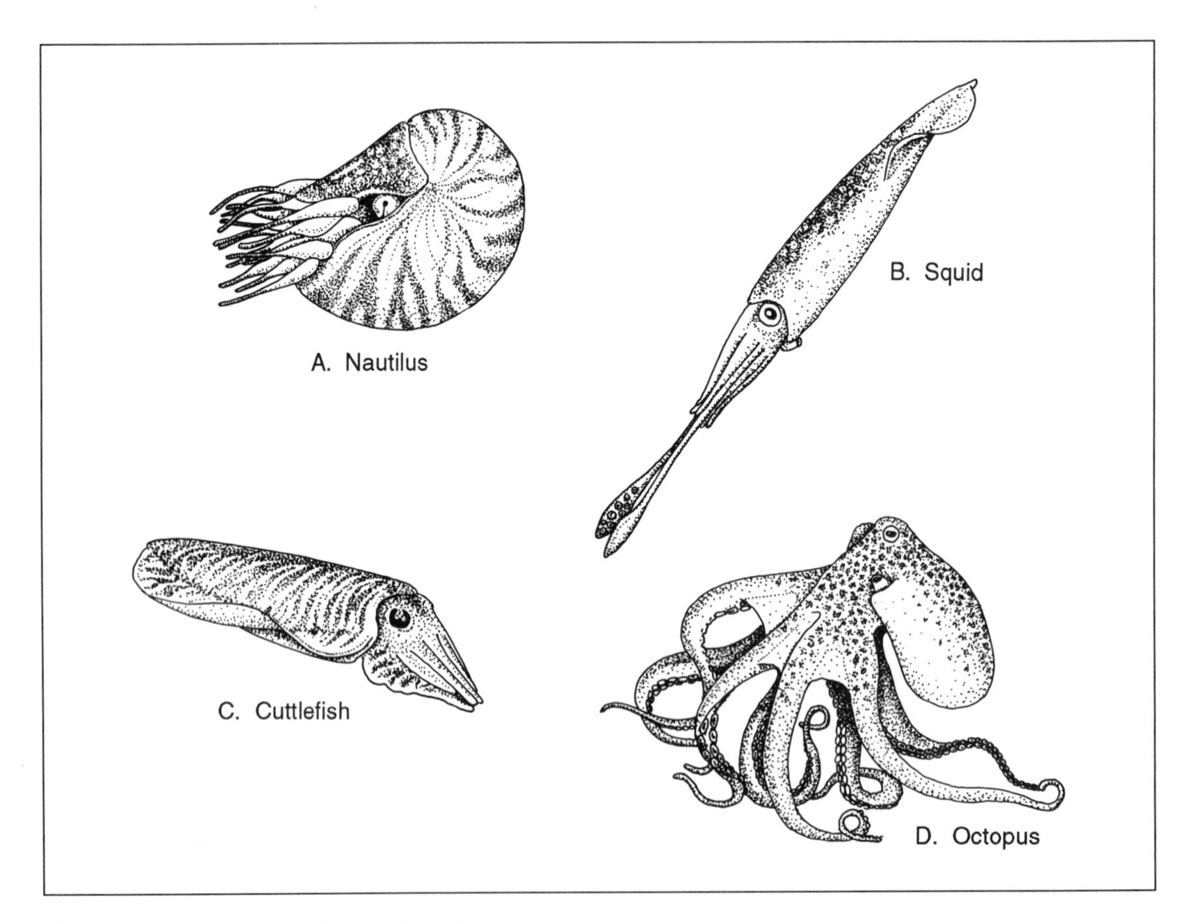

Fig 6–11. Some types of cephalopods

shell, called a **pen,** that looks like a sheet of thick plastic. See (B) in Fig. 6–11. This long, thin shell helps support the body. The cuttlefish, a close relative of the squid, has a harder, more brittle plate, called a **cuttlebone.** See (C) in Fig. 6–11. A cuttlebone is made of calcium carbonate ($CaCO_3$) secreted by the animal; in composition it is similar to the shells of other mollusks. Gas moving in and out of chambers in the cuttlebone lets the cuttlefish move up and down in the water. Cuttlebones are often put in bird cages for the bird to peck on, sharpen its beak, and eat the calcium, a necessary nutrient.

In the mouth of the squid is a **beak** shaped much like the beak of a parrot. The beak is not part of the shell but a separate toothlike structure. When a squid catches prey, such as a fish, it bites off and swallows chunks of it. The squid has a small radula but does not use it for getting food.

The octopus is a cephalopod that has no shell at all. Its only hard body part is its beak, which, as in the squid, is not a remnant of the shell. See (D) in Fig. 6–11. Because an octopus has no hard skeleton, its soft body can squeeze through tiny openings in a reef and hide in crevices or between rocks. Octopuses in aquariums are notorious for their ability to escape.

The octopus is also a master of camouflage, using pigment in its skin cells to quickly change its skin color to blend into its surroundings. These skin cells, called **chromatophores,** contain an elastic sac filled with pigment. The cells are attached to a set of muscle cells. When the muscle cells contract, they pull the chromatophore out flat, spreading the pigment over a larger area and making the skin darker. When the chromatophore is smaller, the skin is lighter. The cells can change shape very rapidly, producing a pulsating pattern of complex color changes. Squids also have chromatophores, which they use to indicate their mood to fellow squids.

In cephalopods the primary swimming organ is the muscular **mantle,** which forms a chamber that opens to take in seawater. When the mantle closes forcefully, seawater ejected through the **siphon** jet-propels the animal in short bursts. Both squids and octopuses change course by quickly redirecting their siphon. They steer by pressing their arms together. They can speedily elude an attacking predator. They can also squirt **ink** from the ink sac into the water, creating an ink cloud for camouflage and confusing the predator.

The squid can also wave its paddle-shaped fins to move slowly forward or backward. The fins also aid the squid in steering and in stabilizing its movements.

The octopus has no fins. It spends most of its time crawling around the bottom, capturing prey with its arms and the suction cups lining the inner surfaces of the arms. After capturing its prey, the octopus bites it, injecting both a poison and digestive enzymes. The enzymes soften the food before the octopus sucks it into its stomach for further digestion.

Most cephalopods are relatively small. But the giant octopus, which lives along the west coast of the United States, can grow to 1.5 m or more. The giant squid, the largest of invertebrates, reaches lengths of 15 m. Prints in early books on voyaging show giant squid attacking ships. Whether the prints depict real or imagined events, they do show the enormous size of these animals. See Fig. 6–12.

Fig. 6–12. An old print showing a giant squid attacking a ship

ACTIVITY 4

Examine the internal and external features of a squid.

(Optional) Cook and eat squid.

MATERIALS

- fresh or defrosted squid
- wax paper
- newspapers
- dissecting scissors or scalpel
- blunt probe
- microscope slide
- dissecting microscope
- ingredients for cooking squid listed in Table 6–6 (optional)

PROCEDURE

1. Lay the squid dorsal side down on a piece of wax paper laid over some newspapers. Lay the squid with its head to the left and its siphon up. See Fig. 6–13.

2. Reach under the animal and remove the pen from the dorsal side by grasping it firmly with your fingers and pulling it free from the mantle.

3. Using a scalpel or dissecting scissors, cut the mantle from its anterior edge next to the siphon to its posterior tip. Do not cut into the internal organs.

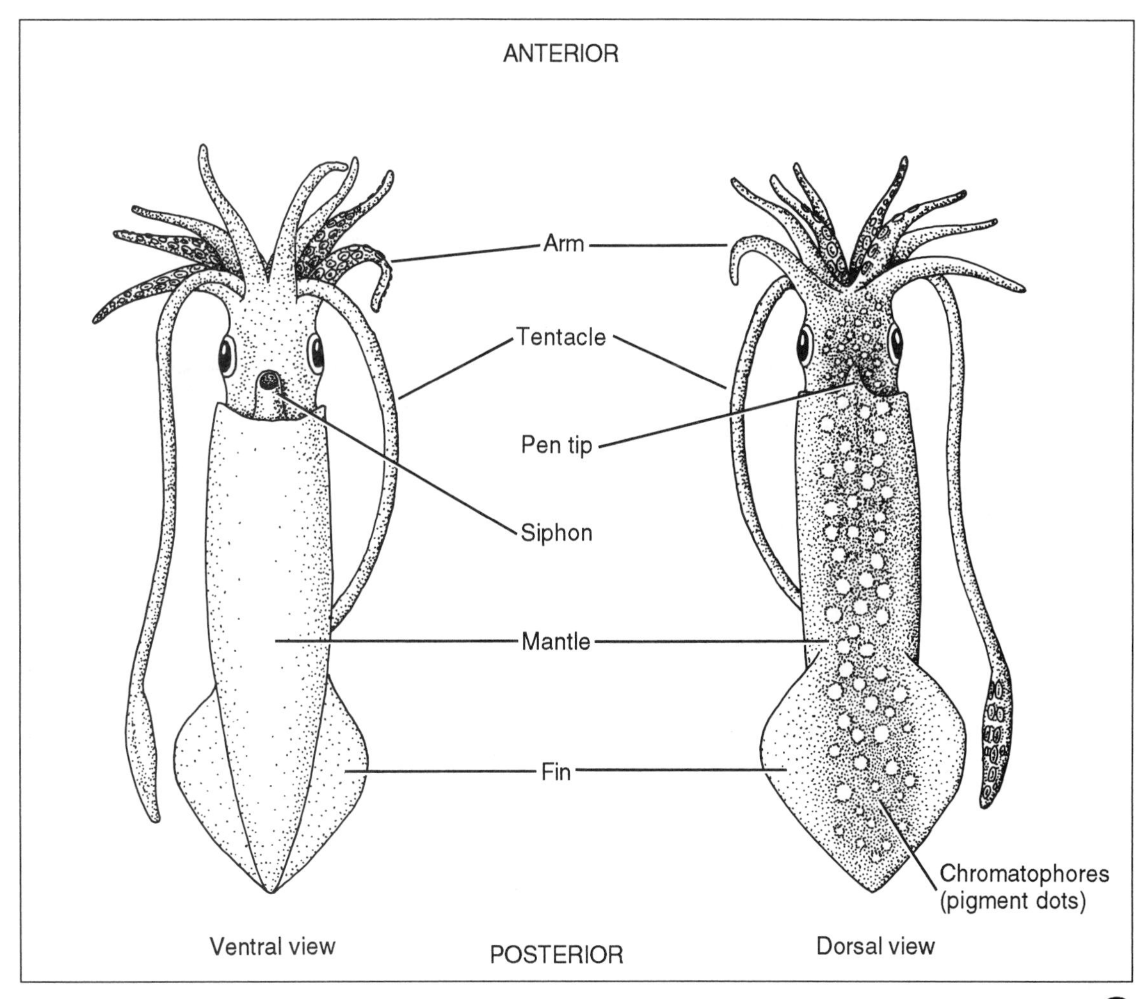

Fig. 6–13. External anatomy of a squid

4. Using a blunt probe, find these structures and describe their functions. Refer to Fig. 6–14 as needed. Draw the structures in Fig. 6–15.

a. caecum	f. ovary or testis
b. intestine	g. gills
c. pen	h. chromatophores
d. ink sac	i. kidney
e. heart	j. nidamental gland

5. Examine a single sucker from an arm.
   a. Cut off a 0.5-cm piece of the arm and place it on a glass slide.
   b. View it under the dissecting microscope.
   c. Draw a single sucker in your notebook.

6. Observe the chromatophores, small

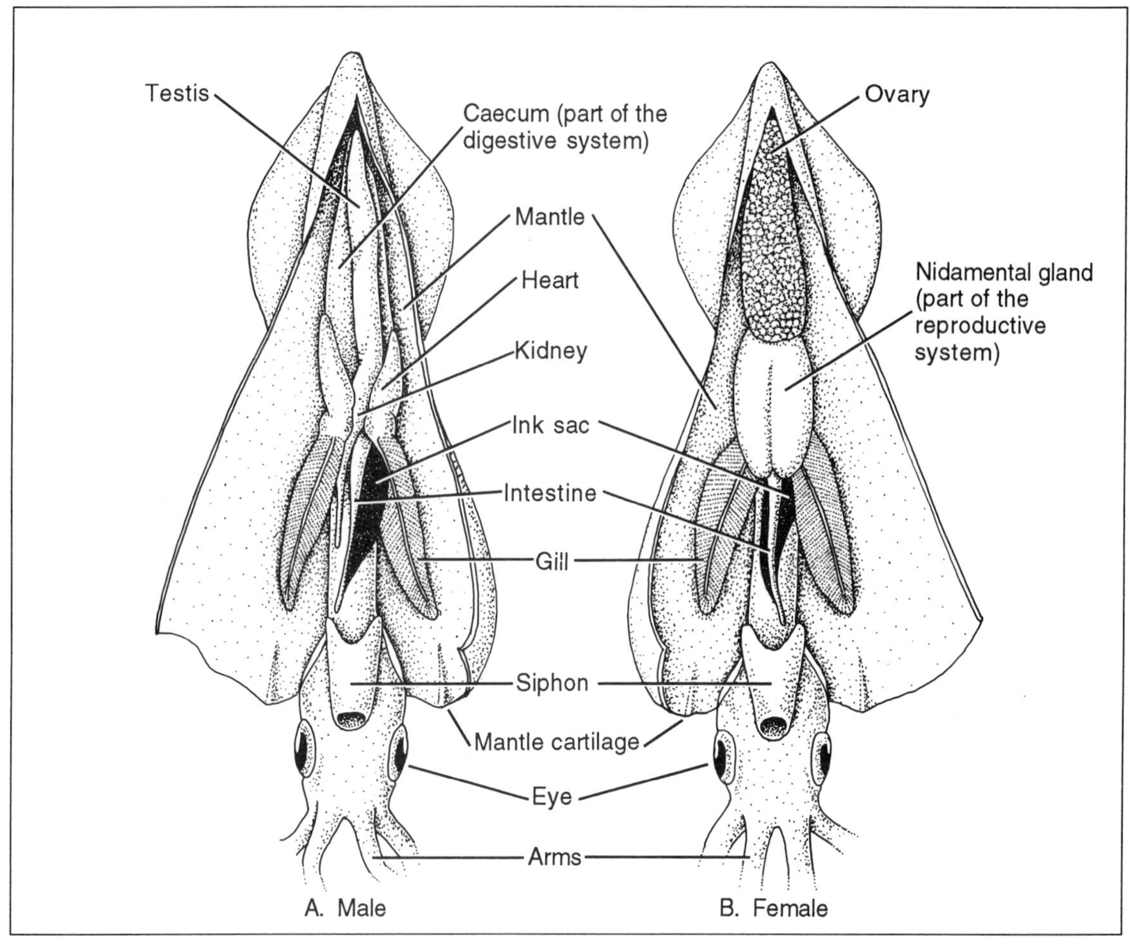

Fig. 6–14. Internal anatomy of a squid

frecklelike spots on the outer layer of the mantle. Cut out or peel off a small piece of the skin that contains the spots. Observe at about 20X under a dissecting microscope. Stretch the skin, noting any apparent change of color. Record your observations.

7. Remove the beak.
   a. Cut the arms from the head with a scalpel at line (A) as shown in Fig. 6–15.
   b. Pull out the beak. Wash it and save it. Sketch it in your notebook.
   c. Remove the internal organs and wrap them in a plastic bag or newspaper. Give them to your teacher or save them for feeding aquarium organisms.
   d. Carefully wash the mantle and arms,

Fig. 6–15. Outline of a squid

Table 6–6. Squid recipes

1. Chili squid
16-oz can stewed tomatoes
8-oz can chili beans
basil, oregano, and bay leaves
8-oz Portuguese sausage, sliced
onion, sliced
squid mantles and arms, sliced

Sauté sliced sausage and onions in a hot frying pan. Add tomatoes, chili beans, and herbs. Bring the mixture to a boil. Add the sliced arms and mantles. Simmer until the mantle turns white (2 to 3 min). Serve hot with rice or crackers.

2. Fried squid
egg, beaten
½ cup milk
pinch of salt and pepper
cup of cornmeal
⅓ cup oil
squid mantles and arms

Mix egg, milk, salt, and pepper in a mixing bowl. Dip the squid mantles and arms in the mix and roll lightly in cornmeal. Heat oil in a hot frying pan and cook squid for about 2 min. Serve hot or cold with rice or crackers.

making sure they are very clean. Save them for Procedure 8.

8. (Optional) Cook and eat the squid. Wash your hands well. Work in a sanitary area. Use a favorite recipe or try one in Table 6–6.

QUESTIONS

15. How does the squid's ink help protect it?

16. What are the distinguishing features of cephalopods? What features relate cephalopods to other mollusks? What features of mollusks appear in other phyla?

17. What advantages do cephalopods get from their chromatophores?

18. Describe jet propulsion and control of direction in a squid.

19. Describe several methods of escape (defense mechanisms) used by cephalopods.

20. How does an octopus differ from a squid? List or draw and label the differences.

FURTHER INVESTIGATIONS

1. Collect and compare shells.
   a. Compare valves of clams, oysters, mussels, and scallops. Look for variations within species.
   b. Compare gastropod shells from the Atlantic and Pacific oceans.

2. Look in your supermarket for clams, oysters, or other bivalves.
   a. If possible, bring these to class. Compare their anatomy.
   b. Using a mollusk, prepare a food for the class. Some suggestions are clam chowder, clam fritters, and linguini (noodles) with clam sauce. Make a class recipe book.
   c. Test recipes for cephalopods. Try various cooking methods—boiling, baking, broiling, and smoking.

3. Find out why bays and estuaries are good places for clam, mussel, and oyster beds. How is the taking and eating of oysters restricted? What is the basis for these restrictions?

4. Attend a meeting of a malacological association (a shell club) or invite a member to speak to the class. Find out about shell clubs at local museums and aquariums.

5. Study mollusks in their natural environment.
   a. Find out about gastropod habitats and seasonal fluctuations in population. Report to the class.
   b. Study octopuses and squids. Determine what they eat and how they find and catch prey. What other behaviors do you see? If you cannot study octopus or squid in their natural habitat, observe them at an aquarium.
   c. What animals eat mollusks? Make a list of animals that feed on bivalves, gastropods, and cephalopods.

6. By using references and speaking to health experts, learn the role of gastropods in the life cycle of parasitic worms that invade humans and their pets. (Liver flukes and heartworms are examples.)

7. Some people say that the octopus is the most intelligent of invertebrate animals. See references to learn about octopuses, especially their brains, eyes, and sensory organs. Report to the class.

8. An old saying advises, "Never eat shellfish in months without an 'r' in their names." What seafoods are considered shellfish? Why might the month make a

difference in whether shellfish are safe to eat?

9. Use references to learn about land snails and slugs. How can they survive without being constantly in water? Which are considered gourmet food? Which are considered pests? Which are considered threatened or endangered species?

10. Seashells appear throughout history in art and in literature. Find how shells are used as symbols in religion, in mythology, and in native arts.

11. Striped zebra mussels in the Great Lakes may have been accidentally introduced from a ship's bilge water. Learn about them and the environmental problems they have caused.

12. How does living in a shell affect the arrangement of internal organs in gastropods? Use references to learn how the digestive system and other systems are arranged in various mollusks.

13. Loss of habitat has threatened many freshwater, terrestrial, and marine mollusks. Use library references to learn about mollusks in your area and other places in the nation. Which species have become extinct or greatly reduced in number? What, if anything, do you think should be done to protect them? Should their protection be allowed to hinder or stop real estate development projects, dam construction, logging or farming industries? Set up a debate or panel discussion in class.

7. Arthropods

Many familiar species belong to the phylum **Arthropoda**—insects, spiders, scorpions, centipedes, and millipedes on land; crabs, crayfish, shrimp, lobsters, and barnacles in water. See Fig. 7–1.

Arthropods are considered the most successful animals on earth. The phylum includes more species and more individuals than all other groups of animals combined. Over 85% of all known animal species are arthropods.

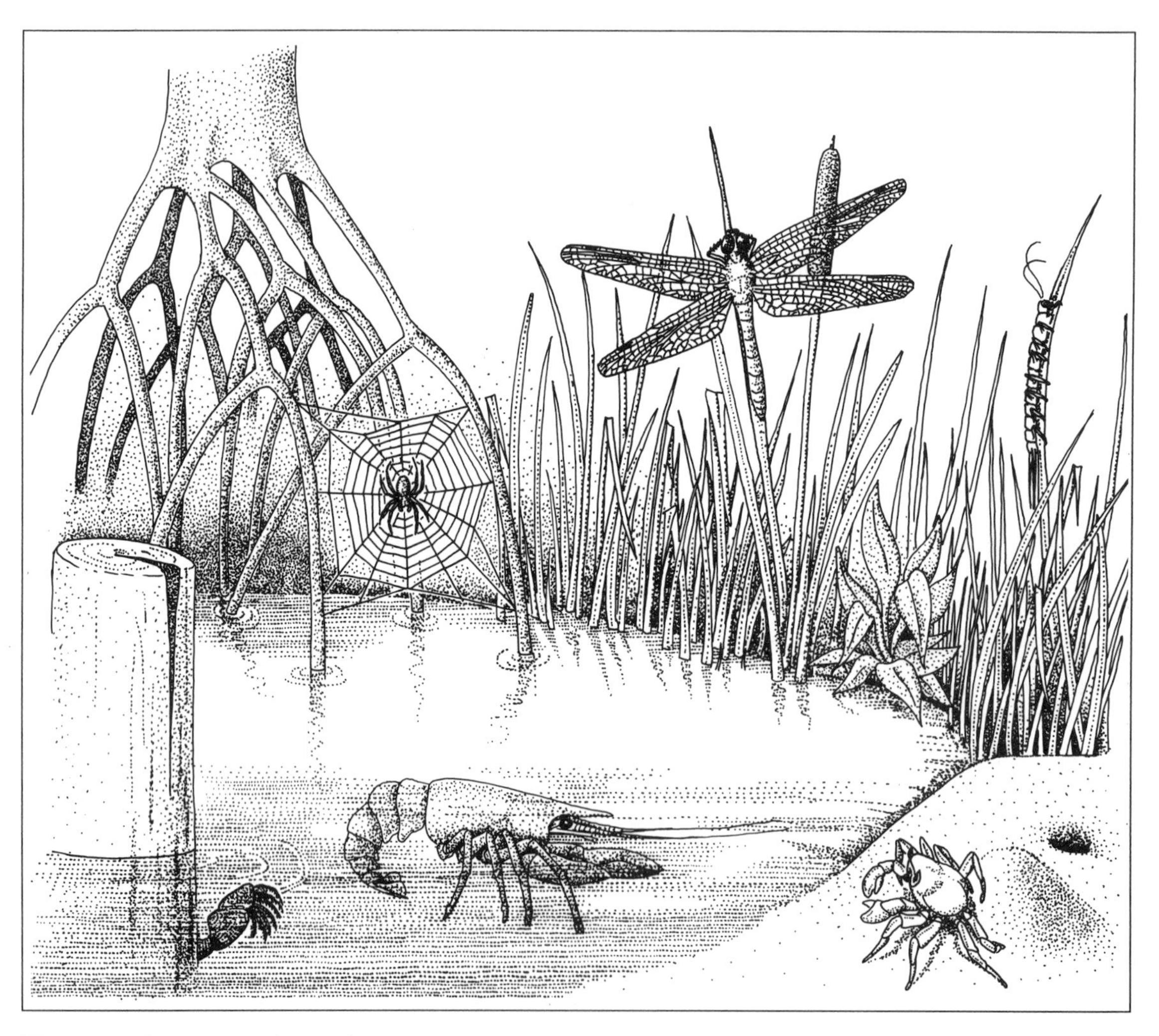

Fig. 7–1. Common arthropods

See Fig. 7–2. They live in the widest range of habitats and eat the greatest varieties of food. Consider how many kinds of animals you can find in your schoolyard. The number of kinds of arthropods (ants, flies, mosquitoes, cockroaches, beetles, spiders, and so on) vastly exceeds the number of kinds of vertebrates (humans, dogs, cats, mice, rats, and so on).

Most arthropods have developed a hard, protective **exoskeleton** (outer shell). Some groups, such as crabs and barnacles, secrete calcium carbonate into the exoskeleton, making it thick and hard. To grow, arthropods must molt (shed) their exoskeletons periodically. During the molt, they form a larger exoskeleton to allow for expansion.

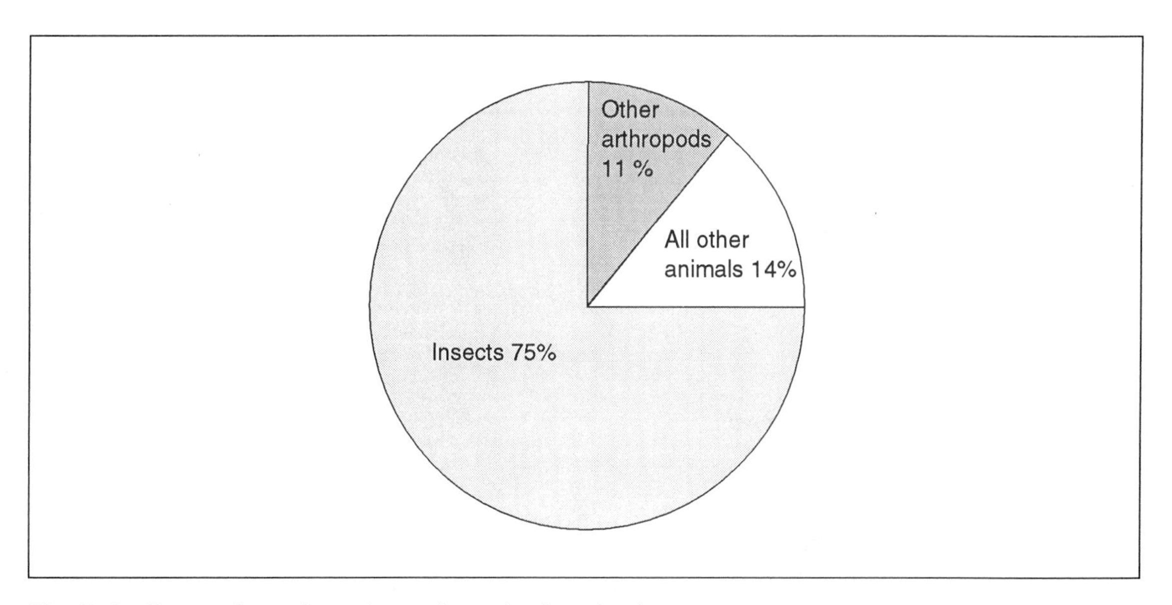

Fig. 7–2. Comparison of numbers of species in animal groups

The word **arthropod** (G. *arthro* = joint; G. *pod* = foot) refers to a unique feature of the group—jointed legs, called **appendages,** which vary widely in number and function. Many appendages are used for eating, feeling, sensing, mating, respiring, walking, or defending themselves.

The combination of an exoskeleton and jointed appendages is something like a suit of armor worn by medieval knights. The muscles for movement are attached to the inner surface of the exoskeleton. See Fig. 7–3. Vertebrates such as fish and humans have an internal skeleton, called an **endoskeleton,** with muscles attached to its outer surface.

An arthropod's body is divided into segments, like those of the earthworm. In species like millipedes and centipedes, the segments are quite similar to each other. See (A) in Fig. 7–4. In other species, like an ant, the segments are clustered in major body regions. Insects have an abdomen of several segments and a

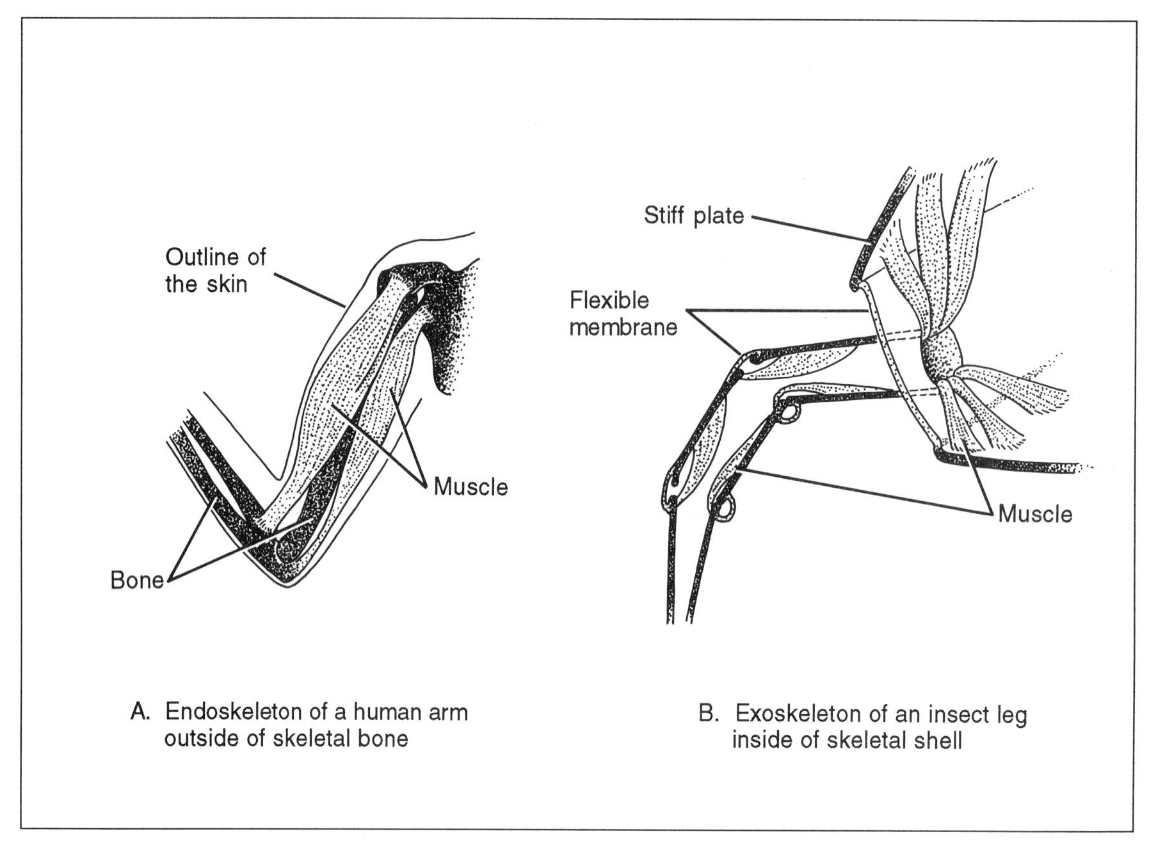

Fig. 7–3. Muscle attachment on an endoskeleton and an exoskeleton

separate head and separate thorax. See (B) in Fig. 7–4. In crabs, shrimp, lobsters, and crayfish, the head and thorax fuse in a single section called a **cephalothorax** (G. *cephalo* = head; G. *thorax* = breastplate). See (C) in Fig. 7–4.

Most segments have a pair of attached jointed appendages. The posterior pairs commonly function as swimming legs **(swimmerets)**, the middle pairs as walking legs, and the anterior pairs as food-getting apparatuses **(maxillae** and **mandibles)** or as sensory organs **(antennae)**. See Fig. 7–6.

Crustacea

Most marine arthropods belong to a group called **Crustacea.** The word first referred to the crusty exoskeleton of organic material called **chitin,** which distinguishes this group from mollusks, whose hard shells are made of calcium carbonate. Most crustaceans live in the ocean, where they are so abundant that they are often called "insects of the sea." Some species of crustaceans live in fresh water; a few—isopods and pill bugs, for example—live on land. See Fig. 7–5.

Crabs, shrimp, and lobsters commonly

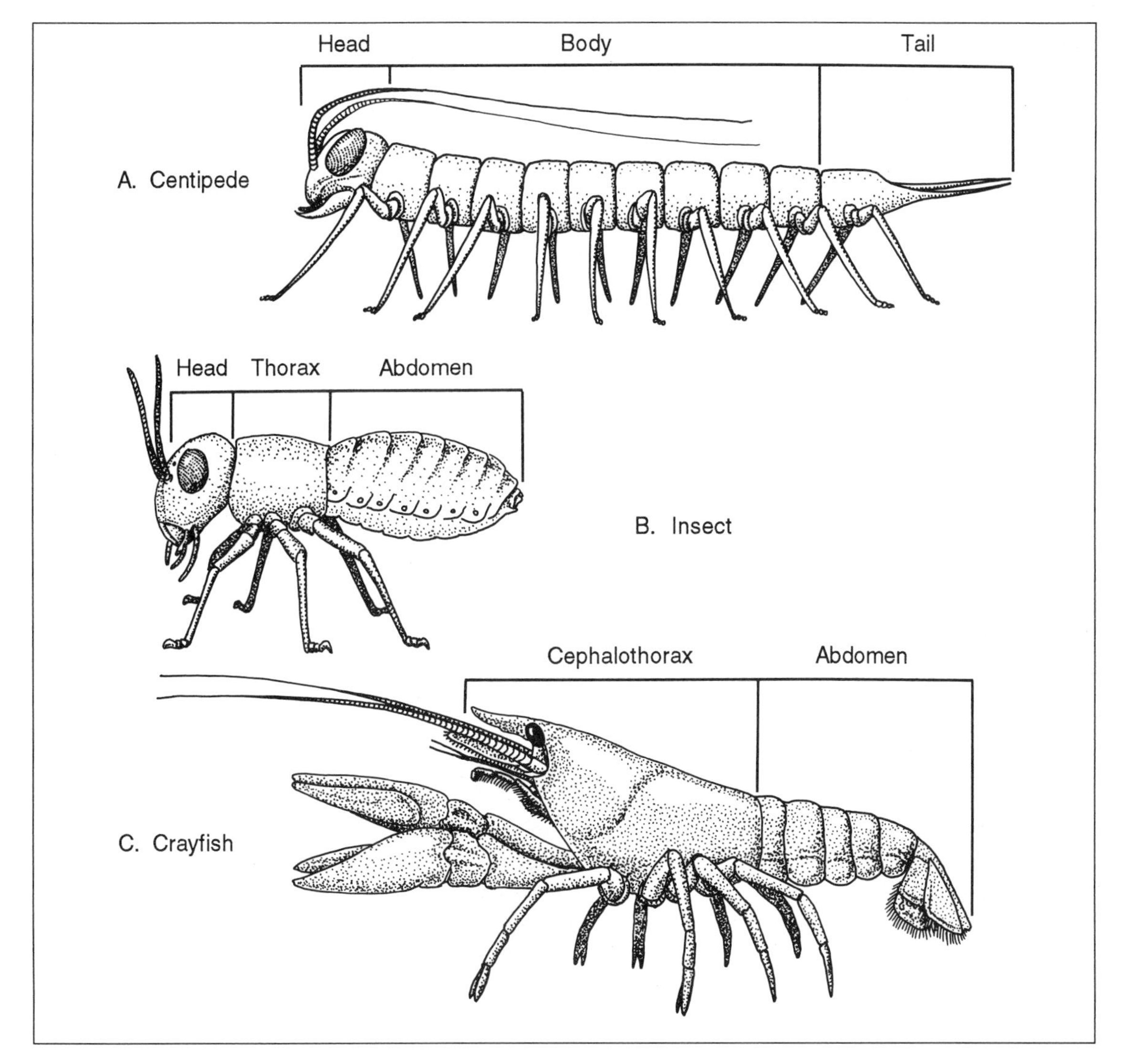

Fig. 7–4. Arrangement of segments in three types of arthropods

live along the shoreline. Some species of shrimp, called krill, spend their lives as plankton, drifting in the surface waters of the open oceans. Crayfish are common in freshwater lakes and streams. All these animals are used as food, both by larger animals and by humans. Some are considered delicacies. We will use crustaceans readily available in markets to study the anatomical features of arthropods. Many species are easily kept in an aquarium and can be used to study behavior.

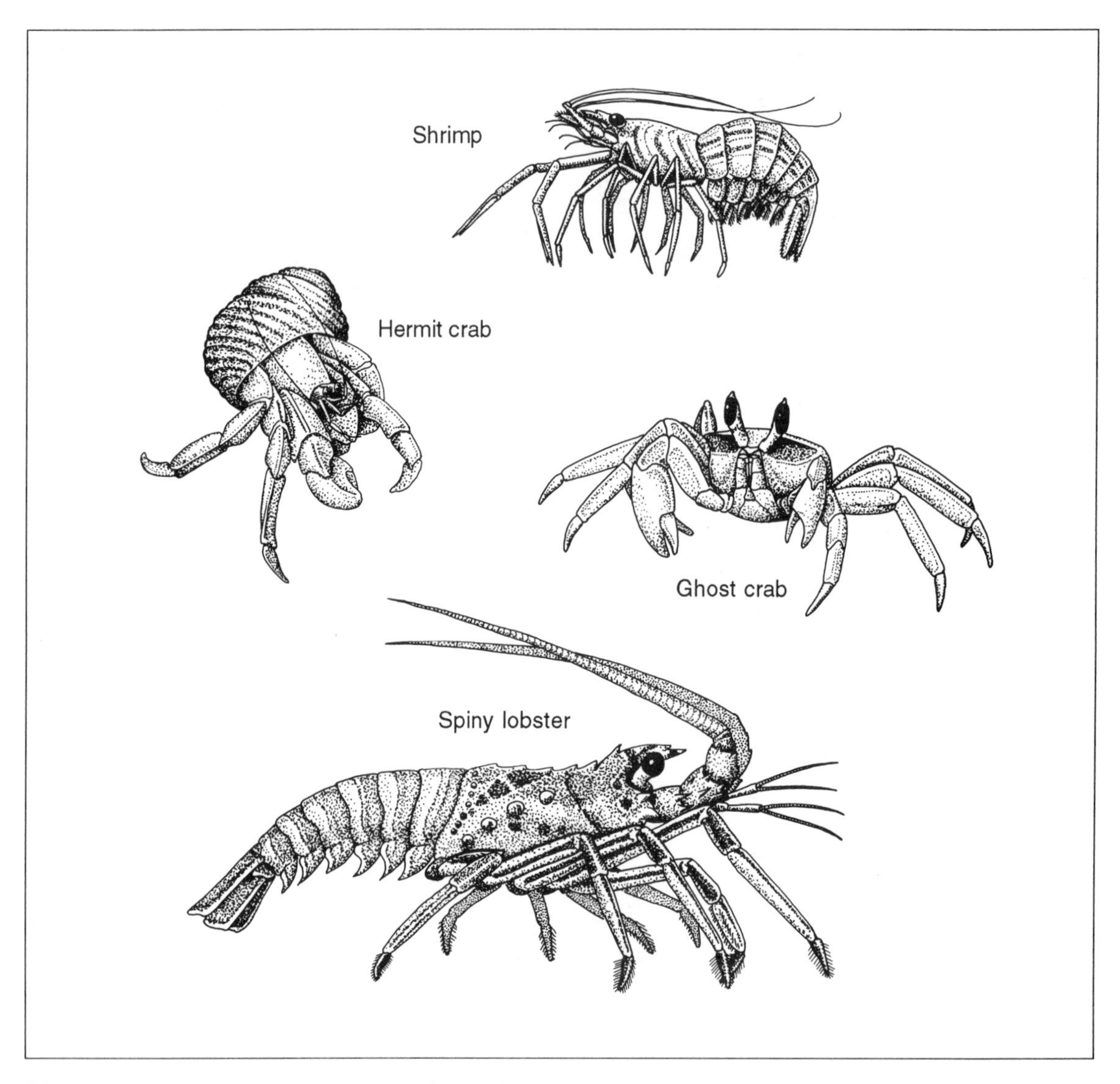

Fig. 7–5. Some larger crustacean arthropods

In the next activity you will identify the sex of an arthropod. Lobsters and crayfish have external structures from which you can tell their sex. Males and females are most readily identified by their swimmerets, the appendages on the abdomen. The female swimmerets have hairs, making them look like feathers; the male swimmerets are relatively hairless.

In the male, the openings through which sperm pass out of the body are at the base of the last walking legs. During mating the male transfers the sperm by using the first pair of its abdominal swimmerets (behind the walking legs). In males, the swimmerets are large and point toward the front of the body. When brought together in the midline of the body, these two appendages form a tube through which sperm pass to the female. The female keeps the sperm in a saclike receptacle whose opening is between the third pair of walking legs. The openings of the female reproductive tract are at the base of the second pair of walking legs. Some days or weeks after receiving the sperm, the female releases several hundred fertilized eggs. These eggs become attached by a gluelike secretion to her swimmerets, where they hang like grapes on a stem for weeks to months until hatching.

In crabs the abdomen is much smaller than in lobsters and crayfish, and the reproductive structures are not as easy to see. In males the abdomen is narrow and fits into a groove on the under side of the cephalothorax. In females the abdomen is flat and broad, covering most of the underside of the cephalothorax.

ACTIVITY 1

Study the structures of a crustacean and determine their functions.

MATERIALS

- whole shrimp, lobster, or crayfish
- newspapers or dissecting pan
- copy of Workbook Fig. 7–6
- dissecting scissors
- forceps
- dissecting microscope
- blunt probe

PROCEDURE

1. Lay a fresh shrimp or crayfish on its side in a dissecting pan or on newspapers.

2. Using information in Table 7–1 and Fig. 7–6, find the animal's external anatomical structures.

3. Determine the sex of the specimen from the description of the differences between males and females.

4. Carefully remove the side of the carapace with scissors and forceps to expose the gill chamber. Count the gills and note how they attach to the body.

5. Use a dissecting microscope to observe the surface of the eye. Note the many regular-shaped surfaces, called **facets.** These are the surfaces of individual eyes. Thousands of these eyes make up the **compound eye.**

6. To expose the internal organs, remove the gills and the rest of the carapace from one side of the cephalothorax. Also remove a strip of the exoskeleton along the dorsal surface of the abdomen. Be careful to avoid damaging the delicate internal organs. Using the diagram of the organs of a crustacean in Fig. 7–7, identify the following systems and organs:
   a. circulatory system: heart, dorsal blood vessels, ostia (openings into the heart)
   b. digestive system: mouth, stomach, digestive gland, intestine, anus

Table 7–1. Glossary of external anatomical features of a crustacean

Abdomen. The segmented section of the body behind the one-piece cephalothorax.

Antennae (the singular is *antenna*). The second pair of appendages in the cephalothorax. They are long, jointed feelers used in touching and tasting. *Antenna* is also a general term for a long external sensory organ.

Antennules. The branched first pair of appendages in the cephalothorax. They are short, jointed antennae used in touching, tasting, and keeping equilibrium.

Carapace. The exoskeleton shield covering the head, thorax, and gill chamber.

Chelipeds. The first pair of large walking legs which in some species have pinchers called chelas (KEE luhz) that are used for attack or defense.

Gill chamber. The compartment on the lateral side of the cephalothorax housing the gills.

Mandibles. Appendages near the mouth used for grinding food.

Maxillae (the singular is *maxilla*). Appendages near the mouth used for manipulating food.

Maxillipeds. The first three appendages behind the mouth; used for manipulating food.

Rostrum. The extension of the carapace between the eyes.

Stalked eyes. Eyes on a raised stem. These eyes, which have many facets or subunits, are called compound eyes.

Swimmerets. Small appendages attached to the abdomen; used for swimming and by the female for carrying and aerating eggs.

Telson. A tail-like extension of the last segment in the abdomen; used with the uropods in backward swimming.

Uropods. Paddlelike pair of swimmerets on the last segment of the abdomen; used in swimming and in protecting eggs.

Walking legs. Five pairs of leglike appendages attached beneath the cephalothorax.

c. reproductive system: testis or ovary (may be absent in immature specimens)
d. nervous system: brain, ventral nerve cord, ganglia

QUESTIONS

1. How does the exoskeleton of an arthropod compare with
   a. the exoskeleton of a mollusk?
   b. the endoskeleton of a fish?

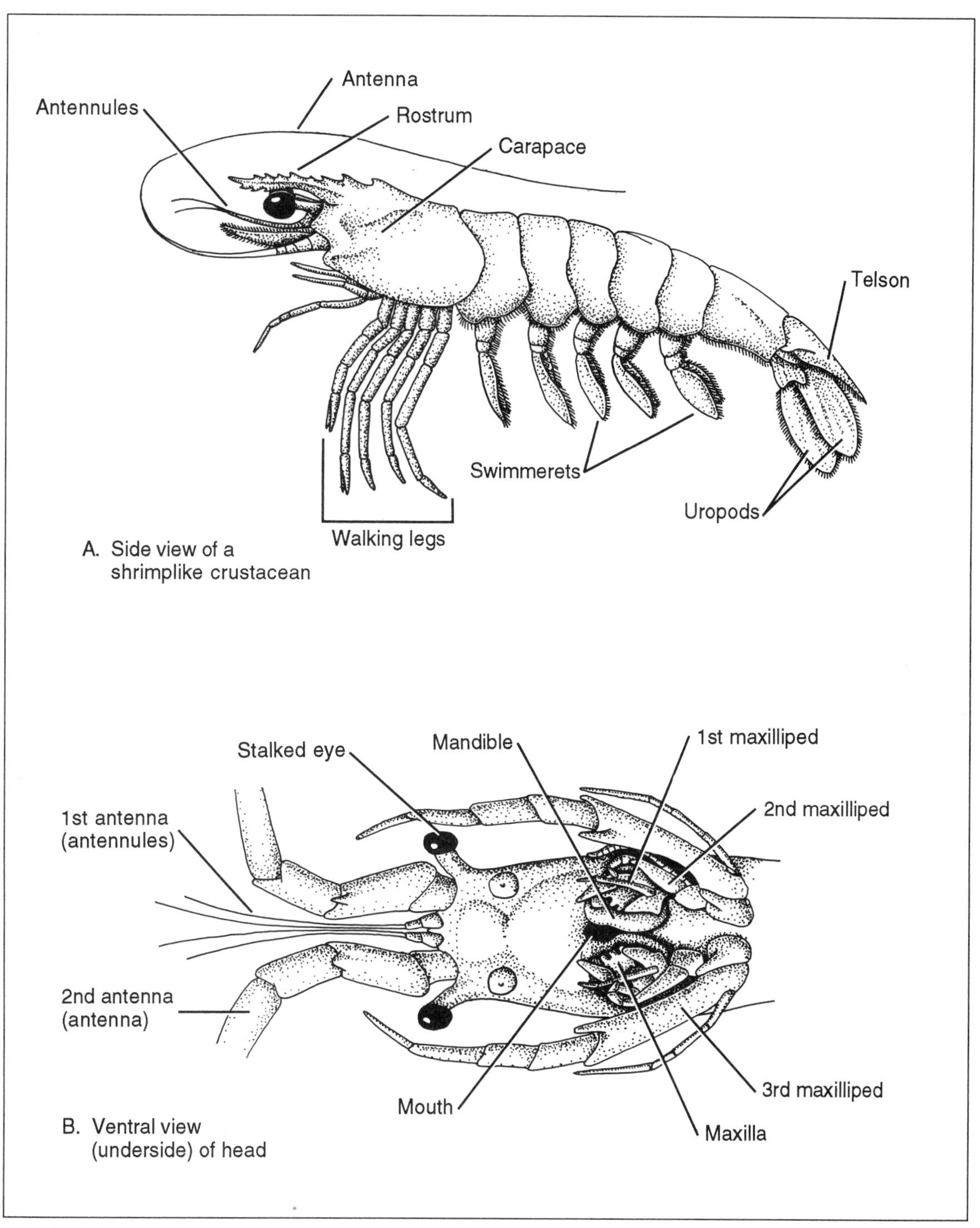

Fig. 7–6. A shrimplike crustacean

Ⓦ

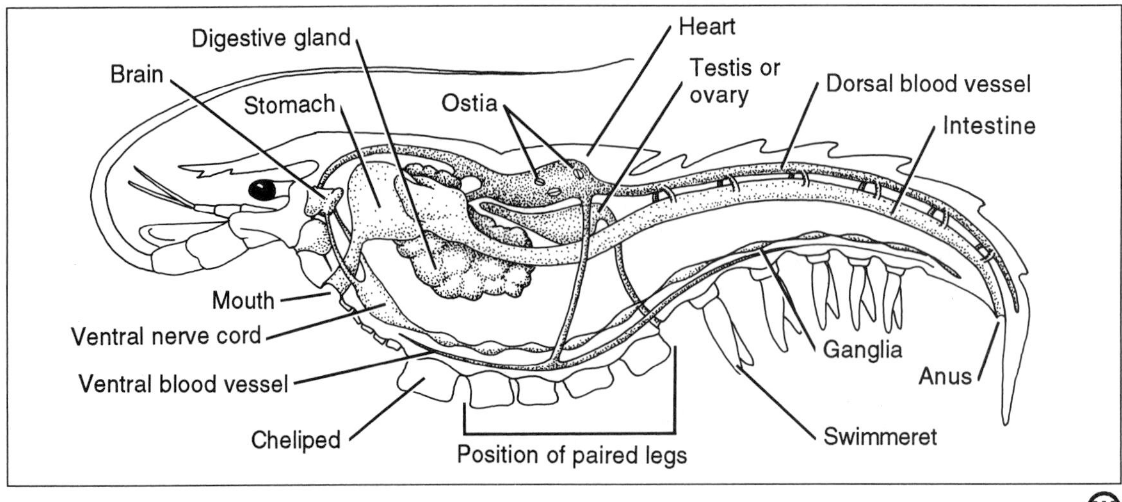

Fig. 7–7. Internal organs of a crustacean

2. Which appendages are attached to the cephalothorax? Which are attached to the abdomen?

3. Which appendages have attached gills?

4. Which sections of the body are most flexible?

5. How does the arrangement of gills in the crustacean differ from the arrangement in fish?

6. How does the circulatory system of a crustacean differ from that of a fish?

7. Even though a crustacean has no large veins, shops sell "deveined" shrimp. What anatomical part does deveining remove?

8. How does the location of the nerve cord of arthropods compare with that of vertebrates? Of polychaete worms?

9. What is the difference between a simple eye in vertebrates and a compound eye in arthropods? If necessary, use reference books to find the answer.

10. Fill in the characteristics of phylum Arthropoda in Table 1–3, Comparison of animal phyla by features, in Topic 1 of this unit.

Behavior of Crustaceans

Of all marine invertebrates, crustaceans have the greatest variety of ways of responding to their environment. We can watch many of their behaviors in the laboratory. These behaviors can tell us much about the way crustaceans operate in the wild. Be prepared for rapid movements, some of which are best captured on video or motion picture film for close analysis.

We will experiment with a crustacean—a shrimp, a crab, or a freshwater crayfish.

ACTIVITY 2

Observe the behavior of a crustacean.

MATERIALS

- live shrimp, crab, or crayfish
- 5- or 10-gal established aquarium (seawater or freshwater)
- small piece of fresh or frozen fish
- 8-in length of sewing thread
- blunt probe
- eyedropper
- blue or red food coloring

PROCEDURE

1. Put a live crustacean (crab, shrimp, or crayfish) in a beaker or shallow aquarium of seawater or freshwater, depending on its natural habitat. Use enough water to cover the animal. Give the animal time to rest and get used to its surroundings.

2. Observe the natural behavior of the animal. Make the following observations and record your data in Table 7–2.
   a. Tie a small piece of fish on a thread and hang it in the water in front of the animal. Note the action of the antennae, antennules, and mouth appendages in getting food.
   b. When the animal moves forward, observe how the walking legs move and in what order.
   c. Touch the animal with a probe until it moves its abdomen. Describe how it moves. Observe how it defends itself after being probed.
   d. Observe and record how the swimmerets move. Describe what causes the animal to respond.
   e. Add a small drop of food coloring to the water near the front of the animal. Note how the dye moves through the gill chamber. Sketch

Table 7–2. Movement of crustacean body parts during various behaviors 

Body part	Feeding	Walking	Swimming	Escaping
Antennae				
Antennules				
Maxillae and mandibles				
Walking legs				
Abdomen and telson				
Swimmerets				

the pathway of the dye in Fig. 7–6.

QUESTIONS

11. What anatomical parts does a crustacean use for
    a. swimming?
    b. eating?
    c. sensing food?
    d. attacking or defending itself?
    e. escaping predators?

12. From your observations describe how the crustacean used its appendages in protecting itself, in circulating water through its gills, and in walking, swimming, and eating.

13. From your observations of crustacean behaviors, tell how you might go about catching them for food. Describe what you might do and explain your reasoning.

14. What might be the functions of the rostrum? What is your evidence?

15. Describe respiration in a shrimp, crab, or crayfish. What are the structures used and the pathways of respiration?

ACTIVITY 3

Observe the behavioral interactions of several shrimps or freshwater crayfish in a small area.

MATERIALS

- 6 to 8 live shrimp or crayfish
- 5- or 10-gal aquarium (seawater or freshwater)
- 10- or 20-gal established aquarium (seawater or freshwater)
- paper towels
- fingernail polish

PROCEDURE

1. Observe the interactions between two animals by size and by sex.
   a. Use two shrimp (or crayfish) of similar size. Try to use animals that have never been together before. Determine the sex of your animals.
   b. Place each animal in a small aquarium by itself. Record your observations for 5 min in Table 7–3.
   c. Put the two animals together in a small aquarium filled with seawater (fresh water for crayfish). Record your observations for 5 min in Table 7–3.
   d. Repeat Procedure 1 with pairs of animals of unmatched sex and animals of different size.
   e. If you need help with behavior terms, refer to Unit 1, Table 9–2.

2. Observe the behavior of several animals over a longer time.
   a. Set up a large aquarium with an undergravel filter and aeration stones. Add seawater for marine shrimp or fresh water for crayfish. Ask your teacher for directions if needed.
   b. Put objects such as stones or jars in the aquarium to serve the animals as hiding places. Pile the objects to form small "caves." Try a variety of stones and jars—different colors, sizes, and shapes—as living places

Table 7–3. Behaviors of crustaceans Ⓦ

Crustacean type		Size	Sex	Observation
1 animal per bowl	Animal A			
	Animal B			
2 animals per bowl	Animal A			
	Animal B			

for shrimp or crayfish. Use other substrates such as shells, small rocks, or pottery fragments.

c. Mark 6 to 8 animals to make them easy to identify. (This step is unnecessary if each animal has a unique distinguishing feature.) Here is a way to mark them:
   1) Carefully dry the carapace with a paper towel.
   2) With nail polish, mark the carapace of each animal with dots or stripes to identify it. (This will not hurt or distress the animal.)
   3) In your notebook, record the markings, size, and sex of each animal.

d. Put the marked animals in the aquarium. Watch the interactions among them for several days. Note especially if any animals establish and defend a territory. Note patterns of dominance and aggression.

e. Record your observations in your notebook each day.

QUESTIONS

16. What body postures and movements show aggressive behavior? Defensive behavior?

17. What effect does a difference in sex or body size have on the interaction of two animals? Describe in detail the interactive behavior between two animals of
    a. the same size and sex.

b. the same size but different sex.
c. the same sex but different size.

18. If territories were established, how long did it take the animals to establish them in the large aquarium? Did sex and size relate to the establishment of territories? Did all animals claim a territory? Did these animals defend their territories? If so, did the territories have distinct boundaries? Did the territories remain the same over a long time?

19. How would the animals' behaviors be useful in their natural environments?

FURTHER INVESTIGATIONS

1. Consult references to compare the anatomy of a crab, a lobster, an ant, and a bee. Make drawings to show similar and dissimilar features.

2. Report on the farming of shrimp, crab, lobster, or crayfish. Compare the size, the technology, and the economic importance of this kind of farming in your state and other states. Compare crustacean farming with fish farming. What environmental issues affect crustacean farming?

3. Collect dried arthropod molts for the class collection. Find information on the process of molting in arthropods.

4. Learn more about where crabs or shrimp live in natural environments. How, if at all, are their bodies adapted to their habitats? What do they eat and, in turn, what animals prey on them?

5. Many people think that barnacles are mollusks. Read references to learn about the anatomy and life history of barnacles. Explain what makes them arthropods. Learn of their economic impact on the shipping industry, which must cope with barnacles growing on ship hulls.

6. Visit a seafood store. Find out what kinds of arthropods are sold for food. Compare prices of arthropods (shrimps, crabs, lobster, crayfish) with prices of fish, mollusks (clams, squid), beef, and chicken.

7. Collect recipes using shrimp, crab, lobster, and crayfish. Start a classroom seafood recipe book.

8. Find out what commercial and medicinal products are extracted from arthropod by-products. An example is *chitoson,* which is extracted from the carapaces of crabs for use in making fibers, films, and artificial human skin.

9. What is the nutritional value of shrimp, crabs, and lobster? How do they compare with fish in protein, fat, and calories?

10. Look for examples of crustaceans in art, music, and literature. Some examples are representations in jewelry, cartoons, and advertising. Find examples of imagery in our language, such as calling someone "crabby" or a "shrimp."

8. Echinoderms

Some of the most common ocean organisms—sea stars, sea urchins, sea cucumbers, brittle stars, and feather stars—belong to the phylum **Echinodermata,** named for the spines or bumps covering the outer surface of the bodies of many of them (G. *echino* = spiny; L. *derm* = skin). See Fig. 8–1. All members of this phylum are radially symmetrical, the body usually being divided radially into five parts or multiples of five. All have a nerve ring and a water vascular system (explained in this topic). They have calcium carbonate endoskeletons, ranging from microscopic spicules to visible plates. All live in the ocean.

The five-sided radial structure of echinoderms makes the body strong. See Fig. 8–2. A five-sided skeleton is stronger than a four- or six-sided one because the line of weakness cannot run directly across the body. Even a three-sided body plan is weaker than a five-sided one.

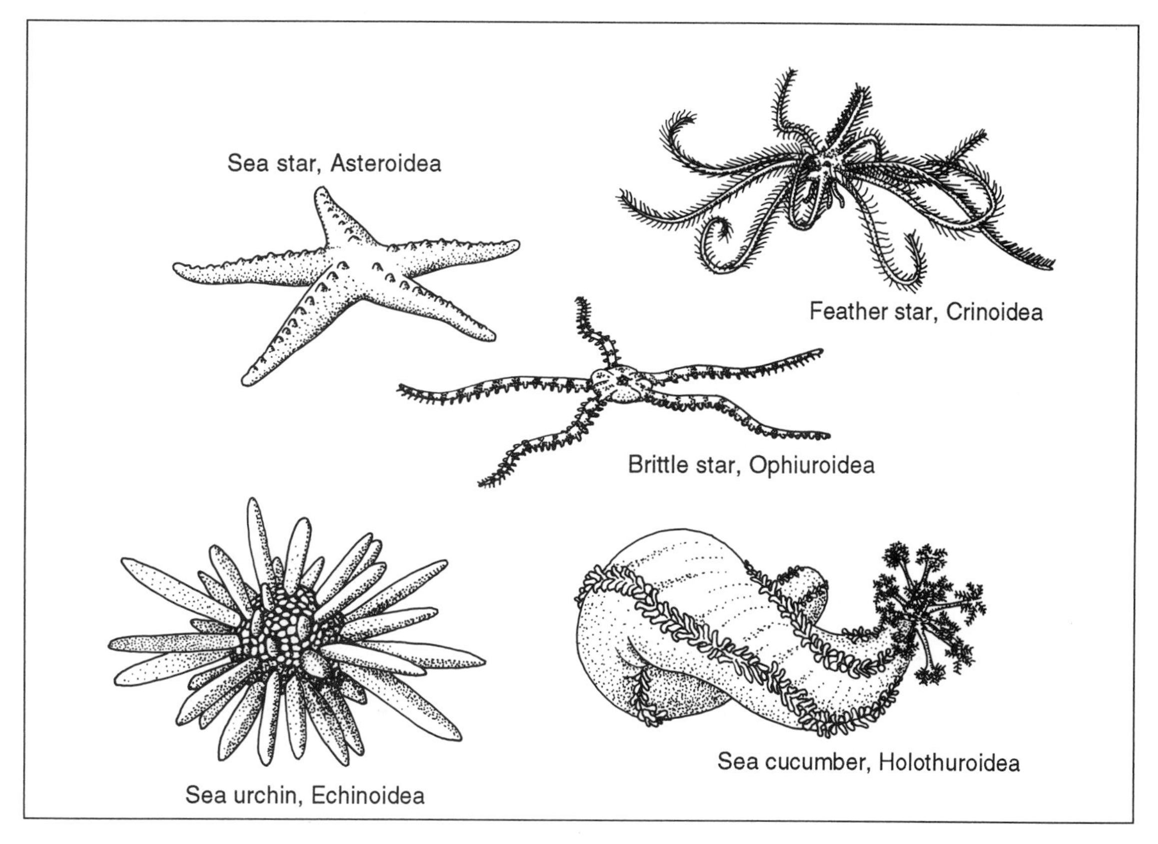

Fig. 8–1. Types of echinoderms

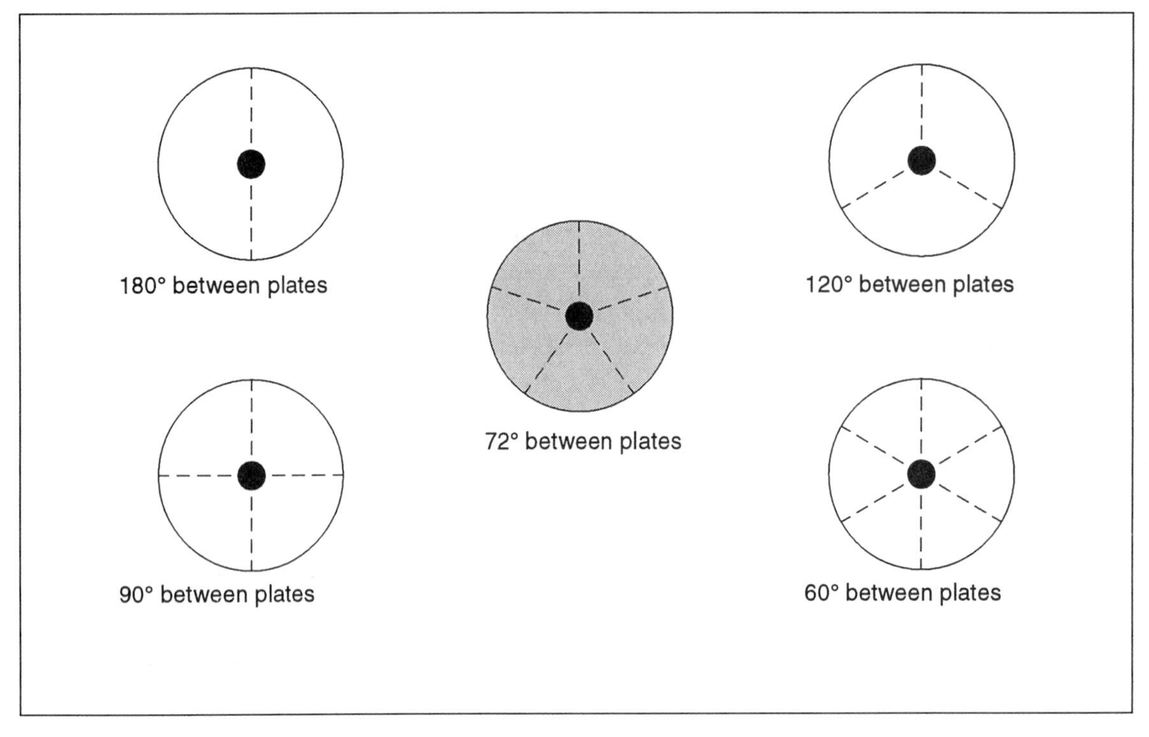

Fig. 8–2. Lines of weakness across various body plans. The dashed lines mark lines of weakness.

Sea Urchins

Sea urchins belong to the class **Echinoidea,** named for the movable spines projecting from the body like a hedgehog's spines (G. *echinoid* = like a hedgehog). Sea urchins are common around the world, from the ocean's shoreline to its great depths, from tropical waters to the far reaches of the Arctic. Sea urchins are relatively small; most of them can fit in your hands. The spines protect the animal and help it move and get food. The long, thin, sharp spines of some sea urchins easily penetrate the skin of anyone who steps or sits on one. See Fig. 8–3. In some species, toxic chemicals on the tissues covering the sharp spines make its stab extremely painful. See (A) in Fig. 8–3. Other species, with thick, blunt spines, are safe to handle. See (B) in Fig. 8–3. A few species that live in the shallow-wave surge zone on rocky seashores have spines modified into flat, broad plates that offer little resistance to strong wave action. See (C) in Fig. 8–3. The spines of sea urchins protect them from most predators.

Skeleton

The soft inner organs and tissues of sea urchins are protected by a hard **test,** a skeleton composed of plates of calcium carbonate. See Fig. 8–4. The plates interlock in a tight geometric pattern that makes the skeleton rigid. Because the test is covered by very thin

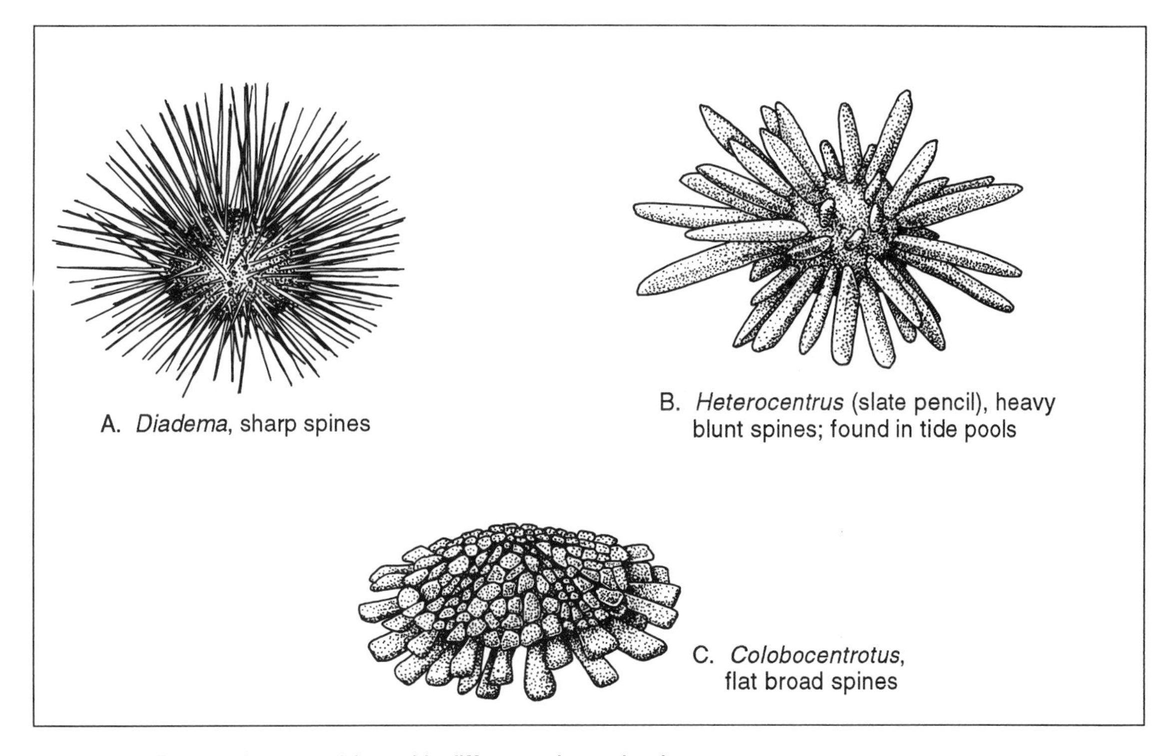

Fig. 8–3. Types of sea urchins with different-shaped spines

skin or epidermis, it is considered an endoskeleton. Most of the plates have tiny pores through which internal organs of respiration protrude into the seawater. The spines attach to the plates on **tubercles,** ball-and-socket joints with muscles attached around the base, supporting the spines and moving them. The teeth are attached to a complex series of up to 35 bones called **ossicles** (L. *ossic* = small bone). All their mouth parts together are called **Aristotle's lantern.**

ACTIVITY 1

Observe details of the skeleton of a sea urchin.

MATERIALS

- dried sea urchin test with spines removed
- pen flashlight
- separated pieces of a sea urchin test
- dried sea urchin test with spines intact
- hand lens (optional)
- dried specimen of Aristotle's lantern
- 8½ x 11-in sheet of cardboard (optional)
- glue (optional)

PROCEDURE

1. Find repeating patterns on the test of a sea urchin.
   a. Use a dried sea urchin test. Identify individual plates, pores, and tubercles.

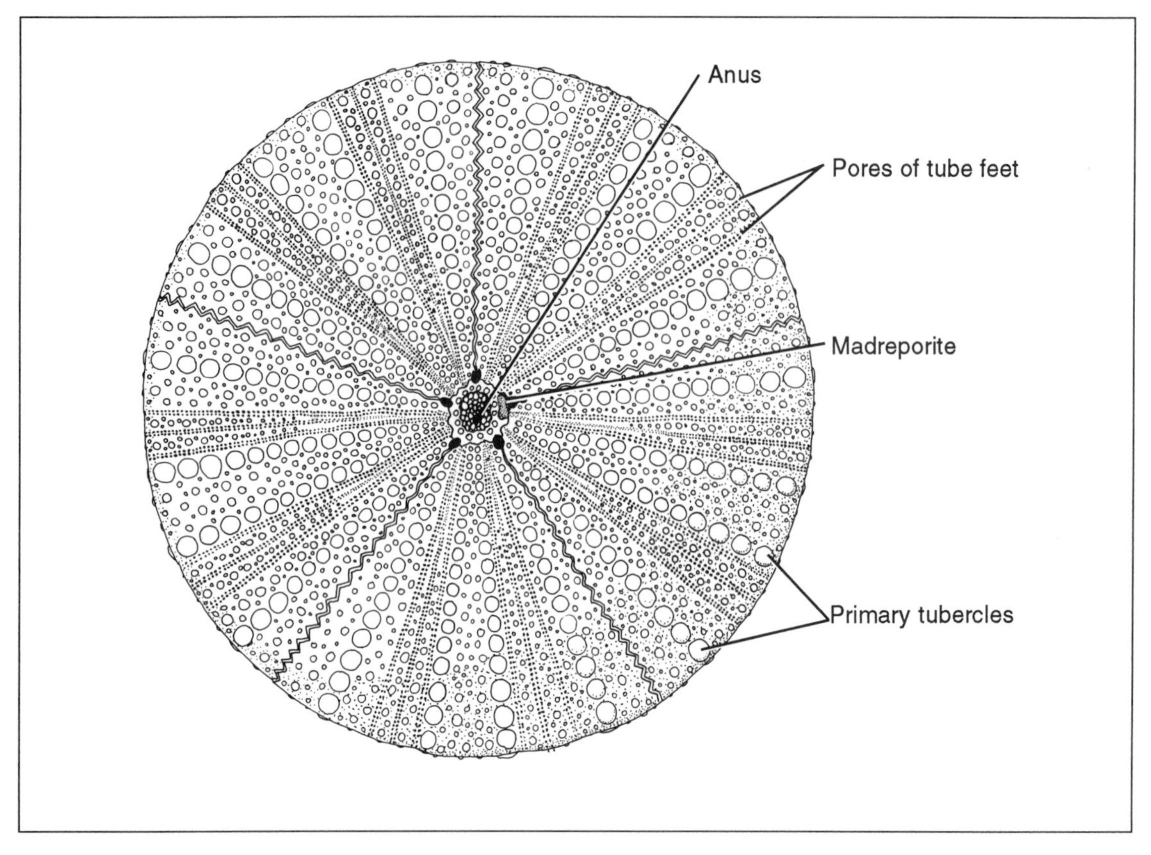

Fig. 8–4. Dorsal view of a sea urchin test (internal skeleton) without the spines

b. Looking at the top, examine the test for repeating patterns of plates, pores, and tubercles. Count the number of these patterns around the test.
c. In a dark corner or a darkened room, shine a small penlight into the test through the large opening to examine the pores.

2. Concentrating on a section of the test, look for details of repeating patterns of plates, pores, and tubercles.
   a. Find the number and shape of individual skeletal plates within the unit. Seeing is often easier if you view the test from the inner surface through the large opening.
   b. Draw the pattern of skeletal plates, tubercles, and pores as accurately as you can.

3. Compare a complete test with separated plates of a test of the same species. Try to fit the plates together to form a single unit.

4. Compare a test without spines and a dried test with spines intact.
   a. See how the spines attach to the test and what patterns the spines make.
   b. On tests with spines attached, look for spines of different lengths. See how they are distributed over the test. Look for variations among the spines.

5. Determine the arrangement of skeletal parts of the Aristotle's lantern.
   a. Using a dried Aristotle's lantern, examine how the teeth are attached to the rest of the skeletal parts.
   b. (Optional) If enough lanterns are available, carefully dismantle one and lay out the pieces in an organized arrangement. Carefully glue the pieces of the lantern on cardboard for display.

6. Repeat Procedures 1–5 with other species of sea urchins if they are available.

QUESTIONS

1. How many repeating units make up a sea urchin test? What is the shape of each unit? What parts and structures appear in each unit? How are the plates arranged within each unit? What is the possible advantage of this number of repeating units?

2. How is the skeleton of a sea urchin like the skeleton of a lobster? How is it different? See Topic 7, Arthropods, for information if necessary.

3. From your observations, tell how the spines attach and move. Make a series of sketches to illustrate your description.

4. What are some advantages of having spines and a rigid test? What are some disadvantages?

5. Where would you expect urchins with long, brittle spines to live? Where would urchins with short, thick spines live? Explain your reasoning.

6. How do the teeth of a sea urchin attach to the Aristotle's lantern bones? How does it compare with the attachment of teeth in your own mouth? From your analysis of the bones and teeth of Aristotle's lantern, explain how this structure operates in scraping food from rocks.

Feeding and Digestion

Most sea urchins are herbivores. They scrape algae from hard substrates with five toothlike structures in the mouth on the lower surface of the body. The teeth are attached to the skeletal structure called Aristotle's lantern, which you studied in Activity 1. Small bits of food move through a long digestive tube to be digested and absorbed. Indigestible material passes out through the anus, opposite the mouth. See (D) in Fig. 8–14.

Water Vascular System

The **water vascular system** is a complex series of canals running throughout the sea urchin's body. See Fig. 8–5. This system is unique to the echinoderms. It is a hydraulic pressure system that aids in movement. The canals are water-filled tubes that open to the outside through a skeletal plate called the **madreporite** (L. *madre* = mother; L. *pori* = small hole) lying on the surface near the anal opening. Water enters and leaves the tubes through this sievelike plate.

A sea urchin moves about with **tube feet,** tiny, delicate projections attached along the side of a water-filled tube called a radial canal. Tube feet extend through the small holes in the skeleton to the outside. These feet are grouped in five regions. Most sea stars, sea urchins, and sea cucumbers have suction cups at the tips of their tube feet. In some sea stars and brittle stars the tube feet are shaped like little paddles.

In an animated cartoon you may have seen someone in suction-cup shoes walking up a wall and across a ceiling. The tube feet of sea urchins work in much the same way. Water enters and leaves the **radial canal** through the madreporite. From the radial canal water enters the tube feet and the **ampullae,** which act like the bulbs of eyedroppers. Valves keep water from flowing back into the radial canal. See (A) in Fig. 8–6.

When a valve closes and the ampulla muscles contract, squeezing the ampulla, water shoots into the tube foot, extending it. See (B) in Fig. 8–6. When the tube foot comes in contact with hard substrate, its center withdraws, forming a cup and producing a vacuum much as a rubber suction cup does. The tube foot clings to the substrate because the water pressure on its outside edge is greater than the pressure inside its suction cup. When the muscles of the ampulla relax, water moves back into the ampulla, flattening the cup and releasing the vacuum. See (C) in Fig. 8–6.

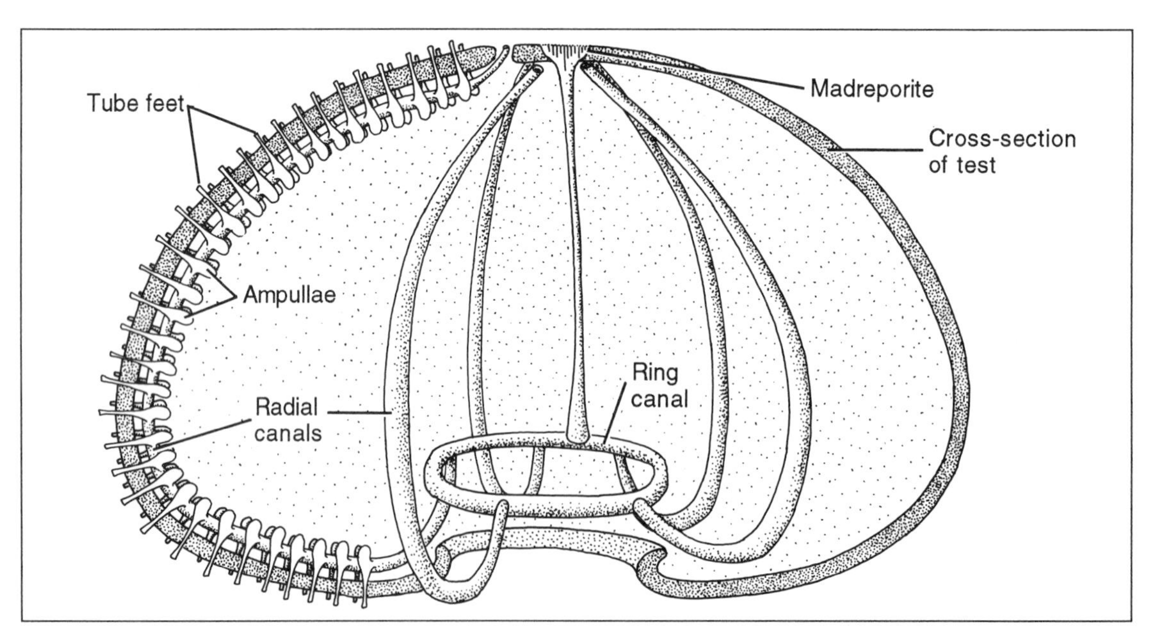

Fig. 8–5. Water vascular system of sea urchin

Protection

Besides spines, some sea urchins and sea stars have small jawlike pinchers attached to stalks at the base of their spines. These pinchers are called pedicellariae (L. *ped* = foot; L. *icellus* = little). A pedicellaria snaps open if something touches its outer surface; it snaps shut if it is touched on its inner surface. Some pedicellariae are toxic, containing a small poison gland. Others have powerful jaws that can crush small organisms.

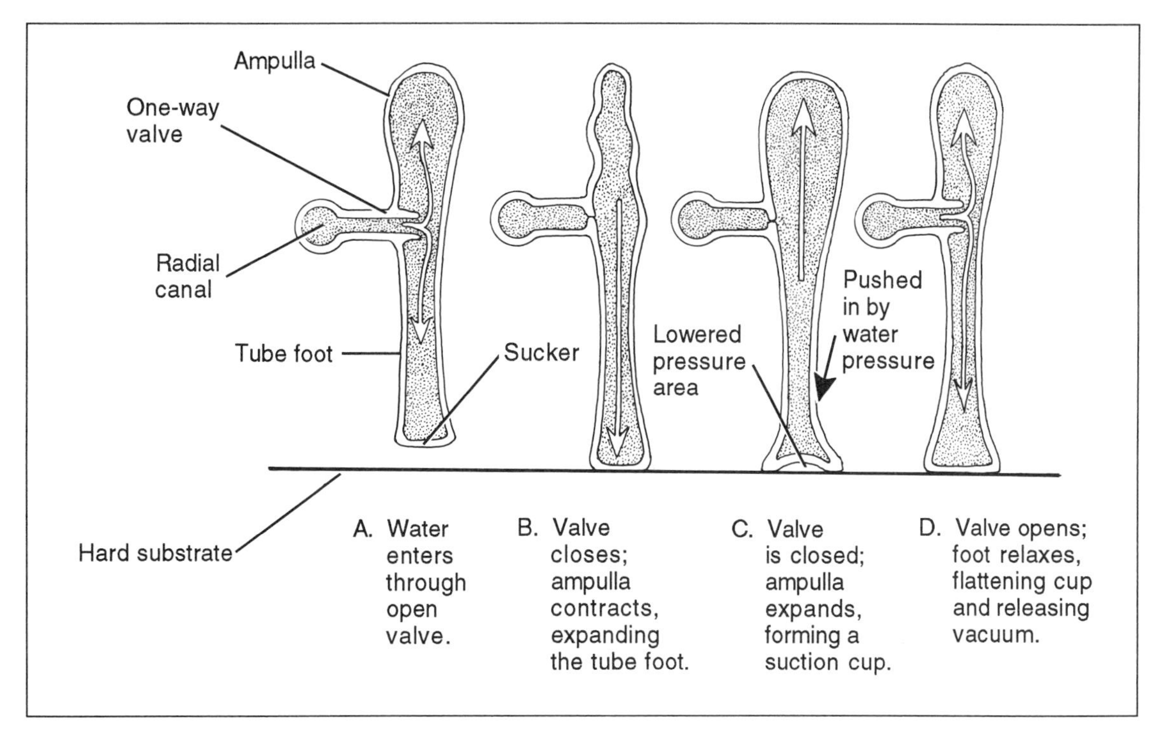

Fig. 8–6. How the valve, tube foot, and ampulla work

ACTIVITY 2 (OPTIONAL)

Observe external structures of a live sea urchin and their functions.

MATERIALS

- live sea urchin
- 20-gal established seawater aquarium
- hand lens
- blunt probe
- copy of Workbook Table 8–1
- cardboard
- assorted debris (sand, algae)
- large culture dish
- 2 blocks of wood
- mirror
- 1-m string or fishing line
- spring scale

PROCEDURE

1. Put a live sea urchin in your observation aquarium and cover it with seawater.
   a. Look for the thin tube feet extending between the spines onto the glass. Watch how they attach to and detach from the surface. Note the distribution of tube feet over the body.
   b. Observe whether the extended length of tube feet varies among parts of the sea urchin.
   c. Compare the position of the tube feet on the living specimen with the position of the holes on the skeleton you studied in Activity 1. Use a hand lens to see fine details.
   d. Look for pedicellariae around the base of the spines. Look for different sizes and structural types of pedicellariae.

2. Perform the following tests on a live sea urchin:
   a. Touch the urchin lightly with a probe on the tube feet, one spine, several spines, pedicellariae, and body surface. After each probing, let the animal relax. Record the urchin's responses in Table 8–1.
   b. Test the response of the urchin to rapid changes of light stimulus. To produce these changes, wave your hand or a sheet of cardboard over the urchin. Record the action of the spines, tube feet, and pedicellariae in Table 8–1.
   c. Turn the urchin upside down and observe how it rights itself. Record in Table 8–1 what the spines and tube feet do.
   d. Put the urchin in the center of the aquarium. Make a current of water around it by moving your hand clockwise through the water. Record in Table 8–1 the movements of the spines and tube feet.
   e. Sprinkle small bits of debris such as sand or bits of algae on the urchin's body. Observe the action of the spines, tube feet, and pedicellariae. Record in Table 8–1.

3. Observe the action of Aristotle's lantern in a living specimen.
   a. Put the urchin in a culture dish of seawater.
   b. Raise the dish by supporting the bottom on two sides with blocks of wood.
   c. Put a mirror between the supports so you can see the underside of the sea urchin.
   d. Put small bits of algae in the container and watch closely what the teeth of Aristotle's lantern do during feeding.
   e. Alternatively, gently hold the sea urchin to the side glass of an observation aquarium until it clings. Observe the action of the teeth.

4. Measure the holding strength of different sea urchins.
   a. Tie two lengths of string together in the center to prepare a bridle to hold the urchin.
   b. Place this bridle about the urchin as shown in Fig. 8–7.

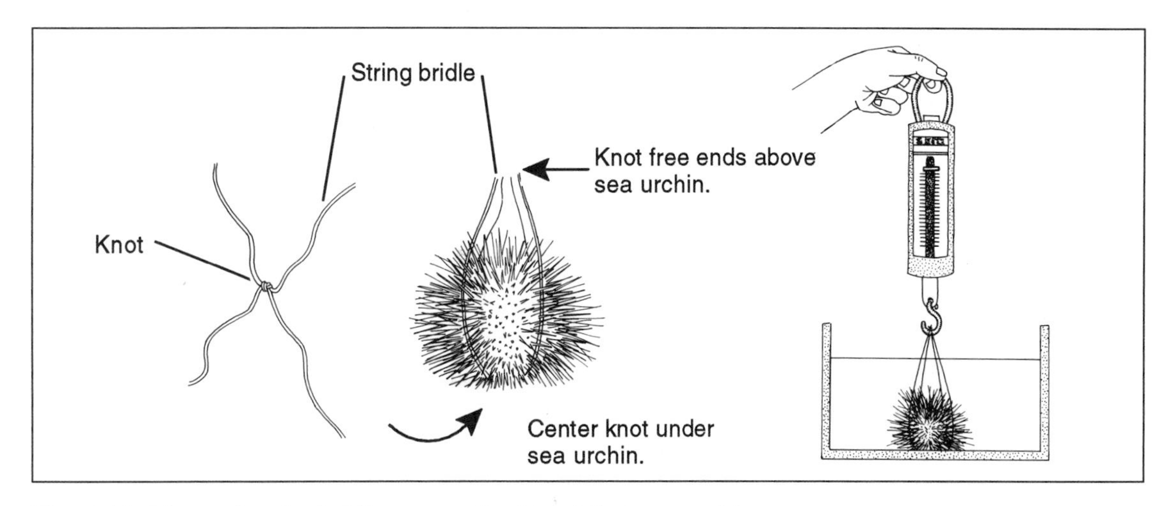

Fig. 8–7. Measuring the holding strength of a bridled sea urchin

Table 8–1. Sea urchin behavior Ⓦ

Type of experiment	Response
Area touched Tube feet Single spine Test Several spines Pedicellaria	
Rapid light changes Spines Tube feet Pedicellaria	
Inverted animal Spines Tube feet	
Water movement Spines Tube feet	
Removing debris Spines Tube feet Pedicellaria	
Holding strength Initial trial After 5 min Average holding strength	

c. Return the bridled urchin to the aquarium and let it attach itself to the bottom glass.
d. Attach a spring scale to the bridle to measure the urchin's holding strength. See Fig. 8–7.
e. Slowly pull on the spring scale until the urchin releases. Record the total holding strength of your urchin in Table 8–1.
f. Put the urchin back on the bottom glass of the aquarium and let it rest for 5 min. Repeat Procedures 5.c. through 5.e. and record the holding strength of the second trial.
g. Calculate the average strength of the urchin. Record your data in Table 8–1.

QUESTIONS

7. How does a suction cup work? Explain in words and drawings.

8. How does a tube foot work? Explain in words and drawings.

9. How does the distribution of tube feet in a live sea urchin compare with the arrangement of holes in the test of a skeleton of a sea urchin of the same species?

10. From your observations of the live sea urchin, describe in detail how the spines attach and move. Make a series of drawings to supplement your description.

11. How are the spines and tube feet used by the sea urchin to move around?

12. How does a sea urchin right itself when upside down? What structures does it use? What forces in its natural environment might turn a sea urchin over?

13. How do sea urchins keep their body surfaces clean and free of particles? What structures do they use? Suggest why being able to keep themselves clean is an advantage to them.

14. From your observations, tell how responsive sea urchins are to changes in light and water movement. What is your evidence?

15. If we had to hang by our hands from a bar, we'd soon tire. We might hang on for 5 to 10 min. Yet most echinoderms hold to objects for long periods. How can they hold on for so long? How is this ability an advantage to these animals in their natural environment?

16. Review your measurements of a sea urchin's holding strength. What other factors should be considered in getting a more precise result?

Sea Stars

Sea stars belong to the class **Asteroidea** (G. *asteroid* = like a star). See Fig. 8–8. Like sea urchins, sea stars inhabit the oceans worldwide, from tide pools and the nearshore to deep-ocean seafloors. Sea stars are predators, crawling over the ocean bottom in search of prey. They feed not only on slow-moving or sedentary mollusks such as snails, clams, oysters, and mussels but also on dead organisms lying on the bottom. One species, the crown of thorns, consumes so much live coral that it has done massive damage to reefs in the Pacific. Sea stars come in a range of sizes, reaching up to 1 m in length, but most are much smaller. Sea stars may be red, blue, or many other colors. One is called the chocolate chip star; its tan body is covered by blunt, dark brown spines, resembling a chocolate chip cookie.

Most sea stars have a central disk with five radial arms; some species have 15 to 40 arms. A few have arms so short that they barely protrude. Their bodies look like pincushions.

Skeleton

The sea star's skeleton, like the sea urchin's, is an endoskeleton consisting of small plates of calcium carbonate embedded in the epidermis. These plates, called **ossicles,** are much smaller than those of sea urchins. The sea star's ossicles are connected by muscles and connective tissue to form a network that lets the arms bend and twist into shapes to fit any contour. Some sea stars have spines extending from the ossicles, making them prickly and defending them from predators.

Water Vascular System

Sea stars have a water vascular system and tube feet much like those of the sea urchins. They project from **ambulacral grooves** (L. *ambul* = walk) along the arms. The tube feet are used mainly for clinging and moving. In some sand-dwelling sea stars the tips are

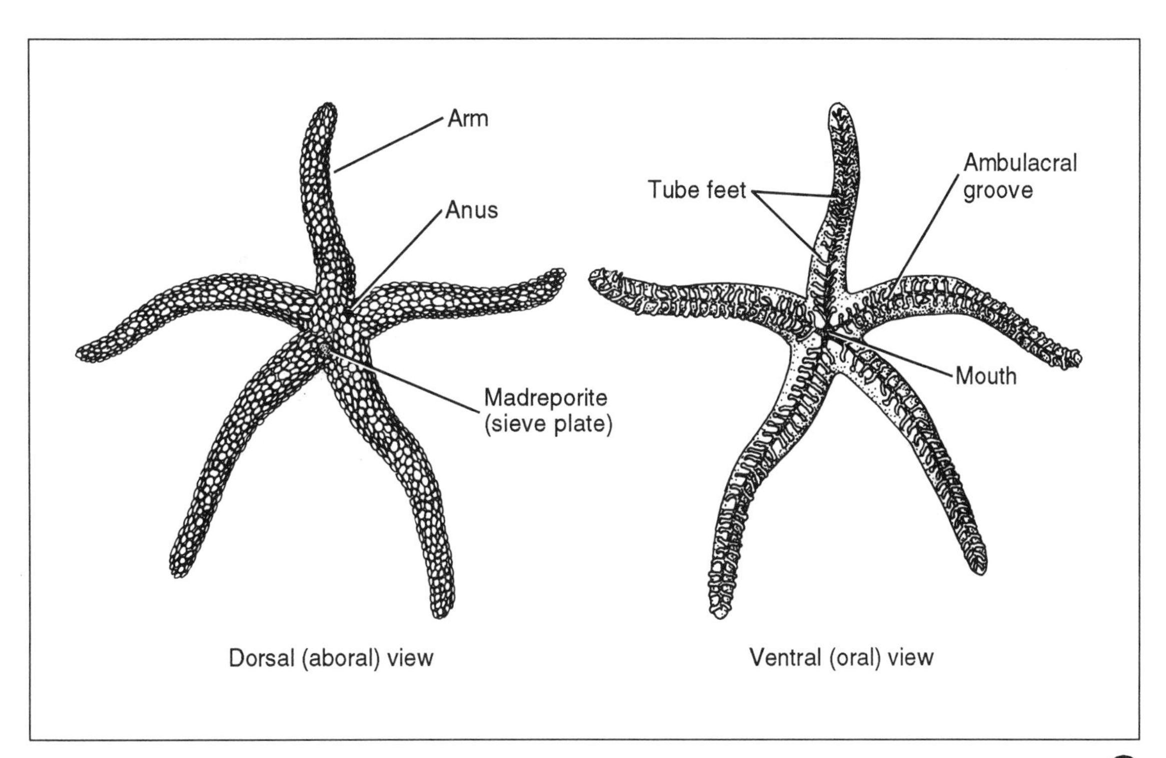

Fig. 8–8. Two views of a sea star

Ⓦ

paddle-shaped, making them efficient for "walking" and burrowing.

Feeding and Digestion

The mouth of a sea star opens into the stomach in the central disc. The anus is on the upper surface. See (A) in Fig. 8–15. Most sea stars are carnivores. Although a sea star has no teeth, it can eat coral polyps and mollusks by pushing its stomach out of the body, spreading it over its prey, and digesting it. To eat a clam, the sea star grasps the bivalve in its arms, attaches its suction cups to both shells, pulls steadily until the shells open slightly, and extends its stomach into the clam. In this way it preys on clams whose shells are open as little as 0.1 mm. After the sea star digests and absorbs the tissues of its prey, it sucks its stomach back into its own body. The arrangement of the digestive tract in a sea star is shown in (A) in Fig. 8–14.

Regeneration

Sea stars have remarkable powers of regeneration. Many species can regenerate a whole arm that breaks off. These regenerated pieces are called comets. See Fig. 8–9.

QUESTIONS

17. Sea stars have no teeth, yet they eat other animals (corals, mollusks). How might they do this?

18. Two powerful adductor muscles hold the shells of a clam together. Humans have trouble opening a live clam, yet a sea star can pull them apart. How might they do this?

19. Clam fisheries found that their clam beds were being eaten by sea stars. So they cut the predatory sea stars into pieces when they found them in the clam beds. But the numbers kept increasing. How was this possible? Using your knowledge of sea star regeneration, suggest alternative methods of reducing the problem of sea star predation on clam beds.

Brittle Stars

Brittle stars are the most abundant of the echinoderms. About 2,000 species inhabit the ocean floor worldwide, from the shoreline to great depths. In some areas, clusters of millions of brittle stars thickly carpet the bottom. They are rarely seen because they are active only at night, hiding under rocks and in crevices during the day.

Protection

Brittle stars have long, flexible arms attached to a small central disc. See Fig. 8–10. These animals got the name *brittle star* because an arm often breaks off if they are captured. The broken arm is left wiggling as the rest of the brittle star scoots away. The missing arm regenerates quickly. Most brittle stars are small with a central disc diameter usually less than 3 cm, but the arms may be up to 10 cm long.

Skeleton

Skeletal ossicles form a series of scaly plates along the arms, and a series of large cylindrical ossicles runs through the center of each arm. These ossicles look somewhat like the row of vertebrae in a fish skeleton. They are connected by muscles that contract, pro-

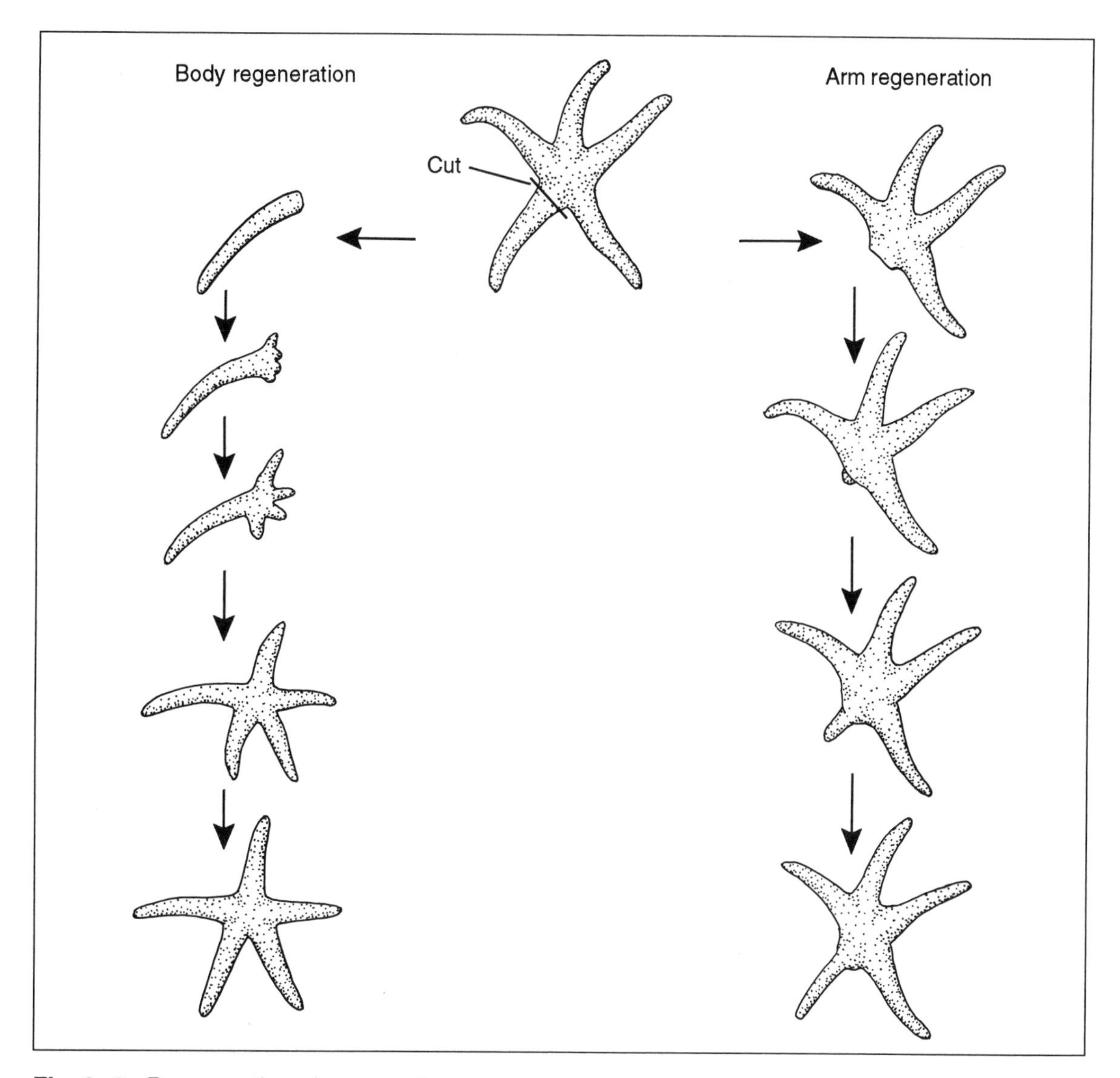

Fig. 8–9. Regeneration of an arm of a sea star

ducing a snakelike action. This characteristic movement gives the class its name, **Ophiuroidea** (G. *ophi* = snake; G. *uroid* = like a tail). It is also the basis for another common name, **serpent star.** Because of this movement, brittle stars appear to be dangerous, but they are harmless to humans. A row of movable spines projecting from the sides of the arms helps the animal move along the bottom. Although the arms appear to be radial, one or two of them usually lead in pulling the animal along while the others trail. See Fig. 8–11.

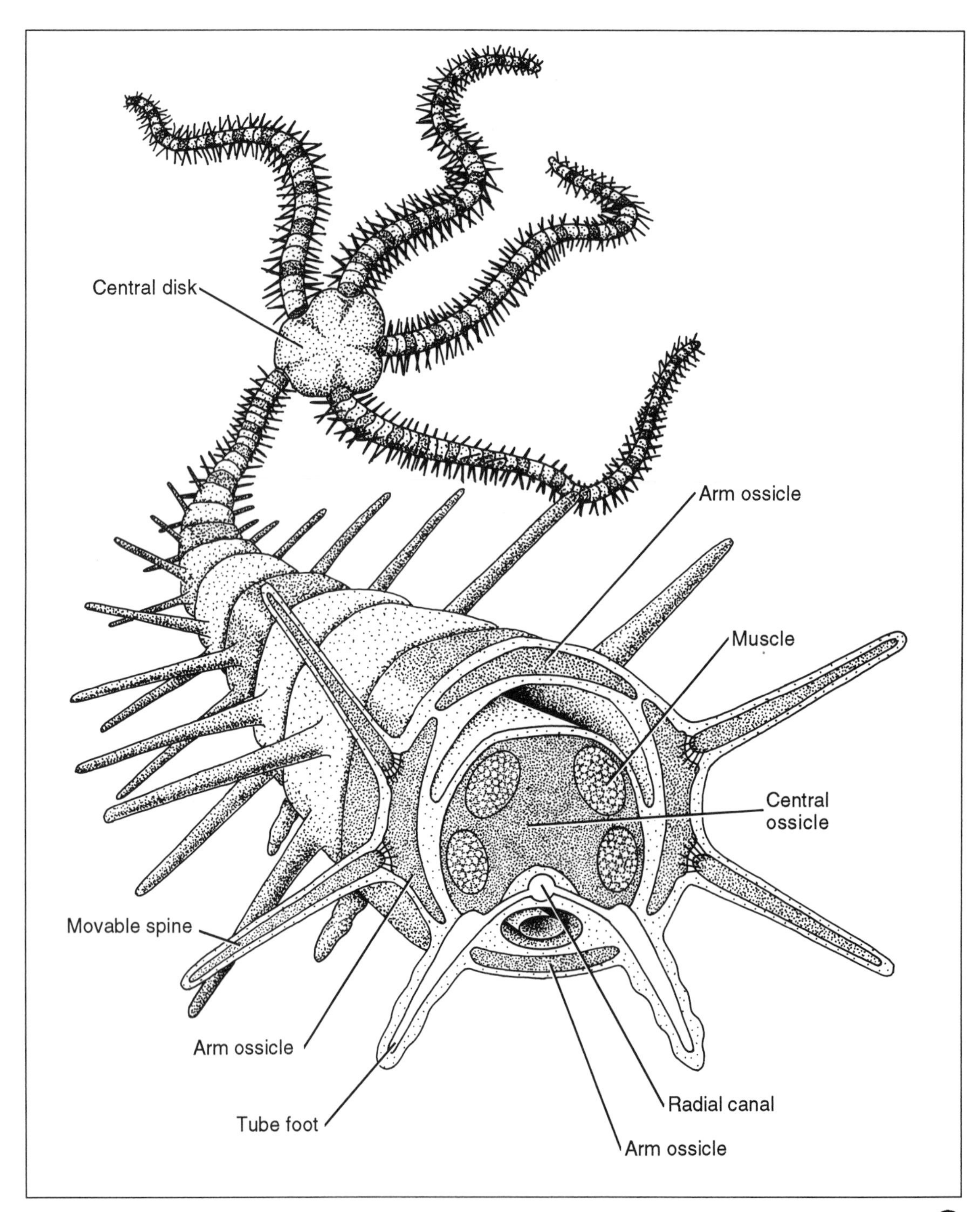

Fig. 8–10. Brittle star showing an enlarged cross-section of one arm

Ⓦ

Feeding and Digestion

These animals feed on detritus—small particles of food—on the bottom. Some brittle stars curve their arms up to collect food particles suspended in the water. The tube feet, shaped like pointed tentacles, are used mainly for collecting food. One tube foot passes particles to another toward the mouth. The food then passes into the stomach, where it is digested. Brittle stars have no anus; they eject undigested material through the mouth.

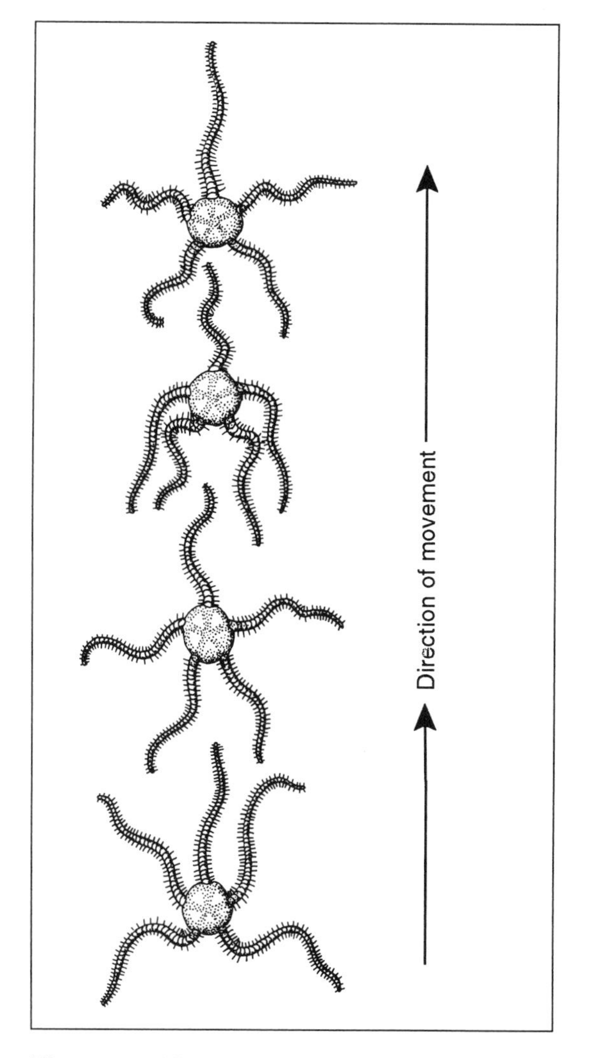

Fig. 8–11. Movement of a brittle star with one arm leading

Sea Cucumbers

Sea cucumbers are pickle-shaped animals with feathery tentacles at one end. They are often mistakenly called worms. Some are like fat pickles a few centimeters long; others are like thin tubes over a meter long. These animals are common residents of reefs and rocky shorelines worldwide. A few species swim constantly in the water, seldom touching the bottom; they are the only members of this phylum to do so. Some Pacific islanders collect sea cucumbers, remove their intestines, and dry the muscular body wall, making a food eaten in many countries, notably China and Japan. Its commercial name is *trepang* (Malay) or *bêche-de-mer* (French). Among other dishes, it is used in soups.

Feeding and Digestion

The digestive system has a mouth at one end, a digestive tube down the center, and an anus at the other end. See (D) in Fig. 8–14. The mouth is ringed with tentacles that are modified tube feet. Some species use their tentacles to take in sediment particles rich in plant and animal matter. See (A) in Fig. 8–12. Other sea cucumbers extend their tentacles to snatch passing food particles (detritus and plankton). See (B) in Fig. 8–12. This behavior makes them look somewhat like sea anemones, and so this class is named **Holothuroidea** (G. *holothuroid*=like a polyp). The digestive tube has a stomach and a long, thin, coiled intestine where food is digested. Indigestible sand

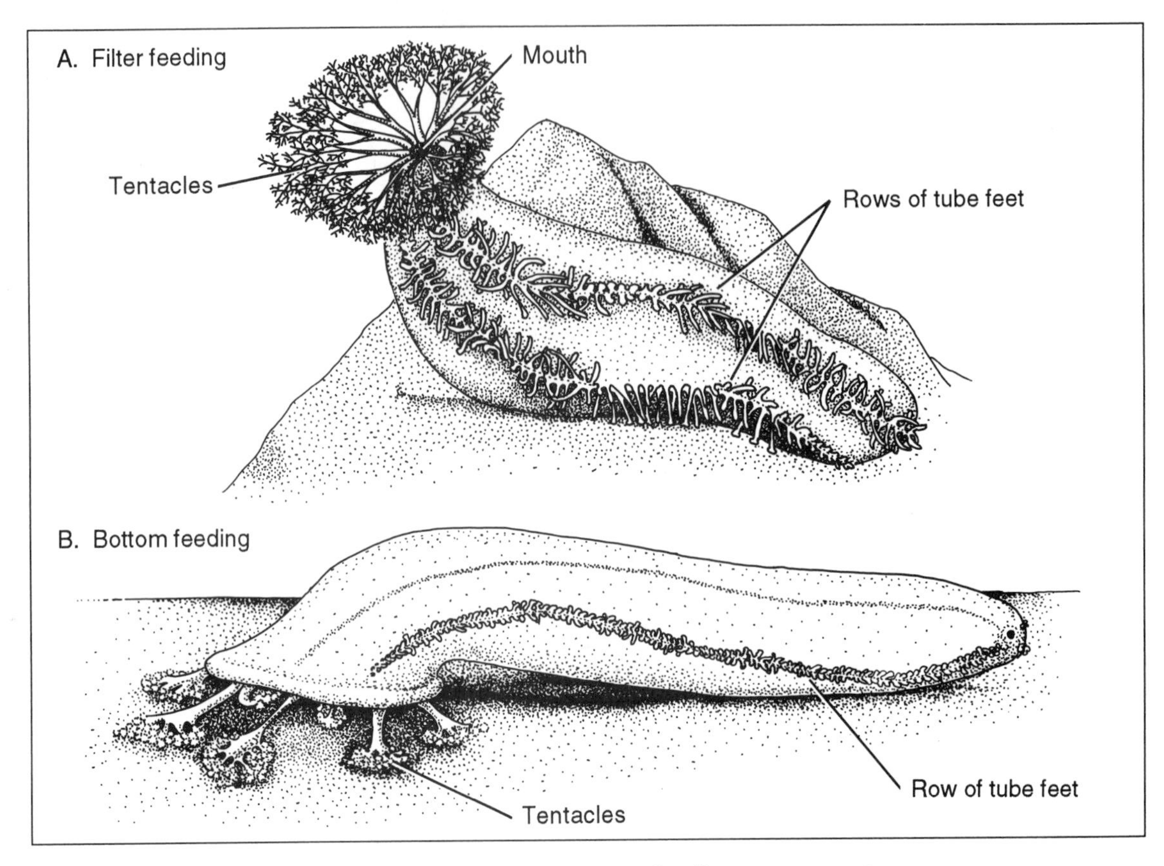

Fig. 8–12. A filter-feeding sea cucumber and a bottom-feeding sea cucumber

and other particles are expelled through the anus. Much the same happens in earthworms, which literally eat their way through soil. See Fig. 8–13.

Skeleton and Muscles

Unlike other groups of echinoderms, sea cucumbers have no large plates or ossicles forming a rigid skeleton. Their skeletal structures are microscopic spicules embedded in the animal's skin. Because the spicules differ by species, they are useful in distinguishing them.

Muscles in the body wall of many sea cucumbers are developed enough to aid in locomotion. When the muscles contract, the body becomes firm and rigid. In some species the muscles are so thin that the internal organs show through the body wall. When these animals are taken from the water, the body wall collapses like thin plastic tubing.

Respiration

Sea cucumbers have an unusual arrangement of their respiratory system. They breathe through an internal structure called a **respira-**

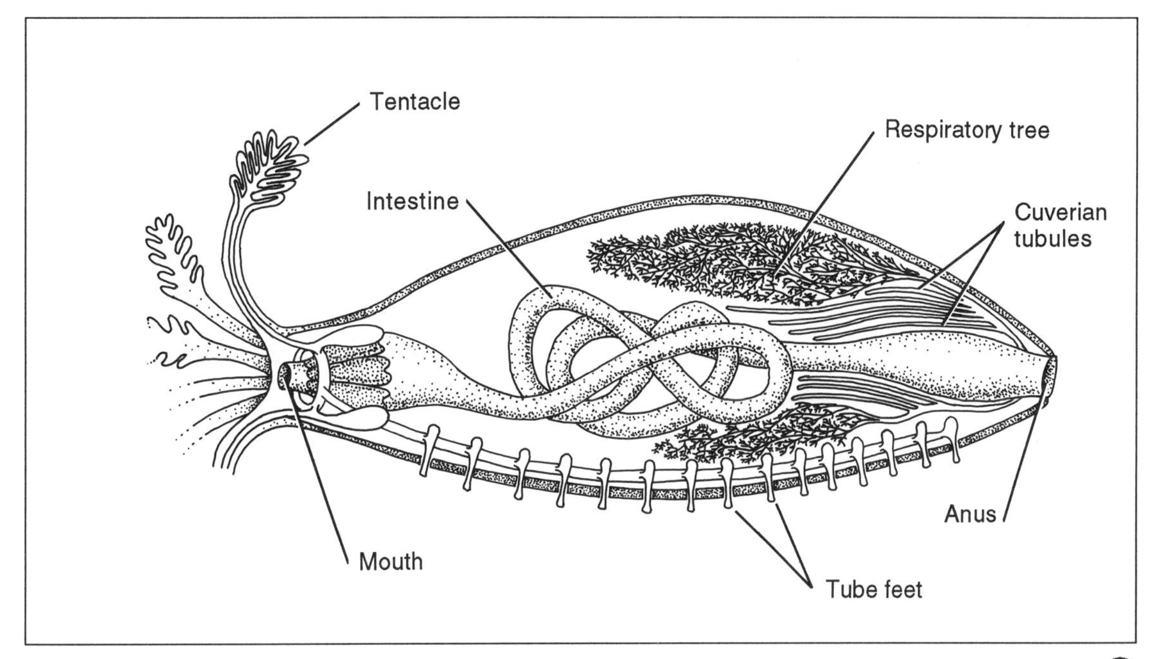

Fig. 8–13. Internal anatomy of a sea cucumber

tory tree, attached to the intestine. See Fig. 8–13. Seawater taken in through the anus fills this branching structure, where body fluids absorb the oxygen. The water is then "exhaled" through the anus.

Because the anus is often open during this respiratory process, other organisms—small crabs and fish among them—sometimes enter and take up residence in the lower digestive tract and respiratory tree. This kind of symbiotic relationship, which benefits the invader with no apparent harm to the host, is called **commensalism.** A few species of sea cucumbers have a set of toothlike projections around the anus to ward off invaders.

Protection

Some tropical sea cucumbers have a bizarre way of protecting themselves. Some branches of their respiratory trees have taken the form of long, slender threads, called **Cuverian tubules.** These tubules contain both a sticky substance and toxic chemicals. When these sea cucumbers are disturbed, they eject sticky threads out the anus, thoroughly entangling any offending organism. The ejected tubules look like strands of limp spaghetti.

Some sea cucumbers can **eviscerate**—forcibly eject their internal organs out the anus. They sometimes perform this unappealing act when they are handled roughly or subjected to warm or stagnant water. Under favorable conditions, the internal organs soon regenerate, and the animal carries on.

ACTIVITY 3

Observe the anatomy and behavior of sea cucumbers.

MATERIALS

- live sea cucumber
- 20-gal established seawater aquarium
- copy of Workbook Table 8–2
- large culture dish
- 2 blocks of wood
- mirror
- algae or detritus
- sea cucumber skin, dried or preserved
- forceps
- dissecting scissors
- microscope slide and coverslip
- liquid household bleach
- compound microscope

PROCEDURE

1. Put a sea cucumber in your observation aquarium and cover it with seawater.
   a. Look for tube feet extending from the body. Find any pattern in the distribution of the tube feet over the body surface.
   b. Observe how the tube feet and the muscles of the body wall are used in locomotion.

2. Test the response of the sea cucumber to stimuli such as touch and water currents; test its photoreception—its response to changes in light.

3. Observe the action of the tentacles when the sea cucumber feeds.
   a. Put a sea cucumber in a large culture dish of seawater.
   b. Support the bottom of the dish on two sides with blocks of wood.
   c. Put a mirror between the supports so you can see the underside of the sea cucumber.
   d. Alternatively, gently hold the sea cucumber to the side glass of the observation aquarium until it clings.
   e. Put small bits of algae or detritus in the container and watch the tentacles during feeding. Note especially whether they sweep particles from the bottom or reach up to filter suspended particles.

4. Determine the rate of respiration of your sea cucumber.
   a. Observe the opening and closing of the anus. Measure the time each opening and closing cycle takes and count the cycles taken per minute (rate of respiration).
   b. For each cycle carefully observe the water movements to see whether the animal is "inhaling" or "exhaling." Record your observations and measurements in Table 8–2.

5. Observe the microscopic spicules in the skin of a sea cucumber.
   a. Take a small piece of skin tissue from a dried or preserved sea cucumber. Or use forceps to lift a tiny piece of skin (a few millimeters across) from your live specimen and snip it off with scissors. (Such a small region will heal quickly.)
   b. Put the piece of skin on a microscope slide. Place a few drops of bleach on

it to dissolve the soft tissue, revealing any skeletal structures.

c. Lay a cover slip over the specimen. Observe it under a compound microscope at low power (100X), then high power (400X).

d. Look for spicules of various shapes and draw each kind that you observe.

6. Record your observations in Table 8–2.

7. Repeat Procedures 1 through 4 with other species of sea cucumbers if available.

QUESTIONS

20. How are tube feet distributed over the body of the sea cucumber you studied? Describe the placement and pattern of rows or groups. How does this distribution compare with the distribution you observed on sea urchins?

21. Which is more important in locomotion of your sea cucumber, tube feet or body movements? Compare your observations with observations by students who studied another species.

22. Describe similarities and differences in locomotion of sea urchins and sea cucumbers.

23. Did your sea cucumber get food by sweeping sand particles from the bottom or by reaching up for suspended food particles? Describe in detail how the tentacles move in getting food.

24. What was the rate of respiration of your sea cucumber? Describe in detail the sequence of movements and direction of water flow in a complete cycle of respiration.

Table 8–2. Observations of anatomy and behavior of sea cucumbers 

Observations of a sea cucumber	Specimen 1	Specimen 2
Tube feet Distribution pattern Action		
Behavioral responses Touch Water movement Changes in light Other		
Tentacles Feeding action		
Respiration Time of inhalation Time of exhalation Rate of respiration		
Spicules	100X 400X	100X 400X

25. How many shapes of spicules did you find in the skin of your sea cucumber? What is the relative abundance of each shape? Compare results with those of students who observed the same species and other species.

Shapes and Symmetry

Most animals that move around have bilateral symmetry. But echinoderms, although they also move, are radially symmetrical, so the terms *anterior, posterior, dorsal,* and *ventral* do not apply. In the echinoderms there are two surfaces. One is the **oral** surface, where the mouth is and the tube feet project. The tube feet are limited to distinct regions called the **ambulacral regions.** The other surface is the **aboral,** which never has projecting external tube feet but sometimes contains the anal opening of the digestive system. All echinoderms are variations on this oral-aboral body plan. See Fig. 8–14.

Sea stars (class Asteroidea) and brittle stars (class Ophiuroidea) have flat bodies with a broad aboral surface facing up and an oral surface facing down. Both groups have arms (usually five) projecting from a central body disc. The ambulacral regions with the projecting tube feet extend along each of the arms. See (A) and (B) in Fig. 8–14.

Like sea stars, the feather stars and sea lilies (class Crinoidea) have arms, but the oral surface faces up, away from the bottom. See (C) in Fig. 8–14. The tube feet extend upward from the oral surface to capture particles of food floating by. Feather stars grasp the substrate with a series of rootlike projections from the aboral surface. Sea lilies have long, stalklike projections from the aboral surface that permanently attach them to the bottom.

Sea urchins (class Echinoidea) have no arms. See (D) in Fig 8–14. The radial body plan is spherical. The oral surface, with ambulacral regions and tube feet, covers most of the sphere. The aboral surface is only a small disc at the top. In most sea urchins, spines also extend from the oral surface, usually between the rows of tube feet.

The radial body plan of sea cucumbers (class Holothuroidea) is tube-shaped, with the aboral surface just a small region at the end opposite the mouth. See (E) in Fig. 8–14. Most of the long body is covered by the oral surface, with tube feet projecting in five rows. Many of the tube feet around the mouth take the form of long tentacles, used for gathering food. The body lies on its side, giving the appearance of bilateral symmetry. The tube feet touching the bottom usually bear suction cups and are used for locomotion. The tube feet on the "upper" part of the body are often simple pointed structures.

ACTIVITY 4

Compare the structures and behaviors of echinoderms.

MATERIALS

- copy of Workbook Table 8–3

PROCEDURE

Fill in Table 8–3 with information from the text and the activities. Wherever possible, focus on similarities and differences of structure, function, and behavior.

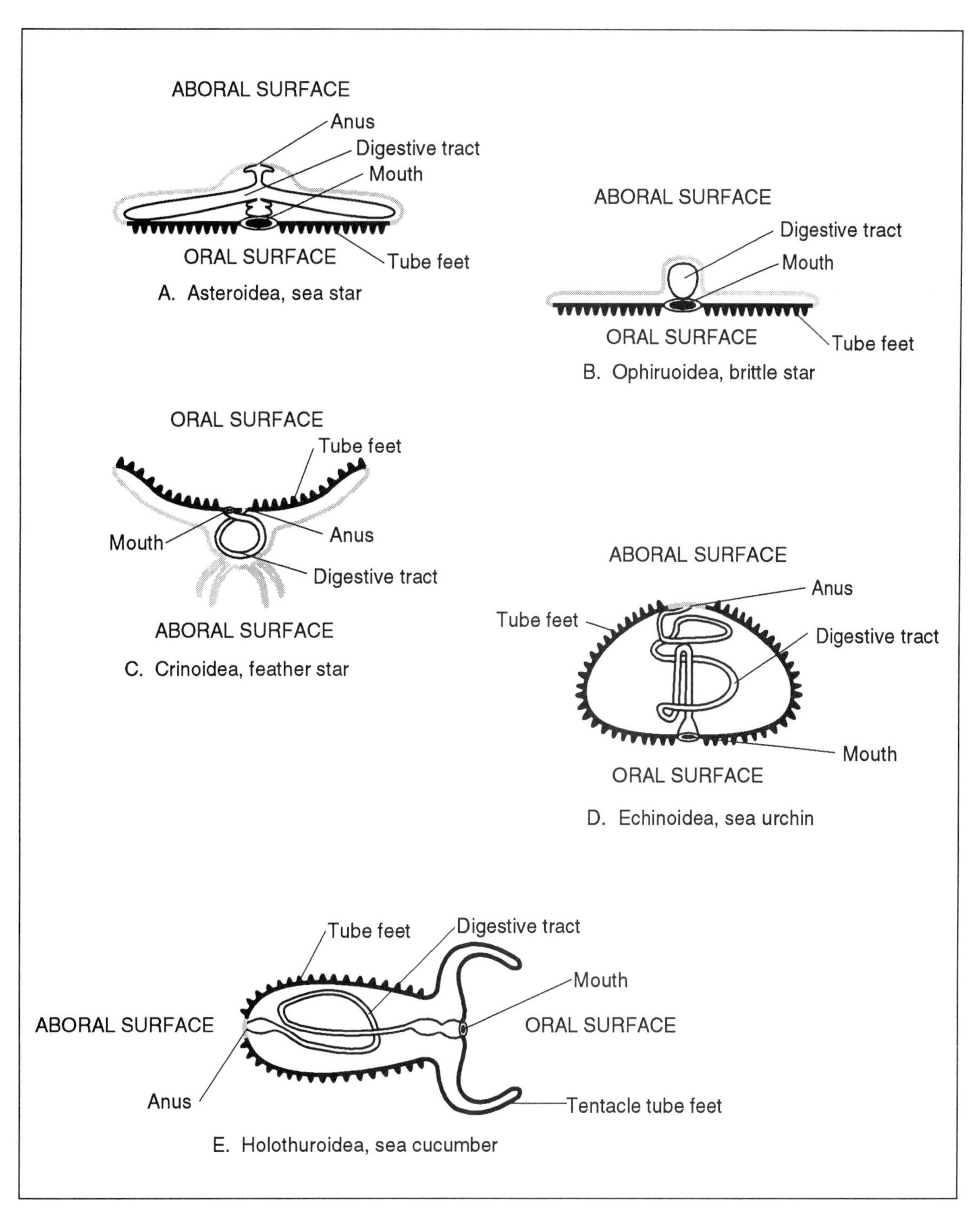

Fig. 8–14. Relations of oral and aboral surfaces among classes of echinoderms

Table 8–3. Comparison of structure, function, and behavior of major groups of echinoderms 

Animal	Method of feeding	Food eaten	Skeletal structure	Type of tube feet	Movement	Protection
Sea urchin			Rigid interlocking plates	Long suction cups covering body		
Sea star	Everts stomach					
Brittle star		Detritus, very small bits				Breaks off arms
Sea cucumber					Muscles in body wall	

QUESTIONS

26. How are tube feet adapted to different uses in the groups of echinoderms?

27. How does the arrangement of skeletal structures differ in sea urchins, sea stars, and brittle stars? How do these differences establish the way these animals move?

28. How do sea urchins, brittle stars, and sea cucumbers protect themselves?

29. Add phylum Echinodermata to Table 1–3, Comparison of animal phyla by features.

FURTHER INVESTIGATIONS

1. Find the holding strengths of urchin species on a given reef, tide pool, or rocky outcropping. Draw an aerial map of the area and mark the location of each species on it. Report on the relation between an urchin's habitat and its ability to prevent being tossed about by waves.

2. Do tube feet regrow? Design experiments or make observations to find the answer.

3. Dissect and study the urchin's water vascular system. Make a model of it for the class.

4. Make and demonstrate a working model of the ball-and-socket structure that attaches a sea urchin's spine to its test.

5. Why might the skeleton of the sea urchin's mouth parts be called Aristotle's lantern?

6. Use a key to identify sea urchins or sea stars for your class collection. If keys are not available, devise them.

7. If you can get a debris-collecting urchin such as a *Tripneustes gratilla* or *Pseudoboletia indiana* for an aquarium observation, notice which objects it transports on its surface. Try objects of different kinds and sizes. What are the possible advantages of debris collecting by some kinds of sea urchins?

8. Collect spicules of sea cucumbers in your region. Mount the spicules on glass slides the same way you mounted sponge spicules in Topic 2.

9. If live sea stars, brittle stars, or feather stars are common in your area, use them for observations and experiments. Repeat some of the activities you did with sea urchins and sea cucumbers, or devise your own. Record your observations and conclusions. Report to your class.

10. Use references to gather information on the damage done by crown-of-thorn sea stars to the Great Barrier Reef of Australia and reefs on other islands in the Pacific Ocean. How do these sea stars do such massive damage to the reefs they live on? What animals prey on these sea stars, limiting their numbers and the destruction they do?

11. Use references to learn about the industry of collecting sea urchins and sea cucumbers (*trepang* or *bêche de mer*) and preparing them for use as food. Report to the class.

12. In 1986 a new class of echinoderms (class Concentricycloidea) was discovered on waterlogged pieces of wood on the bottom of the deep ocean near New Zealand. This was a most unusual discovery, given the centuries of exploration and identification of classes and species of plants and animals. Use references to learn more about this exciting discovery. Report on the discovery and on the anatomy and natural history of these animals.

9. Invertebrate Chordates: Tunicates and Lancelets

Tunicates and lancelets belong to the phylum **Chordata** (G. *chord* = string), which also includes vertebrates, such as fish and humans. The features that make chordates similar to each other but different from other phyla are a notochord, pharyngeal slits, and a hollow nerve cord dorsal to the notochord. At first glance it's hard to imagine that a tunicate and a fish are related, but the lancelets look very much like fish. See Fig. 9–1.

Chordata have the following common features:

1. The **notochord** is a stiff but flexible rod of cells and connective tissue (G. *noto* = back; G. *chord* = string) that gives the phylum its name, Chordata. In some chordates the notochord is a major support structure. In fishes, amphibians, reptiles, birds, and mammals, the notochord

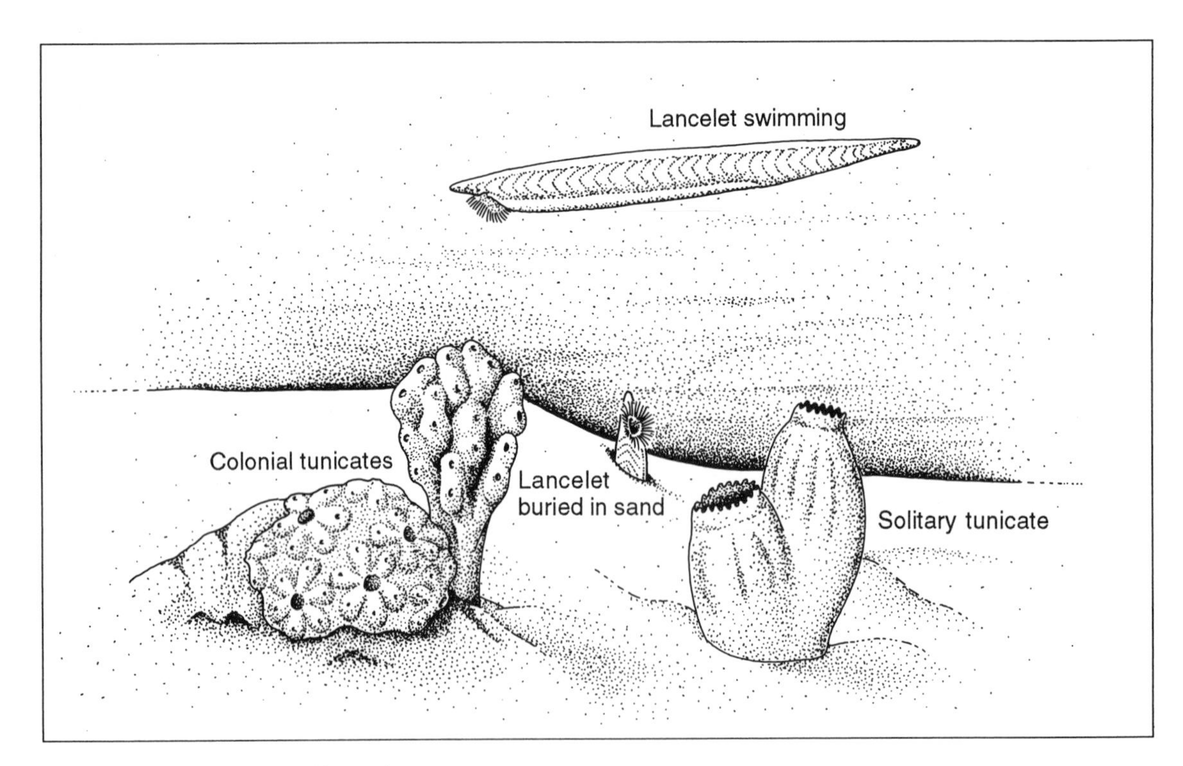

Fig. 9–1. Tunicates and lancelets

is present only in the embryo. Because bony, segmented vertebrae replace it during later stages of development, these animals are assigned to the subphylum **Vertebrata.** Animals such as tunicates and lancelets that have a notochord but never a vertebral column are **invertebrate chordates.**

2. **Pharyngeal slits** are in the **pharynx,** the region of the digestive tract just behind the mouth. In some chordates, such as tunicates, these slits filter food from the water. In other chordates, such as fish, they are respiratory structures. In humans they appear only in the early embryo as a few indentations, not as open slits. They are therefore called **pharyngeal clefts** in a human embryo.

3. The **dorsal hollow nerve tube** lies above the notochord and sends branches of nerve tissue into muscles and other organs and tissues. As the nerve tube grows, its walls thicken, almost eliminating the central hollow space. A dorsal hollow nerve tube is a common feature of all chordates, including humans, in both embryonic and mature stages.

Tunicates

If you spend time on oceanfront beaches or docks, you're likely to find some tunicates attached to rocks or pilings. Tunicates may be solitary (living singly) or colonial (living attached to each other). Some species of solitary tunicates are 7.5 cm (3 in) long, large enough to be picked up. Colonial tunicates are much smaller. Many solitary tunicates look like miniature vases with two necks; some colonial tunicates attached to rocks and pilings resemble fruit gelatin embedded with stars. The point of each star is a tunicate, and the center of the star is the common pore through which they all exhale. Individual tunicates in a colony are very small, but the colony itself can be very large. See Fig. 9–1. Some planktonic kinds of colonial tunicates form huge floating tubes of tunicates, all embedded in the wall of the tube with their mouths pointing outward. These colonies can grow to over 10 m in length.

When solitary tunicates are squeezed, they squirt out jets of water, earning their nickname "sea squirt." Solitary tunicates are usually dull gray, brown, or black. Colonial tunicates can be more colorful, some bright red or yellow, others emerald green.

Some tunicates are eaten by fish and mollusks. But in many species the body contains high concentrations of poisonous substances such as the element vanadium (V) and the compound sulfuric acid (H_2SO_4). In others, spiny calcareous spicules cover the outer surface. The poison and spines protect the animals from predators. Tunicates have no known commercial value.

Tunicate Larval Structure

Tunicates have a notochord only in their larval stage. The notochord supports the whole tail of the larva but just part of its body. This arrangement gives the subphylum its name, **Urochordata** (G. *uro* = tail; G. *chord* = string). See Fig. 9–2.

The larva is a bilaterally symmetrical, free-swimming animal that looks like a tadpole or a lancelet. To swim, it wiggles its tail by contracting muscles on either side of its notochord. An opening on top of the body, called the **oral siphon,** leads to the pharynx. A second hole on top of the body, the **atrial siphon,** leads to the **atrium,** which surrounds the pharynx. The pharynx has pharyngeal slits, also called gill slits. The tunicate cycles water through the oral siphon and down the pharynx, through the pharyngeal slits and into the atrium, then out the atrial siphon.

The ventral surface of the pharynx has a long row of cells that form the **endostyle.** These cells have tiny attached hairs, called cilia, that constantly sway back and forth, sweeping food particles toward the stomach opening. The endostyle also secretes mucus, which traps small particles of detritus and plankton.

In some species of tunicates, the larval stage does not last long and the atrial and oral openings do not develop fully. These larvae do not eat until they are attached to a substrate. Only then do their siphons open.

The larva swims feebly as a planktonic organism for just a few hours or days, then attaches headfirst to the substrate with a set of adhesive projections. See Fig. 9–3. As it slowly grows into an adult, its body changes drastically. It loses its tail, its notochord, and most of its nerve chord. Its two siphons and its pharynx, pharyngeal slits, endostyle, and atrium change size and shift position.

Tunicate Adult Structure

The adult tunicate's outer wall is thick and leathery in many species; in some it is thin, clear, and jellylike. This layer, called a **tunic,** gives the group its common name. See Fig. 9–4.

An adult tunicate gets oxygen and food by taking water through its oral siphon into its pharynx—a sac with slitlike holes that looks like gauze under a microscope. The inside of

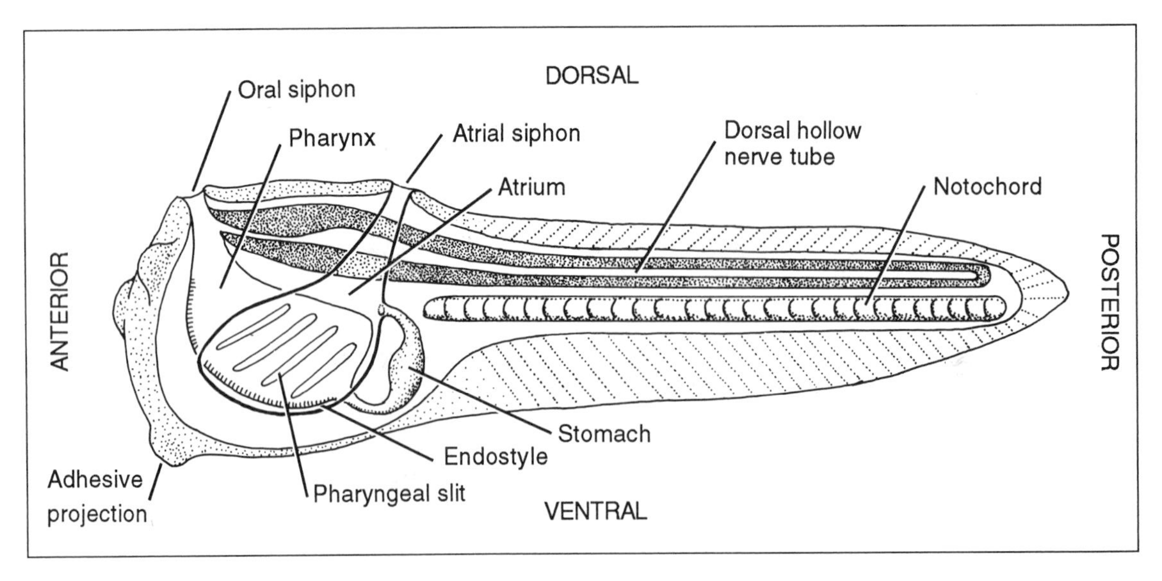

Fig. 9–2. Tunicate larva
Source: Modified from Pearse and Buchsbaum 1987, 743

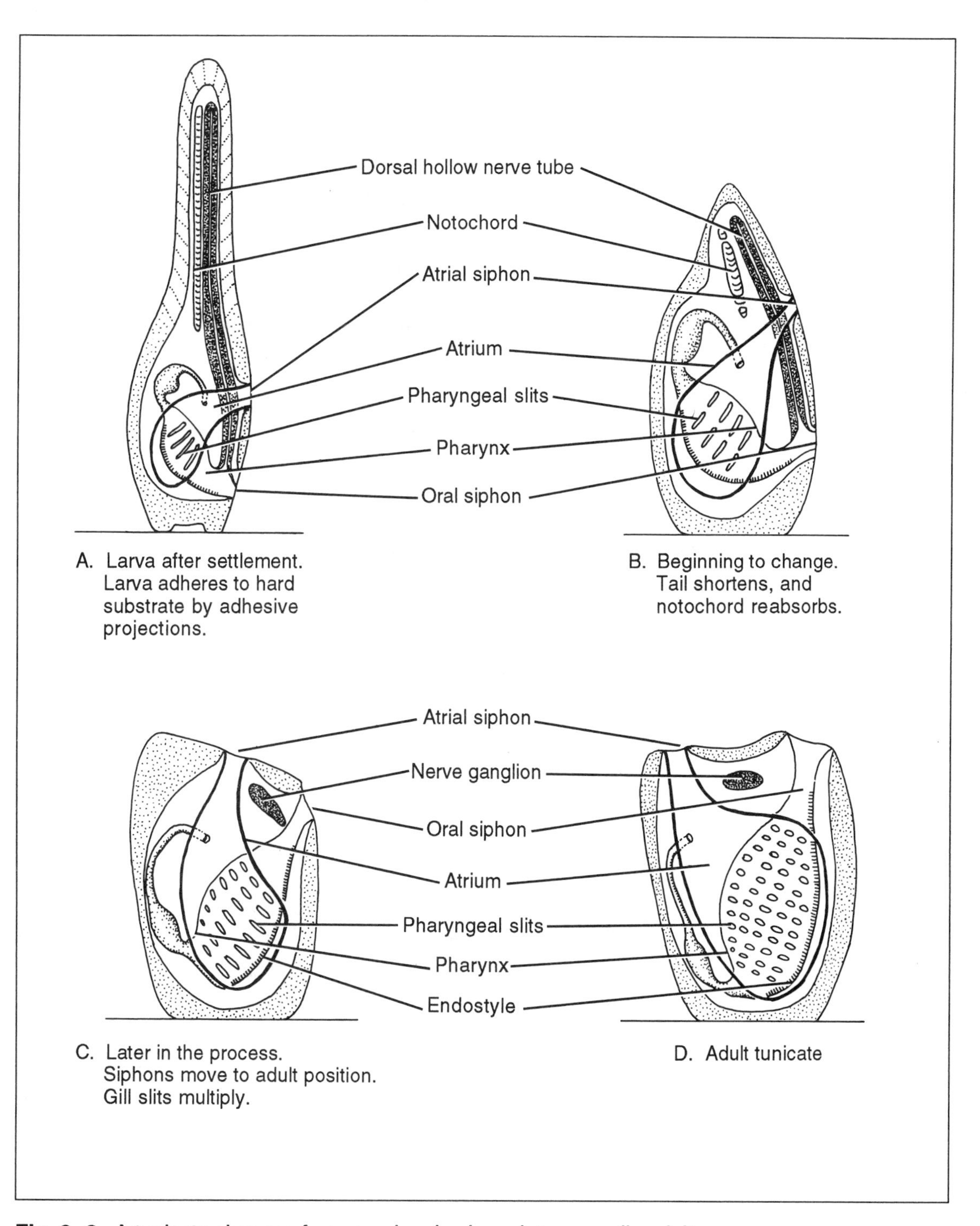

Fig. 9–3. A tunicate changes from a swimming larva into a sessile adult.

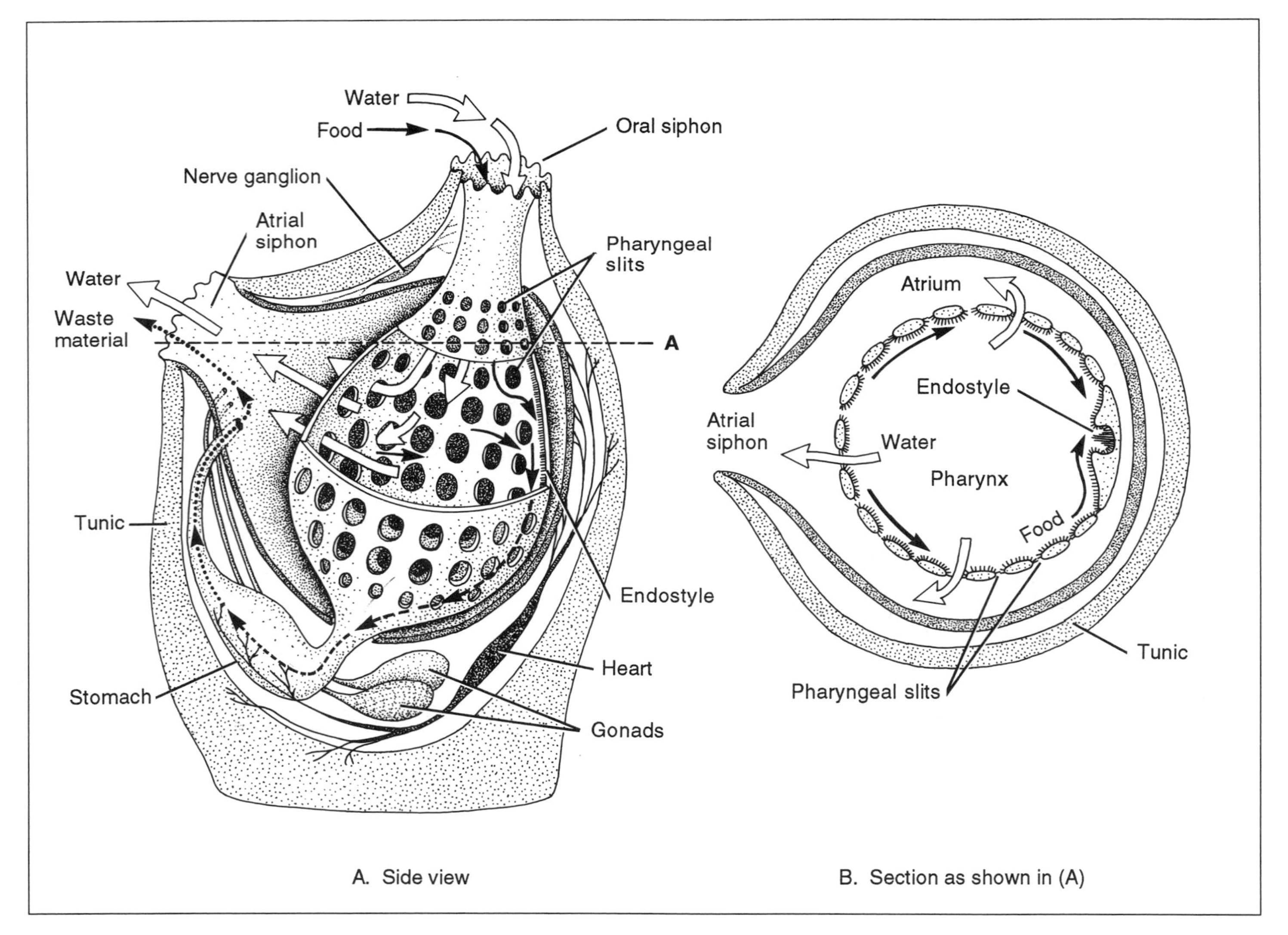

Fig. 9–4. Internal organs of a solitary adult tunicate
Source: Modified from Pearse and Buchsbaum 1987, 739

Ⓦ

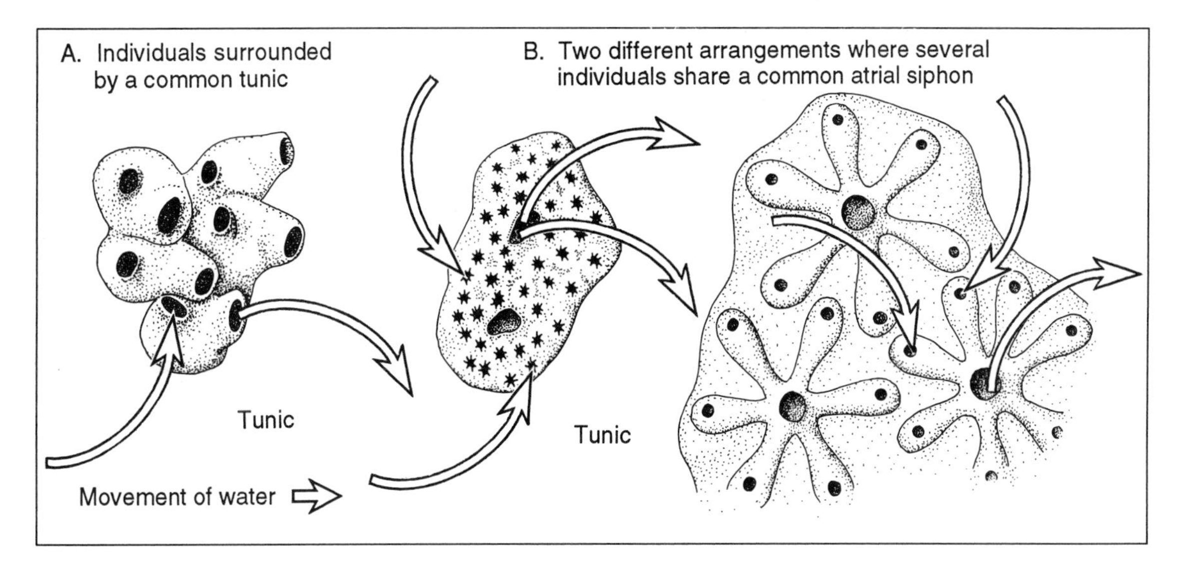

Fig. 9–5. Attachment of individuals in a colonial tunicate

the pharynx has a coating of mucus, secreted by the endostyle. As water flows into the pharynx, the pharyngeal slits take up oxygen and filter food particles in the form of plankton and detritus, which stick to the mucous coating. After filtering, the water flows into the atrium and out the atrial siphon. In this way, some species of tunicates filter more than 100 L of water in a single day.

The food particles trapped in the mucous layer then move along the network of slits into the digestive tract. After digestion, wastes leave via the anus into the atrium. At regular intervals the tunic contracts, squirting water out through the atrial siphon and clearing the atrium of water and particles of feces. It's no wonder that tunicates are often called "sea squirts."

Tunicates have a circulation system with a heart and a network of blood vessels. When the heart contracts, it pumps blood through the blood vessels and cavities that distribute nutrients throughout the body. The tunicate's heart interests biologists because it reverses the direction of flow every few minutes for a reason they do not understand. (Recall that in fish the blood flows through the vessels in one direction because of the action of valves in the heart.)

In the adult tunicate, the dorsal hollow nerve tube of the larva becomes reduced to a cluster of nerve cells, called a ganglion, located between the siphons. See Fig. 9–4. Nerve branches control the movement of the siphons and the movement of the material on the pharyngeal slits toward the digestive tract.

Colonial tunicates form clusters in a number of patterns. In one pattern a single tunic surrounds several individuals. See Fig. 9–5. In another pattern the individuals form a circle and share one atrial siphon.

ACTIVITY 1

Compare the structure and function of larval and adult tunicates.

MATERIALS

- copies of Workbook Fig. 9–4 and Table 9–1
- red and blue pencils

PROCEDURE

1. Use information in the text to complete Table 9–1.
   a. Describe each tunicate structure listed, and tell whether it appears in the larva and the adult.
   b. On your copy of Fig. 9–4, draw red arrows to show the pathway of food and blue arrows to show the pathway of water.
   c. Using information from the text, Table 9–1, and Fig. 9–4, write a paragraph describing the processes of capturing food, digesting it, and eliminating wastes.

QUESTIONS

1. What is the pathway of food and water through an adult solitary tunicate?

2. How is the swimming planktonic larva stage important in a tunicate's life? What can a larva do that an adult cannot? What happens if the larva settles in a spot unsuitable for it?

Table 9–1. Important tunicate structures Ⓦ

Structure	Description and function	Present in larva?	Present in adult?
Notochord			
Dorsal hollow nerve tube			
Pharyngeal slits			
Endostyle			
Oral siphon			
Atrium			
Atrial siphon			
Tunic			
Mucous secretion			
Pharynx			
Digestive tract			
Anus			

3. How do the structure and function of a tunicate's heart differ from those of a fish? Refer as needed to Unit 1, Topic 7, Internal Anatomy.

4. What is the function of the tunic? Use an unabridged dictionary for information on the word *tunic* with reference to clothing. Compare the uses of this word.

Lancelets

Lancelets are small sliver- or arrow-shaped animals rarely longer than 5 cm. Although they can swim, they live mostly on or in sandy and muddy bottoms of warm, shallow ocean waters. See Fig. 9–1. Their outer body surface is so nearly transparent that an observer can clearly see their internal organs. Lancelets feed on diatoms (minute algae) and tiny suspended particles of decaying food matter. During the day they hide in the sand or mud, exposing just their mouths for feeding. At night they may wiggle out and swim about. Lancelets are important as a human food source in southeastern China, where they are collected and sold in large quantities.

Structure

Lancelets have the chordate features in the both the larva and the adult stages. In the adult the notochord runs the full length of the body almost to the tip of the front end. See Fig. 9–6. For this reason scientists assign lancelets to the subphylum **Cephalochordata** (G. *cephalo* = head; G. *chord* = string). Muscles are arranged in V-shaped segments, much as they are in fish, along the entire body on either side of the notochord. When the muscles contract, they pull the notochord from side to side, producing a wiggly swimming motion.

The food-filtering apparatus of lancelets works much as it does in tunicates, but it is arranged differently. See Fig. 9–6. The mouth has two sets of tentacles that trap and capture large food particles. The mouth opens into a large **pharynx** that has slits along both sides. A ventral **endostyle** secretes mucous material that coats the inside of the pharynx. Water with small suspended food particles of plankton and detritus moves through the mouth opening into the pharynx and filters through the slits. The filtered water passes into the atrium surrounding the pharynx and out the atrial siphon on the ventral side of the body. Food and mucous material move into the digestive tract, where the small filtered particles are digested and absorbed. The indigestible remains pass out of the body through the anus behind the atrial opening on the ventral side.

The lancelet's circulatory system has the same basic plan as a fish's, but instead of a heart a lancelet has a large blood vessel in the pharynx ventral to the endostyle. This vessel has muscular walls that pulsate to move the blood. The blood flows through a series of vessels in the pharyngeal arches up to a dorsal blood vessel and then to the other organs of the body.

The nervous system has some similarities to a fish's but also some differences. Following the chordate body plan, the dorsal hollow nerve cord runs the length of the body above the notochord. But there is no anterior enlargement of the nerve tube that could be called a brain. The nerve tube divides into segmental branches that control the contraction of the segmental muscles.

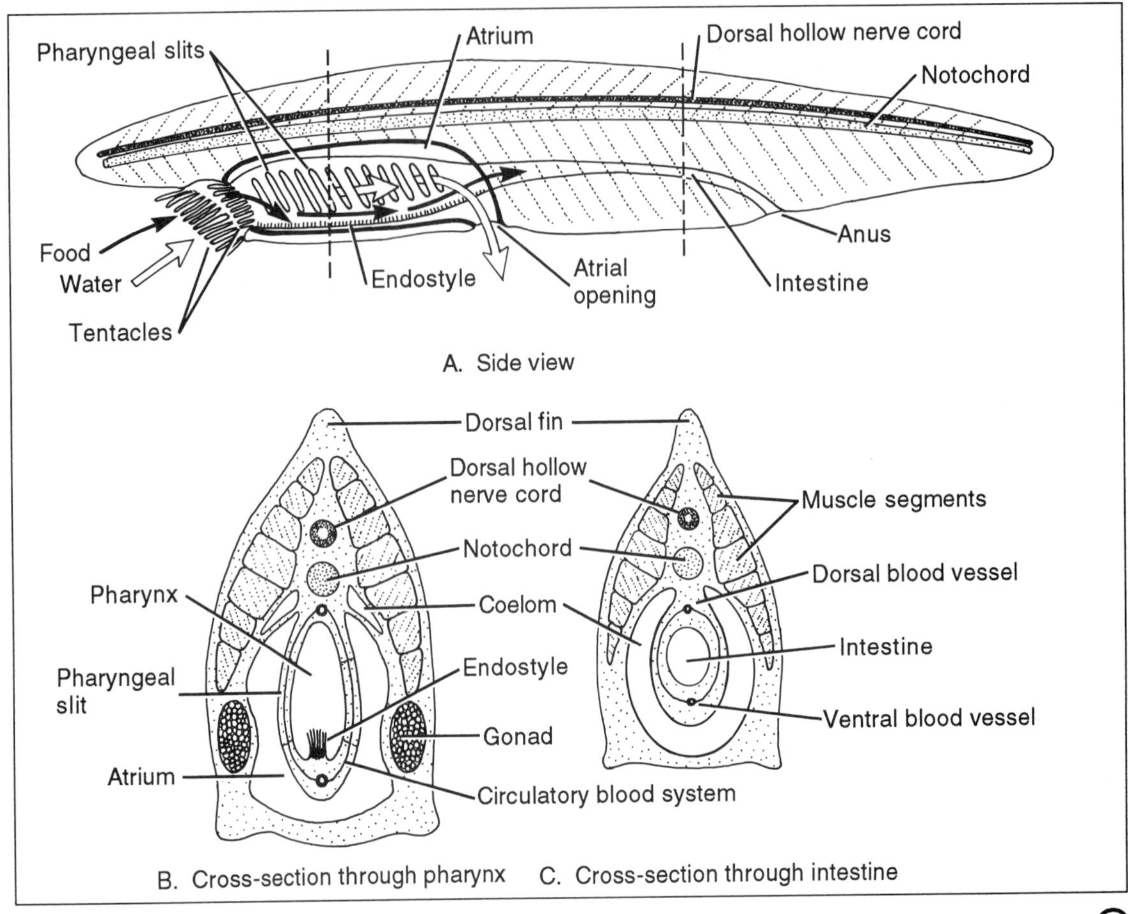

Fig. 9–6. Internal organs of a lancelet

Ⓦ

ACTIVITY 2

Observe the structure of a tunicate and a lancelet.

Study the behavior of a tunicate (optional).

MATERIALS

- solitary tunicate
- lancelet
- small culture dish
- eyedropper
- copy of Workbook Table 9–2
- dissecting microscope
- dissecting scissors or scalpel
- Petri dish
- copy of Workbook Fig. 9–6
- red and blue pencils
- live tunicate (optional)
- large culture dish (optional)
- seawater (optional)
- probe (optional)
- toothpicks (optional)
- carmine particles (optional)

PROCEDURE

1. Study the external structure of a tunicate.
   a. Rinse your tunicate thoroughly but carefully to remove the preservative solution.
   b. Put the tunicate in a culture dish filled with water. As you work, keep the tissues moist by adding water with an eyedropper.
   c. Count the large external openings in the tunicate. Record in Table 9–2.
   d. Put the specimen under the dissecting microscope and look at its external covering. Note its color. Feel the surface with your finger to detect whether it is smooth or rough. Record your observations in Table 9–2.

2. Examine the inside of a tunicate.
   a. With scissors, cut the outer covering or tunic lengthwise from the oral siphon toward the base.
   b. Cover the specimen with water. The water supports and suspends the delicate internal organs and makes them easier to see.
   c. Observe the tunicate with the naked eye and then under a dissecting microscope. Identify as many internal structures and organs as you can.
   d. Draw the internal structure in your notebook.

3. Study the structures of a lancelet.
   a. Rinse the lancelet thoroughly to remove the preservative solution
   b. Put the lancelet in a Petri dish containing water.
   c. Using Fig. 9–6 as a guide, identify the external structures.
   d. Identify the internal structures. The internal organs can be seen through the external body wall, which is thin and usually transparent.
   e. On your copy of Fig. 9–6, draw red lines to show the pathway of food and blue lines to show the pathway of water. Compare the lines on this drawing with the ones you made on Fig. 9–4.

4. (Optional). Observe the behavior and external features of a live tunicate.
   a. Put a live tunicate in a culture dish filled with seawater. Let the specimen remain undisturbed until the siphons open and the water is pumping through the openings.
   b. Observe the color of your specimen. Record in Table 9–2.
   c. Gently touch the surface of your tunicate. In Table 9–2 describe the texture of the tunic— that is, how it feels to the touch.
   d. Use a blunt probe to touch the tunicate on various regions of the body. Observe the response to mechanical stimuli. Record your observations in Table 9–2.

5. (Optional). Observe the path of water circulating through a live tunicate.
   a. Using a toothpick, drop carmine particles at a large opening and watch where they go.
   b. Watch for currents. Record your observations in Table 9–2.

Table 9–2. Observations of tunicates

Observation	Preserved	Living
Number of openings		
Color		
Texture of tunic		
Response to touch		
Path of water circulation		

QUESTIONS

5. What is the function of the pharyngeal slits in a tunicate?

6. What do tunicates filter out of seawater? What happens to the filtered material?

7. (Optional) From your observation of carmine particles, describe the patterns of water circulation through tunicates. Where did the carmine particles go? Compare your observations with the water circulation pathway you marked in blue on Fig. 9–4.

8. From your observations and the reading, describe how tunicates respire.

9. (Optional) Why are tunicates called "sea squirts"? Which of your observations support the use of this name? What is the function of the squirting action?

10. How is a sponge like a tunicate in body structure and function? How does a sponge differ from a tunicate? Refer as needed to Topic 3, Sponges.

11. How is a tunicate like a lancelet in structure and function? How is it different?

12. How is a lancelet like a fish? How is it different?

13. What is the pathway of food and water through a lancelet? See the markings you made on Figs. 9–4 and 9–6 for information. What are the similarities and differences in a lancelet and a tunicate?

14. What are the similarities and differences between the various subphyla of chordates? Using information obtained from your reading and from the activity, fill in Table 9–3.

15. Can the word *invertebrate* be an acceptable term in scientific nomenclature? Give reasons to support your answer.

16. Fill in the features of the phylum Chordata in your copy of Table 1–3, Comparison of animal phyla by features.

Table 9–3. Comparison of structures in groups of chordates 

Subphylum	Urochordata	Cephalochordata	Vertebrata
Organism			Fish
Notochord			Embryo only
Dorsal nerve tube			Adult
Pharyngeal slits			Adult (gills)
Vertebral column			Yes

FURTHER INVESTIGATIONS

1. If you have colonial tunicates in your area,
   a. study their structure and behavior and compare them with those of the specimen you studied in this topic. For each species, locate the pharyngeal slits and other structures and draw them. Share your findings with the class.
   b. study the contents of the gut of several species of tunicates. Compare the gut contents of species of tunicates from different areas.

2. If your teacher can get a live lancelet from a biological supply company or from your local marine environment, study its structure and behavior and compare it with the structure and behavior of a tunicate. Use the descriptions and figures in the text to guide you.

3. At what stage(s) in the development of the human embryo is the notochord prominent? Use references to learn about human embryonic development.

4. There are two small classes of planktonic tunicates, one class consisting of solitary tunicates that retain their larval tail into adulthood, and the second class consisting of both solitary and colonial drifting tunicates. Investigate these two classes and report to the class on how their body shape and lifestyle differ from those of the more common sessile tunicates. Do any animals prey on these tunicates?

UNIT 3
PLANTS

The odor of decomposing flesh wafts over a beach as waves churn up the bodies of fish suffocated in a tomato-soup-red broth of trillions of blooming microscopic plants. Above the low-tide line, mats of brown algae coat the cliff faces, making homes for intricate communities of animals and cushioning them against the crashing waves of storms. In nearshore waters, a school of anchovies glides among the trunks of a great kelp forest, then scatters and darts into hiding as a barracuda dashes at the dispersing silvery throng. Although aquatic plants can kill animals, they also supply them with food, oxygen, and shelter.

In the geologist's calendar of the earth's history are records of a time when the waters held no animals. Locked in the rocks for over two billion years are fossils only of algae. In that beginning time these aquatic plants started the slow process of releasing oxygen from its bondage in carbon dioxide and creating oxygen-rich environments. Only then did animals appear, consuming oxygen and plants for energy and growth and producing carbon dioxide and nutrient waste for plants to grow anew. We will explore how animals and plants depend on each other as we investigate the builders of the chemicals necessary for life in the living ocean, the plants.

Francis M. Pottenger III

1. Seaweeds: An Underused Resource

Seaweeds are large marine algae of the sorts that you may have seen washed up on a beach or floating in shallow nearshore waters. Even if you have never seen live seaweed, you probably eat or use seaweed products more often than you know. They are used as food for humans and animals, as fertilizer or compost for agriculture, as a source of medicine, and as an ingredient in many industrial products.

In this activity we will prepare and taste foods that use seaweeds. Most seaweeds can be eaten raw, cooked, or preserved. Some fresh seaweeds have a soft texture; others are crisp. Boiling softens them and takes out any bitter taste. Dried seaweeds may be eaten dry or presoaked in water to rehydrate them.

How seaweeds are prepared depends largely on cultural or personal preference and on the flavors and textures of the seaweeds. Some seaweed recipes taste best immediately after they are prepared. Others taste better one to several days later. As you begin cooking and tasting seaweeds, think of them as sea vegetables.

Fig. 1–1. Seaweeds are used in many recipes.

ACTIVITY 1

Prepare and taste foods made with seaweeds.

MATERIALS

- cleaning supplies
- copy of Workbook Table 1–1
- fresh *Gracilaria*
- fresh *Codium*
- other fresh, edible seaweeds, as available
- sheets of dried *nori*
- sticks of agar-agar (also called *kanten*)
- other ingredients for a recipe in Table 1–1 or other recipe of your choice
- 1-qt cooking pot
- hot plate
- slotted spoon
- pot holder
- measuring spoons and cups
- kitchen knife
- paper towels
- disposable plates and forks or chopsticks
- 3 x 5-in index cards

PROCEDURE

1. Working with a team, decide on the recipes to use. See Table 1–1. Note that
   a. recipes 1 to 4 use fresh seaweeds,
   b. recipes 5 and 6 use dried seaweeds, and
   c. recipes 7 and 8 use agar-agar *(kanten)* to make gelatin dishes.

2. Read the recipe carefully and plan how to prepare it.
   a. Plan how to obtain the ingredients. Some ingredients, like cooked rice, should be prepared ahead of time.
   b. If you are collecting seaweeds from a shoreline, review the safety and conservation notes in Table 1–2.
   c. Arrange to have a clean kitchen or sanitary area available. Keep your hands clean. Thoroughly clean all cooking utensils.

3. If you are preparing fresh seaweed dishes (recipes 1 to 4 in Table 1–1), here are some general directions to follow:
   a. Rinse the seaweed thoroughly with tap water. It may be chopped into smaller pieces, depending on your recipe.
   b. If you are using *Codium* (recipe 3), omit steps 3.c. and 3.d.
   c. Fill a quart-size (about 1,000 mL) cooking pot with ⅓ cup (about 300 mL) of tap water. Bring the water to a boil.
   d. Put the seaweed in the boiling water. The amount of cooking time to soften the seaweed is up to you.
   e. Use a slotted spoon to remove the seaweed. Drain it on paper towels. Test as you would spaghetti. (Some people prefer crispy, uncooked seaweed.)
   f. Taste the prepared foods.

4. After preparing your assigned recipe and tasting the results, you may wish to modify it. Write your modified recipes on index cards.

5. (Optional) Begin a class seaweed recipe booklet. Include recipes from this activity.

Table 1–1. Seaweed recipes

T = tablespoon; t = teaspoon; c = cup

Fresh Seaweeds

1. *Kim Chee Ogo* (Korean Style)

1/4 lb *Gracilaria* (prepared *ogo*)
1/2 c soy sauce
1/4 c vinegar
grated ginger to taste
grated chili pepper to taste
chopped garlic to taste

Clean *Gracilaria* and boil just long enough to soften it. Drain. Mix the seasonings and add to the *Gracilaria*. (This may be bottled and kept in the refrigerator.)

2. Seaweed *Tsukudani* (use on hot rice dishes)

1/4 lb *Gracilaria*
2 T brown sugar
2 T rice vinegar (or use another mild vinegar)
1/2 c soy sauce
1/4 t MSG (monosodium glutamate)

Clean *Gracilaria*. Bring sugar, soy sauce, and vinegar to a full boil in a pot. Put cleaned algae into the pot with the sauce. Cook to a "mush." (Be careful that it doesn't burn; stir often.) Sesame seeds and chili pepper may be added to taste.

3. Codium Salad

1/4 lb *Codium*
1/2 c rice vinegar
1/2 t sugar
1/4 c diced tomato

Clean *Codium* using only cold water. Do not boil. Add sauce to cleaned *Codium* immediately before serving. *Codium* toughens rapidly in the sauce. Better still, try using the sauce as a dip.

4. Kailua *Ogo* (spicy)

1/4 lb *Gracilaria*
1/2 c vinegar
1 t sugar
1 t diced chives or green onions
1/4 c diced tomato
hot sauce to taste

Follow the directions for *Kim Chee Ogo*.

Dried Seaweeds

Look for seaweed food products in your grocery store. You will find recipes on their packages. Here are two to start with.

5. Hand–Rolled Sushi

Sheets of *nori* cut in half lengthwise
2 c cooked rice, cooled to room temperature
1 T rice vinegar
1 medium carrot, peeled and cut into 3- to 4-in pieces
1 medium cucumber, peeled and cut into 3- to 4-in pieces
1/2 c soy sauce

Slice the carrot and cucumber pieces into narrow strips. Add rice vinegar to cooked rice, stirring thoroughly. Take a sheet of *nori* in the palm of your hand and spoon a heaping teaspoon of rice onto its center and add carrots and cucumbers. Wrap *nori* around rice and vegetables to make a roll. Dip sushi roll in soy sauce, or try the sauce in Recipe 3.

6. Laver Soup

1 c rehydrated *nori*
2 c water
one 10 1/2-oz can beef consommé
juice of 1/2 lemon (or less, to taste)

Tear dried *nori* into pieces. Simmer in water until soft. Bring the water to a boil, then add the consommé and lemon juice. Heat just to boiling. Add a twist of lemon peel in each serving bowl. Serve with crackers or toast.

Table 1–1 *continued.* Seaweed recipes

Agar-agar *(kanten)*

7. Agar Gelatin

1 stick of agar-agar
3 c water
1 c sugar
1 t lemon extract
1 drop yellow food coloring

Soak a stick of agar-agar for 30 min in the water, then boil the agar-agar and water until the stick melts. Add sugar and continue cooking for 10 to 15 more min. Add lemon extract and food coloring, then remove from heat. Pour into a flat pan and refrigerate until the agar-agar thickens and becomes firm.

Note: You can stir in chopped fruits (except fresh pineapple) and nuts after the agar-agar has thickened to the consistency of egg whites.

8. Chicken loaf

1/2 oz agar-agar
2 c chicken meat, chopped
2 c chicken broth, heated
1/2 c minced olives
1/4 c sweet pickles, chopped
2 stalks green onion, chopped
1 t mustard
1 t salt (or less, as desired)
pepper to taste

Add agar-agar to boiling broth. Lower heat and stir until agar is dissolved (a few minutes). Add chicken and remaining ingredients. Place in a clean loaf pan. Refrigerate until firm. Makes 6–8 servings.

Table 1–2. Safety and conservation notes for picking fresh seaweeds

1. **Health notes**
   Collect seaweeds only from areas unpolluted by sewage or other contaminants. (Or buy edible seaweeds from reputable food stores.)

   Pick out and remove attached organisms and any other entangled material. Wash the plants thoroughly in clean tap water.

2. **Ocean safety tips**
   Some seaweeds grow attached to rocks that are exposed to wave action. The rocks may be slippery. The best time to collect seaweed is when the tide goes out. Before collecting, check a tide chart and determine when the tide will come back in and you must leave the area. Observe the wave action before venturing out to collect. Wear protective shoes and gloves. Remain alert to wave action, and never turn your back to the waves.

3. **Conservation common sense**
   a. Learn and obey laws governing the collection of seaweeds and other marine specimens. Laws vary widely by area and season.
   b. The dark red-to-black lumps on some seaweeds are parts of the reproductive structures. Do not collect them. Leave them alone to reproduce.
   c. Collect by picking (or cutting) off only the top portion of the seaweed. Leave the bottom portion (the rootlike holdfast) attached to the rocks to allow the seaweed to regrow.
   d. Collect only as much as you plan to use.

QUESTIONS

1. Why is an edible marine plant called a seaweed and not a sea vegetable? Why are seaweeds not popular as a human food in many parts of the United States?

2. How does cooking affect the colors of seaweeds? What might cause these changes?

3. Describe the flavors and textures of each seaweed you sampled.
   a. What other foods do their tastes remind you of? How would you describe their flavors?
   b. What other vegetables have textures like fresh seaweeds?

4. Which recipe was the most popular with your class? Why? How does food preference or taste affect the popularity of a dish?

ACTIVITY 2

Compare the nutrient value of seaweeds and other foods.

MATERIALS

- graph paper

PROCEDURE

1. Select three foods from Table 1–3. Include a seaweed, a starchy food (bread, rice, or noodles), and the fish.

Table 1–3. Nutritional content of seaweeds and other foods

Type of food material	Percentage per 100 grams					
	% Water	% Protein	% Fat	% Carbohydrate	% Ash & fiber	Calories (kcal) per 100g
Raw (wet) seaweeds						
Gracilaria (ogo)	83.5	1.8	0.2	11.5	3.0	48
Codium	92.9	1.0	1.8	1.8	4.0	11
Dried seaweeds						
Porphyra (nori)	11.7	22.2	1.1	44.3	19.7	235
Gelidium (agar)	8.7	6.2	0.3	80.9	4.6	306
Grain products						
Wheat bread, enriched	31.6	8.8	1.2	57.3	1.5	282
Rice (cooked)	78.5	1.0	0.0	20.3	0.1	88
Noodles (cooked)	75.2	2.7	2.1	19.4	0.7	108
Fish						
Mullet (fresh)	74.1	20.7	3.9	0.0	3.0	124

2. Make graphs to compare the nutrient value of seaweed and other foods.
   a. Decide how to graph the information from Table 1–3 to best compare the percentage of protein, fat, and carbohydrates in 100 g of each of these foods. Label your graphs.
   b. Examine and interpret the information in your graphs.

3. Share your graphs with others in the class. Be ready to explain how you set up and interpreted your graphs.

4. Compare the graphs produced in the class. Decide what information each graph shows. Suggest ways to improve the graphs.

QUESTIONS

5. Of the foods listed in Table 1–3, which is
   a. the highest in percentage of protein?
   b. the lowest in percentage of fat?
   c. the most balanced in carbohydrate, fat, and protein? How did you decide what is balanced?
   d. the most caloric (highest in calories)?
   e. the highest in percentage of ash and fiber?

6. Is water a food? Explain your answer.

7. Why are dried seaweeds higher in nutrient value than raw seaweeds?

8. Which of the graphs was best for comparing nutrient values of seaweeds and other foods? Support your answer.

9. How much fresh seaweed do you think it takes to produce 100 g (about ¼ c) of dried seaweed? Imagine that seaweed is like lettuce. Estimate how much lettuce would have to be put into a dehydrator (a device for drying food) to yield ¼ c of dried lettuce.

10. If seaweed (or lettuce) were the only food available for you to eat, how much would you have to eat to get 2,000 Calories each day? (A Calorie, also called kcal, is 1,000 calories)

11. Would a diet consisting of only seaweeds be healthy over a long period? Give reasons to support your answer.

12. From the foods listed in Table 1–3, what combination of seaweed, grain, and fish would yield a 600-Calorie meal with the highest carbohydrate and protein and the lowest fat content?

Uses of Seaweeds as Food

Although many seaweeds can be eaten, some are tastier than others. Taste, of course, is a matter of preference. Many edible seaweeds are high in fiber—carbohydrates that are not digestible. These seaweeds are like celery or lettuce.

About 3 ounces of dried seaweed has more than the minimum daily requirements of Vitamins A, B–1, and B–2 and half the requirement of Vitamin C as defined by the U.S. Department of Agriculture. Seaweeds also contain other essential vitamins and minerals. An important mineral supplied by seaweed is iodine, needed by our bodies to produce a hormone that regulates cell function.

From ancient times, people who lived near the ocean have been picking and eating seaweeds. Four commonly used seaweeds are *nori, ogo,* dulse, and Irish moss.

Nori is popular in oriental cooking. Sheets of dried *nori* wrapped around vinegared rice and garnishes make a popular Japanese dish called *sushi*. Dried seaweed is also used in soup and meat dishes to add flavor and color. West coast American Indians and Eskimos used this seaweed as a source of salts and trace elements in their diets.

Nori is usually made from dried *Porphyra* species (also called red laver). A single flattened blade with ruffled margins, *Porphyra* is red when young and grayish-purple when older. See Fig. 1–2. It can grow to 15 cm in length and width. *Porphyra* is commonly found in shallow, temperate coastal waters, where it is cultivated on poles and lines set out along sheltered shores. The *nori* industry is the largest seaweed-harvesting industry in the world.

Fig. 1–2. *Nori*

Another popular type of seaweed is called by its Japanese name, ***ogo*.** This seaweed is ***Gracilaria*,** a red alga that is easy to collect because it grows in crisp clumps in very shallow water, often along the margins of fringing coral reef flats. After storms it can be picked in large quantities among the beach-drift on shore. See Fig. 1–3.

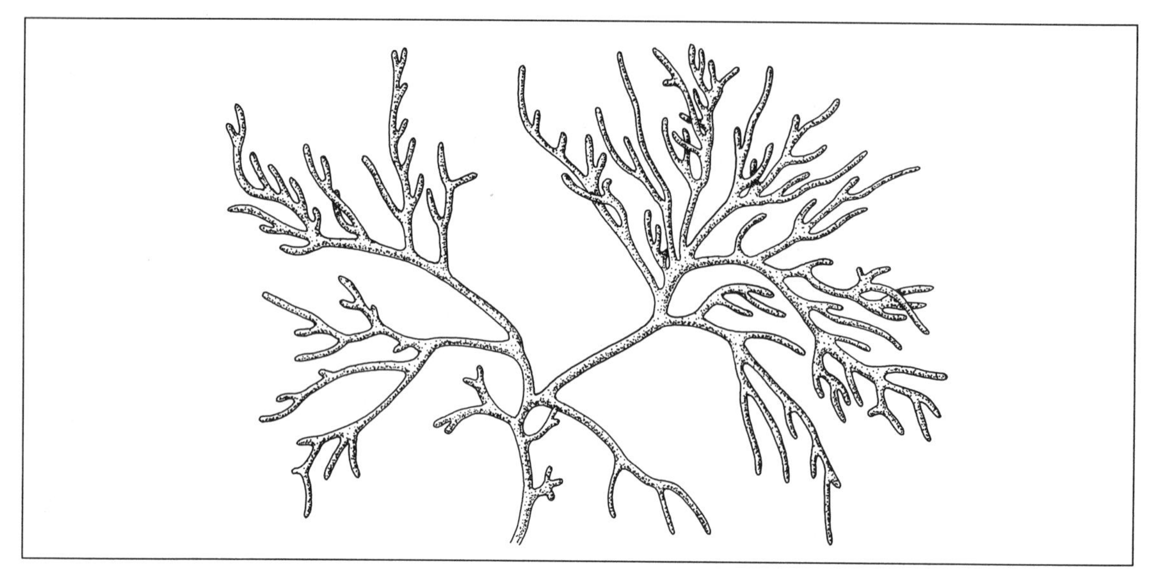

Fig. 1–3. *Gracilaria (ogo)*

Ogo must be washed well with cold water and picked clean of encrusting coral, shrimps, and other organisms before being eaten. The Japanese use more *ogo* than all other ethnic groups put together. It is also popular in Hawaii, where it grows abundantly. *Ogo* is eaten raw or after cooking for a short time. Combined with raw fish and soy sauce, it makes a dish called *poke. Ogo* is also served mixed with other cooked vegetables or added to stews. Fresh *ogo* dishes are sold in the fish or vegetable sections of many grocery stores in Hawaii.

Dulse, known throughout Europe as **red kale,** is the red seaweed *Palmaria palmata.* In Ireland it is eaten with potatoes. It is also used in Maine, along the eastern coast of Canada, and along the Mediterranean in stews and other dishes or served as a relish. Sometimes it is chewed raw, like gum. Dulse adds color to foods and thickens sauces and gravies. See Fig. 1–4.

Rhodymenia sp., another kind of dulse, is found in tidepools and on rocks at the low-tide line along the northern Atlantic and Pacific coasts of the United States. Its thin, rubbery blades 2 to 8 cm tall and 1 to 2 cm wide grow from a short stipe. Its blades are flat and without distinctive markings. Their shapes vary from ribbonlike to oval.

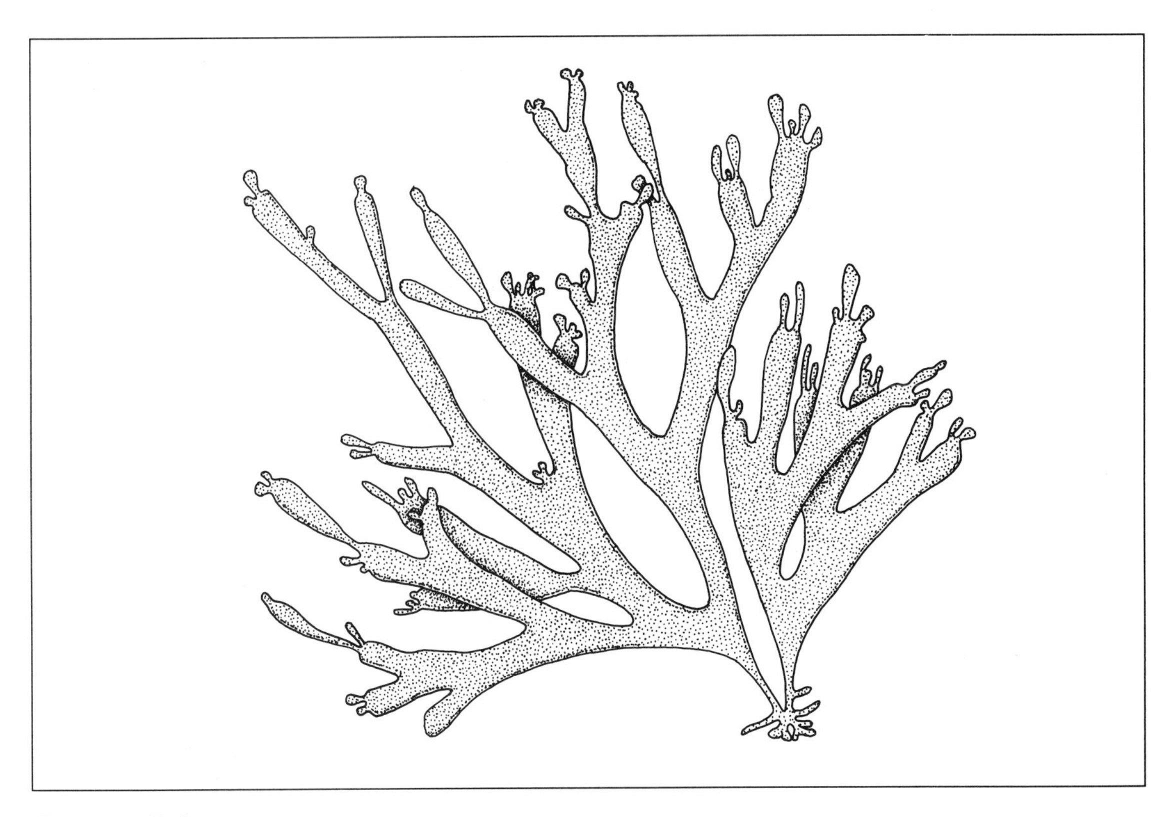

Fig. 1–4. Dulse

Irish moss is the seaweed *Chondrus crispus*, which is widely used in the United States and Europe. See Fig. 1–5. Colonists boiled it with milk and added fruit and vanilla to make pudding desserts. **Carrageenan** is a thickener important in food production. It is extracted from Irish moss or from another seaweed, *Eucheuma*. It is used to thicken ice cream, sherbets, and other frozen foods. It is added to puddings and soups to make them smoother and thicker. *Chondrus crispus* is found from Nova Scotia to Cape Cod, Massachusetts. *Eucheuma* is grown commercially in the Philippines.

Fig. 1–5. Irish moss

Other Uses of Seaweeds

Seaweeds are used as food for animals. Farmers have long known that their cows, sheep, and goats can feed on algal beachdrift with no ill effects. Experiments in processing seaweeds with animal feed began when there was a grain shortage during wars in Europe. Today the feed industry harvests the top meter or so of the fast-growing brown algae **kelp** (*Macrocystis*) off the California coast. Kelp can grow over 30 cm per day, faster than any other plant on earth. Kelp are one of the largest seaweeds, growing up to 50 m tall in areas called kelp beds or kelp forests. See Fig. 1–6.

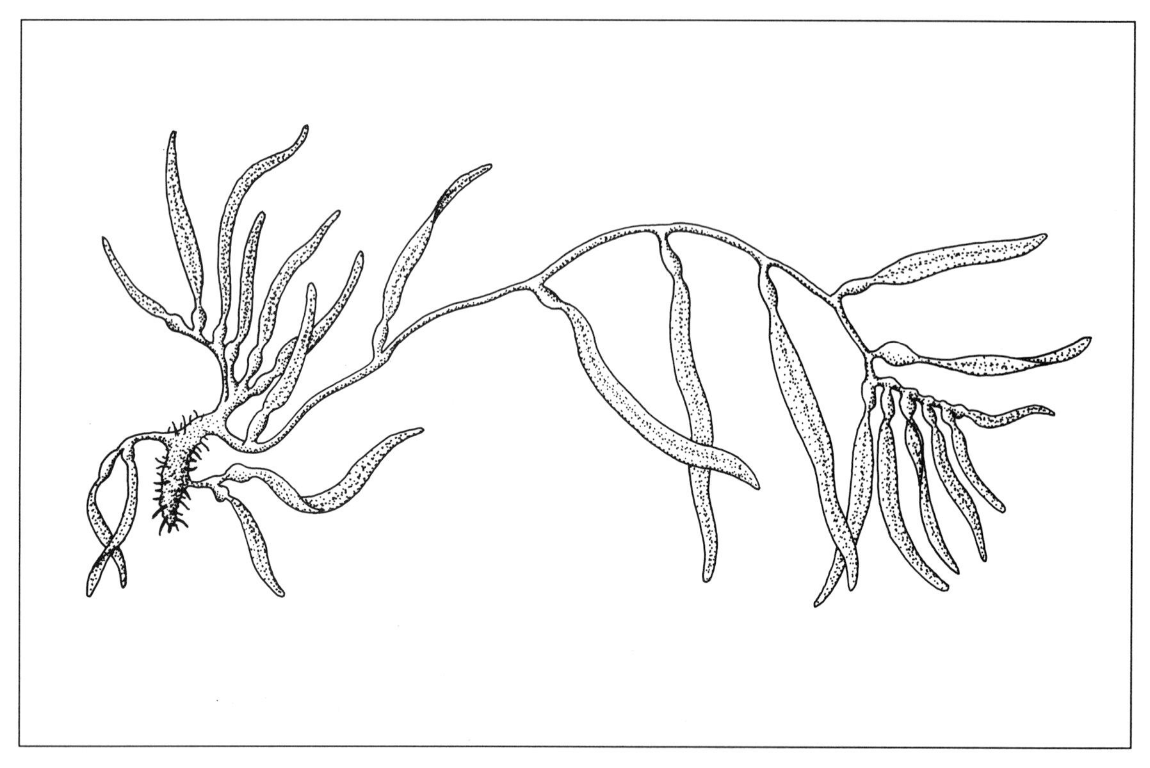

Fig. 1–6. Kelp (*Macrocystis*)

Seaweeds are also harvested and processed to extract minerals and other products. Because they are high in potash (KOH, K_2O) and other minerals, they make good fertilizers. After storms, when detached seaweeds have drifted to shore, they are collected and mixed directly into soil or composted for fertilizer.

Medicinal and industrial products are extracted from seaweeds. Before modern medicine and the pharmaceutical production of drugs, seaweeds were picked and used as remedies for various ailments. Today seaweeds are harvested and processed to obtain many products. See Table 1–4.

Table 1–4. Products from seaweeds

Algin. A substance found in the cell walls of brown algae such as kelp. Because it is water absorbent, it is widely used for thickening, suspending, and emulsifying such products as polishes, cosmetics, and ice cream. Algin is so important to U.S. industries that much time and money have gone into research on ways to increase the harvesting of kelp without damaging the ecology of the kelp beds.

Carrageenan. A red algal extract from Irish moss or other seaweeds. Today it is extracted mostly from the seaweed *Eucheuma*. *Eucheuma* is cultured in warm Pacific waters off countries like the Philippines. Carrageenan makes processed foods thicker and smoother.

Agar. A jellylike substance extracted primarily from the seaweed *Gelidium*. It is used in processed foods as a substitute for gelatin and as an anti-drying agent for foods like cheese, ice cream, and canned meats. Agar is also obtained from *Gracilaria*. It is important as a medium for growing laboratory cultures of bacteria and other organisms.

Ash. Burned seaweeds containing soda (Na compounds) and potash (KOH, K_2O), used in manufacturing glass and soap.

QUESTIONS

13. Make a list of common food products that contain seaweed or seaweed extracts.

14. For what purposes are seaweeds used in cooking?

15. For what purposes are seaweeds used in agriculture and industry?

16. Explain the importance of these seaweed products:
    a. carrageenan
    b. agar
    c. algin

17. What foods have you eaten and what products have you used that probably contained seaweed products?

FURTHER INVESTIGATIONS

1. Search for seaweed products among the foods in your home or in a grocery store or supermarket. Check food labels. Make a list. Share your findings with the class.

2. Look for more seaweed recipes. Make a recipe booklet for use in your classroom or community.

3. Find out how people in other societies use seaweeds. Look for examples from Hawaii and other Polynesian islands, from Japan, China, Malaysia, and other far eastern countries, from Europe, and from colonial America.

4. Find out how seaweeds are harvested commercially and for what purposes.
    a. Learn about ancient harvesting

techniques and traditional uses of seaweeds.

b. Learn how modern technology is changing aquaculture practices. Include aquaculture for food, for sport stocks, and for aquarium enthusiasts.

5. What is meant by a well-balanced diet? How many Calories and how many grams of carbohydrates, protein, and fat should you consume daily? What vitamins and minerals do you need for good health? What role do vegetables play in a well-balanced diet? How could seaweeds help you maintain a well-balanced diet?

6. Learn how commercially prepared agar is used in making bacterial growth media. Invite a bacteriologist to explain how bacteria are cultured, what the cultures are used for, and what precautions to use in handling them.

7. Make your own agar-agar. Collect fresh seaweeds. Wash them in fresh water, put them in a pot, barely cover them with water, and bring to a boil. Simmer for 30 min or until the liquid thickens. Remove from stove and cool to lukewarm. Squeeze the liquid through cheesecloth into a pan. Freeze for 24 hr. Thaw completely, then pour off the water. You are left with straw-colored agar, which you can air-dry and store in a waterproof container.

2. Pressing Seaweeds

Most ocean seaweeds are large algae that grow attached to firm substrates such as rocks, shells, or pilings. For this reason such seaweeds live only along the coastal fringes of continents and islands or from the tops of submerged reefs where there is enough sunlight for them to photosynthesize. Floating seaweeds like *Sargassum* (gulfweed) are exceptions.

Seaweeds vary greatly in size, shape, and color. Some, such as kelp (*Macrocystis*), are giants that rival trees in size; others are only a few centimeters long, with fine, delicate structures. A good time to collect seaweeds is just after storm waves have broken off pieces and carried them to shore. But storm waves generally do not dislodge the holdfasts, so they can regrow.

If you look among detached seaweeds that wash in and out with the waves, you will find a wide variety of specimens. When collected fresh, they can be eaten or used to prepare a reference collection.

In this topic you will learn how to make sets of preserved seaweed specimens by pressing and drying them. Plants collected on a field trip can be pressed for reference and study. Seaweeds artfully arranged and pressed can be used to decorate notepaper or to make a natural collage for framing.

ACTIVITY

Make a collection of pressed seaweeds.

MATERIALS

- 4 recently collected seaweed specimens
- four 8½ x 11-in sheets of white paper
- four 5 x 8-cm labels
- seaweed identification key
- 2 probes or skewers
- dissecting scissors or scalpel
- 30 x 30 x 5-cm or larger pan
- seawater
- basting syringe or pipette
- 8½ x 11-in flexible plastic sheet
- camel-hair paintbrush
- 4 clean newspapers, 4 pages thick
- four 12 x 20-cm pieces of waxed paper or clean cloth
- four 8½ x 11-in sheets of corrugated cardboard
- plant press (2 boards)
- weight or rope
- 3-hole punch
- 3-ring binder
- glue, clear
- pictorial seaweed key (optional)

PROCEDURE

1. Obtain seaweed specimens.
   a. Wash them and remove attached organisms or entangled objects.
   b. Select the best of each specimen for pressing.

2. Assign a number to each specimen and prepare the following:
   a. Get a sheet of white paper 8½ x 11 in. Record the specimen number lightly in pencil on the lower right corner. (When the seaweed is pressed and dried, you will cover the penciled number with a label.)
   b. Prepare the labels now. Write the specimen number and the date and location where each seaweed was found. If you collected the seaweed offshore, record the depth and type of substrate. Record the name(s) of the collector(s). See Fig. 2–1.

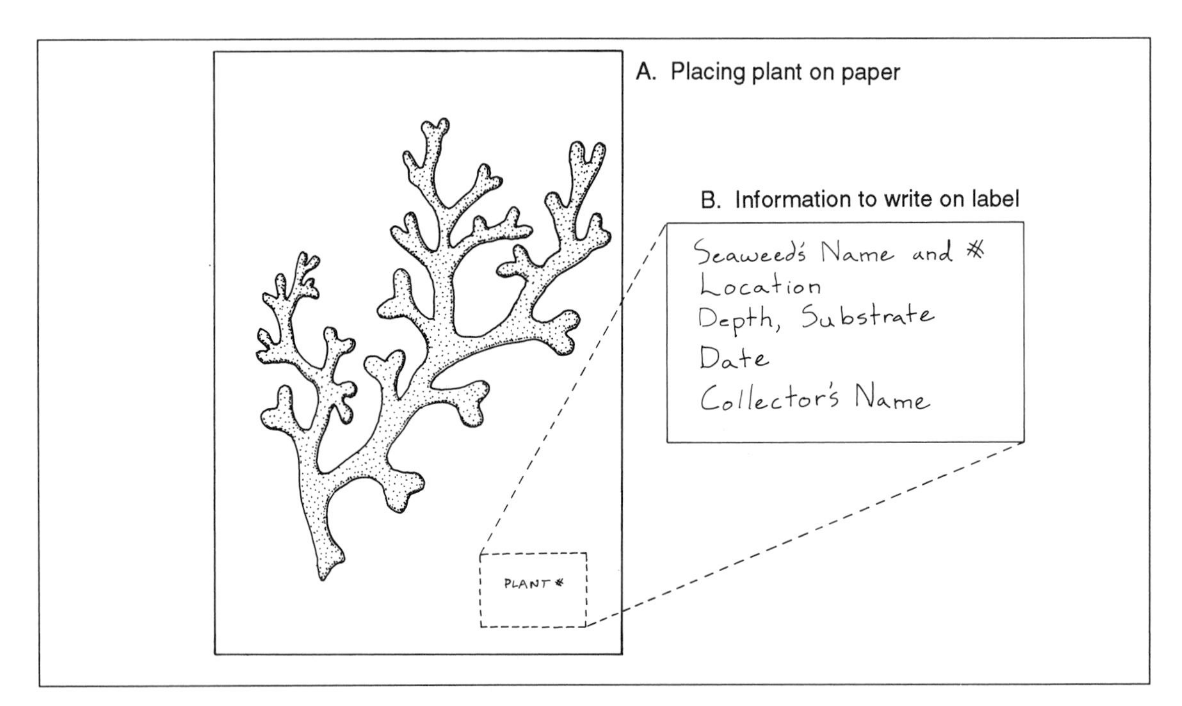

Fig. 2–1. Recording information

3. Press each seaweed specimen as follows:
   a. Lay a piece of white paper on a flexible plastic sheet. The plastic will support the paper when it gets wet.
   b. Select a seaweed specimen and lay it on the white paper. Leave a wide margin on the left side of the paper so it may be punched later and put in a binder. Leave space in the lower right corner for the label.

c. Float out the algae by submerging the paper and the specimen in a pan of seawater about 1 cm deep. This step is called "floating out" the seaweed. See Fig. 2–2. Use gentle jets of water from a basting syringe to move and arrange the features of the seaweed for best display.

d. Arrange the seaweed to show all its important details. Use your fingers or two probes to position it. Separate the fronds and snip off overlapping fronds with scissors. Be careful not to cut the paper.

e. Gently lift the seaweed, paper, and plastic carrier out of the pan. Holding one side, tilt the carrier and let the water drain away slowly.

f. Holding the paper horizontally, inspect the position and arrangement of the specimen. For final arranging, use a paintbrush or jets of water from a basting syringe to separate overlapping fronds and display the plant's features.

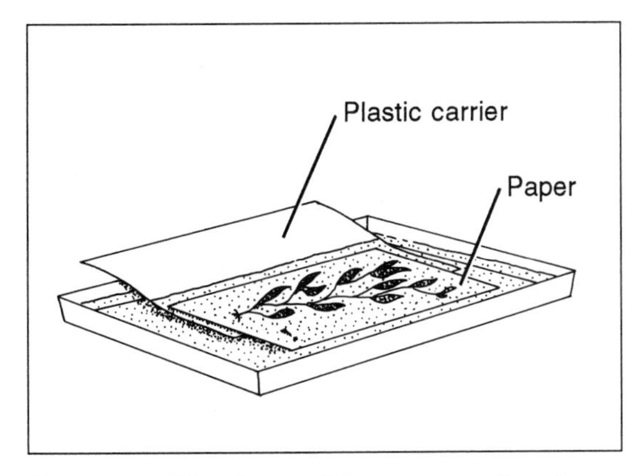

Fig. 2–2. "Floating out" fine seaweed under water

4. Dry the arranged specimen.
   a. Very carefully lift the paper with the specimen from the plastic sheet. Then lay the wet paper with the mounted specimen on an opened newspaper about four pages thick. See (A) in Fig. 2–3. The newspaper will absorb excess water. Cover the specimen with waxed paper or clean cloth to prevent the newspaper ink from staining the specimen and the paper. Fold the newspaper closed, sandwiching the specimen. See (B) in Fig. 2–3. Last, write your name on the outside of the newspaper.
   b. Stack the sandwiched specimens on a desk or a board. Insert a thin piece of corrugated cardboard over every fourth specimen sandwiched in newspaper. Limit the height of the stack to about 30 cm. (The paper on which the specimens are mounted tends to crinkle in stacks higher than 30 cm.) See (C) in Fig. 2–3.
   c. Press the specimens by putting a board on top of the stack and adding a heavy weight or by tying a cord tightly around the stack.
   d. Open the pressed stack every 24 hours. Replace the damp newspapers, waxed paper or cloth, and cardboard as needed. Repeat the procedure until the pressed specimens are completely dry. This will take about a week. The cloths, newspapers, and cardboard can be dried and reused.

5. Remove the dried, pressed specimen mounts. Complete each pressed speci-

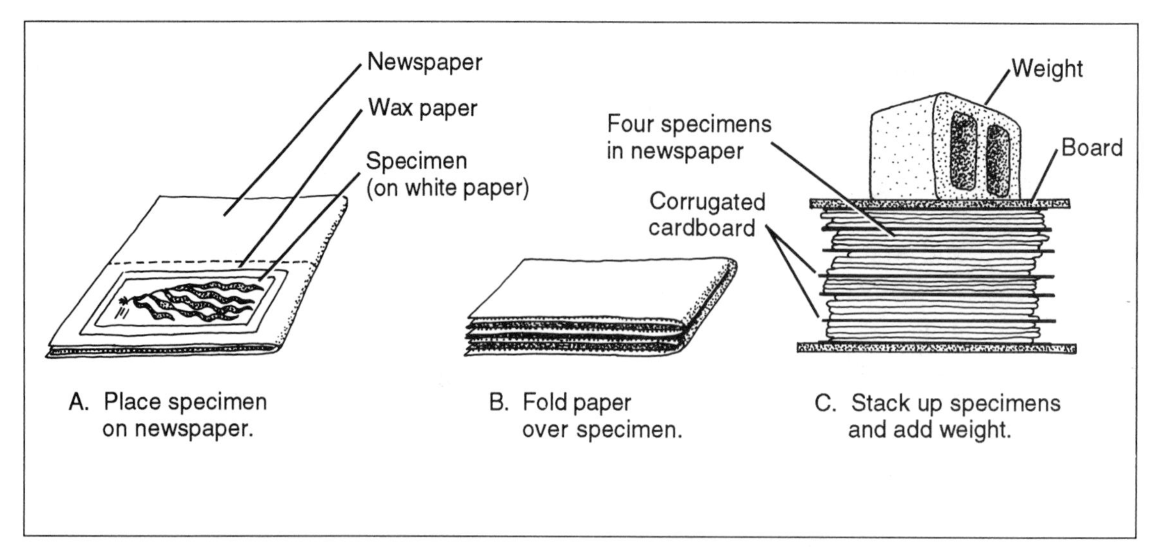

Fig. 2–3. Preparing specimens for drying

men by placing its neatly printed label over your penciled information. Three-hole-punch the page and insert it into the class binder. If a bit of the seaweed loosens from the page, lightly glue it in place with clear-drying craft glue or white glue.

6. (Optional) If a seaweed key is available, identify each specimen.
   a. Most seaweed keys are organized by color (green, brown, and red). Their colors are determined by their pigments. See Table 2–1.
   b. Identify each seaweed from the drawings in the key. Observe the features of each specimen carefully. Compare the specimens with the drawings. Find the drawing that best matches the seaweed.
   c. Record the name of each seaweed on its label.

QUESTIONS

1. When is "floating out" important in preparing a specimen? How else could a seaweed specimen be arranged on mounting paper?

2. List several uses of pressed seaweeds.

3. How might you rehydrate a pressed specimen? (*Rehydrate* means to put water back into a dried specimen.) Compare the appearance of a rehydrated specimen and a fresh specimen.

4. Did any of your pressed specimens stain the white mounting paper? Which species? What use might be made of this observation?

5. Most pressed seaweeds stick well to paper. What makes the seaweeds stick?

Table 2–1. Seaweeds (large marine algae) grouped by apparent color

Green algae (Chlorophyta). Clear, green algae with chlorophyll that is not masked by other pigments. A typical marine example is *Ulva* (sea lettuce), which is found in shallow, sometimes brackish coastal waters of all oceans. Green algae include the **calcareous green algae** that secrete calcium carbonate to form delicate or finely branched skeletons. *Halimeda* is an important calcareous green alga that helps in coral reef growth. When living, it looks green; when dried it looks like branches of oatmeal. (Most of the familiar freshwater algae are also green algae.)

Brown algae (Phaeophyta). In addition to chlorophyll, these plants contain other pigments that color the plant brown, sometimes with olive, greenish, or yellowish casts, but without pink tinges. Most of the familiar dominant large seaweeds that grow on temperate and polar rocky coasts are brown algae. Some are small, with fine features, such as the fan-shaped *Padina.* Others are large, often thick and leathery, and may have floats, such as the many species of kelp. Others are floating seaweeds such as the unattached species of *Sargassum.*

Red Algae (Rhodophyta). These plants are pink or red but may appear brown (as in the *Acanthophora*). In addition to chlorophyll, they contain red, and sometimes blue, pigments. They grow in all oceans and often are the dominant algae in the tropics. Examples are *Gracilaria* and *Chondrus* ("Irish moss"). There are more species of red marine algae than of green and brown marine algae together. Many are used for human food and other products. Red algae include coralline-encrusting algae that appear rose or lavender when alive and white when dried.

Blue-Green Algae (Cyanophyta). Most blue-green algae are microscopic plantlike organisms (cyanobacteria); they are not discussed here with the seaweeds. Ones that are large enough to be considered seaweeds form long, dark green or blackish filaments, strands, or mats. Where nutrients are abundant (especially in polluted areas), they may form thick, dark, slippery films on intertidal rocks or grow attached to other larger seaweeds. At least one species (*Lyngbya*) causes "swimmer's itch," a rash that develops from strands caught in bathing suits.

FURTHER INVESTIGATIONS

1. Make a collection of pressed seaweeds. Identify the specimens.
   a. Compare your specimens with those made in previous classes. Does your information agree with information on earlier specimens? Make corrections as needed.
   b. As you find new samples throughout the year, add them to the class collection of dried seaweed specimens.

2. Compare the seaweeds from two or more beaches. Make a map of each beach

showing the locations of seaweeds. Describe the seaweeds and the substrates, the depth of water, and the distance from shore where they were collected.

3. Make collections several times a year. Compare the collections. Look for evidence of seasonal changes affecting the supply of seaweeds.

4. Design seaweed-decorated stationery or place cards. Arrange seaweeds on sheets of paper. Use two or more pieces to form an algal collage. Press the seaweeds as you did in this topic.

5. When you collect seaweeds, put pieces in a plastic bag and add seawater to form a mini-aquarium. Hold the bag up and look for small animals that may be swimming or moving about on the seaweed. Study the organisms that live in or on seaweed habitats.

6. *Sargassum* is a seaweed commonly attached to rocks along many tropical shores. Yet huge quantities of it float in large areas off the east coast of the United States. Use references to find out where these floating forms come from and how they reproduce. Report to the class.

3. Photosynthesis in the Ocean

Algae and other water plants often look quite different from land plants. But because they also have many similarities, we can use much of what we know about land plants to understand water plants. Perhaps the most important similarity is the ability to carry out photosynthesis.

Photosynthesis

Algae and most land plants contain some form of the green pigment **chlorophyll.** Chlorophyll is a molecule that enables plants to convert sunlight energy into chemical energy. We call this process **photosynthesis.**

To explain photosynthesis we must enter the tiny world of electrons, protons, and neutrons, the subatomic particles that make up atoms. Atoms in turn are the building blocks of molecules. We can get a feel for their size when we realize that it takes over 100 million hydrogen atoms in a row to equal a centimeter. That's about 3 million to stretch across the thickness of this paper. It takes over 100,000 protons side by side to equal the diameter of the hydrogen atom.

Into this tiny world comes energy from sunlight in the form of streams of **photons.** Photons are ultra tiny packages of energy that are much, much smaller than electrons, protons, or neutrons. Like all other forms of energy, photons have the capacity to do work or move things. A photon with sufficient energy can knock an electron out of one chlorophyll molecule. That electron can be captured by other molecules that hold it, using the energy from it to build glucose from CO_2 (carbon dioxide) and H_2O (water). This photosynthetic process is the way light energy is transformed into **chemical energy.**

Once formed, glucose builds and fuels living organisms. The energy in glucose can be used to produce the fats, proteins, and starches that plants use to build, repair, and reproduce themselves. Though many kinds of molecules are built up and broken down in the bodies of organisms, the energy for driving these chemical reactions comes originally from sunlight. Fig. 3–1 shows the basic equation for the photosynthetic process of producing glucose.

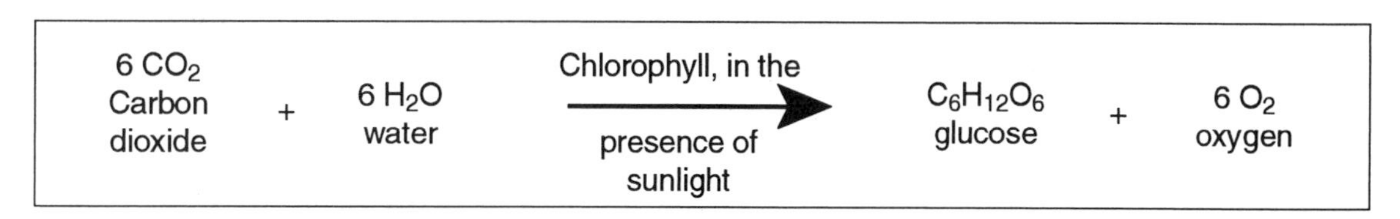

Fig 3–1. Equation for the photosynthetic production of glucose

Animal cells do not contain chlorophyll and cannot photosynthesize. So animals must eat plants or other animals to get the glucose and other molecules they need to build and fuel their bodies.

Respiration

Stored chemical energy is released from glucose in a process called **respiration,** which is a reverse of photosynthesis. Both plants and animals must carry out respiration in order to get the energy needed to survive and grow.

QUESTIONS

1. Write the equation for respiration, the breakdown of glucose ($C_6H_{12}O_6$) to produce body energy. (Sunlight and chlorophyll are not involved in respiration. Energy is a product of respiration.)

2. How does the process of photosynthesis differ from the process of respiration?

3. Under what circumstances does a plant carry out photosynthesis? Respiration?

Solar Energy

The sunlight we see is the same energy that drives the process of photosynthesis, but this part, which we call **light,** makes up only about 40% of the energy received from the sun. The remaining energy takes other forms. About 50% is infrared energy, 9% is ultraviolet energy, and the other 1% is X rays or microwaves. Collectively we call these different forms of solar energy **electromagnetic radiation.**

Photons are packets of energy that behave like both particles and waves. For convenience we describe the amount of energy in a particular kind of radiation in terms of its wavelength or the distance between wave peaks. Radiation with short wavelengths has more energy than radiation with long wavelengths. In short waves there are more energy peaks or "kicks" per unit of length.

The Electromagnetic Spectrum

Visible solar radiation appears as white light, yet when passed through a prism, it breaks up into a rainbow of colors called a **light spectrum.** A spectrum displays light photons of different wavelengths, from the longest, red, to the shortest, violet, with orange, yellow, green, and blue between.

Electromagnetic radiation extends beyond the light spectrum in both directions. This larger spectrum, which includes light, is called the **electromagnetic spectrum.**

At the low-energy end of the electromagnetic spectrum are infrared photons. Though our eyes cannot see it, we feel the warmth from the heat it produces by jiggling whole molecules. Surprisingly, it takes less energy to move a molecule to produce heat than to move a much smaller electron. The reason is that molecules are less tightly bound to each other than electrons are bound together within atoms.

At the high-energy end of the electromagnetic spectrum are the ultraviolet photons, which can destroy many of the molecules of life. Ultraviolet radiation is used as a sterilizer to kill germs, and we experience its molecular destruction in sunburns. Beyond ultraviolet photons are the very intense X rays, which can pass through our bodies to make photos of our body parts.

Wavelengths

Because the wavelengths of the electromagnetic spectrum in the energy ranges of light, ultraviolet radiation, and X rays are quite short, they are often reported in nanometers (nm). A nanometer is very small, only one billionth (0.000,000,001) of a meter, the width of thirty hydrogen atoms sitting side by side. Fig. 3–2 shows wavelengths of solar radiation in nanometers.

QUESTIONS

4. In each pair, which wavelength carries more energy?
   a. infrared radiation or ultraviolet radiation
   b. red light or violet light
   c. X rays or blue light
   d. infrared radiation or X rays

5. What is solar energy? What part of solar

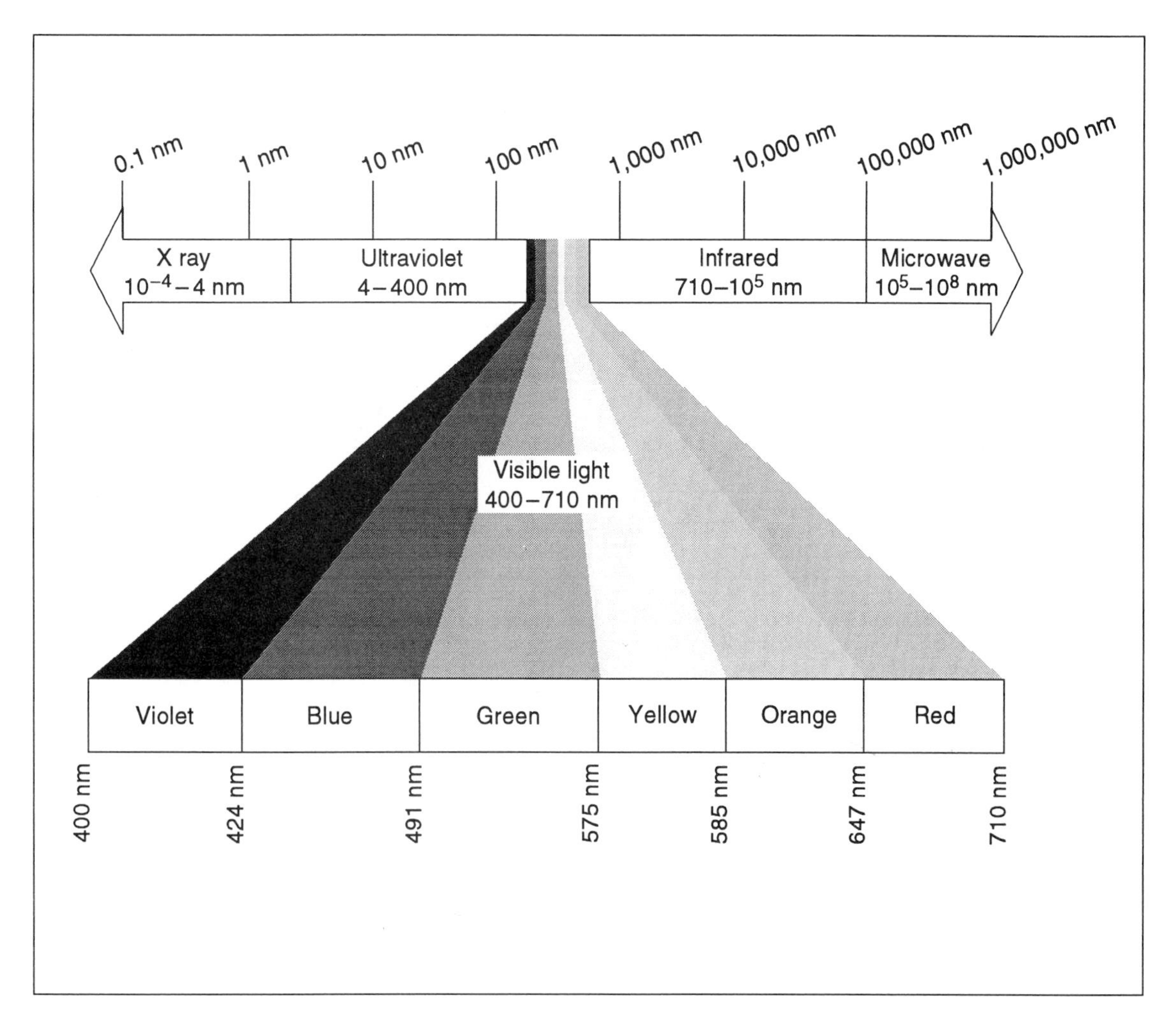

Fig. 3–2. Wavelengths of the electromagnetic spectrum of solar radiation

energy can humans see? What part of solar energy do we call sunlight?

Sunlight and Chlorophyll

Sunlight interacts with the chlorophyll pigments in plants and in plantlike organisms such as blue-green bacteria. **Pigments** are colored materials that reflect light of certain wavelengths while absorbing or capturing light of other wavelengths. **Chlorophyll pigments** absorb sunlight, enabling chlorophyll-containing organisms to carry out photosynthesis. Table 3–1 shows what happens to sunlight energy when it interacts with chlorophyll pigments in a typical plant cell.

To see which wavelengths of light are absorbed by chlorophyll pigments, we can dissolve the pigments from a plant, shine light on them, and measure the wavelengths of light that they reflect. The wavelengths that are

Table 3–1. Sunlight interacting with chlorophyll pigments in a plant cell 

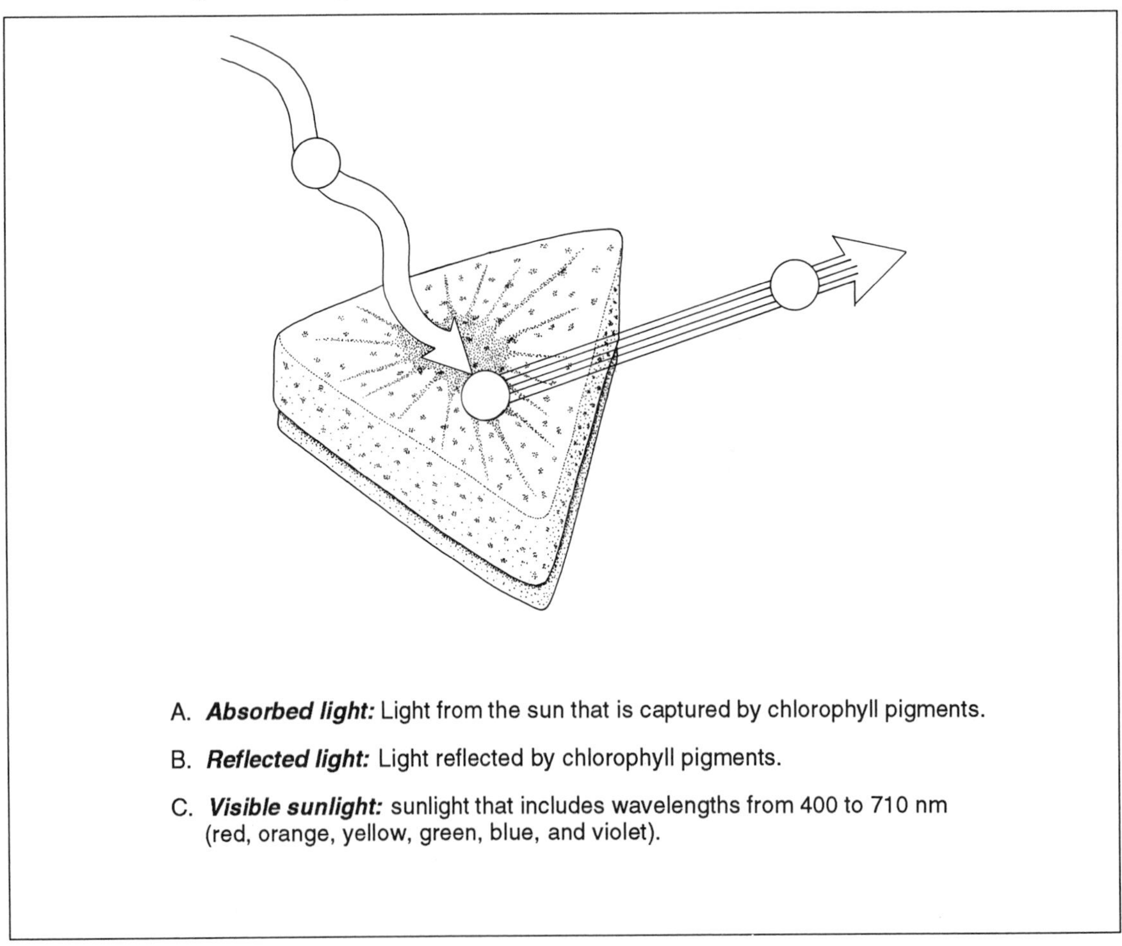

A. ***Absorbed light:*** Light from the sun that is captured by chlorophyll pigments.

B. ***Reflected light:*** Light reflected by chlorophyll pigments.

C. ***Visible sunlight:*** sunlight that includes wavelengths from 400 to 710 nm (red, orange, yellow, green, blue, and violet).

not reflected are absorbed. The graph in Fig. 3–3 shows the results of one such experiment.

Plants also contain other pigments besides chlorophyll, including yellow **xanthophylls** and yellow-orange **carotene** (the pigment that gives carrots their color). Classification of seaweeds (large marine algae) as red, green, or brown is based largely on its apparent color, which in turn depends on the pigments it contains. See Unit 3, Topic 2, Table 2–1 for a list of seaweeds grouped by their apparent color.

QUESTIONS

6. What happens to sunlight as it interacts with chlorophyll pigments in photosynthesis?
   a. Using the terms in Table 3–1, write a letter in each circle to identify what is happening to the sunlight energy.
   b. Write a description of each process shown in Table 3–1.

7. Refer to Fig. 3–3.
   a. What color(s) do the chlorophyll pigments reflect? What color(s) do you see?
   b. What color(s) do the chlorophyll pigments absorb? (Light that is not

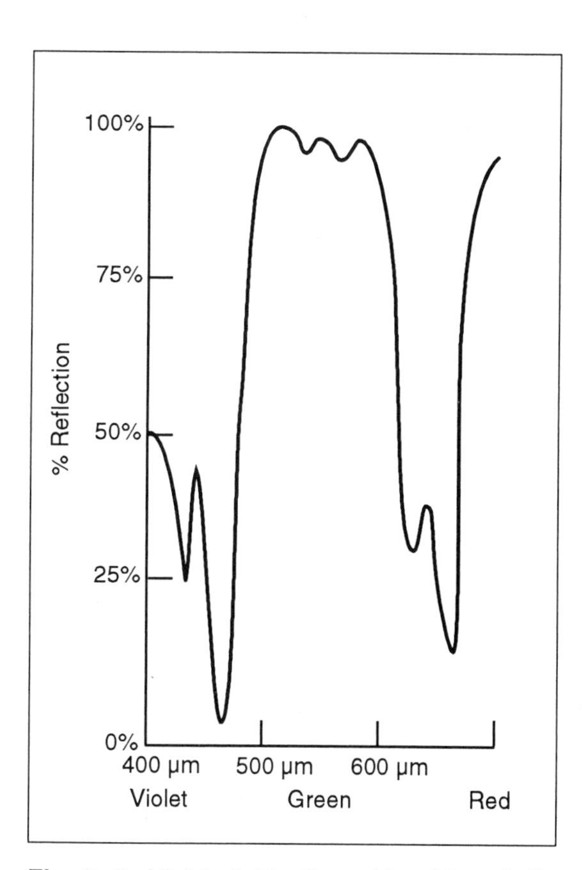

Fig. 3–3. Visible light reflected by chlorophyll pigments Ⓦ

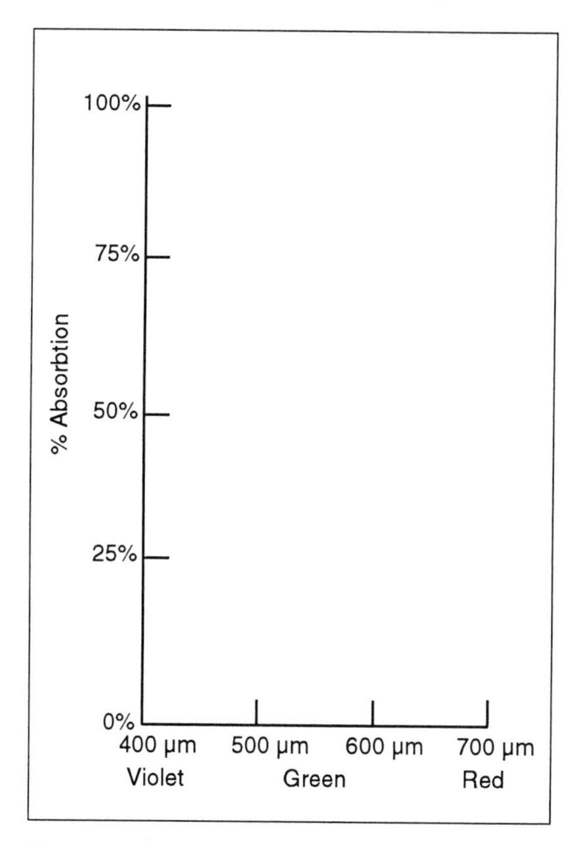

Fig. 3–4. Visible light absorbed by chlorophyll pigments Ⓦ

reflected is absorbed.) How do you know what colors are absorbed?

c. How does the plant use the energy it absorbs?

8. In Fig. 3–4, make a graph showing the percentage of light absorbed by chlorophyll pigments. Use information from Fig. 3–3.

9. What might explain the apparent color
   a. of healthy green leaves?
   b. of pond water?

Euphotic Zone Light

Because sunlight is the primary source of energy for photosynthesis, plants that live in water must live close enough to the surface to receive at least 1% of the incoming solar energy. This layer of water is called the **euphotic zone.** See Fig. 3–5. In clear tropical waters, the euphotic zone may extend to a depth of 80 m. Closer to the poles, sunlight energy does not penetrate as deeply, so the euphotic zone may be less than 10 m deep. In turbid waters, where light-blocking material is suspended, even less light penetrates. Very muddy waters may have a euphotic zone of only a few centimeters.

In clear water the layer beneath the euphotic zone is the **disphotic zone,** which may extend as deep as 800 m. The dim blue light that penetrates this zone is not sufficient to sustain photosynthesis.

These two zones, the euphotic and the disphotic, make up the **photic zone.** Most of the water in the ocean lies beneath the photic zone in the lightless, black ocean region called the **aphotic zone.**

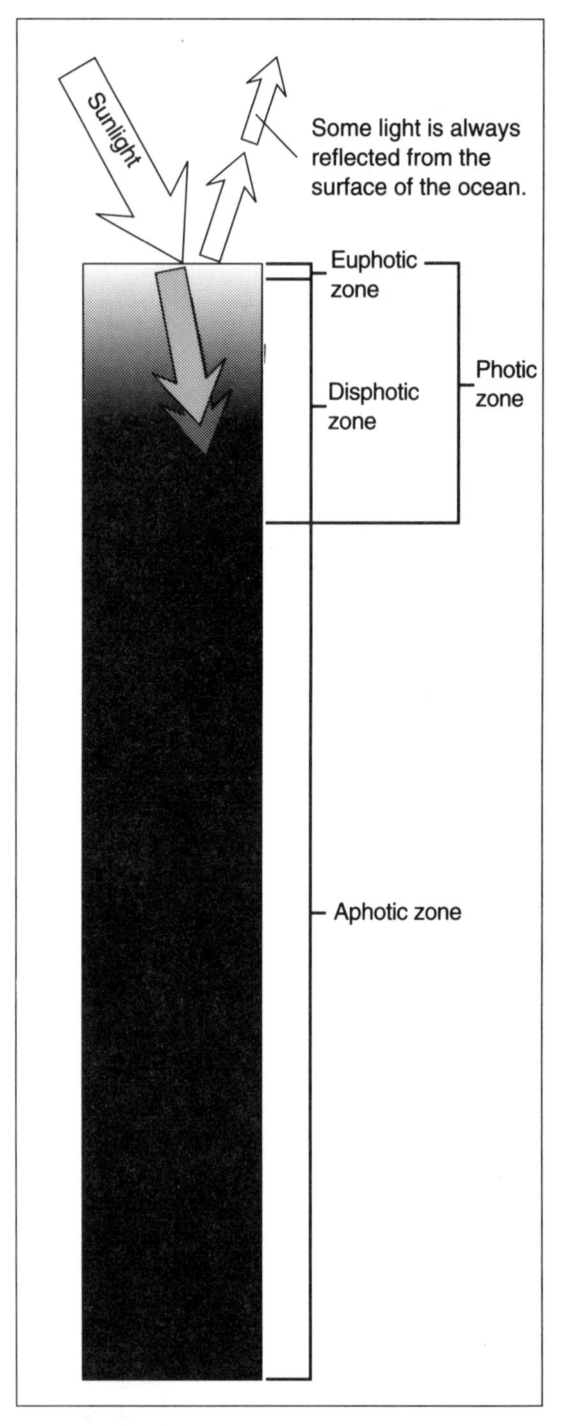

Fig. 3–5. Sunlight penetration of the ocean

Knowing the meaning of *photic* and of *eu-* and *dis-* and *a-* can help you remember the terms:

phot = light or radiant energy
euphotic = having good light
disphotic = having poor light
aphotic = having no light

When sunlight energy strikes the ocean, some of it reflects off the surface back into the atmosphere. The amount of energy that penetrates the surface of the water depends on the angle at which the sunlight strikes the ocean.

Water absorbs nearly all the entering infrared energy from sunlight within 10 cm of the surface. In this very shallow layer it is converted to heat, which raises the water temperature and causes it to evaporate more rapidly. Most swimmers have experienced warm surface water with much cooler water just beneath it. When winds and waves stir the surface waters, heat is transferred to cooler layers below. The place where water temperature changes abruptly from warmer to colder is called the **thermocline.**

Visible light plays a part in photosynthesis. Within the first 10 m, water absorbs more than 50% of the visible light energy, absorbing more red light than blue light. In clear tropical water only about 1% of visible light, mostly in the blue range, penetrates to 100 m (about 300 ft). See Fig. 3–6.

Red light is more strongly absorbed by water than blue-green light is. That is why a diver's red wetsuit appears nearly black at 20 m. At 30 m, water has absorbed nearly all the visible light colors except blues. At that depth, a scuba diver without a flashlight sees all underwater features only in shades of blue. To see a full spectrum of colors, a diver must shine a flashlight directly on an object. Thus both the **intensity** (amount) and the **color** of visible light varies with depth in the euphotic zone.

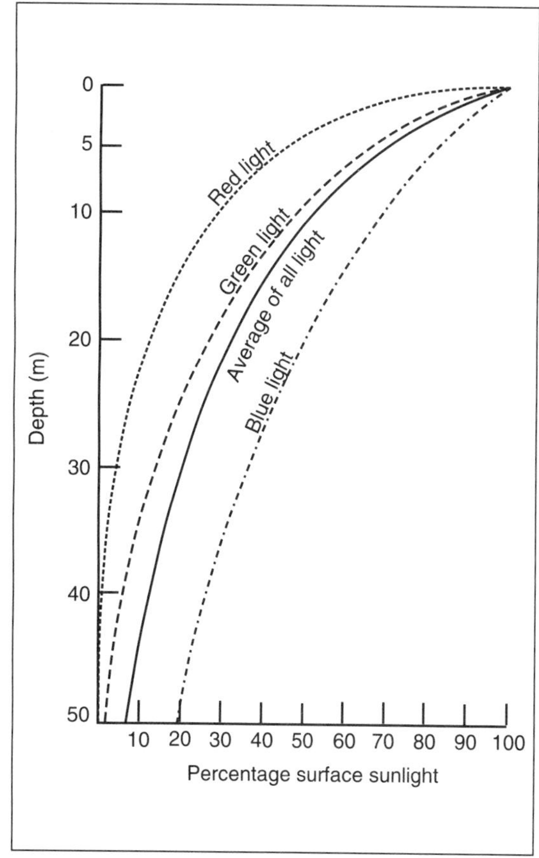

Fig. 3–6. Percentages of different wavelengths of sunlight remaining at increasing depths as sunlight penetrates clear midocean tropical water Ⓦ

QUESTIONS

10. Use information from Fig. 3–6 to complete Table 3–2 showing the percentages of different kinds of light visible in the upper layers of the euphotic zone in clear midocean tropical water.

Table 3–2. Percentages of light available by depth in the upper part of the euphotic zone 

Depth (m)	% Red light	% Green light	% Blue light	% Total visible sunlight
0 (surface)	100	100	100	100
3				
5				
10				
15				
20				
30				
40				
50				

11. How might the reduction in red light from 100% at the surface to 10% at 20 m be explained? Where might the red light go? What percentage of each color of light is left at 20 m?

12. How does depth affect the colors of objects a diver can see at a depth of 5 m into the euphotic zone? At a depth of 30 m into the euphotic zone?

13. Redraw the graph in Fig. 3–6 to show light absorption down to 100 m. Use information from the text in producing your graph.

14. How might the blue color of deep, clear tropical open-ocean water be explained?

15. Why is water in a swimming pool darker blue at the deep end than at the shallow end? Why is some water green and some water blue? Where do these colors come from?

Seaweed Pigments and Light

Photosynthesizing plants contain green chlorophyll and yellow-orange carotene plus other pigments such as yellow xanthophyll. These pigments absorb energy from visible blue light and, to a lesser extent, red light. Because blue light penetrates to about 80 m in clear tropical water, plants can photosynthesize down to this depth.

Seaweeds (large marine algae) are distributed in the euphotic zone according to their preference for intensity and color of the available light. Green algae (which absorb blue and red light) grow from the low-tide line to about 10 m. Red algae (which absorb blue light) grow in the dim light of deeper waters or in shaded areas.

Free-floating microscopic marine algae (phytoplankton) can be so numerous that they block the passage of light though water, decreasing the depth of the euphotic zone. In nutrient-rich shallow waters such as those off Chile and the east coast of the United States, phytoplankton are so abundant that the euphotic zone is no deeper than 5 m.

QUESTIONS

16. In tropical waters what colors and intensities of light are available to the photosynthetic process of
    a. green seaweeds living from 0 to 10 m?
    b. red seaweeds living at 20 m?

17. The depth of the euphotic zone varies from one place to another. How might this be explained?

ACTIVITY

Observe the production of gases in light and darkness.

MATERIALS

- two 400-mL beakers
- aquarium water or prepared distilled water
- 0.25% sodium bicarbonate solution in dropping bottle
- 2 small glass funnels
- 2 sprigs of *Elodea* or similar fresh-water plant
- 2 test tubes
- waterproof marker
- lightproof cloths 0.5 m x 0.5 m
- copy of Workbook Table 3–4

PROCEDURE

1. If you do not have an established fresh-water aquarium, prepare distilled water as follows:
    a. Fill four 600-mL beakers to within 3 cm of the top with distilled water.
    b. Add 2 mL of 0.25% of sodium

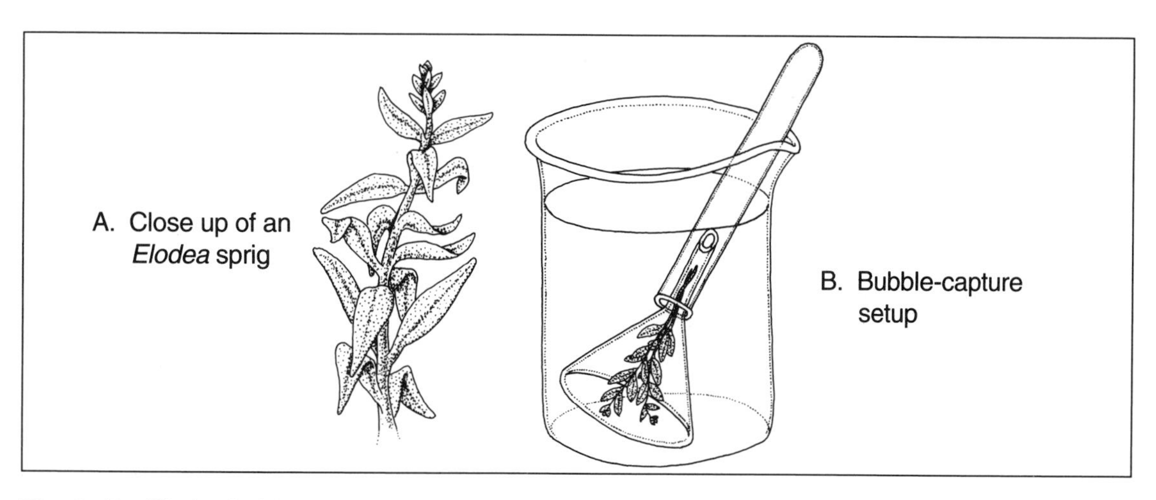

Fig. 3–7. *Elodea* bubble-capture setup

bicarbonate solution to each beaker.

2. Prepare two *Anacharis* bubble setups as shown in Fig. 3–7.
   a. Use one of the beakers of water you prepared in Procedure 1.
   b. Place a sprig of *Anacharis* with a freshly cut stem in a glass funnel.
   c. Invert the funnel with the *Anacharis* inside and sink them to the bottom of the beaker.
   d. Completely fill the test tube with aquarium water or distilled water. Hold your finger over the open end, invert the test tube, and place it over the end of the funnel. There should be no air in the test tube. Your setup should look like Fig. 3–7.
   e. Repeat Procedures 2.a. through 2.d. with a second setup.

3. Test the response of *Anacharis* to light and darkness. Leave both setups in the same lighted area (out of direct sunlight), but cover one with a lightproof cloth.

4. Daily for 4 days, mark with a waterproof marker the volume of gas that has accumulated at the top of each test tube. Invent a way to determine the volume of gas produced daily. Share your inventions. Record your data in Table 3–3.

5. After the first day predict the volume of gas (in mL) that will be produced the

Table 3–3. Volume of gas collected in light and darkness by *Anacharis* Ⓦ

Length of experiment	Volume of gas (mL)			
	Plant in light		Plant in dark	
	Actual volume	Predicted light	Actual volume	Predicted volume
Start	0 mL		0 mL	
Day 1				
Day 2				
Day 3				
Day 4				
Day 5				
Day 6				
Day 7				
Day 8				

next day in each of the two setups over a period of 4 days. Record your predictions in Table 3–3.

6. At the end of 4 days remove the lightproof cloth covering the other *Anacharis*.

7. Once the cloth is removed, measure and record the gas produced by each of the two setups of uncovered plants for another 2 to 4 days.

8. Design and carry out your own experiment to test for differences in intensity of light, color of light, or length of exposure (amount of time that plants are exposed to light).

QUESTIONS

18. How can you explain the gas that was produced in the test tubes?

19. How well did you predict the production of gas in each setup? How, if at all, did the results differ from your predictions?

20. Which treatment gave off the largest volume of gas?

21. What happened to the plant that was covered with a lightproof cloth? How did gas production change after you removed the cloth?

22. If you were to do this experiment using seawater and marine algae, how could you modify the setups to simulate ocean conditions?

Life Without Sunlight

So far as we know, all life on the earth's surface depends ultimately on chlorophyll-containing plants and plantlike organisms for food. Small animals feed on plants, and larger animals prey on smaller animals, forming a **food chain** supported by green plants.

We know that photosynthesis in the ocean is limited to the euphotic zone. Even though we know that animals live below the euphotic zone, oceanographers once assumed that fish and other animals living in the depths are somehow linked to food chains that begin with photosynthesis at the surface. Thus it was assumed that all life in the ocean is linked to photosynthesis.

Imagine the surprise when scientists discovered a microscopic plantlike organism producing sugar in a process much like photosynthesis, but doing so in the black darkness at the bottom of the ocean some 2.5 km (about 1½ mi) deep. In 1977, scientists in deep-sea exploration vehicles explored deep-ocean hot springs off the Galapagos Islands. There they found a single-celled bacterium that contains no chlorophyll but can produce sugar.

These organisms are remarkable in two ways. First, instead of using light as their energy source, they use hot hydrogen sulfide (H_2S), normally a deadly poison to organisms. Second, they live in very hot (65° to 100°C) water that would kill most surface organisms. (Around 2,500 m deep, where the vents are located, ocean pressure is so great that water boils above 370°C. The superheated water from these underwater springs doesn't boil because of the great pressure at that depth.)

Another remarkable fact is the density of

life at the Galapagos springs. The water samples contain a million to a hundred million organisms per milliliter of water—a very high concentration, indicating that this is a rich biological area.

Here, at a depth where no light can penetrate, plantlike bacteria are producing the same glucose, fats, and proteins that photosynthetic plants produce at the surface. Like surface-dwelling primary producers, they are eaten by animals. Clams and giant red tube worms that eat the bacteria are eaten in turn by large white crabs. Even fish live in the ecosystem of the springs. Bottom waters contain oxygen and other nutrients necessary for life. Hydrogen sulfide provides a chemical substitute for sunlight energy. The overall reaction seems to be the one in Fig. 3–11.

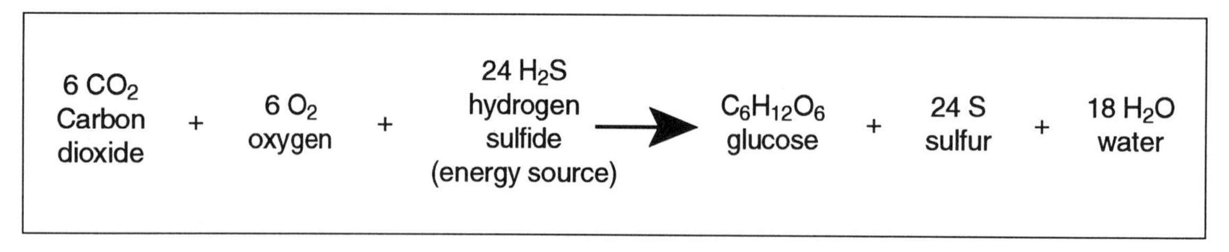

Fig. 3–11. Equation for the hydrogen-sulfide driven synthesis of glucose

QUESTIONS

23. In the equation in Fig. 3–11, what is the source of the hydrogen (H) found in glucose?

24. What is the role of oxygen (O_2) gas in the reaction shown in the above equation?

FURTHER INVESTIGATIONS

1. Using references, find out about plant pigments. Explain how pigments impart color to plants. Explain the light and dark phases of photosynthesis.

2. Set up demonstration(s) for the class showing how light interacts with water. Start with a simple one, like inserting a pencil into a glass of water and observing what happens.

3. Find out about ocean primary production. What areas of the oceans are most productive? What might account for the high productivity of these areas? What might account for the relatively low productivity of other areas?

4. What physical and biological factors might affect
   a. light intensity in the euphotic zone?
   b. light color in the euphotic zone?

5. Use chromatography to study the pigments in plants and seaweeds.
   a. Use references to learn how to extract pigments from plant material. Keep in mind that chlorophyll pigments will dissolve in alcohol or acetone; other pigments (such as

carotene and xanthophyll) will dissolve in water.

CAUTION: Both alcohol and acetone are flammable.

b. Use reference books to learn how to use paper chromatography to separate pigment extract. To do this, you put a small quantity of concentrated pigment extract on one end of a strip of paper, then place that end in a solvent. The solvent will move up the strip, separating the pigments.

c. Try to determine why extraction and chromatographic separations are generally more successful with land plants than with seaweeds.

4. Structural Differences Between Land Plants and Water Plants

Along coastlines, land plants and seaweeds may live only a few feet from each other. Yet the environmental conditions that they must endure to survive are very different. Plants on land must take nutrients and water from the soil. They must take carbon dioxide for photosynthesis from the surrounding air. But air can dry plant parts above ground, and storm winds can blow the plant away.

By contrast, seaweeds are surrounded by all the dissolved nutrients needed for growth, although some may be in short supply, including carbon dioxide for photosynthesis. They never lack the water they need. But in a storm, crashing waves and violent currents can tear seaweeds from the rocks and reefs and sweep them away. In this topic we will investigate the structural differences that permit these plants to live in such vastly different environments.

Vascular Land Plants

The land plants that we commonly see—the trees, shrubs, grasses, and ferns of our forests, fields, and gardens—are vascular plants. These are structurally the most complex among land plants. We will compare them with algae. All **vascular plants** have roots, stems, and leaves connected by a system of **veins**—tubes that carry nutrients and water throughout the plant. Flowering and cone-bearing plants reproduce by seeds, ferns by tiny spores. Roots anchor the plants to the ground and supply them with mineral and water nutrients. Stems, which may grow into trunks, support a photosynthetic factory of leaves. See Fig. 4–1.

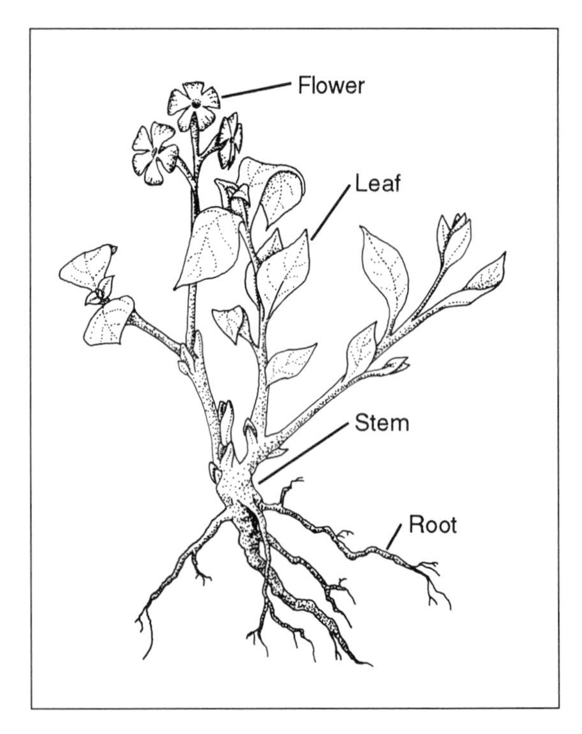

Fig. 4–1. Structure of a flowering vascular land plant Ⓦ

Leaves

A leaf is like a sandwich of cells. The surfaces, called the **epidermis,** are the "slices of bread" of the sandwich. These epidermal layers are usually only one cell thick. As in animals, the epidermis is the outermost layer of cells. A waxy material called the **cuticle** covers the epidermis. The cuticle prevents evaporation of water from the epidermis, protecting the plant from drying out. See Fig. 4–2.

In the epidermis are many tiny holes called **stomates.** These are porelike openings for carbon dioxide (CO_2), oxygen (O_2), and water vapor (H_2O). A stomate has a pair of banana-

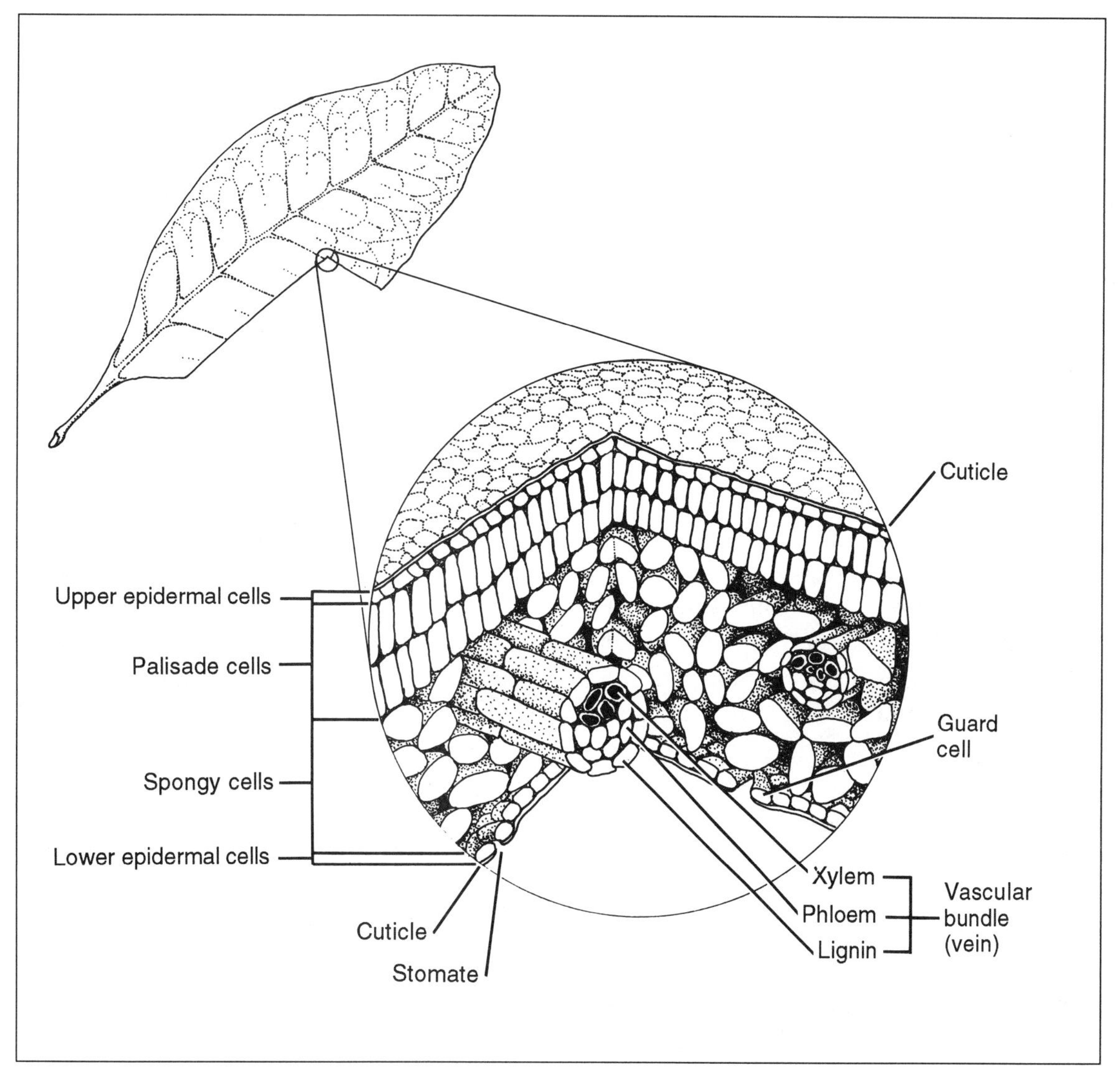

Fig. 4–2. Internal structure of a land-plant leaf

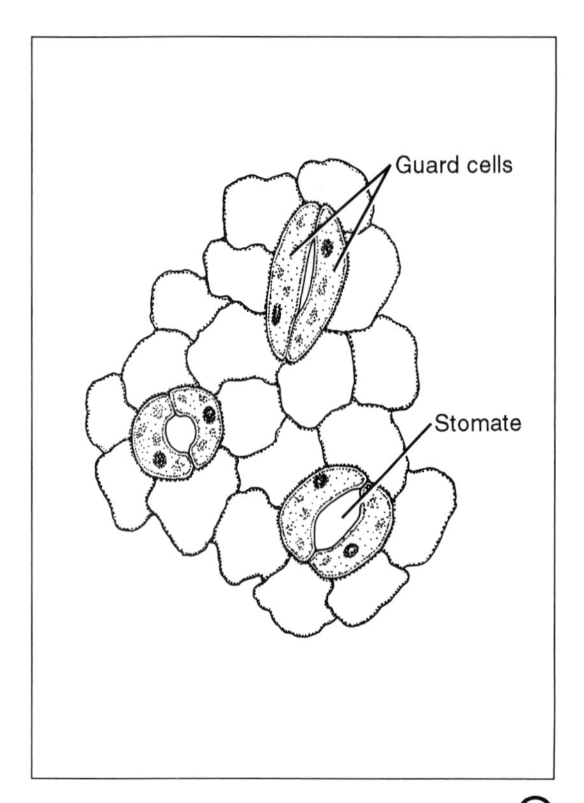

Fig. 4–3. Generalized drawing of stomates ⓦ

shaped **guard cells** that surround it and regulate its size. When the stomates are open, water vapor readily passes out of the plant and CO_2 and O_2 pass in and out. When they are shut, water cannot easily leave the plant. By using stomates and their guard cells, the plant regulates moisture loss and gaseous exchange with the atmosphere. See Fig. 4–3.

Cells That Photosynthesize

Photosynthesis occurs in the leaves and other green parts of a plant. The inner layers of the leaf are filled with **palisade cells** and **spongy cells**. See Fig. 4–2. These cells are rich in chlorophyll pigments that plants need for carrying out photosynthesis and producing sugar. Sugar produced in photosynthesis is used for energy and for making starches, fats, and proteins needed for plants to grow, repair, and reproduce.

Vascular Bundles

If we hold a leaf of a flowering plant up to the light, we see a network of veins. Veins contain **xylem cells,** which carry water and minerals from the roots to the leaves, and **phloem cells,** which carry sugar from the leaves to other parts of the plant. Xylem cells and phloem cells, along with the strengthening **lignified fibers,** form the veins, which are also called **vascular bundles.**

Vascular tissue (xylem and phloem) is an essential characteristic of all true roots, stems, and leaves. Plants that have vascular tissue are called **vascular plants.** See Fig. 4–1.

Vascular Water Plants

Vascular plants that live in fresh water are called **water plants, freshwater plants,** or **aquatic plants.** They evolved from land plants that adapted to living in water. Some water plants, such as water lilies, look like vascular land plants, with flowers blooming on stems. Some are used in fish aquariums. Water plants come in many shapes. Some bear many fine leaves on a stalk, like *Elodea;* others have broad, arrow-shaped leaves, like the sword plant, *Aponogeton*. See Fig. 4–4.

Only two families of vascular plants, both called **sea grasses,** grow in the ocean. They are also called **saltwater plants**, **seawater plants**, or **marine plants**. They grow rooted to the bottom along coastlines, never in the open ocean.

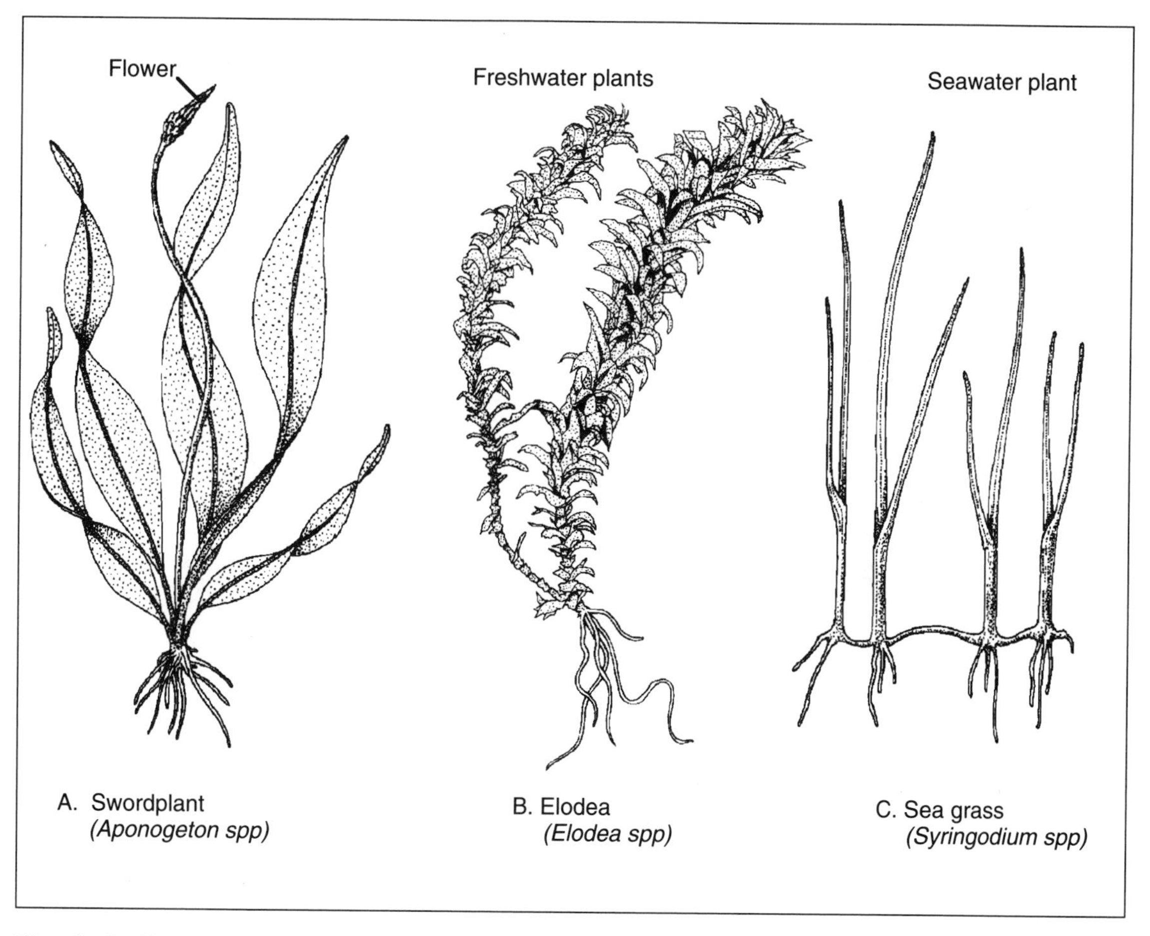

Fig. 4–4. Examples of freshwater and marine water plants

Some vascular plants thrive in salt marshes and estuaries, living half in and half out of the ocean. *Spartina*, for example, lives in salt marshes. Mangroves are small trees that live in estuaries with their roots partly submerged. Water in estuaries regularly varies in salinity with the tide and with rain and runoff. Incoming tides bring salty seawater; outgoing tides bring fresh water from upriver. Like other vascular plants, mangroves have true roots, stems, and leaves containing vascular tissue.

Seaweeds

Seaweeds are large marine algae classified as **macrophytes** (G. *macro* = large; G. *phyt* = plant). They are not vascular. Structurally a seaweed has three parts; a **holdfast,** a **stipe,** and a **blade** (which is sometimes broken up into leaflets). Although a holdfast looks like a root, it is not a true root because it has no vascular tissue. But it functions like a root, securing the seaweed to its substrate. A stipe, which looks like a stem, connects the blade or blades to the holdfast. But because stipes and blades have no vascular tissue, they are not considered stems and leaves. See Fig. 4–5.

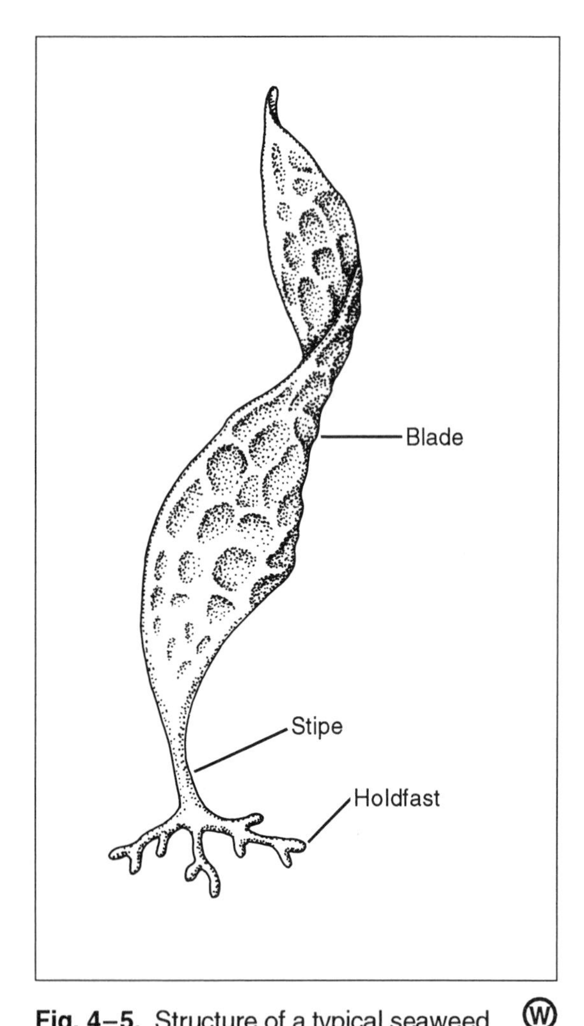

Fig. 4–5. Structure of a typical seaweed Ⓦ

Seaweeds are supported by the water around them. Because water continuously bathes them, supplying nutrients and carrying away wastes, they don't need a vascular system.

Photosynthesis occurs in algae, which, like vascular plants, use sugar for energy and for synthesizing other substances. In seaweeds, photosynthesis takes place primarily in the cells of the **medulla.** See Fig. 4–6, a cross-section of a typical seaweed.

The growth of seaweeds is limited by wave action, by herbivorous grazing animals, by nutrients in the water, by salt concentration of the water, and by the amount of sunlight. Sunlight varies from day to night and from season to season. The amount of sunlight penetrating the water also varies with the depth of the water and with turbidity caused by suspended particles in the water.

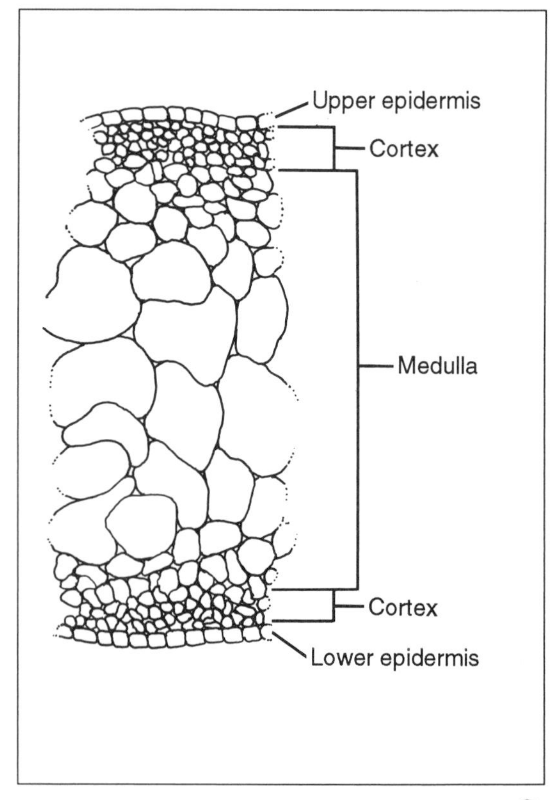

Fig. 4–6. Cross-section of a seaweed Ⓦ

QUESTIONS

1. What are the distinguishing characteristics of
   a. vascular land plants?
   b. vascular water plants?
   c. seaweeds?

2. Describe the similarities and differences between
   a. roots and holdfasts.
   b. leaves and blades.
   What are the functions of these structures?

3. How do seaweeds and vascular land plants compare in their structures and processes for
   a. photosynthesis?
   b. intake and distribution of nutrients?
   c. removal of wastes?
   d. exchange of gases?

ACTIVITY

Compare the characteristics of vascular land plants, vascular water plants, and seaweeds.

MATERIALS

- See lists for each test.

PROCEDURE

1. Divide the class into three teams to carry out one of the following tests on each type of plant:
   Test 1. Stomates
   Test 2. Cuticle
   Test 3. Lignin

2. Record your results. Prepare a team report to share your findings with the class.

3. After completing your tests and listening to the reports, go to the Summary Procedure at the end of this activity.

Test 1. Stomates

Compare the number of openings (stomates) on the surfaces of vascular land plants, vascular water plants, and seaweeds.

MATERIALS for Test 1

- at least two leaves or blades from
  a land plant from a hot, dry environment
  a land plant from a shady, moist environment
  a vascular freshwater plant
  a seaweed
- paper towels
- clear or pale fingernail polish
- 4 microscope slides and 8 coverslips
- fine-tipped waterproof marker
- forceps or toothpick
- compound microscope
- copy of Workbook Table 4–1

PROCEDURE for Test 1

1. In this activity we will use a nail polish "cast" for finding the number of stomates and their distribution in at least one sample of each of the following:
   a. a land-plant leaf from a hot, dry environment
   b. a land-plant leaf from a shady, moist environment
   c. a vascular freshwater plant
   d. a seaweed

2. With tap water, wash the leaves and blades. Pat them gently with a paper towel and let them dry in air.

3. For each plant, use two leaves or blades. For land plants, paint a thin patch of nail polish about 1 cm^2 on the upper surface of one leaf, a similar patch on the lower surface of the other leaf. For the blades of seaweeds or leaves of aquatic plants, you can paint long, narrow patches instead. (Using two leaves or blades will keep them from sticking to any other surface.) The dried polish will make a cast, or impression, of the surface features of the leaves and blades.

4. Prepare the microscope slides. Use one slide for each type of plant. With a fine-tipped waterproof marker, label each slide as shown in (A) in Fig. 4–7.
   a. Write the plant name or specimen number on the left of the slide.
   b. Write a *U* on the left where you will put the sample from the upper epidermis.
   c. Write an *L* on the right where you will put the sample from the lower epidermis.

5. Place the casts of stomates on the slides as follows:
   a. When the casts are dry, peel them off with the tips of the forceps or the pointed end of a toothpick.
   b. Place the casts from one plant on a slide with the side of the cast that touched the plant's surface facing up. Place the upper epidermal cast on the left and the lower epidermal cast on the right. See (B) in Fig. 4–7.
   c. Place a coverslip on each cast.

6. Observe the casts with a compound microscope. Record your observations in Table 4–1.
   a. Place a slide on the microscope stage. Focus at low power (40X), then at high power (100X). If stomates are present, they will resemble Fig. 4–2.
   b. Draw what you see at each power. Record the magnification.

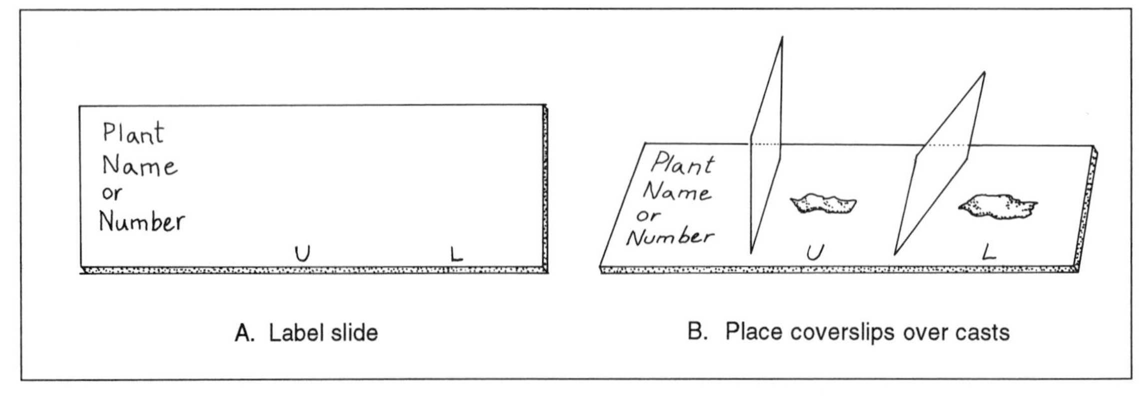

Fig. 4–7. Placing dried stomate casts on a microscope slide

7. Estimate the number of stomates you can see in the microscopic field. Record the data in Table 4–1.

8. Prepare to report the results of your work to the class.

QUESTIONS for Test 1

1. How did you estimate the number of stomates visible in the microscopic field?

2. For each plant, tell
   a. the numbers of stomates on its upper and lower epidermis.
   b. the patterns, if any, in the stomates on the two surfaces.

3. Compare the abundance of stomates on plants from different environments.
   a. Which plants have the most stomates? On which surface(s) did these stomates appear?
   b. Which plants, if any, had very few or no stomates? On which surfaces?
   c. Did any plants have stomates on just one surface? Which plant(s)? Which surface?

4. Compare the numbers and patterns of stomates on
   a. land plants from hot, dry environments and from shady, moist environments.

Table 4–1. Test 1. Comparison of stomate patterns and numbers in plants Ⓦ

Field	Magnification	Sketch of upper epidermis	Number of stomates in microscopic field	Sketch of lower epidermis	Number of stomates in microscopic field
Land plant from a hot, dry environment __________ (name)					
Land plant fom a shady, moist environment __________ (name)					
Vascular freshwater plant __________ (name)					
Seaweed __________ (name)					

b. vascular freshwater plants and seaweeds.
c. vascular freshwater plants and land plants.

5. From your observations, write a hypothesis to explain how these plants have adapted to different environments.

Test 2. Cuticle

Compare vascular land plants, vascular water plants, and seaweeds for the presence of a waxy cuticle.

MATERIALS for Test 2

- samples from
  a land plant from a hot, dry environment
  a land plant from a shady, moist environment
  a vascular freshwater plant
  a seaweed
- 4 microscope slides and coverslips
- single-edged razor blade
- Sudan IV stain solution in dropping bottle
- paper towels
- compound microscope
- copy of Workbook Table 4–2

PROCEDURE for Test 2

1. In vascular land plants, a waxy coat over the epidermis called the **cuticle** controls water loss. The Sudan IV staining method is an indicator for waxy cuticle layers on the upper and lower surfaces of leaves.

2. Cut a cross-section of a leaf from a plant in a hot, dry environment. Your teacher will demonstrate the technique described below. Use care in handling the razor blade.
   a. Place a 2-cm^2 piece of the leaf on a microscope slide.
   b. Put your index finger on the leaf at a 45° angle to the slide. Hold the razor blade in a vertical cutting position as shown in Fig. 4–8.
   c. Slowly lower your index finger as you make rapid, thin cuts in the leaf with the razor blade. Make 20 to 30 slices. When you finish, your finger

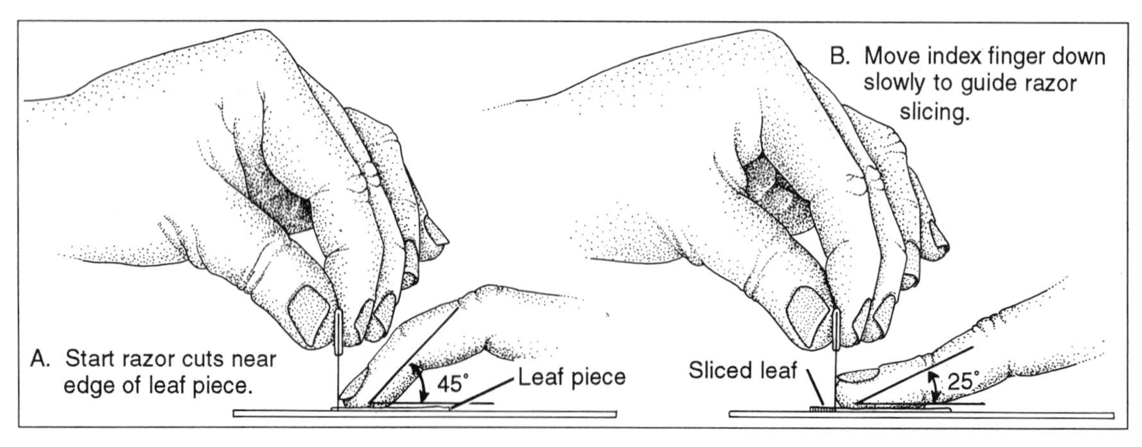

Fig. 4–8. Technique for slicing tissue into cross-sections

should be at the 25° position shown in Fig. 4–8.

CAUTION: Take care not to slice the tip of your finger.

d. Use two or three of the thinnest, most transparent slices. Discard the rest.
e. Position the thin slices on their sides so that you can see the exposed inner tissue. Add two drops of Sudan IV stain. Lay a coverslip over the slices. After 1 min, draw off the excess stain by placing a small piece of paper toweling along one edge of the coverslip.

3. Observe the cross-sections with a compound microscope at low magnification (about 40X). Record your observations in Table 4–2.
   a. Look for the cuticle below the lower and above the upper epidermis. If a cuticle is present, it will be pink or light red from the Sudan IV stain. Note any differences in the thickness of the cuticle.
   b. Draw the structures you see. Label the upper and lower epidermis and the cuticle. On your drawing, shade the stained areas. Record the magnification.

4. Repeat Procedures 1 through 3 using a leaf from a plant in a shady, moist environment, a leaf from a vascular freshwater plant, and a blade from the seaweed. Select thick leaves and blades for making cross-sections so that you can easily see the upper and lower surfaces when you view the section on its side.

5. Prepare to present your findings to the class.

Table 4–2. Test 2. Comparison of cuticle in plants

Leaf or blade sample	Drawing of cross-section
Land plant from a hot, dry environment __________________ (plant name) (magnification)	
Land plant from a shady, moist environment __________________ (plant name) (magnification)	
Vascular freshwater plant __________________ (plant name) (magnification)	
Seaweed __________________ (plant name) (magnification)	

QUESTIONS for Test 2

6. How did you select the thinnest sections to stain?

7. For each plant, tell whether it had a cuticle and how thick it was on
   a. the upper surface.
   b. the lower surface.

8. On which plant(s) was the cuticle thickest? On which surface? How might this be an advantage to the plant?

9. On which plant(s) did you find little or no cuticle? Is the cuticle missing from both surfaces? How might the lack of a cuticle be an advantage to the plant?

10. Compare the presence or absence of cuticle on
    a. land plants from hot, dry environments and from shady, moist environments.
    b. vascular freshwater plants and seaweeds.
    c. vascular freshwater plants and land plants.

11. What relationships, if any, did you find between plant environments and the presence of cuticle in the plants? How might the presence of cuticle relate to adaptation to different environments?

Test 3. Lignin

Test for the presence of a stiffening substance (lignin) in cells of vascular land plants, vascular freshwater plants, and seaweeds.

MATERIALS for Test 3

- stem samples from
  - a land plant from a hot, dry environment
  - a land plant from a shady, moist environment
  - a vascular freshwater plant
  - a seaweed
- 4 microscope slides and coverslips
- single-edged razor blade
- phloroglucinol stain in dropping bottle
- paper towels
- hydrochloric acid (3N HCl) in dropping bottle
- forceps
- compound microscope
- copy of Workbook Table 4–3

PROCEDURE for Test 3

1. Lignin is a material that stiffens plant cell walls, making plants stiff and woody. Phloroglucinol stains lignin pink. See Fig. 4–2.

2. Prepare and stain a thin cross-section of a stem from a plant in a hot, dry environment.
   a. Using a single-edged razor blade, cut six thin cross-sections from a land-plant stem onto a microscope slide. Follow the directions given in Test 2, Procedure 2, and illustrated in Fig. 4–8. Select two of the thinnest sections and discard the others.
   b. Place the cross-sections on a slide and cover them with two drops of phloroglucinol stain. After 2 min, remove the excess stain by drawing off the liquid with the edge of a piece of paper towel.

c. Cover the stained cross-sections with two drops of hydrochloric acid (3N HCl).

CAUTION: Hydrochloric acid (HCl) can produce chemical burns. If you get it on your skin or clothing, wash it off at once with a large quantity of water and notify your teacher.

d. Using forceps, place a coverslip over the cross-sections. After about 1 min, draw off the excess acid by touching a paper towel to one edge of the coverslip.

3. Observe the stained cross-sections with a compound microscope at low magnification (about 40X).
   a. Look for tissue areas that stain pink. These contain lignin.
   b. Draw a cross-section in Table 4–3. Make arrows to show the structures that turned pink with this stain. Record the magnification.

4. Repeat Procedures 1 and 2 using a stem from a plant in a shady, moist environment, a stem from a vascular freshwater plant, and a stipe from a seaweed.

5. Analyze your data and prepare to share your findings with the class.

Table 4–3. Test 3. Comparison of lignin in cross-sections of plants 

Leaf or blade sample	Drawing of cross-section
Land plant from a hot, dry environment ______________________ (plant name) (magnification)	
Land plant from a shady, moist environment ______________________ (plant name) (magnification)	
Vascular freshwater plant ______________________ (plant name) (magnification)	
Seaweed ______________________ (plant name) (magnification)	

QUESTIONS for Test 3

12. Describe the procedure for drawing off excess staining fluid from the cross-sections.

13. Describe the distribution of lignin in each plant.

14. Which plants have
    a. the most lignin? Where is the lignin in the cross-section?
    b. the least lignin?

15. Compare the amount of lignin in
    a. land plants from hot, dry environments and shady, moist environments.
    b. vascular freshwater plants and seaweeds.
    c. vascular freshwater plants and land plants.

16. What relationships, if any, did you find between plant environments and the amounts of lignin in the plants? How might the distribution of lignin relate to adaptation to different environments?

SUMMARY PROCEDURE

1. As each team reports, summarize the results. In Table 4–4 use a (+) to indicate that a plant has that characteristic or a (–) to indicate that it does not have it.

2. Complete Table 4–5 by describing the plant structures that enable each kind of plant to adapt to each environmental factor listed.

Table 4–4. Comparison of plant characteristics Ⓦ

Plant specimen	Test 1. Stomates		Test 2. Cuticle	Test 3. Lignin
	Upper	Lower		
Land plant from a hot, dry environment				
Land plant from a shady, moist, environment				
Vascular freshwater plant				
Seaweed				

Table 4–5. Plant structural adaptations to environmental factors 

Environmental factors	Vascular land plant structures	Vascular freshwater plant structures	Seaweed structures
Water intake Water loss			
Exchange of oxygen & carbon dioxide gases			
Gravitational stress			
Mechanical stress			
Nutrient supply			

QUESTIONS

4. What structural differences did you find in land plants and water plants that adapt them to their environments?

5. What structure, if any, in each of the following plants helps to prevent drying out?
   a. plants that live in dry, hot environments
   b. plants that live in shady, moist environments
   c. plants that live in fresh water

6. Which plants do not have stomates? How do these plants exchange water, carbon dioxide, and oxygen with their environment?

7. Which plants have lignin? What advantages and disadvantages does lignin give them?

8. Without a cuticle, how does a plant prevent water loss? For which type(s) of plants is water loss an environmental problem?

9. Compare the following types of plants:
   a. plants from hot, dry surroundings

and ones from shady, moist environments
   b. freshwater plants and land plants
   c. freshwater plants and seaweeds

10. How might the presence or absence of the structures you listed in Table 4–4 be related to the environment in which the plant grows? Give specific examples.

FURTHER INVESTIGATIONS

1. Test for lignin, cuticle, and stomates in a variety of plants of different sizes and environments, including
   a. beach plants.
   b. desert plants.
   c. wetland (marsh) plants.
   d. plants in your yard.
   e. aquarium plants.
   f. water lilies.

2. From the environment in which a land plant lives, predict the appearance of the cross-section of a leaf. Test your prediction by staining and examining cross-sections of a leaf.

3. Make cross-sections of a variety of algae structures and compare them with the one in Fig. 4–6.

4. Using library references, learn how dehydration techniques are used to preserve foods. Some foods are air-dried, some are freeze-dried, and others are baked or microwaved dry.

5. Find out how to use an oven or a microwave to dry and preserve herbs. Demonstrate the procedure to the class.

6. Use botany reference books to learn more about the structural differences
   a. among seaweeds and other marine algae. Learn more about the structures and life cycles of green algae (*Chlorophyta*), brown algae (*Phaeophyta*), red algae (*Rhodophyta*), and blue-green algae (*Cyanophyta*).
   b. among vascular land plants and water plants. Look especially at the few flowering plants (angiosperms) that live partly or completely submerged in water, such as eel grass, turtle grass, marsh grass, and mangrove.

5. Coastal Strand Plants

For most people, a visit to a seashore beach is a pleasant summer experience. A cool breeze, a dip in the ocean, and a nap on the sand add up to a relaxing day. But for plants that live along the shoreline, it is a harsh environment. The constant breeze evaporates moisture from leaves and soil. Saltwater spray from breaking waves blows inland, coating the leaves. When the water evaporates, it leaves a crust of salt. Rainwater washes the salt into the sandy soil, leaving it salty when the water evaporates Plants that cannot tolerate these conditions die, leaving only a few hardy species to dominate the region. In this topic we will study how these rugged coastal plants have adapted to their environment.

ACTIVITY 1

Simulate the effects of salt spray on plants.

MATERIALS

- 2 potted beach plants with watering dish
- 2 potted inland plants with watering dish
- watering can
- plastic wrap
- spray bottle filled with seawater
- spray bottle filled with fresh water
- scissors
- red and black pencils
- copies of Workbook Fig. 5–1 and Table 5–2
- overhead transparency (optional)
- red and black overhead transparency pens (optional)
- tests for stomata and cuticle from Topic 4 (optional)

PROCEDURE

1. Set the plants where they will get northern light. Let them adjust to the classroom climate for about a week. Water the soil regularly with tap water.

2. Before you begin this experiment, predict which plant(s) will be the most tolerant to salt spray, the coastal plant or the inland plant. **Tolerant** here means able to survive the most punishment from salt spray. Record your prediction and reason for it in your notebook.

3. When you are ready for the experiment, cover the moist soil of all plants with plastic wrap to prevent moisture loss and buildup. Use one plant of each type for a control, the other for the experiment.

4. Working with your partners, spray the experimental plants with seawater spray and the control plants with freshwater spray, following a schedule like the one in Table 5–1. This schedule will simulate the irregularity of sea spray along coastlines. Spray the plants lightly; do not drench them.

5. At the same time each day, estimate the amount of foliage injury. **Foliage injury** is any leaf discoloration such as browning, yellowing, spotting, or wrinkling. Each day, record the following data in Table 5–2:
   a. On the first day, observe and count the leaves on each plant. Note their normal appearance so that you will be able to identify an injured leaf.
   b. Each day after spraying begins, observe and count the injured leaves. Record the count and calculate the percentage of injured leaves as follows:

$$\frac{\text{No. of injured leaves}}{\text{Original no. of leaves}} \times 100 = \text{percentage of injured leaves}$$

6. Check periodically to see if the potting soil under the plastic wrap needs tap water. Keep the soil moist.

7. On the sixth day, wash the salt from the leaves and stems by spraying them with tap water.
   a. Hold the potted plant horizontally to make sure that no salt enters the potting soil. Spray until the water flows freely off all the leaves. Do this for all the plants.
   b. After washing the plants, do not apply any more salt water.

8. Observe the plants every day for 10 days. Determine which plants best survived the salt spray.

Table 5–1. Schedule for salt spraying

Day	8 a.m.	11 a.m.	1 p.m.	3 p.m.
1	spray			
2	spray			spray
3	spray	spray		spray
4	spray	spray	spray	spray
5	spray			

Table 5–2. Plant response to spraying Ⓦ

Plant treatment	Days									
	1	2	3	4	5	6	7	8	9	10
Coastal plant control (sprayed with fresh water) 1. Number of original leaves 2. Number of injured leaves 3. Percentage of injured leaves 4. Number of new leaves 5. Other observations										
Coastal plant experiment (sprayed with seawater) 1. Number of original leaves 2. Number of nijured leaves 3. Percentage of injured leaves 4. Number of new leaves 5. Other observations										
Inland plant control (sprayed with fresh water) 1. Number of original leaves 2. Number of injured leaves 3. Percentage of injured leaves 4. Number of new leaves 5. Other observations										
Inland plant experiment (sprayed with seawater) 1. Number of original leaves 2. Number of injured leaves 3. Percentage of injured leaves 4. Number of new leaves 5. Other observations										

9. Graph the data from Table 5–2.
   a. Use a red pencil for the coastal plants. Plot the data for the control plant and graph it as a dotted line. Then plot the data for the treated plant and graph it as a solid line. See Fig. 5–1.
   b. Using a black pencil for the inland plants, repeat Procedure 9.a.
   c. If overhead transparency film and marking pens are available, trace the graph on a transparency so you can share it with your class.

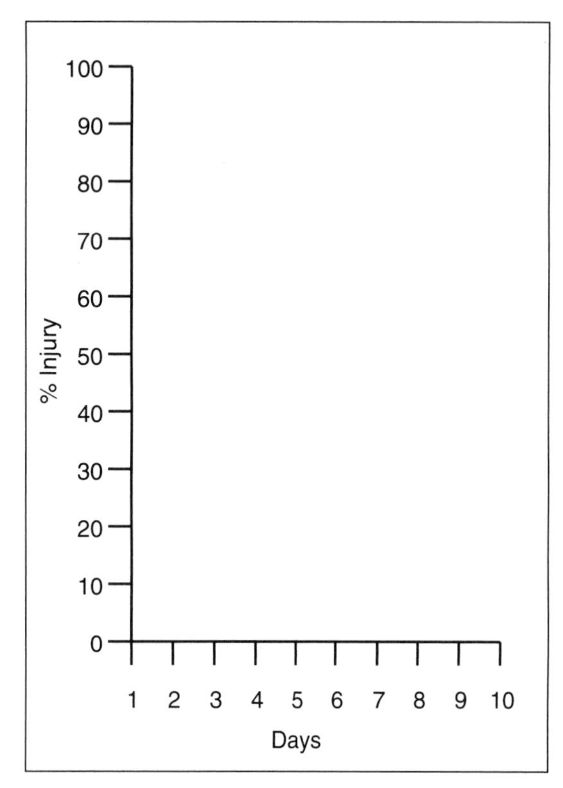

Fig. 5–1. Plant response to salt spray and freshwater spray

10. Be ready to describe and interpret your results with the class.

11. (Optional) Test for differences in stomata and waxy cuticle in inland plants and coastal plants. See Topic 4, Structural Differences Between Land Plants and Water Plants.

QUESTIONS

1. What is meant by salt tolerance?

2. Which plant was more salt-tolerant, the inland plant or the coastal plant? Suggest an explanation for the differences that you observed.

3. How did an increased quantity of salt spray affect
   a. the inland plant?
   b. the coastal plant?

4. What effect did washing the leaves with fresh water have
   a. on the inland plant?
   b. on the coastal plant?

5. What was the control in this experiment? What is the purpose of having controls? Why were the controls sprayed with fresh water?

6. Compare your test results with other teams' results.
   a. Make a data table showing the results of all tests on inland and coastal plants.
   b. Review the data. If necessary, revise your answers to Questions 2 and 3.

7. Which seasons of the year and types of weather would deposit the most salt on the leaves and stems of coastal plants?

Osmosis

Plants perform the basic life processes in their cells, which are bathed outside and inside with liquids that carry molecules of water, wastes, and nutrients. In vascular plants and seaweeds a liquid surrounds the cell.

All cells are enclosed in membranes. These membranes have tiny holes just large enough to permit the passage of water, waste molecules, and nutrient molecules. But the holes do not allow very large molecules of protein or fat, which are essential to the cell's structure, to leave the cell. Such membranes are called **semipermeable** membranes.

The spreading of material from an area of high concentration to an area of lower concentration is called **diffusion.** You can observe diffusion by putting a drop of food coloring in a glass of water. The food coloring moves slowly in all directions, eventually spreading evenly through the water. As the food coloring diffuses to a region of low food-coloring concentration, the water diffuses to an area of low water concentration, into the drop of food coloring.

Water moves through a membrane in a special kind of diffusion called **osmosis.** As in all diffusion, molecules tend to move from a place of high concentration to a place of low concentration.

When the concentration of large molecules is higher in the cells than in the surrounding cell sap, water molecules enter the cell by osmosis, causing the cell to swell. When the concentration of water inside the cell is greater than the concentration of water in the surrounding cell sap, water flows out of the cell, causing the cell to shrink.

To function properly, living plant cells must maintain a minimum amount of water. Since most chemical reactions need water, loss of water below the minimum level causes cells to malfunction and eventually to die. See (A) in Fig. 5–2. Excess water entering a cell may create enough pressure to disrupt structures within the cell or even to rupture the cell. See (B) in Fig 5–2. Many cells have developed ways of controlling the amount of water within them.

QUESTIONS

8. What is diffusion? Describe how it would disperse salt in a beaker of water.

9. How is osmosis similar to and different from diffusion?

10. How do plant cells get needed nutrients from cell sap? How do they get rid of wastes?

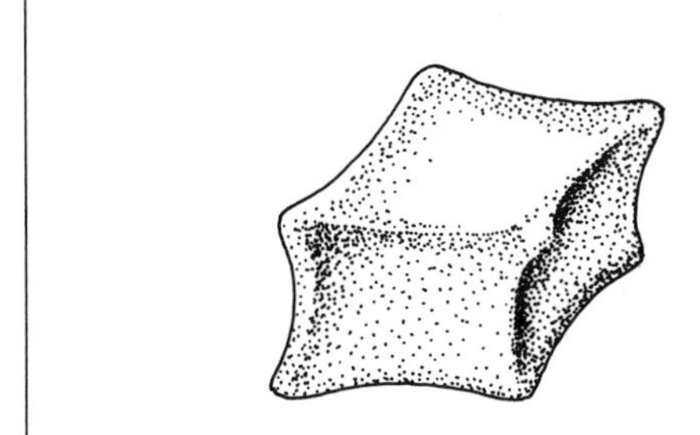

A. Cell with insufficient internal water. The membrane shrivels.

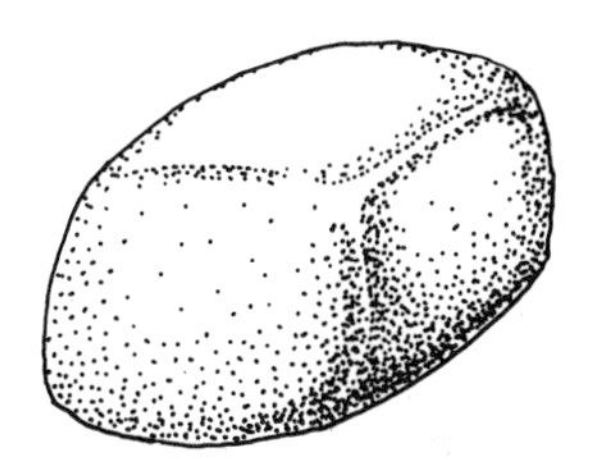

B. Cell with excess internal water. The membrane swells.

Fig. 5–2. Osmosis in plant cells

Salinity tolerance refers to the range of salt concentrations that an organism can survive in. Distilled water contains no salt. Its salinity is 0%. Fresh water in a lake, a river, or a stream has a lower salt concentration than the cell sap of the plants that live in and around the water. The average salinity of seawater, where seaweeds live, is about 3.5%. The salt spray that coats coastal land plants has a higher salt concentration than the cell sap of the land plants.

ACTIVITY 2

Test the salinity tolerances of a freshwater plant cell, a land-plant cell, and a marine algae cell.

MATERIALS

- plants: *Croton*, *Elodea*, and *Cladophora* (or *Ulva*)
- scalpel or single-edged razor blade
- 3 microscope slides and coverslips
- solutions in dropping bottles:
  0% (distilled water)
  6 % salt solution (about double the concentration of seawater)
- compound microscope
- copy of Workbook Fig. 5–3
- paper towels
- copy of Workbook Table 5–3

PROCEDURE

1. Test the salinity tolerance of a freshwater plant exposed first to fresh water (0% solution), then to salty water (6% solution), and again to fresh water (0% solution.)
   a. Using a scalpel or a single-edged razor blade, make thin cross-sections from the tip of an *Elodea* leaf. Place the section on a slide and cover it with a drop of distilled water (0% solution) and a coverslip. Observe it through the microscope at low power. Select an area of the section where you can easily see individual cells. Carefully draw a group of cells and their internal parts in (A) in Fig. 5–3.
   b. Observe the same cells exposed to a 6% salt solution. Note the time that you begin. Add 2 drops of the 6% salt solution to one edge of the coverslip. Touch a paper towel to the opposite edge of the coverslip to draw the saltwater solution across the sample. Look for changes in the arrangement of the internal cell structures. View for 2 minutes; then draw the internal cell structures in (B) in Fig. 5–3.
   c. Replace the salt solution with the 0% distilled water solution by placing two drops of distilled water at one edge of the coverslip and touching the other edge with dry paper toweling to draw off the saltwater solution. Record the total exposure time to the saltwater solution. Total exposure time begins when you first expose the cell to the salt water; it ends when you finish replacing the salt water with distilled water.
   d. Observe what happens to the cells. Draw your observations in (C) in Fig. 5–3.
   e. Determine whether there was recovery of the cells. **Recovery** is the

return of the cells and their contents to their original shape and size. Compare (C) with (A) in Fig. 5–3. Record your conclusion in Table 5–3.

A. Cells exposed to 0% salt solution (distilled water)	B. Cells exposed to 6% salt solution	C. Cells returned from 6% salt solution to 0% solution
Vascular freshwater plant	Vascular freshwater plant	Vascular freshwater plant
Land plant	Land plant	Land plant
Seaweed	Seaweed	Seaweed

Fig. 5–3. Drawings of plant cells exposed to freshwater and saltwater solutions 

Table 5–3. Recovery of plant cells exposed to salt solutions 

Plant	Exposure time to salt solution (min)	Recovery (Yes or No)
Freshwater plant *(Elodea)*		
Land plant *(Croton)*		
Seaweed (marine algae) *(Cladophora)*		

2. Repeat Procedures 1.a. through 1.e. using the land plant and the alga. Record your results in Fig. 5–3 and Table 5–3.

QUESTIONS

11. How did the response of the cells to fresh water differ
    a. in land plants?
    b. in freshwater plants?
    c. in seaweeds?

12. How are your observations in this activity related to osmosis?

Coastal Plant Zonation

In salt concentration and amount of available fresh water, the beach is like a desert. Because few plants can adapt to such harsh conditions, plant populations in a coastal environment are not as diverse as in other areas.

Even among plants adapted to living in coastal and desert environments, some are more resistant to drying and some are more salt-tolerant. These differences contribute to the zonation of coastal plants. **Zonation** is the progressive change in types of organisms within one kind of ecological community, such as a shoreline community. Plants that can survive and reproduce in a difficult area have a better chance of monopolizing that area. See Fig. 5–4.

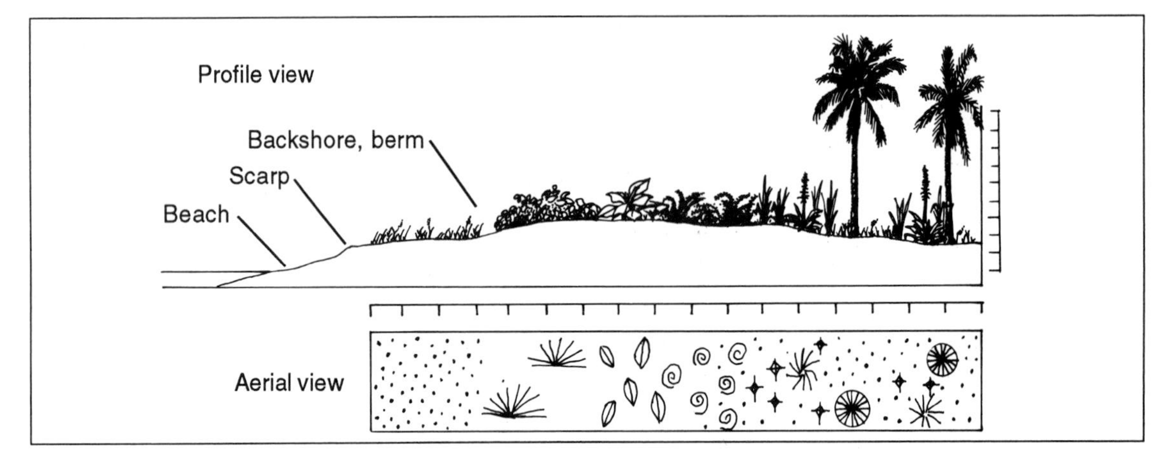

Fig. 5–4. Zonation of plants on a coastal strand

ACTIVITY 3

Identify common beach plants and describe their features.

Describe coastal plant zonation along a transect line.

Relate physical characteristics of plants to zonation.

MATERIALS

- transect line, 25–50 m, marked at 5-m intervals
- clipboard, pencil, and paper
- camera (optional)
- 25 white tags with strings
- 25 plastic bags or envelopes
- copies of Workbook Table 5–4
- plant identification books
- plant press (see Topic 2)

PROCEDURE

1. Select a beach study site. Look for an area with two or more overlapping plant populations within 50 m of the scarp. The **scarp** is the sharp, steplike falloff in the beach caused by wave action. See Fig. 5–4.

a. Lay the transect line perpendicular to the shoreline. Begin your study along the transect line where the vegetation begins and goes inland.
b. Sketch a profile of your study site. The horizontal and vertical scales of the profile should be fairly accurate. See the example in Fig. 5–4.

2. Walking inland along the transect line, identify species of plants.
   a. For each species, measure its location along the transect line where the plants are distributed.

   NOTE: Many coastal areas are now protected to prevent erosion. Read and obey posted signs.

   b. Determine whether the species is common or rare in that region of the transect. Record the information in Table 5–4.
   c. Sketch the location and abundance of each species on your profile sketch of the transect. See Fig. 5–4 for an example of a profile sketch showing species and abundance of plants.

3. Collect samples of each kind of common plant, including seeds, roots, leaves, and flowers if possible. Common plants are ones that are abundant in an area. Do not collect samples of plants that are scarce in the study area. Instead, sketch or photograph them.
   a. For each specimen prepare a tag with a number and symbol to identify it.
   b. Put each tagged specimen and its seeds in a plastic bag. You will use the specimens in Procedure 4.

4. After returning to class, do the following with your specimens:
   a. Complete Table 5–4. Use reference books to identify each specimen by its scientific name. Make checks in the columns that best describe the root, stem, and leaf features of each specimen.
   b. Prepare a permanent pressed collection of the common coastal plant species you found. Include a drawing of the plant's seed. (For information on pressing and labeling specimens, see Topic 2, Pressing Seaweeds. You will not need to float the specimens out in water.)

QUESTIONS

12. Describe the zonation of the plants along the transect line.

13. Which plants are common
    a. near the scarp?
    b. on the back shore?
    c. farther inland?

14. What features, if any, do plants in the same habitat have in common? What is your evidence?

15. What relationships, if any, are there between plant features and plant zonation along a beach?

16. Compare the results from your transect study with others' results from their

Table 5–4. Features of common coastal plants

Features	Plant #___	Plant #___	Plant #___	Plant #___	Plant #___	Plant #___
Plant name						
Location along transect						
Abundance of plant (common or rare)						
Leaf type						
Grass blade type						
Wide with blunt tip						
Wide with pointed tip						
Flat, thin leaves						
Fat, puffy leaves						
Lobed edge on leaves						
Leaf texture						
Waxy						
Smooth						
Hairy						
Stem type						
Woody stem						
Green stem						
Swollen stem						
Many branching stems						
Single stem per plant						
Root type						
Fibrous mass of roots						
Single root (taproot)						

studies. Were the same kinds of plants found in the same or different kinds of habitats? How could this be explained?

FURTHER INVESTIGATIONS

1. Conduct a zonation study of plants from a freshwater site, such as a lake, marsh, or stream. Compare your results with the results of your coastal plant study.
2. Study the relationships between plants and the formation of sand dunes. Observe coastal changes over two months. Decide how, if at all, these are related to coastal plants.
3. Set up an experiment to determine the effect of salt on the root systems and seeds of plants. How important are root

systems and seeds to beach plants?

4. Design and carry out an experiment to determine the ability of inland plants and coastal plants to tolerate watering the soil with water of different salinities.

5. Design and test ways for using seawater or brackish water for agriculture. Use library references to find what progress has been made in using brackish water or seawater to grow crops to alleviate food shortages.

6. Seaweed Beach Drift

Most seaweeds attach themselves to rocks or other hard surfaces, so they grow along rocky coastlines, in tidepools, and in offshore areas with solid substrates. They seldom grow in mud or shifting sand. On solid surfaces they often coat the tops, sides, and even the crevices.

Seaweed distribution along coastal shores and in tidepools depends on the plants' tolerance for agitation by waves, air exposure during low tides, and changes in water temperature and salinity. Storm waves dislodge seaweeds and set them adrift. Some seaweeds break up naturally as they mature.

In this topic we examine **driftweeds**, the seaweeds that wash ashore. This term includes unattached seaweeds, like *Sargassum*, that may be carried to shore by winds, waves, currents, and tides.

Every year huge amounts of seaweed are washed onto beaches. Driftweeds often wash in and out with the waves, annoying waders when weeds wrap around their ankles. During low tides the driftweeds often lie in clumps or rows along the high-tide line. Storms can deposit piles of driftweeds high up on the beach.

On first arrival, driftweeds are fresh and potentially usable as food or fertilizer. Sea birds and crabs forage among them to pick off attached animals to eat. Swarms of tiny herbivorous crustaceans consume some of these seaweeds, but some remain to dry and decay on the beach.

In this activity we will sort through fresh driftweed to learn more about the kinds of seaweeds that grow offshore and to determine what kinds of animals live among the seaweeds.

QUESTIONS

1. How might each of these conditions change the environment in which seaweeds grow?
   a. low tides
   b. freshwater runoff after heavy rains
   c. rising water temperature in a tidepool

2. What environmental factors might
   a. dislodge seaweeds?
   b. deposit them on shore?

3. Is driftweed commonly or rarely deposited on a beach? Explain your reasoning.

4. What are some possible
   a. uses for seaweed beach drift?
   b. reasons why people often ignore seaweed beach drift?

5. What eventually happens to seaweed beach drift? Where does it go?

ACTIVITY

Examine fresh seaweeds collected from beach drift.
Look for animals that live among these seaweeds.

MATERIALS

- rubber gloves
- two 5-gal buckets with handles and lids
- 10 reusable gallon-size plastic bags
- waterproof marker
- balance
- key to local seaweeds (optional)
- magnifying lens or dissecting microscope

PROCEDURE

1. Collect one bucketful of fresh seaweeds that you find washed upon the beach. Half-fill the second bucket with seawater.

   CAUTION: Wear rubber gloves as you work with the seaweeds. Watch for possible entangled objects like fishhooks or stinging organisms like jellyfish (the Portuguese man-of-war, for example).

2. (Optional) While at the beach, sit in a safe area and observe
   a. evidence of waves, currents, and tides that bring the driftweed to shore.
   b. animals eating seaweeds or foraging among them for food.

3. Determine the percentage composition of the collected seaweeds in the bucket. Record the information in Table 6–1. Make additional tables as needed.
   a. Weigh each dry, empty gallon-size bag. Mark each bag with its mass and an identification number.
   b. Rinse the seaweeds in the second bucket of seawater. Drain the water from the seaweeds and save the bucket of drained seawater for Procedure 5.
   c. Put all the rinsed seaweed into large, preweighed plastic bags. Use as few bags as possible. Weigh the total mass of the seaweeds and the bags. Subtract the bag mass from the total mass. Record the total wet mass of the seaweeds in Table 6–1.
   d. Now separate the seaweeds, sorting each kind into its own dry, preweighed plastic bag. Weigh each bag of seaweed, and record its mass.
   e. Calculate the percentage composition by mass of each kind of seaweed as follows:

$$\text{\% Composition of one kind of seaweed} = \frac{\text{total mass of one kind of seaweed}}{\text{total mass of all seaweeds in the bucket}} \times 100$$

4. (Optional) Using a key to common seaweeds, identify the seaweeds you collected. Record the names in Table 6–1. Write the names on the bags with the seaweeds.

Table 6–1. Percentage composition of a sample of seaweed beach drift Ⓦ

Team # ________ Sample site: ________	Bucket # ________	Date: ________
Seaweed name by genus (and species, if known)	Wet mass (g)	% Composition
	Total wet mass of all seaweeds: ________ (g)	100%

5. As soon as possible, observe the animals associated with the seaweeds. Describe or sketch your observations in Table 6–2.
   a. Search for encrusting animals such as sponges, tunicates, mollusks, or corals. Work with a small clump of seaweed at a time. When you find an encrusting animal, tear off a small piece of the seaweed with the animal attached. Use a hand lens or dissecting microscope to view the animal. Identify the animals to their phylum level and, when possible, to their class.
   b. Look for small swimming animals in the rinse water from Procedure 3.b.

Table 6–2. Animals found in seaweed beach drift

Ⓦ

Team # _______ Bucket # _______ Date: ____________

Sample site: ____

Animals by phylum	Sketches and descriptions of animals
Protista (single-celled animals such as foraminifera, protozoa)	
Porifera (sponges)	
Cnidaria (anemones, jellyfish, coral)	
Platyhelminthes (flatworms)	
Annelida (segmented worms)	
Echinodermata (sea urchins, sea stars, brittle stars)	
Mollusca (bivalves, gastropods, cephalopods)	
Arthropoda (crustaceans, insects)	
Chordata (tunicates, lancelets, small fish)	

Pour the seawater into an empty resealable gallon-sized plastic bag. You now have a temporary aquarium. Hold it at eye level.

c. Look for moving animals among the seaweeds. Put one or several pieces of each kind of seaweed in the plastic-bag aquarium. Hold the bag at eye level. Look carefully for movement among the seaweeds.

6. Look for entangled objects among the seaweeds. These may be manufactured things such as fish line and hooks or shredded plastic debris. Watch also for entangled organisms like jellyfish. Record your findings.

QUESTIONS

6. According to your calculations of percentage composition, which seaweed in your sample is the most abundant? From evidence of waves, currents, tides, and wind, where do you think the seaweed grows?

7. In the sample you studied,
   a. what animals were living in or on seaweeds?
   b. how, if at all, were animals living in seaweeds adapted to their habitat? Give examples.
   c. how might you describe the relationships between these animals and the seaweeds?

8. Did you find animals in all of the seaweeds? Did some animals appear to prefer specific kinds of seaweeds? Describe your findings.

9. The procedure called for wearing rubber gloves for handling seaweed beach drift. Suggest reasons for wearing the gloves.

10. Assuming that the seaweeds are fresh and edible, how would you prepare them for eating? Refer to Topic 1, Seaweeds as a Food Resource.

11. To what extent do unraveled ropes, fishing lines, and pieces of nets resemble seaweeds? How could their resemblance be a problem to animals?

FURTHER INVESTIGATIONS

1. Observe a beach to determine how often driftweed washes ashore. Record and interpret your observations. What factors appear to be associated with beach drift washing ashore? Decide whether there is a predictable periodic or seasonal pattern to their appearance. If possible, examine bathymetric charts for areas where seaweeds might grow.

2. Each time driftweed appears on your beach, look for seasonal change in its components. Identify the dominant seaweeds for each drift period or season.

3. Use some of the fresh seaweed as a fertilizer. Set up an experiment to determine its effectiveness. Prepare a demonstration of its use as a fertilizer.

4. Look for seeds and nuts from land plants in the beach drift. Try to determine where they may have come from. Try to germinate (grow) the drifted seeds. Determine

what kinds of seeds tolerate long soaking in seawater. Learn more about plants that have dispersed by drifting from place to place in the ocean.

5. Conduct quantitative studies of the distribution of living, attached nearshore seaweeds. Practice using transect lines. See Topic 5.

6. Seaweeds grow rapidly in nutrient-rich waters. In nearshore locations where runoff carries fertilizers into the ocean, coral reefs may be covered by seaweed that smothers the polyps and kills the reef. Learn about efforts to protect coral reefs.

7. Learn about different cultural and traditional uses of seaweeds. Invite a guest speaker to class.

8. Collect driftwood. Suggest ways of using it. Share your ideas with the class.

UNIT 4
ECOLOGY

Alone on the beach, I thought about Lahua's story. Lahua was born on a tropical island. She remembered how in her childhood the island had supplied everything needed for food, boats, nets, houses, and clothing. Lahua's people knew the ways of peace and solved their conflicts in ceremonial council.

Then soldiers and sailors speaking another tongue came with great machines and turned the island into a fortress. Lahua's people could no longer fish or farm. They had to eat food from cans and boxes and live in galvanized huts built for them. In time the war ended, and a new group of outsiders came, telling the council that the island's people could become rich if the council would sell the rights to the minerals in the island. These outsiders promised that the people could have their island back after the minerals were removed. After meeting for many days, the council agreed to the bargain. Lahua and the others took the money and went to live in a friendless world beyond their island.

Today the island's reef has been blasted to open a harbor for great ore ships, and the land is being planed flat as bulldozers and earthmovers carry off the mineral treasure. Lahua's home is now a sterile rock.

In muted ways, Lahua's story is ours as we fill in our coastal wetlands for industries, dam our rivers or change their courses, choke our creeks and canals with wastes, and overharvest our waters.

With this cautionary tale we take up a study of interactions of plants and animals with their environments—interactions that make life possible in the sea and on land but that human actions disrupt. The hope for sustaining our environmental heritage depends on our collective knowledge of these interactions and our commitment to use our global resources wisely.

Francis M. Pottenger III

1. Global Ecological Systems

Ecology is the study of the interactions among organisms and their environments. If we are to study the ecology of the oceans, we must describe the plants and animals that live there. We must also describe how the oceans and life in them interact as part of the global environment.

For explaining the ecology of an area, we often group things into **categories.** Then we use these categories to generalize about the way nature behaves. Categories are particularly handy in generalizing about **interactions**—the way things behave in relation to each other.

One technique for showing interactions is to draw arrows from a category that is acting (attracting, radiating, destroying, etc.) to each of the categories it acts upon. A diagram showing interactions between categories is called a **systems diagram.**

ACTIVITY

Make a systems diagram showing interactions between categories of things that make up the earth's global environment.

MATERIALS

- copies of Workbook Fig. 1–1 and Tables 1–1 and 1–2

PROCEDURE

1. Identify categories of things that belong to and interact with the global environment.
   a. Begin with the categories in Table 1–1. Examine both the definitions and their symbols.
   b. Decide whether these cover all the major categories in the global environment. You may add, delete, or modify any categories, definitions, or symbols. Record your changes in Table 1–1.
2. Make a systems diagram of the global environment that shows interactions between the categories. Work in pencil

Table 1–1. Possible categories for a systems diagram of the global environment Ⓦ

Category	Symbol
Biological environment (nonhuman). All plants and animals on the earth other than human beings.	
Physical environment (nonhuman). All the land, ocean, atmosphere, weather, climate and other nonliving (abiotic) features not constructed or produced by humans.	
Humans. Men, women, and children. By the year 2000, the human population will be close to 6 billion.	
Technology. Things and processes made by humans.	
Sun. The star at the center of our solar system, around which the earth and planets revolve and from which they receive heat and light. Energy from the son is called radiant energy, solar energy, or sunlight.	
Moon. The natural satellite revolving around the earth affecting tides.	
Planets, stars, and other objects in space. All natural heavenly bodies except the sun and the moon.	
Other.	

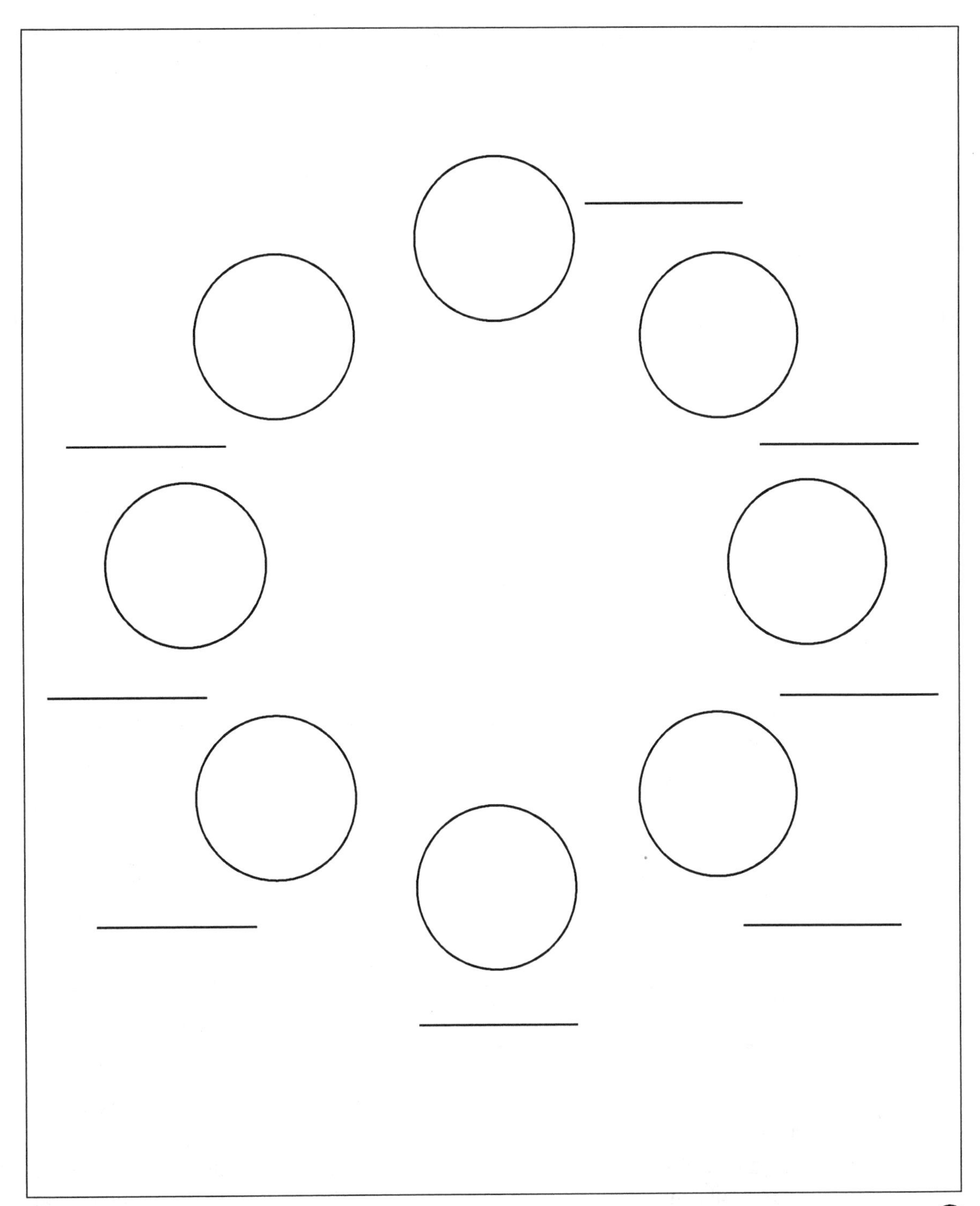

Fig. 1–1. Systems diagram of the earth's global environment

Ⓦ

Table 1–2. Interactions between categories in a systems diagram of the global environment Ⓦ

Category	Interaction line numbers	Line points to category	Nature of interaction
Biological environment (nonhuman)			
Physical environment (nonhuman)			
Humans			
Technology			
Sun		Biological environment	The sun supplies light, gravity, and solar energy to the biological environment
Moon			
Planets, stars, and other natural objects			
Other			

because you will modify your diagram in Procedure 4.

a. Start with a copy of Fig. 1–1. Let each circle represent a category in Table 1–1. Sketch each category symbol in a circle and write its name in the blank next to that circle.

b. Show interactions between categories by drawing lines connecting categories that interact. At the end of each line, draw an arrowhead pointing to the category acted upon. If interactions go in both directions, draw arrowheads on both ends of the line.

3. Describe how each category interacts with other categories.
   a. Start with one category circle. Number each interaction line that goes from that category circle to other circles. Then go to the next circle and continue numbering the lines until they are all numbered.
   b. Beginning with the first category and the first interaction line, record in Table 1–2 what the arrow points to and describe the interaction. For example, if you select the interaction line that points from the sun to the biological environment, you might write, "The sun supplies light, gravity, and solar energy to the biological environment."
   c. Complete Table 1–2 by describing each interaction in your systems diagram.

4. Modify your systems diagram to show the relative impact of one category on another. One by one, erase and redraw each arrow as follows: Use an arrowhead with double lines (⇒) for a major (large) impact; use an arrowhead with a single line (→) for a minor (small) impact.

QUESTIONS

1. From the arrowheads you drew, tell how many categories
   a. interacted in one direction.
   b. interacted in both directions.
   Give examples of each.

2. Which category or categories have
   a. the fewest interactions with the others?
   b. the least impact on the others?
   Suggest reasons that could explain your findings.

3. Which category or categories appear to have
   a. the most interactions with others?
   b. the greatest impact on others?
   Give evidence to support your answer.

4. In Table 1–1, humans were not included in the category "Biological environment."
   a. Suggest reasons for categorizing humans separately.
   b. Suggest reasons for including humans as part of the biological environment.

5. Table 1–1 separates humans from the natural physical environment. What are some human-made physical environments? Give reasons why these should not be included in the category "Physical environment." Then give reasons why they should.

6. Should humans and technology be in separate categories in Table 1–1, or should they be combined? Explain your reasoning.

7. How should the following be included in the study of global ecology?
   a. humans
   b. technologies

   Give reasons to support your answer.

8. Using the category terms you selected for your systems diagram, define
   a. ecology.
   b. environment.
   c. global environmental systems.
   d. environmental interactions.

FURTHER INVESTIGATIONS

1. Using library references, find other examples of systems diagrams and bring them to show the class.

2. Use systems diagrams to show interactions in different kinds of environments. For example, make a systems diagram of a healthy aquarium in the classroom. Or make a systems diagram of a meadow or the solar system.

2. Agents of Environmental Change

Now we turn from the larger global environmental categories that we used in Topic 1 to components within a smaller local environment and how they change.

Figure 2–1 is a composite picture showing many of the components in a local environment. Many are undergoing change, such as the forest and the mountains. Also pictured are some of the agents that produce the changes. Fire, for example, is burning the forest, and rain is eroding the mountains.

ACTIVITY

Identify the environmental components being changed and the agents causing the changes shown in Fig. 2–1.

MATERIALS

- copies of Workbook Fig. 2–1 and Table 2–1

PROCEDURE

1. Study the drawing in Fig. 2–1 for components and agents producing change in that environment.
   a. In the first column in Table 2–1, list at least six of the components in Fig. 2–1 that are undergoing change.
   b. In the second column, categorize each component by choosing the best term from the list to the right and writing its abbreviation.

Bio for living (biotic) things, excluding humans, or for processes produced by them.

Phys for land, ocean, atmosphere, and other abiotic (nonliving) components of the earth or for processes produced by them.

HT for humans and their technologies or for processes produced by them.

A for astronomical objects such as the sun, the moon, and the planets or for processes produced by them.

   c. For each change, identify the agent(s) causing it. Record agents in the third column.

Fig. 2–1. Our changing environment

d. In the fourth column, categorize each agent of change, using the abbreviations in Procedure 1.b.
e. In the fifth column, write a description of each change.

2. Estimate the **time scale** (length of time) for each change. Use or modify the time intervals given below. Record your estimate in column 6.
   a. minutes to days
   b. years to decades
   c. centuries (hundreds of years)
   d. millennia (thousands of years)
   e. millions of years

3. Estimate the **space scale** (size of the affected area) for each change. Use or modify the terms below. Record your estimate in column 7.
   a. mini changes: changes limited to one community or a part of it
   b. local changes: changes limited to one or a few states or small countries

Table 2–1. Environmental changes

1. Component undergoing change	2. Component category	3. Agent(s) acting on the component	4. Agent category	5. Description of change	6. Time scale	7. Space scale
(Example) Forest	Bio	Fire	Phys	Burns down trees	Minutes to days	Mini

c. regional changes: changes affecting large areas, such as oceans, large countries, or whole continents
d. global changes: changes affecting the whole earth

QUESTIONS

1. What kinds of components change? What kinds do not change?

2. How do the physical and biological components of the environment act as agents
   a. to change other components of the environment? Give examples of how the land, ocean, and atmosphere interact.
   b. to change structures made by humans? Give examples.

3. Which agents tend to build up structures? Tear them down? In what ways, if any, do the agents that tend to build up structures differ from agents that tear them down?

4. Which cause greater changes in the environment, nonhuman agents or humans and technological agents? Support your answer with evidence.

5. Give examples of environmental changes over the past 10 years where the rate has
   a. speeded.
   b. slowed.
   c. fluctuated.
   d. held constant.

6. What types of changes are
   a. immediate?
   b. gradual?
   c. fluctuating?
   d. long-lasting?
   e. reversible?
   f. desirable?
   g. undesirable?

   Give some examples and explain your reasoning.

7. List two or more actions that governments can take to protect
   a. the global (worldwide) environment from destructive change.
   b. habitats (places where plants and animals live).
   c. endangered species.

8. List two or more new discoveries or technologies in the last 10 years that are likely to affect the environment, and describe the changes we might expect.

9. List two or more actions that organizations other than governments can take to protect the environment.

10. List two or more actions you can take to help protect the environment. Which of these are you willing to do? Which will you do?

FURTHER INVESTIGATIONS

1. Make posters of an imaginary environment to show how it might have changed. Show it
   a. a million years ago.

b. a thousand years ago.
c. 200 years ago.
d. 50 years ago.
e. today.
f. 50 to 100 years from now.

2. Investigate long-term changes in your local environment. Distinguish between changes caused by natural agents and changes produced by humans and their technologies.

3. Invite speakers to your class to talk about changes in your community. Invite
   a. a geologist to talk about how the land changed.
   b. a historian to talk about how people settled and developed the land.
   c. an environmentalist to talk about local environmental problems and issues.
   d. a real estate developer or city planner to talk about planned changes.

4. Using library references, learn about organizations that work to protect, conserve, and manage
   a. coral reefs.
   b. forests.
   c. wildlife, including both plants and animals.
   d. marine sanctuaries.

3. Global Energy Budget

Almost all (99.98%) of the energy reaching the earth's atmosphere and surface is **solar energy,** the kind that comes from the sun in the form of light and other radiant energy. The earth's hot core, the moon's gravitational tidal pull, and fossil fuels provide the remaining 0.02%. Included in this 0.02% is energy from earthquakes, volcanoes, and gravitational erosion.

At the equator an average of about 20 million kilocalories (2 x 10^7 kcal) of solar energy falls on each square kilometer of atmosphere each minute of the day. This is enough energy to raise the temperature of the water in a full-sized swimming pool to its boiling point (100°C) each minute. But not all of the incoming solar energy is converted to heat. Roughly 29.42% is reflected back into space. About 46.94% is absorbed as heat, 23.00% drives the water cycle, and only 0.045% drives the winds and water currents. The remaining 0.58% of the energy drives the photosynthetic processes of plants. Only about 54% of all photosynthesis takes place on the land.

Energy drives events in nature. Energy is never lost from the universe. It can change form and scatter, but the total remains constant. For example, light energy can kick air and water molecules into motion, producing heat, winds, currents, and evaporation. Light energy can be stored in the chemical bonds of sugar and starch molecules that plants make in photosynthesis. Heat, chemical bonds, and movement of objects are examples of different forms of energy. Each day's supply of light energy from the sun is quickly converted to one of these forms of energy. Chemical energy and energy of movement eventually are converted to heat energy. On the average, the amount of energy coming to the earth's surface every 24 hours is the same as the amount it loses.

Where does the energy go? The atmosphere and the surfaces of land, water, and ice all throw energy back into space as infrared radiation. (We sense **infrared** energy as **heat.**) Living things use the chemical bond energy stored in sugar and starches to move, reproduce, and keep warm. In these bodily processes, the stored chemical energy is released, and it too is converted to infrared radiation (heat) and beamed into space. Once energy becomes heat, it is quickly lost from Earth.

ACTIVITY

Diagram the energy budget of the earth. Build a schematic of the global energy budget. Account for how energy is used at the earth's surface.

MATERIALS

- copies of Workbook Table 3–1 and Figs. 3–1 and 3–2
- calculator (optional)
- flashlight
- globe of the earth

PROCEDURE

1. Using information from the background reading, complete Table 3–1.
   a. Make a list of **inputs** (sources) of global energy. Indicate the percentage from each source.
   b. Calculate or copy the percentage of energy used in the listed global environmental processes.

Table 3–1. Global energy data 

Energy inputs and uses	% Energy input	% Energy use
Global energy inputs: Solar energy		
Energy from other sources		
Global energy uses: Reflected solar energy		
Absorbed by Earth's surface as heat		
Drives weather and climate (wind, waves, currents)		
Drives water cycle		
Drives photosynthesis on land		
Drives photosynthesis in the oceans		
Total energy		

2. Interpret Fig. 3–1 and complete it to show the global energy budget.

3. Compare the amount of energy reaching the earth's atmosphere and surface (input) with the amount leaving the earth (**output**). Complete the diagram in Fig. 3–2.

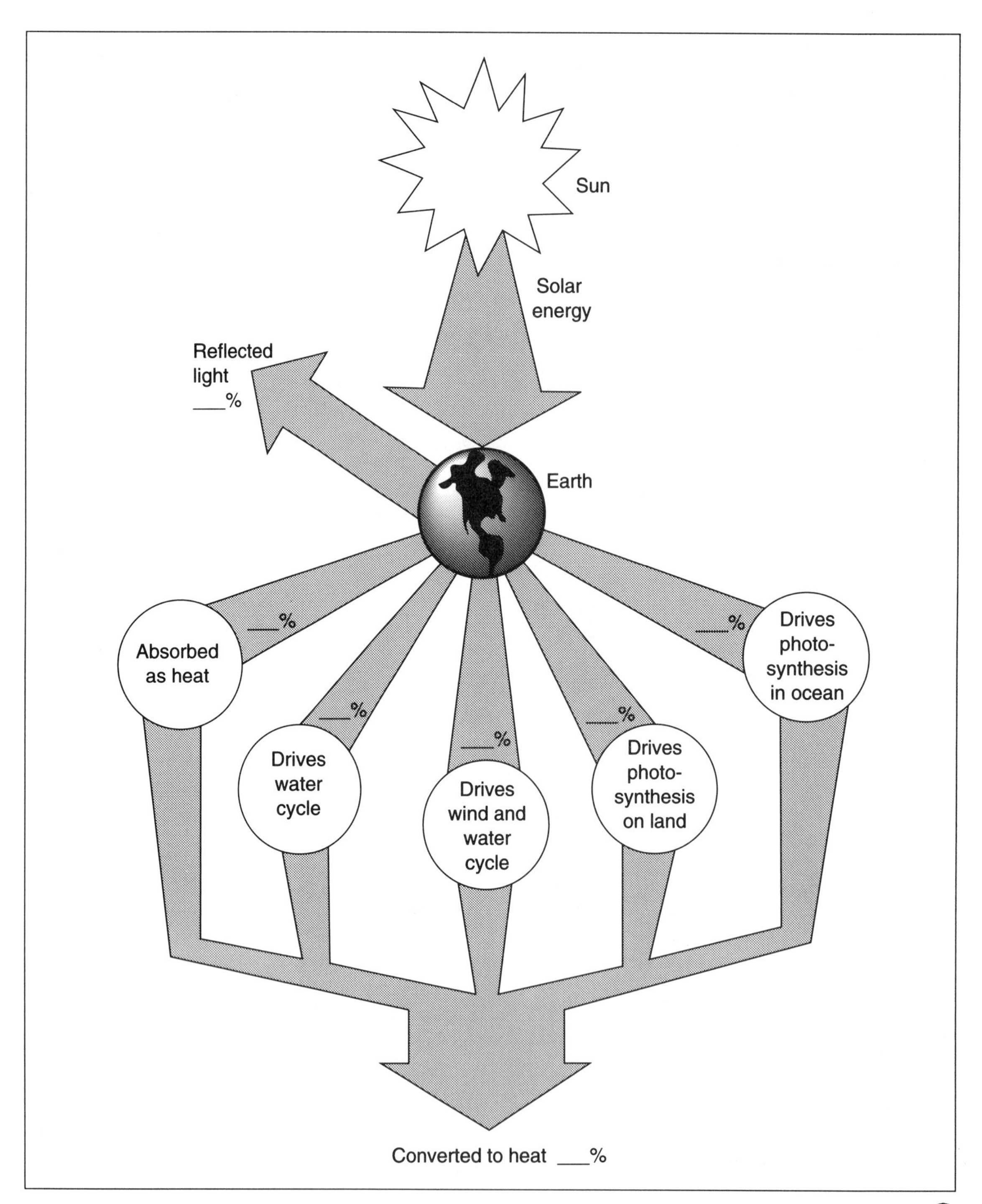

Fig. 3–1. Global energy budget

Ⓦ

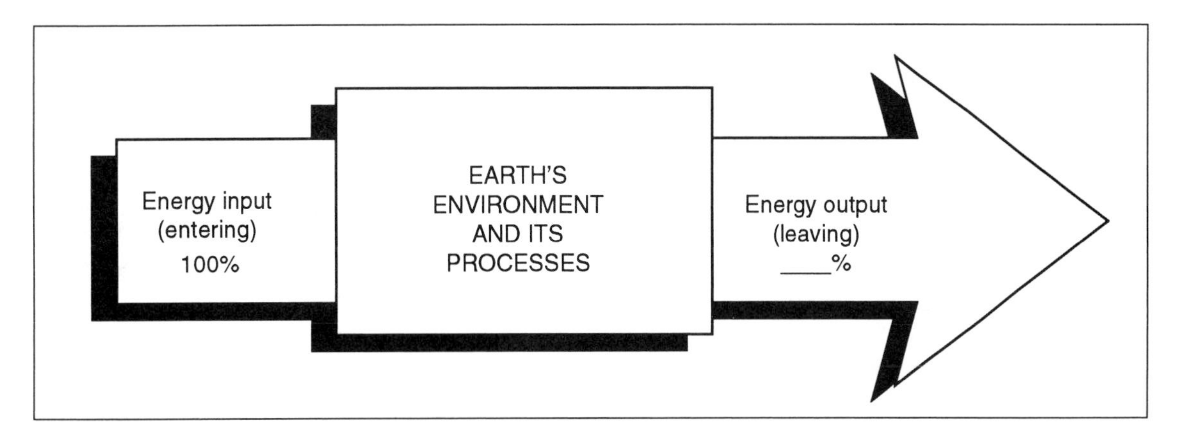

Fig. 3–2. Summary of global energy budget

Ⓦ

4. Using a flashlight and a globe of the earth, simulate the events shown in Fig. 3–3. Show how the axial tilt of the earth affects the amount of solar energy reaching the earth's surface. Demonstrate changes in incoming solar energy
   a. in different seasons.
   b. at different latitudes.

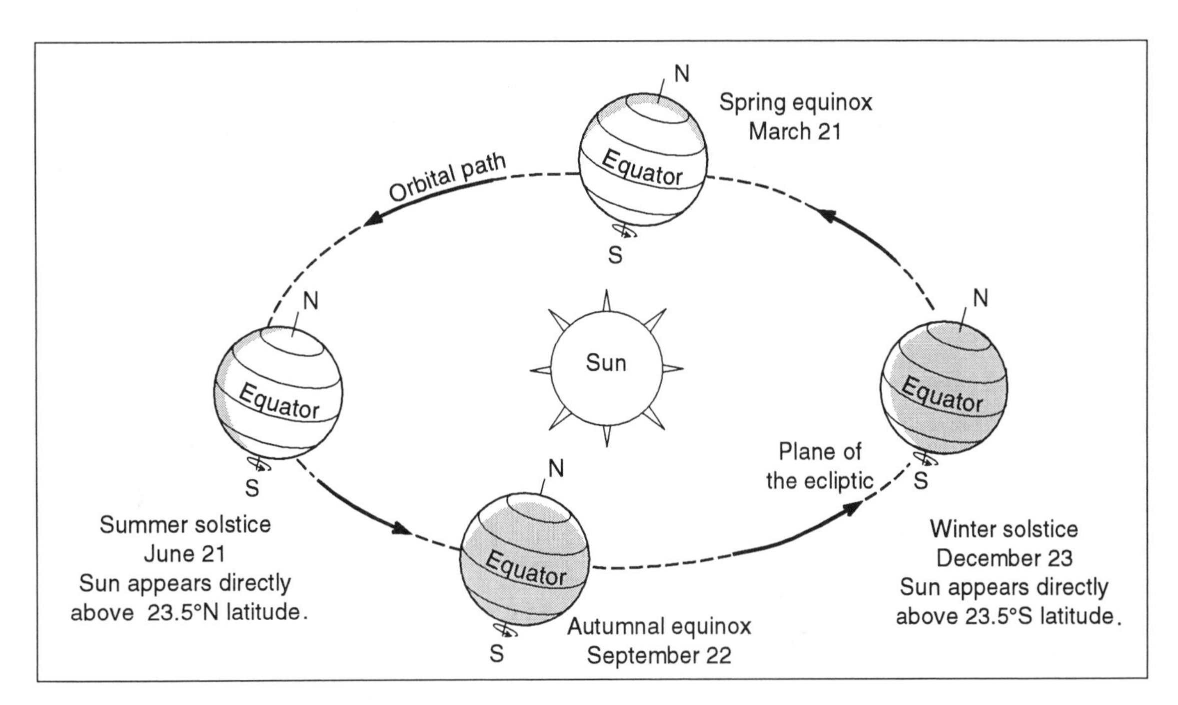

Fig. 3–3. Relationship between Earth's solar orbit and seasons in the northern hemisphere

QUESTIONS

1. Using your category terms from Topic 1 and terms for environmental components and agents of change from Topic 2, describe the following:
   a. how energy is absorbed at the surface of the earth by land, sea, and air
   b. how energy interacts with water
   c. the ways that winds, waves, and currents distribute energy
   d. how energy is used in photosynthesis

2. Make a pie chart showing how energy is expended (used) in the earth's environment. Decide whether to include or exclude reflected solar energy.

3. What might happen to the earth's surface and atmosphere if the incoming energy were greater than the outgoing energy?

4. The total energy the earth receives from the sun each minute is 2.55×10^{15} kcal. The earth's area is 5.12×10^{8} km^2.
   a. On average, how much solar energy falls on each square kilometer of the earth?
   b. How does this figure compare with the 2×10^{7} kcal/km^2/min of energy measured at the equator? What might account for differences?

5. Explain any differences between the average solar energy and the amounts of energy reaching the equator. Refer to Unit 2, Topic 4, Fig. 4–14 for information to help in your explanation. Account for any factors that might apply, including these three:
   a. distance of the earth from the sun
   b. the shape of the earth
   c. the earth's tilted axis

6. Does photosynthesis produce more plant growth on land or in coastal oceans? Suggest explanations.

FURTHER INVESTIGATIONS

1. Using library references, make a diagram to illustrate different kinds of **radiant energy** (energy that travels in waves). Include radio waves, television broadcasting waves, microwaves, infrared radiation, visible light, ultraviolet radiation, X rays, and gamma rays. Show the diagram to the class.
   a. Show which portion of the wave spectrum is solar light (generally between 0.15 and 4 micrometers).
   b. Show which portion of solar light is visible to humans. Identify the wavelengths for red, orange, yellow, green, blue, and violet.
   c. Distinguish between UV-a and UV-b radiation.

2. Learn more about the structure of the earth's atmosphere and its role in regulating global energy.
   a. Make a diagram showing the locations, temperatures, densities, and compositions of the troposphere, the stratosphere, the mesosphere, and the thermosphere.
   b. Find out which layers are associated with weather, climate, and ocean currents. Also find out which layers

help protect life on Earth from harmful ultraviolet radiation.

3. Gases in the atmosphere help to insulate the earth, keeping it warm enough for life.
   a. What natural processes help maintain the earth's atmosphere and temperature?
   b. How might agriculture, the use of fossil fuels, and other human activities be changing the composition of the atmosphere?
   c. Read about the greenhouse effect, the warming of the earth caused by the buildup of manufactured gases in the atmosphere. Report to the class on evidence and controversies associated with the greenhouse effect.

4. The earth's atmosphere and climates have changed dramatically in the past. Invite a geologist to your class to talk about these changes.

5. Learn more about ozone in the atmosphere. How does it form? How does it regulate the global flow of energy? What human activity is affecting the ozone?

6. The amount of energy measured at the equator is 2×10^7 kcal/km^2/min. Using this figure, calculate the amount of energy falling on 1 km^2 of surface at the equator during a month's time (kcal/km^2/mo).

7. Learn more about the relationship between solar energy and climate on Earth. How constant is energy from the sun? How do changes in solar energy affect climates on Earth? Learn more about research on solar energy and its effects, including
   a. sunspots, with apparent 11-year recurring cycles.
   b. magnetic cycles every 22 years.
   c. solar flares.
   d. the rotation of the sun.

8. How might knowledge about solar energy be important to
   a. farmers?
   b. weather forecasters, meteorologists, and climatologists?
   c. economists and investors?
   d. coastal city planners?

9. How do scientists measure solar radiation? Find out how astronomical observatories, balloons, rockets, and satellites are used to study energy from the sun. Report on measurements of the "solar constant" and "total radiation."

10. Sunburns can be both painful and dangerous. What should people know about UV-a and UV-b? What should they do to protect themselves from harmful effects of solar radiation?

4. Bioenergetics

We know from experience that we can satisfy our need for nourishment by eating. We share with other animals the problem that our bodies do not produce many of the complex biological molecules that make up our bodies and that we use as sources of energy. We, like other animals, must have food to get these needed molecules into our bodies.

In this topic we examine the food needs of animals and learn how eating plant materials ultimately satisfies those needs. The study of how energy and matter pass from one living organism to another is called **bioenergetics.**

Producers, Consumers, and Decomposers

Biomass is the matter in living things. Food is edible biomass. Plants and bacteria that produce their own food are called **producers.** Plants produce their own food through photosynthesis.

All other organisms must consume food (other plants and animals) to satisfy their need for the chemical materials that build their bodies and supply energy for life processes. **Consumers** cannot produce their own food. All animals, including humans, are consumers.

Decomposers are special kinds of consumers that feed on **detritus,** which includes wastes (used biomass) from living organisms and remains of dead organisms. In the ocean, bacteria decompose detrital biomass into simpler substances such as nitrates and phosphates. These simple substances, released by the bacteria as wastes, provide the nutrient chemicals essential for the growth of new plants. Bacteria serve a vital role in recycling matter in the environment.

In the ocean, detritus and the bacteria that feed on it are found throughout the water column and on the seafloor. Oceanographers use the term **marine snow** to refer to floating detritus, whose whitish particles look like snow in the sea. Marine snow consists of the soft organic material, fecal pellets, and skeletal remains of dead plankton plus smaller inorganic particles of mud or clay. Marine snow is an important kind of detrital biomass in the open ocean.

Feeding Relationships of Consumers and Decomposers

There are several ways to describe the role of an organism in consuming food. One system classifies animals as herbivores, carnivores, omnivores, or detritivores. Animals that eat only plant material for food to build and run their bodies are **herbivores** or **grazers.** Animals that eat other animals for food are **carnivores.** Carnivores often specialize in eating herbivores. Animals that eat both plant and animal food are **omnivores.** Humans are omnivores. **Detritivores** eat detritus and decompose it into simpler substances.

Since all animals are consumers, plant-eating animals may also be described as **primary consumers** and animals that eat primary consumers as **secondary consumers.**

These in turn are eaten by **tertiary consumers,** and so forth. See Table 4–1.

Another way to classify organisms is to assign them a **trophic level,** also known as a **nutrition level.** This system puts plants and some bacteria in the first trophic level, abbreviated as T1. Primary consumers are in the second trophic level (T2), secondary consumers in the third level (T3), and so on. See Table 4–1.

Table 4–1. Classification of organisms by food role and by trophic level

Symbol	Organism
T6	***Quinary consumers.*** Animals that eat quaternary consumers.
T5	***Quaternary consumers.*** Animals that eat tertiary consumers.
T4	***Tertiary consumers.*** Animals that eat secondary consumers.
T3	***Secondary consumers.*** Animals that eat primary consumers.
T2	***Primary consumers.*** Animals that eat producers.
T1	***Producers.*** Organisms that can carry out photosynthesis. They include green plants, plantlike organisms, and some kinds of bacteria.
D	***Decomposers.*** Bacteria and other organisms that consume marine snow (detritus).

ACTIVITY 1

Develop food chains showing relationships between predators and prey.

MATERIALS

- *HMSS* Open Ocean Ecology Game playing cards
- copy of Workbook Table 4–3
- colored pencils

PROCEDURE

1. Study the game cards. Each card represents one organism in a marine ecosystem and shows its eating habits.
   a. Note the kinds of information on each card. See Fig. 4–1.
   b. An organism's normal diet always consists of organisms from the trophic level below it. For example, a copepod (T2) eats diatoms and dinoflagellates (T1), or a fish larva eats copepods and crustacean larva.
   c. Some cards carry the notation "Also eats," followed by the names of organisms that the animal eats from its own trophic level. For example, the shark (T6) eats swordfish (T6), in addition to organisms in T5.

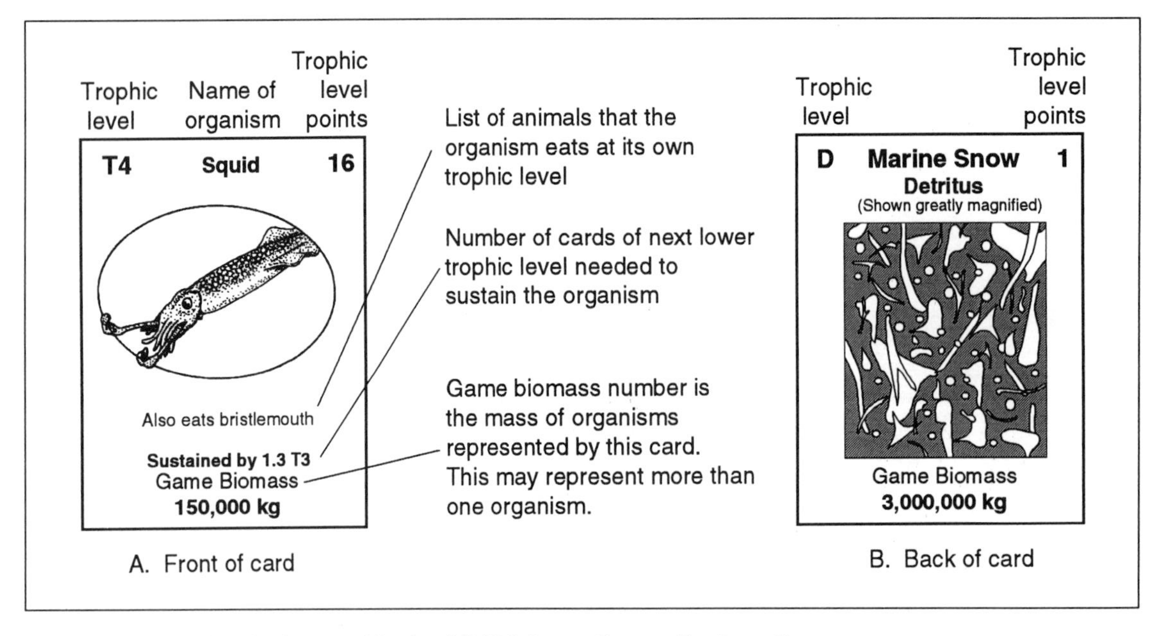

Fig. 4–1. Sample playing card in the *HMSS* Open Ocean Ecology Game

2. Sort the cards into trophic levels indicated by the (T) number in the upper left corner of each card. Remove all Bacteria cards from the deck. Hold these for Activity 3.

3. Build three **food chains.** In your notebook, make a sketch showing the organisms in each chain.
   a. Start with a producer (T1) card. Then select an herbivore (T2) card showing an organism likely to eat the T1 organism. Lay these on the table.
   b. Keep selecting higher trophic level cards and arranging them to show a sequence of **predators** (animals doing the hunting) and **prey** (animals hunted and eaten). See Table 4–2 for information about the organisms.
   c. Sketch each food chain. Draw arrows between organisms from the prey pointing to the predator. See Fig. 4–2.

4. Complete Table 4–3 as follows:
   a. Write in the trophic level numbers.
   b. List examples of organisms at each trophic level.
   c. Indicate whether each organism is a herbivore, carnivore, omnivore, or detritivore.

QUESTIONS

1. Compare the three food chains that you constructed.
   a. How are they similar? Different?
   b. Which is the longest chain? The shortest?

Table 4–2. Information about organisms on the *HMSS* Open Ocean Ecology Game cards

Trophic level T1

Coccolithophore. Extremely small single-celled photosynthetic plant. Makes up 45% of the total phytoplankton in the surface waters. Primary producer in the ocean.

Diatom. Single-celled photosynthetic plant. Very common in the surface waters of all oceans. Floats by means of oil droplets in the cell.

Dinoflagellate. Small photosynthetic organism in the surface waters. Moves by means of flagella (whiplike structures). Some species are phosphorescent. A few species are toxic, producing red tides.

Trophic level T2

Copepod. Makes up 70% of the zooplankton in some regions of the ocean. Eats phytoplankton, especially diatoms. Traps phytoplankton in bristles on appendages. Bristles near the mouth form a basket that catches phytoplankton as they swim. Also eats some zooplankton.

Crustacean larva. Temporary member of the plankton. Small, gradually grows larger. Settles to the bottom when larger. Feeds on phytoplankton when small, eats zooplankton as it becomes larger.

Foraminiferan. Very abundant. Secretes a hard shell. Extensions of the cell, called pseudopods, catch phytoplankton, especially coccolithophores and diatoms. Some species grow larger and live on the bottom.

Trophic level T3

Arrow worm. Dominant group of small predators in the ocean. Eats mainly copepods. Also eats crustacean larvae and small fish larvae.

Fish larva. Eats foraminiferans, copepods, and crustacean larvae when small. Larger sizes eat larger animals.

Krill. Small shrimplike animal with bristles on appendages. Traps copepods, foraminiferans, and small crustacean larvae. Also eats diatoms and fecal pellets of other small animals.

Trophic level T4

Anchovy. Small fish, very numerous in certain parts of the ocean. Swims in large schools. Has gill rakers capable of filtering small objects from the water passing over the gills. Eats krill, arrow worms, small fish larvae.

Bristlemouth fish. Small fish living in deeper waters of the open ocean. Large mouth, fine gill rakers. Feeds on small prey but may eat fish as large as itself. Eats krill and squid but will feed on anything available.

Squid. Open-ocean mollusk that swims in large groups. Migrates vertically from the surface of the ocean at night to great depths in the daytime. Eats shrimp, small fish and fish larvae, crustaceans, and worms.

Trophic level T5

Bonito. Fast-swimming open-ocean predator. Eats small fish and squid.

Jack. Predator hunting in schools. Feeds on fish that also swim in schools and on smaller predators such as mackerel and bonito.

Mackerel. Small open-ocean schooling predator. Feeds on schools of smaller fish and squid.

Small oceanic white-tipped shark. Active, dangerous predator. Feeds on smaller fish, squid, and may eat carrion (dead animals). Also eats larger fish such as mackerel, bonito, and jacks when available.

Trophic level T6

Dolphin. Large, fast-swimming marine mammal. Eats squid and smaller carnivorous fish such as mackerel, jacks, bonito.

Great white shark. One of the largest, most dangerous predators in the ocean. Eats fish, seals, dolphins, swordfish, turtles, people, carrion, and marine debris.

Killer whale. One of the largest marine mammal predators in the ocean. Eats dolphins, great white sharks, swordfish, seals.

Swordfish. Large open-ocean predator. Feeds on schools of smaller predatory fish such as mackerel, jacks, bonito.

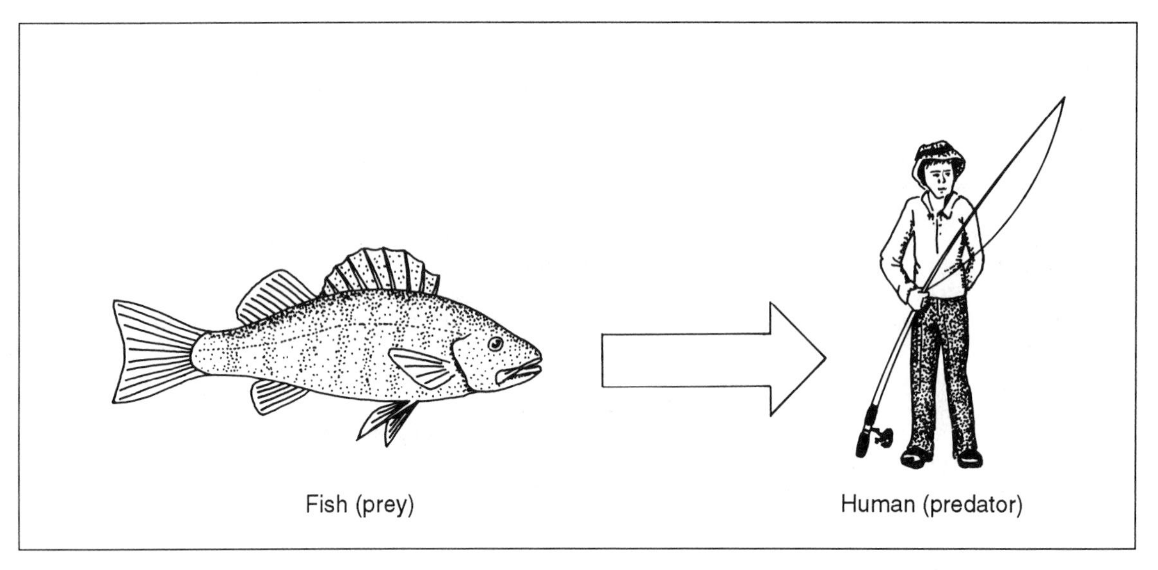

Fig. 4–2. Human predator-prey relationship

Table 4–3. Nutritional description of organisms Ⓦ

Production/consumption role	Trophic level number	Herbivore, carnivore, omnivore, or detritivore	Examples
Producers			
Primary consumers			
Secondary consumers			
Tertiary consumers			
Quaternary consumers			
Quinary consumers			
Bacteria			

In this activity we diagram feeding relations in the whole ecosystem of the *HMSS* Open Ocean Ecology Game. Then we look at the productivity of this ecosystem stated in the amount of biomass (the total weight of living organisms) in the ecosystem over one year. (For this game, organisms and their feeding habits are simplified to make it easier to study the ways that matter and energy move through an ecosystem.)

ACTIVITY 2

Develop a food web.
Investigate the role of decomposers.
Diagram the flow of energy and cycling of matter in the biosphere.

MATERIALS

- *HMSS* Open Ocean Ecology Game playing cards
- lined paper
- colored pencils
- copy of Workbook Fig. 4–3

PROCEDURE

1. Make a **food web** for this ecosystem.
   a. Sort the trophic level cards into piles. Do not include bacteria. Start with the three food chains from Activity 1 and add one card from each pile in each trophic level.
   b. Copy the names of the organisms on lined paper by trophic (T) levels. Write the name of the T1 organism at the bottom, the T2 organism above it, T3 above T2, and so forth. Leave spaces between the levels and between the names.
   c. Draw a box around each name.
   d. Determine what each animal eats. (Animals usually eat organisms from the trophic level below their own.) Draw arrows between each organism and the organisms that eat it.
   e. On each line draw an arrowhead pointing to the predator. See Fig. 4–2.

2. On the food web, identify the three food chains you developed in Activity 1. In each chain, connect the organisms with a colored line or other distinctive marking.

3. Now use the Bacteria cards that you set aside in Activity 1 and the cards that have "Marine Snow Detritus" on the back. Add the names on these cards to your food chains and webs. Decide how many to use and where they fit best.

4. Complete the diagram in Fig. 4–3 as follows:
   a. Using boxes to represent organisms, arrange them according to their feeding relationships. You may need to add or remove boxes, depending on the classification system you use. Label each box with a descriptive name.
   b. Using a red pencil, mark the path of the flow of energy from the sun through the biosphere. Note that at each step, some energy is lost to the environment as heat.
   c. Using a green pencil, trace the path of matter as it cycles through the biosphere.

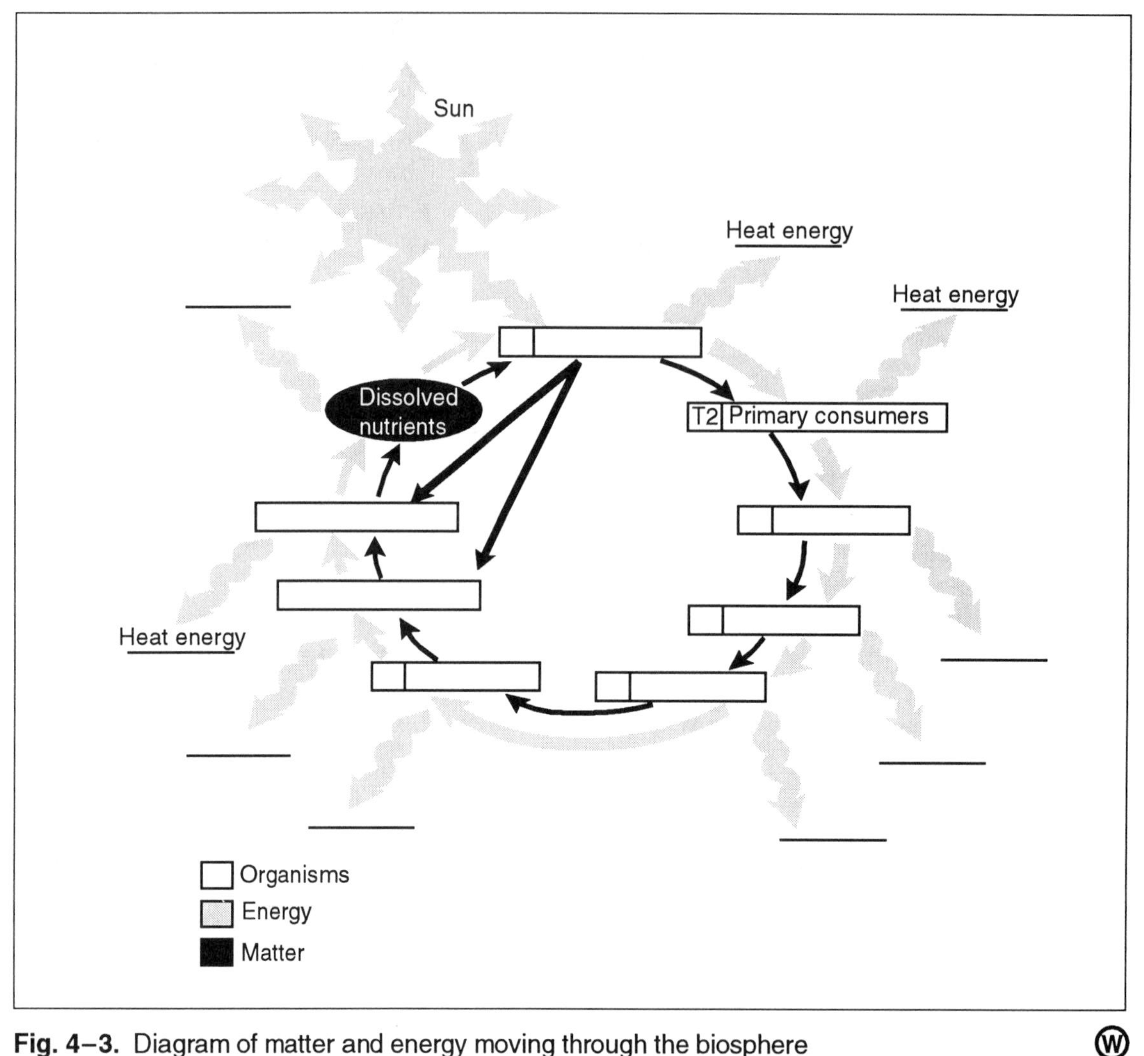

Fig. 4–3. Diagram of matter and energy moving through the biosphere

d. Add arrows where needed to show the path of matter and energy from the trophic levels to detritus and bacteria.

QUESTIONS

2. How does a food web differ from a food chain?

3. Which gives a more complete picture of events in ocean environments, a food web or a food chain? Explain your answer.

4. What do the arrows in the food web represent? Answer in terms of biomass and energy.

5. How does marine snow form? What is it made of? Why is it called marine snow?

6. Describe how adding bacteria and marine snow to a food chain makes a **cyclic system.** What is cycled?

7. Describe the energy inputs and outputs in the biosphere by answering these questions:
   a. How does energy enter the biosphere?
   b. How is energy transferred from one organism to another organism?
   c. What do living things use energy for?
   d. How is energy lost in the biosphere? In what form is it lost? Where does it go?

ACTIVITY 3

Play the Trophic Level Game.
(Optional) Construct a biomass pyramid.

MATERIALS

- *HMSS* Open Ocean Ecology Game board
- *HMSS* Open Ocean Ecology Game cards
- 2-m length of white wrapping or shelving paper (optional)
- meter ruler (optional)

PROCEDURE

1. Play the *HMSS* Open Ocean Ecology Game.
   a. You have probably already used the game cards in Activities 1 and 2. If not, become familiar with the information on the cards. See Fig. 4–1.
   b. Your teacher will give you a game board and a set of rules for playing the game. Read the rules and become familiar with the layout of the gameboard. See Fig. 4–4.
   c. Play the game and record the points for each play. The winner is the player with the most trophic level points at the end of the game.
   d. As you play, develop strategies for making the maximum number of points on each play.

2. When the game is over, keep the cards on the game board as you carry out the following steps:

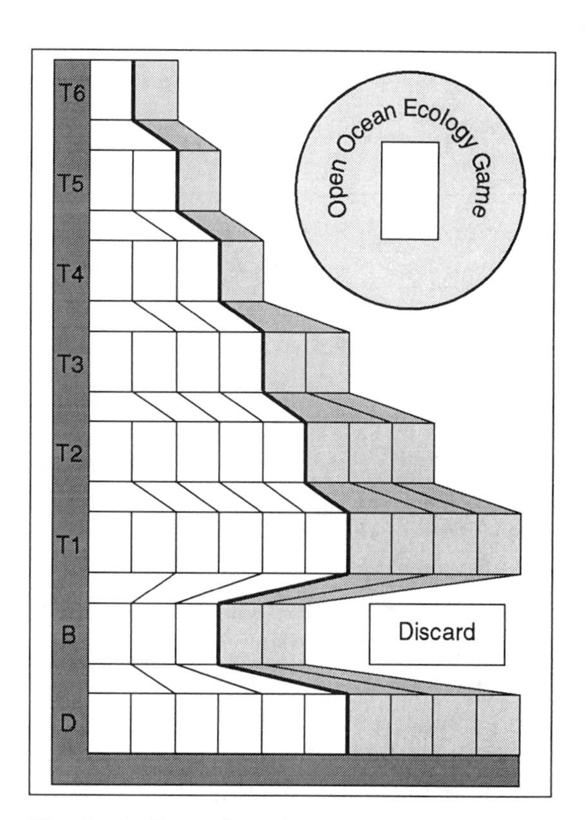

Fig. 4–4. Game board

a. Count the cards supported at each trophic level on the game board. Count only the cards that lie to the left of the heavy black guideline. Record the counts in Table 4–4.

b. Look at a card from each trophic level. Find the game biomass (stated in kilograms). Record this number for each trophic level.

c. Calculate the trophic level biomass as follows:

Number of cards in trophic level x game biomass per card = trophic level biomass

Example for Trophic Level 6:

1 T6 card x 1,000 kg of game biomass = 1,000 kg trophic level 6 biomass

Table 4–4. Biomass supporting each trophic level 

Trophic level	Number of cards in each trophic level	Game biomass per card	Trophic level biomass
6	1	1,000 kg	1,000 kg
5			
4			
3			
2			
1			
Bacteria			
Marine snow detritus			

3. (Optional) Construct a biomass pyramid from the data in Table 4–3. The pyramid will consist of a series of stacked rectangles. Each rectangle will represent a trophic level, and the length of the rectangle will represent the biomass of that trophic level. An incomplete biomass pyramid is shown in Fig. 4–5.
   a. Lay a 2-m length of wrapping or shelving paper on a long table or on the floor.
   b. Draw a faint pencil line across the width of the paper at the 1-m mark.
   c. Starting with marine snow, determine the length of the rectangle to represent its biomass.
      1) Use 1 cm of length to represent 1,000,000 kg of biomass.

2) Calculate the length of the rectangle by dividing the detrital biomass by 1,000,000. See Table 4–4.

d. Draw a rectangle of the length that represents the detritus biomass. Center the rectangle on the faint pencil line. See Fig. 4–5.

e. Repeat Procedures 3.c. and 3.d. for all other trophic levels.

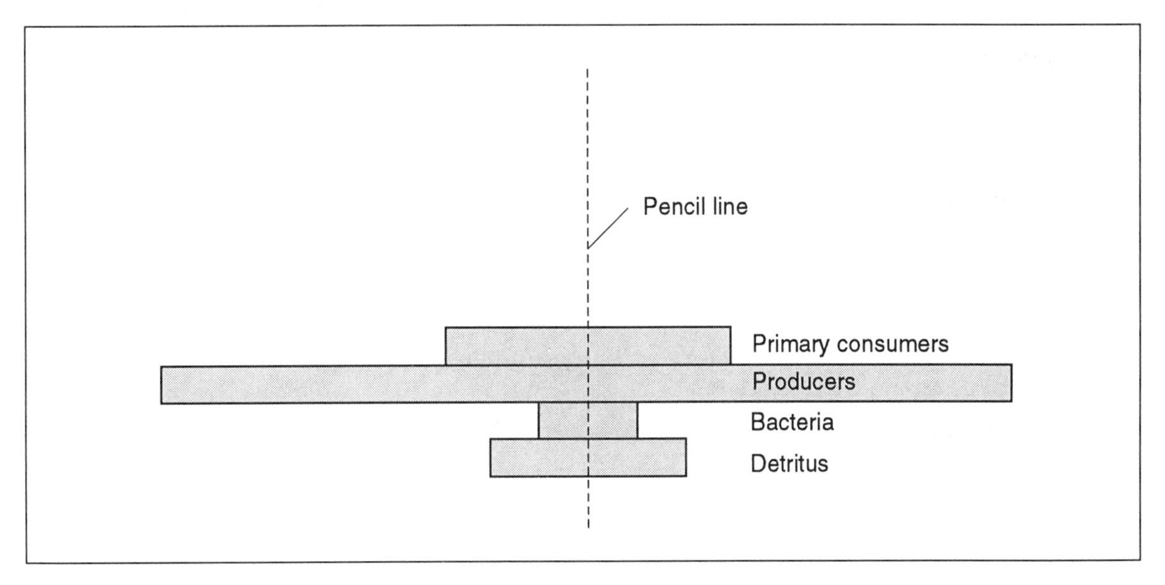

Fig. 4–5. Biomass pyramid showing some trophic levels

QUESTIONS

8. What game-playing strategies won the most points?

9. How well does the Open Ocean Ecology Game simulate the real world?
   a. In the game, if there are not enough lower trophic level cards to support a higher trophic level card, the higher card either cannot be played or must be discarded. What happens in the open-ocean environment that is like this? Give examples.
   b. What other situations from the game simulate real-world conditions?
   c. In the open ocean, when, if at all, do situations occur that resemble the game-playing strategies that won the most game points?
   d. What are some conditions (both natural and technological) that occur in the open ocean but are not simulated in the game?

10. What percentage of the total living biomass in this game is made up of plant biomass (T1)?

11. How much plant biomass (T1) must a primary consumer (T2) eat to produce 1 kg of body weight? Show your calculations.

12. For every 1 kg of T6 organisms such as a killer whale, how many kilograms of plant biomass had to be produced and consumed in the food web?

13. Baleen whales are toothless whales that eat krill. How many kilograms of plant biomass would it take to support 1 kg of baleen whale?

14. It takes about 1,000,000 kcal to produce 25,000 kg of biomass at the first trophic level. About how much energy is required to support a 1,000-kg killer whale?

15. If you were going to develop an ocean ranch to grow whales for meat, would you want to grow baleen whales or killer whales? Explain your answer.

16. Assume that the total T1 biomass represents 100% of the energy that originally entered the Open Ocean Ecology ecosystem. Calculate the percentage of this total energy transferred to each trophic level.
    a. How much of the original energy is left at the T6 level?
    b. How efficient is the transfer of energy from one trophic level to the next?

17. If you assume that the Open Ocean Ecology Game represents food available for humans,
    a. what trophic level holds the most food? How suitable is this food for human consumption?
    b. at what trophic level should humans fish or hunt the sea? Justify your answer.

18. How does the biomass pyramid represent the amount of biomass in each trophic level? If you reduced the length of the rectangle at the producer level to only one-tenth of its present length, what would happen to the length of the rectangles at higher trophic levels? Describe how changes in the natural environment could bring similar results.

19. Using examples from this topic, define the following terms:
    a. bioenergetics
    b. trophic relationships
    c. flow of energy in the biosphere
    d. cycling of matter in the biosphere
    e. biological productivity

FURTHER INVESTIGATIONS

1. Experiment with changing the game rules.
    a. Consider adding natural changes such as changes in seasons and El Niño events.
    b. Consider adding humans and technologies, such as high-tech fishing equipment or a change in the fishing laws.

2. Modify or change the cards to simulate

one of the following marine and aquatic ecosystems:
   a. coral
   b. wetland
   c. inland lake
   d. open ocean
   e. nearshore coast

3. Using systems analysis, make diagrams showing
   a. the inputs and outputs of producers, consumers, and decomposers.
   b. the movement of matter and energy among producers, consumers, and decomposers.

4. Using the systems diagrams from Further Investigation 3, use colored pencils
   a. to show inputs and outputs of photosynthesis and respiration.
   b. to trace the movement of carbon, oxygen, nitrogen, and phosphorus through the ecosystem.

5. A **population** is a group of similar organisms, and a **community** consists of populations occupying a given area. Using these terms, describe
   a. the interactions among populations in the open-ocean community represented by the game cards.
   b. a real-world example, including humans.

6. Look for other examples of environmental simulations. Check for computer games as well as board and card games. Share your discoveries with the class.

7. Investigate how scientists are using computer simulations to study the ecology of land and ocean environments. Select one simulation project and learn as much about it as you can. Find out what basic scientific concepts the simulation uses and what data are based on the predictions. If possible, invite an expert to speak to the class, or find a video showing how the simulation works.

5. Plankton

Most of the living organisms in the oceans we never see and rarely hear about. They are the plankton that float at or near the surface in ocean and freshwater environments. **Plankton** (G. *planktos* = drifting) are organisms that drift passively or swim so weakly that they cannot move against even a modest current.

Although most plankton are too tiny to see, they are very abundant in the surface waters of oceans all over the globe. Plankton constitute 95% of the oceans' biomass. They sustain the food chains of the open ocean. Because of their huge numbers, they are crucial not only to the ecology of ocean environments but also to the ecology of the whole planet. Plankton are classified in three ways:

1. the kind of organism, either as plants (phytoplankton) or animals (zooplankton);
2. how long they exist as plankton, either permanent (holoplankton) or temporary (meroplankton); and
3. by size, ranging from microscopic to larger than humans.

We will use each of these three categories in our investigations of plankton.

Plant and Animal Plankton

Just as we classify sea and land organisms as plants or animals, we classify plankton as plants and plantlike organisms (phytoplankton) or animals (zooplankton). See Tables 5–1 and 5–2.

Phytoplankton

Phytoplankton (G. *phyto* = plant; G. *planktos* = drifting) are unattached, mostly microscopic plants and plantlike organisms that float at or near the surface of the ocean and freshwater lakes, ponds, rivers, and streams. Phytoplankton live in the euphotic zone, the uppermost layer where enough sunlight penetrates so that they can photosynthesize—generally not deeper than 80 m. When they photosynthesize, they convert carbon dioxide and water into sugar and oxygen. They also absorb nutrients necessary for growing and building their bodies.

Phytoplankton play vital roles in both ocean and global ecology. All life on Earth depends on energy from the sun captured by plants in photosynthesis. Phytoplankton are the primary producers of the open ocean. Oceans cover 70% of the earth's surface, and phytoplankton are the dominant organisms. Thus phytoplankton play major roles not only in producing food but also in regulating oxygen and carbon dioxide in the oceans, and ultimately in the atmosphere as well.

Phytoplankton populations are very sensitive to changes in their physical environment, such as changes in sunlight (seasonal changes and heavy cloud cover, for example), and the amount of dissolved nutrients available to them.

Table 5–1. Examples of common permanent phytoplankton, the holoplankton.

Cyanobacteria, sometimes called **blue-green bacteria** or **blue-green algae**, are relatively simple plants, the smallest of the phytoplankton. Because of their high concentrations, especially in such areas as the Red Sea and the Gulf of California, they contribute significantly to oxygen and food production. High-powered microscopes are needed to view many of these algae.

Coccolithophores are plantlike organisms, so named because they are covered with coccoliths, calcium-containing plates embedded in a gelatinous material. They live mainly in open, warmer seas. Sometimes they appear in great numbers in coastal waters, giving the water a milky look. They are an important food for filter-feeding animals. When these organisms are eaten by consumers, their plates are excreted in fecal pellets and accumulate on the seafloor. Although they have two whiplike appendages, called **flagella,** for locomotion, they are very weak swimmers.

Diatoms (G. *diatomos* = cut in half, referring to their pillbox shape) are more common in cold waters. They appear yellow-green or brownish. They may be found as single cells or as chains of cells. Their shells, made of silica, have shapes that aid in flotation. Some forms dwell on the bottom; some are attached to other plants, animals, or hard surfaces.

Dinoflagellates (G. *dinos* = rotating, referring to how they swim) are more common in warmer waters. Seasonally, they cause dense blooms called "red tides." They are usually brownish and one-celled. Some ingest food as animals do. Many are bioluminescent; that is, they glow. Some have shells of cellulose, a complex carbohydrate.

Silicoflagellates are just slightly larger than dinoflagellates. Some forms do not photosynthesize. They have star-shaped internal skeletons made of silica.

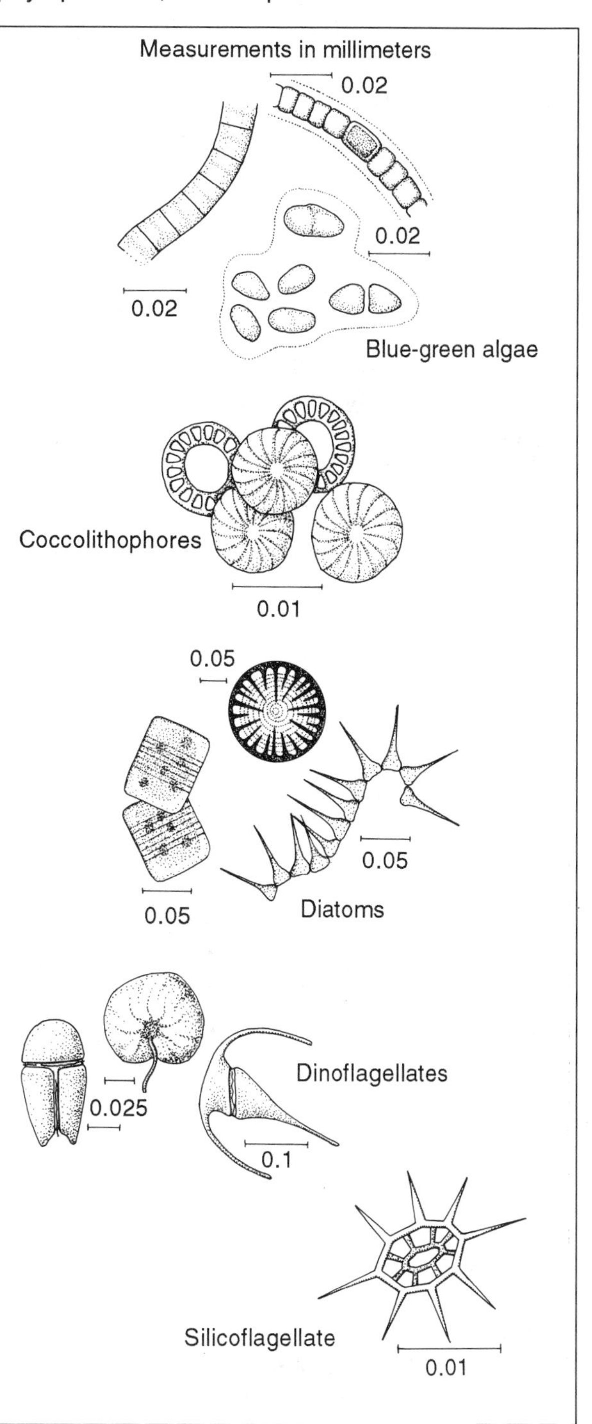

Zooplankton

Zooplankton (G. *zoo* = animal; G. *planktos* = drifting) are animals and animal-like organisms (mostly **protozoans**, primitive animals, generally single-celled). Like all animals, they must consume food to obtain energy and materials to carry out life processes. Zooplankton also depend on phytoplankton for producing oxygen.

Zooplankton that feed on phytoplankton are herbivores (trophic level 2). These grazing animals are sometimes described as "the cows of the sea." Zooplankton that feed on other zooplankton are carnivores; those that feed on phytoplankton and zooplankton are omnivores. Both carnivorous and omnivorous zooplankton are trophic level 3 animals.

Zooplankton are used as food by many other animals, including small and large fish. Small fish like the anchovy (7 to 21 cm) feed on plankton in huge schools of thousands of individuals. The largest fish in the ocean, the whale shark, feeds on zooplankton. Huge baleen whales, the largest mammals in the ocean, also feed almost entirely on zooplankton. The world's largest animal is the 150-ton blue whale. A blue whale's stomach can hold up to 2 tons of krill. Even sessile (nonmoving) organisms, like sponges that filter-feed and corals that capture small food particles, also depend on zooplankton for food. Thus the zooplankton play important roles in ocean food chains.

Zooplankton populations quickly increase when phytoplankton are abundant. Typically, after phytoplankton populations increase, zooplankton graze on it and also reproduce rapidly into larger populations.

Permanent and Temporary Plankton

Plants and animals that live their entire lives as plankton are called permanent plankton, or **holoplankton** (G. *holo* = whole). All the phytoplankton in Table 5–1 are holoplankton. Animals (zooplankton) that are holoplankton include jellyfish, krill, salps, and arrow worms. See Table 5–2.

Temporary plankton, or **meroplankton** (G. *mero* = temporary), drift only in their early stages. For example, the eggs and sperm (the gametes) of seaweed move by means of flagella. Sessile seaweeds release their swimming gametes into the surrounding water, where they swim about in search of a compatible gamete to fertilize. After the eggs and sperm unite, they quickly settle to the bottom to develop into attached seaweeds.

Animal meroplankton are **larvae,** the stage between an embryo and an adult. As they mature, these animals either settle to the bottom, as crabs do, or become stronger swimmers, as fish do. Table 5–3 shows some examples of zooplankton that are meroplankton.

Having a larval stage gives an organism two advantages. First, it provides a way to disperse the organisms over wide areas by using the surface currents of the ocean to sweep larvae away from their place of origin. This is a useful adaptation for sessile organisms. Second, animal larvae develop rapidly into a form capable of obtaining their own food. Because of their early ability to feed, such animals need neither long-term care by adults nor a large supply of stored food (the yolk in a chicken's egg is the chick's stored food supply).

Table 5–2. Examples of common permanent zooplankton, the holoplankton

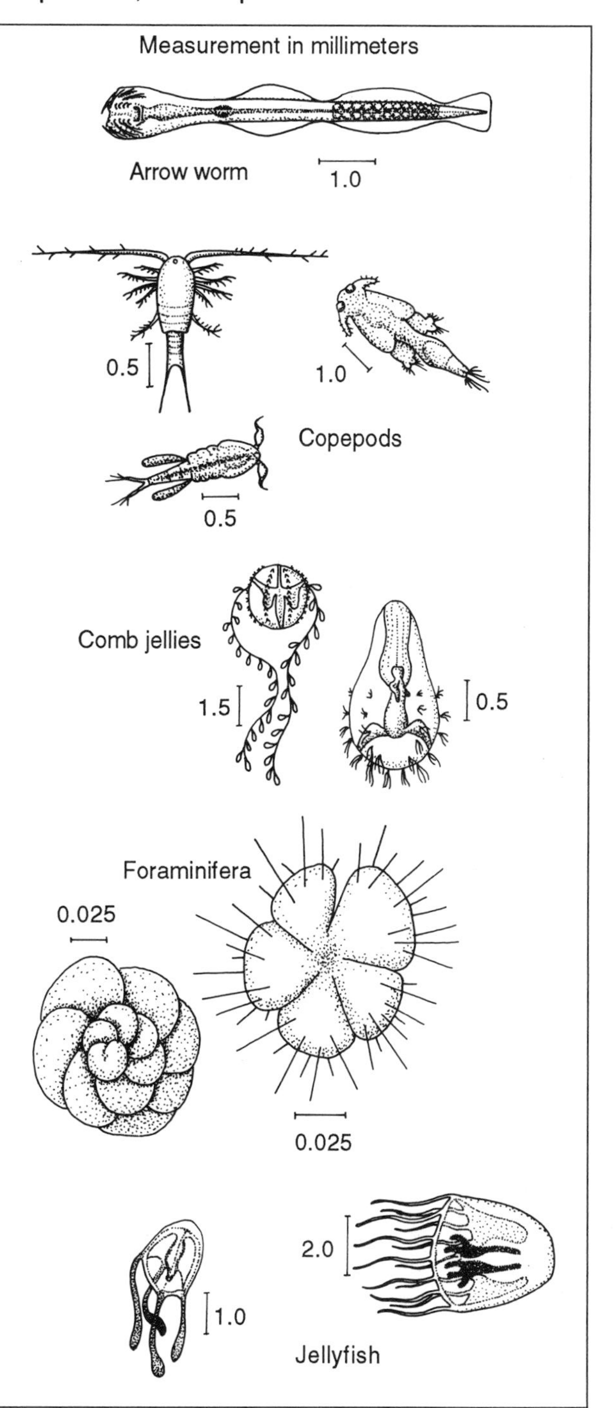

Arrow worms or chaetognaths (G. *chaeto* = bristles; G. *gnath* = jaw) are nearly transparent. They can grow to 2–5 cm. They are carnivores that voraciously prey on other zooplankton. Their abundance, controlled by food supply, varies seasonally. Scientists sometimes use them to identify water masses.

Copepods (G. *cope* = oar; G. *pod* = foot) are crustaceans, the most abundant of the zooplankton. They are omnivorous, eating diatoms, copepods, fish eggs, larvae, and other small organisms. They have two jointed antennae extending from the head and one to several rudimentary eyes or pigment spots capable of detecting light or "seeing" shadows.

Comb jellies or ctenophores are gelatinous and resemble jellyfish. They have no stinging cells and a different propulsion system. They are not classified as jellyfish.

Foraminifera are microscopic one-celled protozoans. They secrete a chalky, calcareous test (outer skeleton or shell) that may consist of one or more spherical chambers. Through small holes in the shell, they push out temporary jellylike arms called pseudopods (G. *pseudo* = false; G. *pod* = foot), which they use to capture smaller organisms like diatoms and other protozoans for food. When foraminiferans reproduce or die, their tests sink to the seafloor. They are more common in warmer waters. Most forms are bottom-dwellers, and not plankton.

Jellyfish (medusae) are bell- or umbrella-shaped organisms of the phylum Cnidaria. Tentacles hanging down from the bell capture prey. Some, like the box jellyfish and Portuguese man-of-war, have powerful, even deadly, stings.

Table 5–2 *continued.* Examples of common permanent zooplankton, the holoplankton

Krill (order Euphausia) include many species of shrimplike crustaceans. Some grow to 5 cm and weigh as much as 1 g. Krill live in dense schools in polar waters. Most are filter-feeders; others have grinding jaws to accommodate larger particles. Krill are an important food for invertebrates, fish (including herring, mackerel, and other commercially harvested fish), penguins and other seabirds, and great filter-feeding whales, including the largest of all animals, the blue whale.

Pteropods, sometimes called sea butterflies, are gastropods (marine snails) whose foot has modified into wings. They produce large, sticky mucous parachutes that trap food particles. Pteropods living at the surface eat phytoplankton; those in deeper water eat zooplankton. Pteropods occur in modest numbers in all seas but are especially numerous in warmer waters. At death, their calcareous shells sink to the seafloor.

Radiolarians are one-celled organisms that secrete often complex and beautiful tests (outer skeletons or shells) made of silica. Some have long glasslike spines. Their name derives from their spherical shapes that resemble tiny suns with many rays. They feed on small animals and plants. Many have symbiotic algae, called zooxanthellae, living within them. The algae photosynthesize, manufacturing food and oxygen that are available to the radiolarian. When they reproduce or die, their tests sink to the seafloor, adding to the sediment layer.

Salps are floating tunicates (organisms that belong to phylum Chordata). They are characteristically cylindrical, tubular, or barrel-shaped. Most are microscopic in size. A few reach 12 cm or more. The action of their heart and circulatory system can be seen through their transparent bodies.

Tintinnids are small bell-like protozoans. Their bodies are encased in a tubular shell. Around the mouth are hairlike cilia that drive tiny phytoplankton into the mouth as they beat.

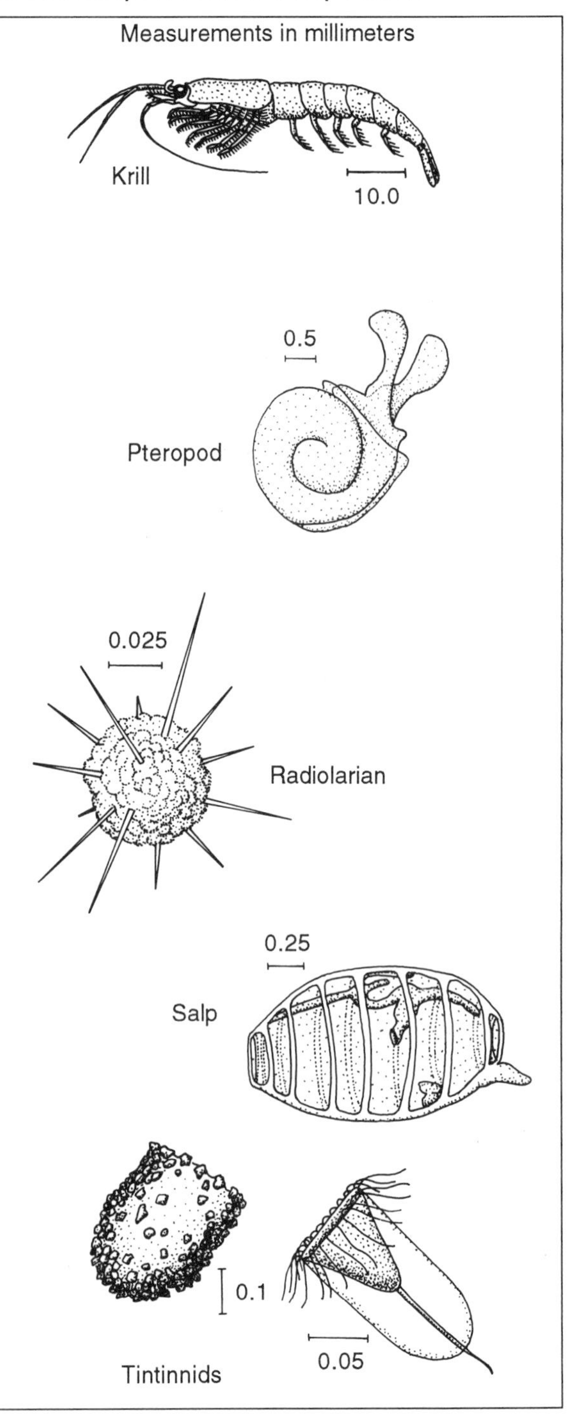

Table 5–3. Examples of common temporary zooplankton, the meroplankton

Crustacean larvae (arthropods) include shrimp, slipper lobsters, crabs, and barnacles. All begin life as larvae. Most are meroplankton.

Cnidarian larvae, such as coral larvae, are called planulae. These are bullet-shaped zooplankton that can drift for many days or weeks until they settle out and begin to form coral polyps.

Echinoderm larvae, such as sea stars, sea urchins, sand dollars, brittle stars, and sea cucumbers, are all found among the plankton.

Fish larvae do not usually look like the adult fish we know. Many egg-laying fish hatch into immature larval forms that drift as zooplankton. Fish larvae are eaten by many larger animals. They in turn feed on smaller organisms.

Mollusk larvae such as gastropod (marine snail) larvae are called **veligers.** Veliger refers to expanded, flexible mantle-like tissue (the vellum) that can be drawn inside the shell. Many veligers are pigmented on the four corners of their vellum.

Worm larvae have many shapes and live as plankton. The larvae of the ribbon worm (a Nemertina) are shaped like helmets. Some contain the young juvenile worm inside their body. Early developmental forms of the flatworms (Platyhelminthes) are among the meroplankton living near the bottom waters. Sipunculid worms also spend a brief time at the beginning of life as meroplankton.

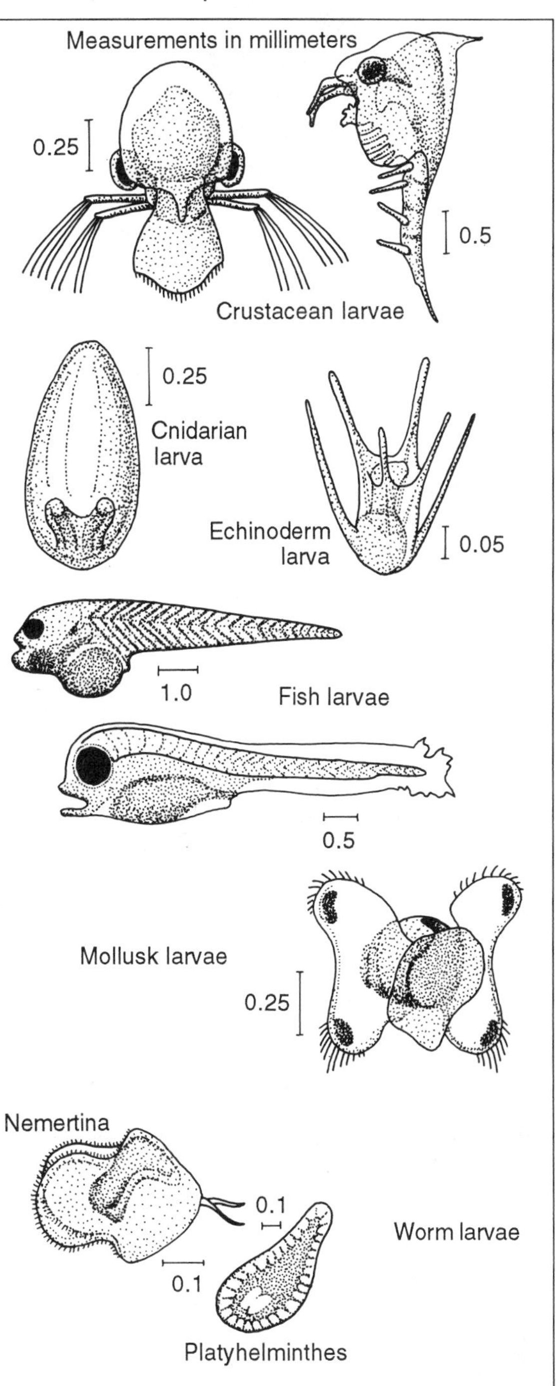

Plankton Size

Plankton vary widely in size. Phytoplankton are generally smaller than the zooplankton. The smallest are the cyanobacteria, so small that they can only been seen under powerful microscopes. Some zooplankton are exceptionally large, such as giant 10 m long salp colonies (a colonial tunicate), giant jellyfish up to 2.5 m in diameter and 40 m long, and the ocean sunfish (4 m long), which swims so poorly that it is considered plankton. See Fig. 5–1.

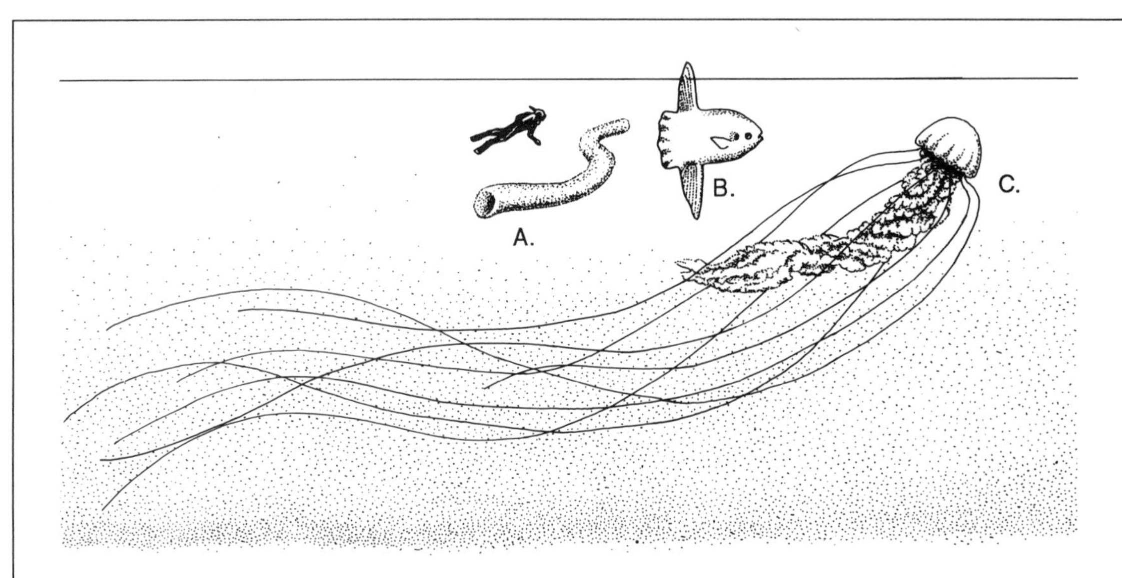

A. Salp colony. Salp colonies of *Pyrosoma* (G. *pyro* = fire; G. *soma* = body) consist of hundreds of thousands of small planktonic tunicates bonded together in a gelatinous tube. The tube is closed at one end. The mouths of the salps point outward; their atriums point inward. When the cilia lining the pharynx beat, water currents flow through the tube and out the open end, propelling the colony slowly through the water. Pyrosoma colonies are bioluminescent (G. *bio* = life; L. *lumin* = light); when disturbed by mechanical, chemical, or light stimulation, salps in a small area of the tube may light up brightly, and waves of light travel down the length of the tube. This behavior may startle a potential predator. Scientists noted this bioluminescence when naming them.

B. Ocean sunfish. Ocean sunfish are also referred to by their scientific name, *Mola mola.* They are large, sluggish predators of jellyfish, comb jellies, or other invertebrates they can suck into their mouths. Molas are thought to be one of the most fertile of all vertebrates, for the female produces close to 30 million eggs at a time. One of the largest of all bony fish, it can reach 4 m in length and 1500 kg in weight. Molas get their name "ocean sunfish" for their habit of lying still on the surface of the water, as if basking in the sun.

C. Giant jellyfish. *Cyanea* are gigantic jellyfish that occur in all northern waters, where they can reach lengths up to 40 m. Their ability to give very painful stings makes it fortunate that they live in waters too cold for most swimmers to enter. Thus most people are safe from their stings.

Fig. 5–1. Relative sizes of exceptionally large zooplankton compared to a human diver

Scientists who study plankton have developed a size classification system based on ranges, from very large to microscopic. This system allows them to refer to organism sizes without giving actual dimensions each time. See Table 5–4.

Table 5–4. Size classification of plankton

Name	Size	Examples
Megaplankton	> 20 cm	Portuguese man-of-war, jellyfish, salp colonies, ocean sunfish
Macroplankton	2 cm to 20 cm	Salps, shrimps, krill
Mesoplankton	0.2 to 20 mm	Copepods, comb jellies, fish larvae, pteropods
Microplankton	0.02 to 0.2 mm	Diatoms, tintinnids, dinoflagellates
Nannoplankton	0.002 to 0.02 mm	Coccolithophorids, cyanobacteria

ACTIVITY 1

Investigate the abundance of phytoplankton in the ocean.

Determine what animal phyla are found in the plankton.

MATERIALS

- copies of Workbook Tables 5–5, 5–6, and 5–7
- Open Ocean Ecology Game cards
- reference books (optional)

PROCEDURE

1. From your experience with the Open Ocean Ecology Game in Topic 4, give evidence to support the claim that over 95% of the biomass of the ocean is planktonic.
   a. Go through the game cards and pick out all organisms that are plankton.
   b. List the plankton and nonplankton by trophic level in Table 5–5. Record the number of cards for each organism.
   c. Find the game biomass written on each organism card. Record in Table 5–5.
   d. Calculate the biomass for each trophic level. Information for the phytoplankton has already been entered into the table.
   e. Calculate the total planktonic and nonplanktonic biomass.

2. Calculate the percentage of total biomass at each trophic level. Record data in Table 5–5.
   a. Calculate and record the percentage of biomass at each trophic level as follows:

$$\frac{\text{Trophic level biomass (kg)}}{\text{Total biomass (kg)}} \times 100\% = \text{\% biomass at that trophic level}$$

b. Calculate and record the percentage of biomass that is planktonic and nonplanktonic.

Table 5–5. Plankton in the Open Ocean Ecology Game 

Trophic level	Number of cards in deck	Game biomass per card	Trophic level biomass (in kg)	% Biomass at each trophic level
Plankton Phytoplankton (T1) Zooplankton (T2) Zooplankton (T3)	16	32,000,000	512,000,000	
Total plankton biomass				
Nonplankton T4 T5 T6				
Total nonplankton biomass				
Total biomass (plankton + nonplankton)				100

3. Complete Table 5–6, summarizing information on plankton in Tables 5–1, 5–2, 5–3, and 5–4. Include the size, kind, and type of residency in the plankton for each organism you use as an example.

Table 5–6. Examples of common plankton 

Size	Phytoplankton		Zooplankton	
	Holoplankton	Meroplankton	Holoplankton	Meroplankton
Megaplankton				
Macroplankton				
Mesoplankton				
Microplankton				
Nannoplankton				

4. Complete Table 5–7 showing relationships between types of plankton and the animal phyla we studied in Unit 1, Fish, and Unit 2, Invertebrates.
   a. For each phylum listed, do any of the animals live as larval plankton? If so, they are meroplankton, so write "yes" in the table. Record examples.
   b. Write "yes" for each type of animal that is a permanent plankton (holoplankton). Record examples.
   c. Write "yes" for each type of animal that eats phytoplankton. Record examples.

Table 5–7. Common marine animals and their relationship to plankton 

Phylum	Are any of these animals meroplankton (temporary plankton?)	Are any of these animals holoplankton (permanent plankton?)	Do any of these eat plankton?
Porifera Sponges			
Cnidarians Sea anemones Jellyfish Corals			
Worms Platyhelminthes Annelids Arrow worms			
Mollusks Bivalves Gastropods Cephalopods			
Arthropods Shrimp Lobsters Crabs			
Echinoderms Sea urchins Sea stars Sea cucumbers			
Invertebrate chordates Tunicates Lancelets			
Vertebrate chordates Fish			

QUESTIONS

1. How do plankton obtain their food?
   a. What is the source of food for phytoplankton? For zooplankton?
   b. Where do plankton fit in open-ocean food chains and food webs?

2. Which of the organisms in the Open Ocean Ecology Game are
   a. permanent plankton (holoplankton)?
   b. temporary plankton (meroplankton)?

3. Using information from the Open Ocean Ecology Game and Table 5–5, answer these questions:
   a. Most plankton are tiny or even microscopic. Consider the percentage of the biomass that is phytoplanktonic. What factors might explain why the percentage of plankton in the ocean is so great? Explain your answer in terms of food chains and trophic levels.
   b. The largest organisms on Earth–great blue whales, great white sharks, whale sharks, and giant squids–live in the ocean. In your opinion, why is the percentage of these huge, nonplanktonic animals so low? Explain your answer in terms of food chains and trophic levels.

4. Use information from the text readings and Table 5–6 to support or refute the following statements:
   a. All zooplankton are meroplankton.
   b. All phytoplankton are holoplankton.
   c. Most phytoplankton are smaller than zooplankton.
   d. All plankton are small.
   e. All phytoplankton are single cells.
   f. Meroplanktonic zooplankton are larvae.
   g. The largest planktonic invertebrates are holoplankton.
   h. Meroplanktonic zooplankton are smaller than holoplanktonic zooplankton.

5. In Unit 1, Fish, you investigated free-swimming fish. What relationship, if any, is there between fish and plankton? Use Table 5–7 and give examples in your answer.

6. How are plankton important sources of food
   a. to filter-feeding organisms? Give examples.
   b. to sessile (nonmoving) organisms? Give examples.

7. How might having a larval planktonic (meroplankton) stage be an advantage to sessile organisms?

8. From the information in Tables 5–1 to 5–4, what general statements, if any, can you make about the size of a planktonic organism and whether it is
   a. a phytoplankton?
   b. an herbivore?
   c. a carnivore?

9. Many fish and some mammals eat plankton. Would you classify them as herbivores, omnivores, or carnivores? Why?

10. What might be the advantages and disadvantages of a fish laying its eggs in an area rich in plankton?

11. Sketch two food chains, one with phytoplankton at the T1 level and the other with seaweed at the T1 level. Keep in mind that, in general, small herbivores eat small plants.
    a. Which food chain is shorter?
    b. Which of the two chains would humans be more likely to fish? Support your answer.

ACTIVITY 2

Collect and observe live plankton.
Test reactions of live plankton to light.
Observe and describe adaptations that help plankton float, swim, and capture food.

MATERIALS

For making a plankton net

- wire clothes hanger
- pliers with a cutting edge
- nylon stocking or pantyhose
- scissors
- needle and thread
- three 2-ft lengths of line
- weights (small lead sinkers)
- collection jar, plastic
- 1-ft length of line

For plankton collection

- copy of Workbook Table 5–8
- centimeter ruler with millimeter markings
- tow line (at least 50 m)
- 1-gal bucket of seawater
- 1-gal observation jar, plastic, wide-mouthed
- seawater hydrometer
- thermometer
- tide chart

For measuring water quality

- water color comparator
- Secchi disk
- dissolved oxygen test kit (optional)
- pH test paper (optional)
- dissolved nitrate test kit (optional)
- dissolved phosphate test kit (optional)

For observing plankton

- eyedropper
- small Petri dish or well slide
- dissecting microscope
- 1.5% methyl cellulose solution (optional)
- cardboard pieces for light shield
- flashlight or other bright light

PROCEDURE

1. If you can't borrow a plankton net, make one. See Fig. 5–2.
    a. Shape a wire coat hanger into a hoop. Twist the ends together with pliers. See 1.A. through 1.C. in Fig. 5–2.
    b. Use a nylon stocking or one leg cut from pantyhose.
    c. Fold its top over the hoop and sew it in place. Leave three evenly spaced ¼-in gaps for tying the line to the ring. See 2.A. in Fig. 5–2.
    d. Make a bridle by knotting the three lengths of line together at one end. Tie the loose ends to the hoop at the gaps. See 2.B. through 2.C. in Fig. 5–2.

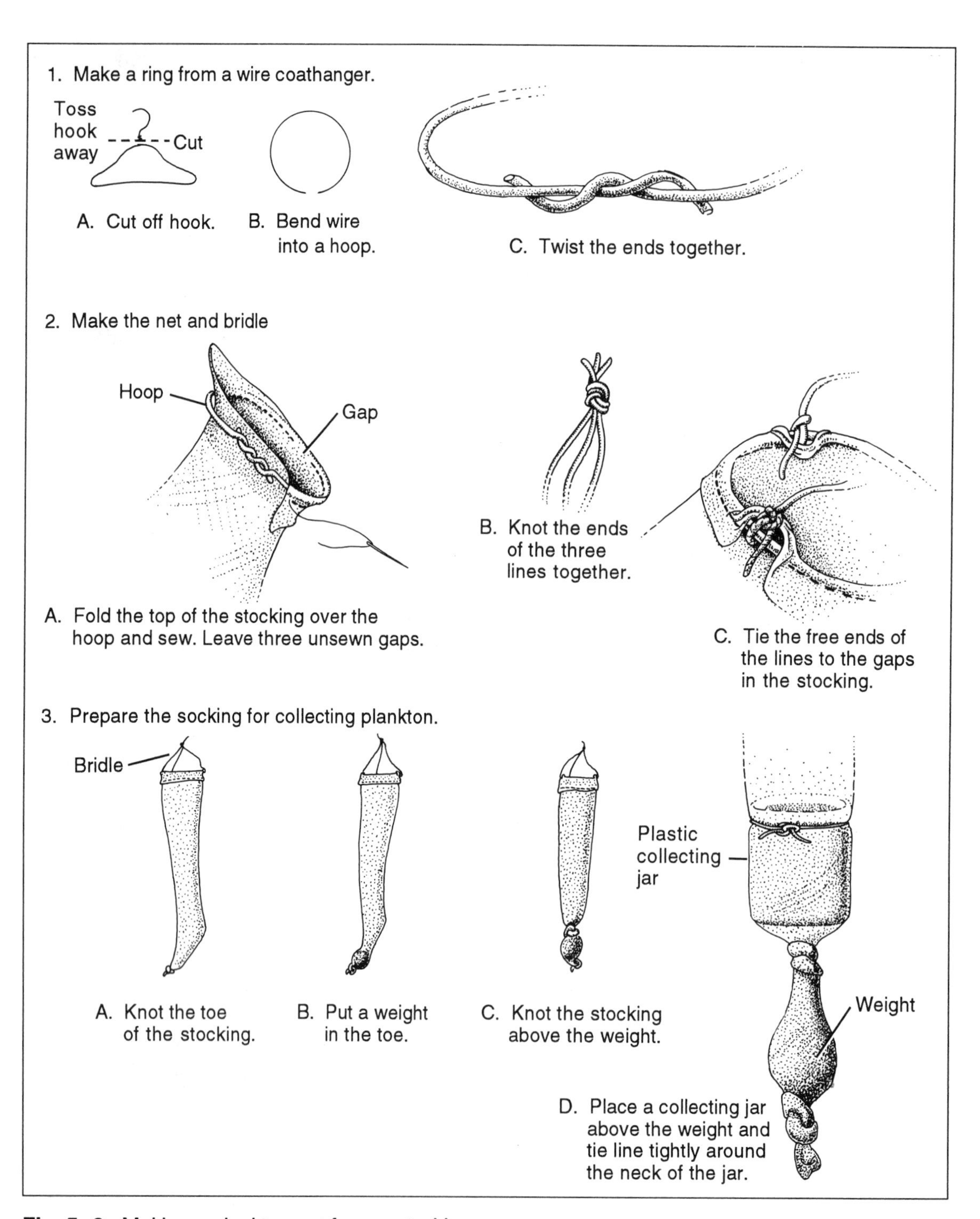

Fig. 5–2. Making a plankton net from a stocking

e. Knot the toe end of the stocking as shown in 3.A. through 3.C. in Fig. 5–2. Insert a weight into the net, pushing it down as far as the knot. Hold it in place by tying a second knot above the weight.
f. Put a collection jar above the weight and tie the nylon net tightly around the neck of the jar with the line. See 3.D. in Fig. 5–2.

2. Estimate the mesh size of your net when stretched during a plankton tow. Use a centimeter ruler with millimeter markings. Record the mesh size in Table 5–5.
   a. From Table 5–4, predict and record the size(s) of the organisms that you will probably capture with the net.
   b. From Tables 5–1 to 5–3, predict the kinds of organisms that you might capture. Record your predictions in your journal.

3. Collect plankton in the plankton net.
   a. Attach a tow line to the bridle.
   b. Fill a bucket with water from your sampling site for rinsing the organisms out of the net and into the collecting jar.
   c. If possible, tow the net behind a boat. Lower the net into the water. The weight will sink the toe end, but the bridle will keep the net open. If you have no boat, try other ways of collecting plankton—for example, by walking back and forth along a long pier or by tying the net to a vertical piling where currents flow. You will have to experiment to find
      1) the best time of day to tow the net (sunrise, midmorning, noon, midafternoon, sunset),
      2) how many minutes to tow the net, and
      3) what depth to keep the net during the tow.
   d. Haul in the net slowly to keep it from twisting and to keep water flowing into the net instead of around the opening.
   e. Lift the net from the water by the bridle. Pour water down the inside of the net to wash the plankton into the collecting jar.
   f. Untie the line around the collecting jar and lift the jar from the net without spilling its contents. Pour the sample from the collection jar into the observation jar.
   e. Turn the net inside out. With a little water, rinse any trapped organisms from the net into the collection jar. Add them to the observation jar.

4. Measure and record the salinity, water temperature, and tide conditions.
   a. Use a hydrometer to measure salinity in parts per thousand (‰). Use a thermometer to measure temperature in degrees Celsius (°C).
   b. Use a tide chart to determine tide height and whether the tide is coming in (a flood tide) or going out (an ebb tide).
   c. Note the cloud cover (cloudy, partly cloudy, clear sky). Record data in Table 5–8.
   d. (Optional) If you have equipment

Table 5–8. Plankton collection data sheet

Ⓦ

1. **Location** ____________ Date ____________ Tow # ______

Time in water ________ AM PM   Time out of water ________ AM PM   Tow duration ________ min

Tow method ____________________________

Plankton net diameter ________ cm   Mesh size ________ mm   Collection jar volume ________ mL

2. **Sampling conditions**

Average tow depth ____________________________

Water temperature________ °C   Tide height ________   Water color ________

Salinity ________ ‰   Wind ________   Cloud cover________

pH________   Evidence of currents ____________________

Dissolved oxygen ________   Dissolved nitrates ________   Dissolved phosphates ________

Other observations ____________________________

____

3. **Initial sample**

Approximate volume collected ________ mL   Approximate % alive ________ %

4. **Drawings of plankton**

available, make other measurements of water quality like those shown in Table 5–8. Record data.

5. Observe living plankton under a microscope.
   a. Fill an eyedropper with plankton and squeeze it into a small Petri dish. Observe the organisms at 20X to 40X through a dissecting microscope. (If they are moving too fast for close observation, add a drop or two of 1.5% methyl cellulose solution or put the sample in the refrigerator for a few minutes.) Sketch what you observe.
   b. Using the information in Tables 5–1 to 5–3, identify as many of the organisms as you can. Use other references as needed.

6. Determine how the plankton respond to light. Lay a light shield over one end of the Petri dish. Shine a light on different parts of the dish. Observe at 20X whether the plankton move toward or away from the light.

7. Because plankton are living organisms, they consist of water plus other substances. Hence their bodies are normally denser than water. Look for body structures that help plankton to
   a. float and remain afloat.
   b. swim forward or backward.
   c. change direction.
   d. capture food.

   Make sketches and record your observations.

8. When you finish, follow your teacher's instructions for preserving or disposing of the plankton.

QUESTIONS

12. What were the sizes of the organisms you captured in your net? What sizes did not appear in your sample?

13. Was the sample mostly phytoplankton or zooplankton? How do you know?

14. From the results of your plankton tow, what can you tell about the relative abundance of
    a. plants?
    b. herbivores?
    c. carnivores?

15. What hypothesis might explain the distribution you found in Question 14?

16. What organism was the largest? What does it probably eat? What probably eats it? Explain your reasoning.

17. Which organism was the most abundant in the sample? What does it probably eat? What probably eats it? Give reasons to support your answer.

18. How might the mesh size of a plankton net determine the kinds of organisms it captures?
    a. What types of plankton would you expect to capture in a net with a large mesh? How representative would this sample be of all the plankton in an area? What kinds of organisms

might escape through the net?
b. Which kind of plankton is most likely to be underrepresented in a plankton tow?

19. Some plankton have hard skeletons; others, such as jellyfish, have soft gelatinous bodies. How might the kind of skeleton affect the catch in a plankton tow?

20. After you rinsed the organisms from the net into the observation jar, what happened to dead organisms and organisms that were badly injured by towing or rinsing?
    a. How did you know that these were dead or badly injured organisms?
    b. What do your observations tell you about what happens to dead plankton in the ocean? Where do they go when they die?

21. What color(s) were the plankton in your sample?
    a. About what percentage were colorless? How might lack of color be an advantage? Were the colorless ones phytoplankton or zooplankton? How do you know?
    b. What colors might be advantageous for phytoplankton? For zooplankton?
    c. Some plankton are iridescent, like the copepod Sappharina. How might iridescence be an advantage?

22. How did the plankton respond to light?
    a. Did all the plankton respond the same way?
    b. When are plankton most likely to retreat to deeper water? Explain your reasoning.

23. Using examples that you observed, describe structural adaptations that aid zooplankton in
    a. floating.
    b. swimming.
    c. moving up and down in the water column.

24. Zooplankton that eat phytoplankton are called herbivores or grazers. Where are these herbivorous zooplankton likely to be found?

25. Other zooplankton prey on herbivorous zooplankton. But if plankton are weak swimmers, how can they hunt? What structures do zooplankton use to capture food? Give some examples from Table 5–2.

26. **Scavengers** are organisms that eat dead food. Unlike communities of land animals, communities of plankton contain few scavengers. Why? Explain your reasoning.

27. If you were to make more plankton tows,
    a. what time of day would probably yield the largest and smallest samples?
    b. what tide conditions would yield the largest and smallest samples?
    c. what other factors—wind, waves, temperature, currents, and water depth—would affect the yield?

28. Oceanographers have found that zooplankton migrate as much as 300 m up and down the water column each day. See Fig. 5–3.
    a. When the midday sun strikes the surface of the water directly, where would you expect to find zooplankton? Give reasons to support your answer.
    b. When the sun sets, what happens to plankton? Give reasons to support your answer.

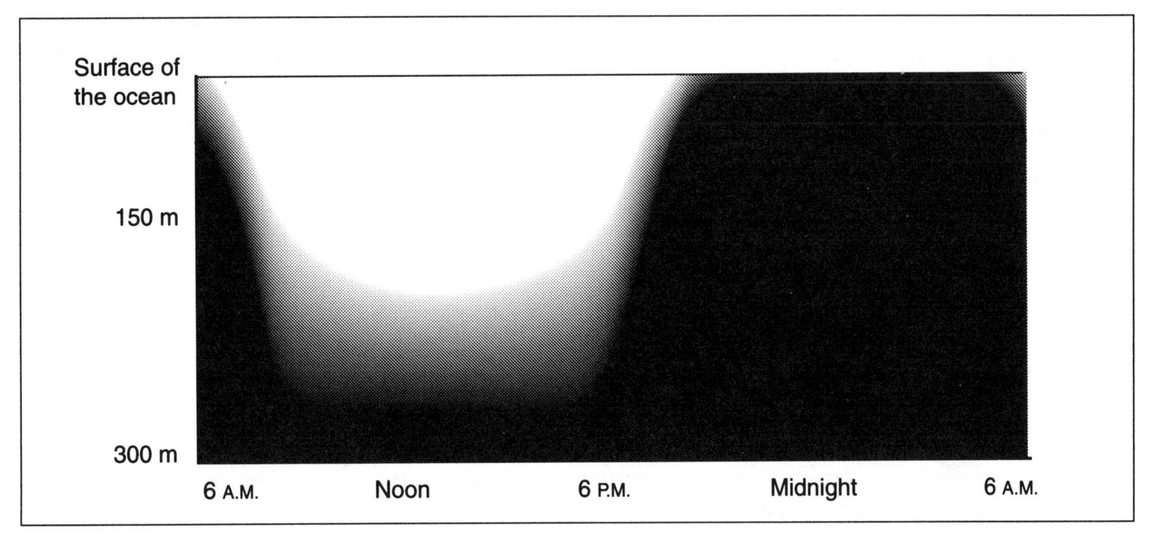

Fig. 5–3. Vertical migration pattern of plankton during a 24-hour period

Plankton as Agents of Change

Because plankton are so abundant, they are one of the key agents of change in the ocean. They exchange gases and nutrients with seawater and create wastes (detritus) that alter the ocean environment.

Interactions with Seawater

Phytoplankton change the concentration of dissolved gases in the ocean. During the day, if there is enough light, they photosynthesize, removing dissolved carbon dioxide (CO_2) from seawater and combining it with water to release oxygen (O_2). Both day and night they respire, removing dissolved oxygen from seawater.

Phytoplankton play a critical role in determining the availability of dissolved oxygen in seawater. During the day they produce more oxygen through photosynthesis than they use in respiration. At night they continue to respire. During a phytoplankton bloom, very large numbers of plankton deplete the dissolved oxygen supply, causing organisms to die.

Phytoplankton's role in gas exchange goes beyond affecting the ocean environment. Since the ocean and atmosphere interact and exchange gases, phytoplankton also play important roles in regulating atmospheric gases.

Phytoplankton selectively absorb elements from seawater and use them to build body parts. Phytoplankton, for example, need nitrogen (N) and phosphorus (P) to build soft tissue, and some require calcium (Ca) or silicon (Si) to build hard skeletal structures. When these materials are abundant in seawater, phytoplankton rapidly grow and multiply; when the materials are depleted, the population drops.

Biological Sediments

Zooplankton eat phytoplankton, but they cannot digest their hard skeletons. The skeletons, made of either calcium carbonate ($CaCO_3$) or silicon dioxide (SiO_2), are also indigestible to other animals. The skeletons pass through animal digestive tracts, then are expelled as one of the substances in waste **fecal pellets.** Uneaten plankton that simply die without being eaten also add skeletal detritus to the ocean.

Some of the plankton skeletal materials eventually sink to the seafloor, where they accumulate as **biogenic sediments** (G. *bio* = life; G. *genic* = producing). Calcium carbonate ($CaCO_3$) sediments, or **calcareous muds**, consist mainly of the skeletal remains of coccolithophores, foraminiferans, and pteropods. Silicon dioxide (SiO_2) sediments, or **siliceous muds**, consist mainly of the skeletons of diatoms and radiolarians. See Fig. 5–4. These plankton are illustrated in Table 5–1 or 5–2.

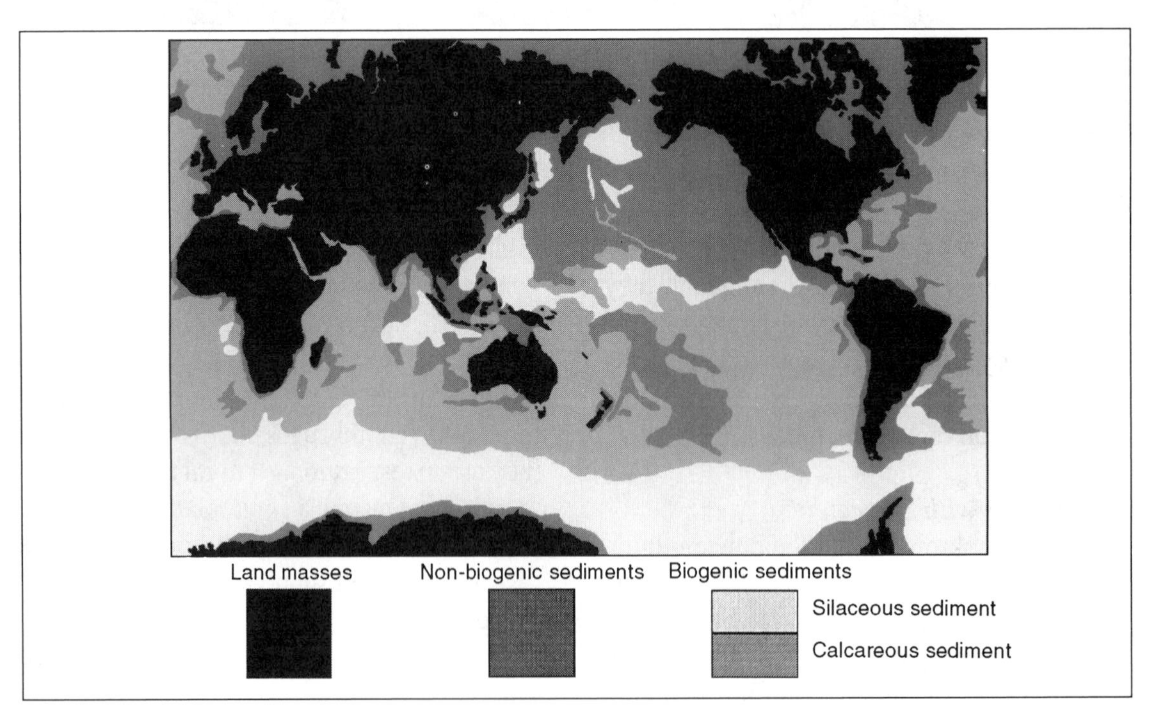

Fig. 5–4. Plankton create beds of sediment across the oceans.

Recycled Nutrients

Organic detritus is soft, nonskeletal biological material that decomposers can digest. The soft parts of dead plankton, along with digestible material in their fecal pellets, make up much of the organic detritus in the ocean. This detritus serves as food for **decomposer bacteria** (detritivores), which convert the detritus into simpler substances that dissolve in seawater, making them available as nutrients for phytoplankton.

Where there are enough nutrients (phosphates and nitrates) in surface layers of the water and enough sunlight to support photosynthesis, phytoplankton flourish. However, they can multiply so quickly that they deplete the surrounding water of nutrients. In the open ocean the dead phytoplankton settle to the bottom, carrying their nutrients with them. The surface water is therefore depleted of nutrients, preventing further growth of phytoplankton. In these regions, because of the lack of phytoplankton, the water is a transparent blue. Most of the open ocean is like this.

Winds, waves, and currents stirring the water distribute dissolved nutrients. Currents can move water near the seafloor back up to the surface. Water near the seafloor is especially rich in nutrients from sediments. This water may take 500 years or more to recycle to the surface unless the area has **upwellings,** currents flowing upward from depths of 200 m or more. Upwellings carry nutrient-rich cold water to the surface. If sunlight is sufficient, phytoplankton flourish in areas with upwellings. So do other organisms that depend on plankton for food. Most of the best fisheries are near continents where upwelling occurs.

Marine Snow

Oceanographers coined the name **marine snow** for the small floating, drifting, or slowly sinking bits of detritus in the ocean. Marine snow consists of the soft organic material, fecal pellets, and skeletal remains of dead plankton plus smaller inorganic particles of mud or clay. Marine snow particles are often several millimeters across, making them easily visible to divers and submersible operators. They also show up in underwater photographs.

When marine snow particles collide, they often stick loosely together, sweeping the seawater of smaller particles as they sink. And marine snow can just as readily fall apart.

About three-fourths of marine snow is either eaten or decomposed in the photic zone—the zone that light penetrates. Most falls apart or is eaten in the upper 1,000 m of the ocean. But about 0.01% sinks to the seabed, adding to the biological sediments deposited on the seafloor.

Only recently have oceanographers understood the importance of marine snow as a source of food and nutrients. Because marine snow drifts from the surface into deeper waters, it provides food for organisms at all depths.

Marine snow was underestimated in earlier research on ocean food productivity, largely because its particles often break apart in sampling nets. Using sediment traps, oceanographers have found far more marine snow in the oceans than they expected—so much more that they have doubled their estimate of the biological productivity of phytoplankton.

The Greenhouse Effect

Scientists who study the greenhouse effect are especially interested in phytoplankton and marine snow. **Greenhouse effect** refers to global warming, the potential warming of the earth from the buildup of carbon dioxide and other gases in the atmosphere. An increase in CO_2 prevents heat from leaving the atmosphere and flowing into space. The CO_2 acts like the glass in a greenhouse, trapping heat in the atmosphere that could eventually cause worldwide warming. Such global warming could bring a rise in sea level, floods along coasts, and disruptive shifts in climate.

Carbon dioxide (CO_2), the major gas in the greenhouse effect, dissolves in the ocean, where phytoplankton use it to build skeletal structures of calcium carbonate ($CaCO_3$). Although most of the skeletal material is recycled, the amount that sinks to the seafloor can stay there for thousands of years. Some scientists have suggested that stimulating phytoplankton productivity may be one way of removing excess carbon dioxide from the atmosphere.

Phytoplankton are much like the forests on land. They both use CO_2 to photosynthesize and build their plant structures, and both produce excess oxygen during daylight. Some scientists think that phytoplankton are more important than land plants in controlling CO_2 levels.

QUESTIONS

29. What is the relationship between phytoplankton in the ocean and the concentrations of carbon dioxide and oxygen
    a. in the ocean?
    b. in the atmosphere?

30. How do phytoplankton change nutrient availability in surface waters?

31. How are biological sediments found on the seafloor explained?

32. What is marine snow and how is it related
    a. to plankton?
    b. to recycling of nutrients in seawater?
    c. to the food web?

33. What are some reasons that scientists who study the greenhouse effect are interested in plankton?

Plankton Responses to Environmental Changes

Because phytoplankton are very sensitive to changes in their environment, their numbers vary throughout the year. Sudden periodic increases in phytoplankton population are called **plankton blooms.**

Since phytoplankton form the basis of the food chain, blooms are quickly followed by increases in populations of grazing zooplankton, then of predators that feed on herbivorous zooplankton. For this reason the size of the phytoplankton population tells much about the biological productivity of the ocean.

Environmental factors related to changes in phytoplankton population size are summarized in Table 5–9.

QUESTIONS

34. See Fig. 5–5, which shows seasonal variations in phytoplankton populations over a year in open-ocean temper-

Table 5–9. Environmental factors related to phytoplankton population size

Sunlight. Increased light increases photosynthesis. Factors that decrease sunlight include nights, winters, and cloudy skies.

Nutrients. Increased supplies of nutrients (containing nitrogen [N] in the form of nitrates, phosphorus [P] in the form of phosphates, and potassium [K]) speed phytoplankton growth causing population explosions (blooms).

Temperature. Warm temperatures speed the growth of many living organisms.

Temperature layering (stratification). Layering occurs when the sun heats surface water, preventing it from mixing with colder, denser water. When phytoplankton deplete nutrients in upper layers, layering prevents nutrients in deeper waters from mixing into surface waters.

Grazing. Phytoplankton blooms provide abundant food for herbivorous zooplankton, stimulating the growth of their population. Because zooplankton graze on phytoplankton, the phytoplankton population falls until larger predators control the zooplankton populations.

Dissolved oxygen. Phytoplankton and all other organisms respire continuously, taking in dissolved oxygen, During the day photosynthesis by phytoplankton produces oxygen, increasing the dissolved oxygen content of the water. At night the phytoplankton continue to respire but stop photosynthesizing, and the dissolved oxygen decreases. If the oxygen is severely depleted, large numbers of organisms can die.

ate zone waters (such as in the North Atlantic Ocean).

a. What factors account for the spring bloom?
b. How can the summer plateau be explained?
c. What factors might explain the fall bloom?
d. What happens to the phytoplankton population during the winter? What environmental factors might account for this change?

35. How, if at all, would the phytoplankton population graph differ for
    a. tropical waters? Give reasons to support your answer.
    b. polar water? Give reasons to support your answer.

36. **Upwellings** occur mostly in coastal waters. During an upwelling, cold, deep currents flow to the surface, bringing nutrient-rich water into the euphotic zone.

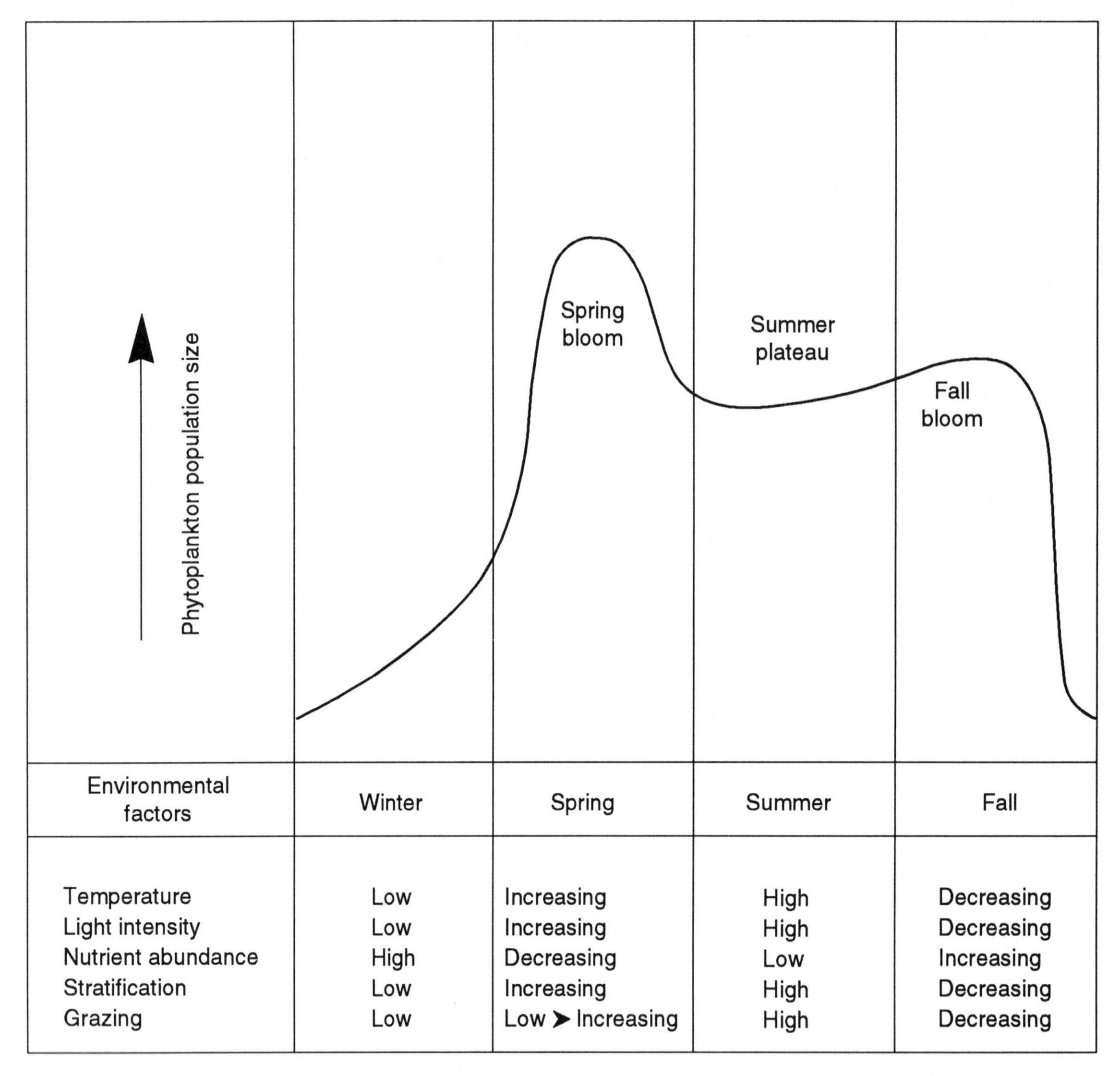

Environmental factors	Winter	Spring	Summer	Fall
Temperature	Low	Increasing	High	Decreasing
Light intensity	Low	Increasing	High	Decreasing
Nutrient abundance	High	Decreasing	Low	Increasing
Stratification	Low	Increasing	High	Decreasing
Grazing	Low	Low ➤ Increasing	High	Decreasing

Fig. 5–5. Phytoplankton population size over one year (midlatitude, temperate waters)

a. What happens to phytoplankton populations during an upwelling?
b. What happens to the zooplankton population?
c. How does an upwelling affect fish populations in an area?

37. Ecologists use the term **eutrophic** to describe lakes and ponds where nutrients are so abundant that they promote a plankton bloom. What might happen to a pond in late spring if nutrients were added, perhaps in the form of dissolved

fertilizers from nearby gardens or farms, and the pond water became eutrophic?

a. What would happen to freshwater plants and phytoplankton in the pond?
b. What would happen to the zooplankton population? To other animals in the pond?
c. What would happen to the oxygen level in the eutrophic pond during the day?
d. During the night, under normal non-eutrophic conditions in the pond, what happens to the dissolved-oxygen concentration?
e. During the night, under eutrophic conditions, what happens to the dissolved-oxygen concentration? How might this affect the plants and animals in the pond?

38. How might pollution affect plankton in the ocean? In lakes and ponds?

ACTIVITY 3

Diagram chemicals taken in and given off by phytoplankton.
Describe how phytoplankton interact with their seawater environment.
Investigate the relations between phytoplankton, marine snow, and the greenhouse effect.

MATERIALS

- copies of Workbook Figs. 5–6 and 5–7
- colored pencils

PROCEDURE

1. Make a diagram showing the materials taken in and given off by a phytoplankton cell. Start with Fig. 5–6. Refer to Unit 3, Topic 3, for information on the chemical reactions of photosynthesis and respiration.
   a. Using a green pencil, draw arrows showing the chemicals taken in from the seawater during photosynthesis.
   b. Using the same green pencil, draw arrows showing the products of photosynthesis.
   c. Using a red pencil, show the chemicals used by phytoplankton cells during respiration in the phytoplankton cell.
   d. Using the same red pencil, show the products of respiration.
   e. Using a yellow pencil, show the chemicals used by phytoplankton cells during growth and skeleton formation.
   c. Using a brown pencil, show what happens to the parts of the phytoplankton cell when it dies and breaks up.

2. Diagram the role of phytoplankton in the cycling of matter in seawater. Start with Fig. 5–7.
   a. In green pencil, draw arrows showing the food chain that begins with phytoplankton. Make the arrows point to each organism doing the eating.
   b. In red pencil, indicate the sources of the organic detritus in marine snow.

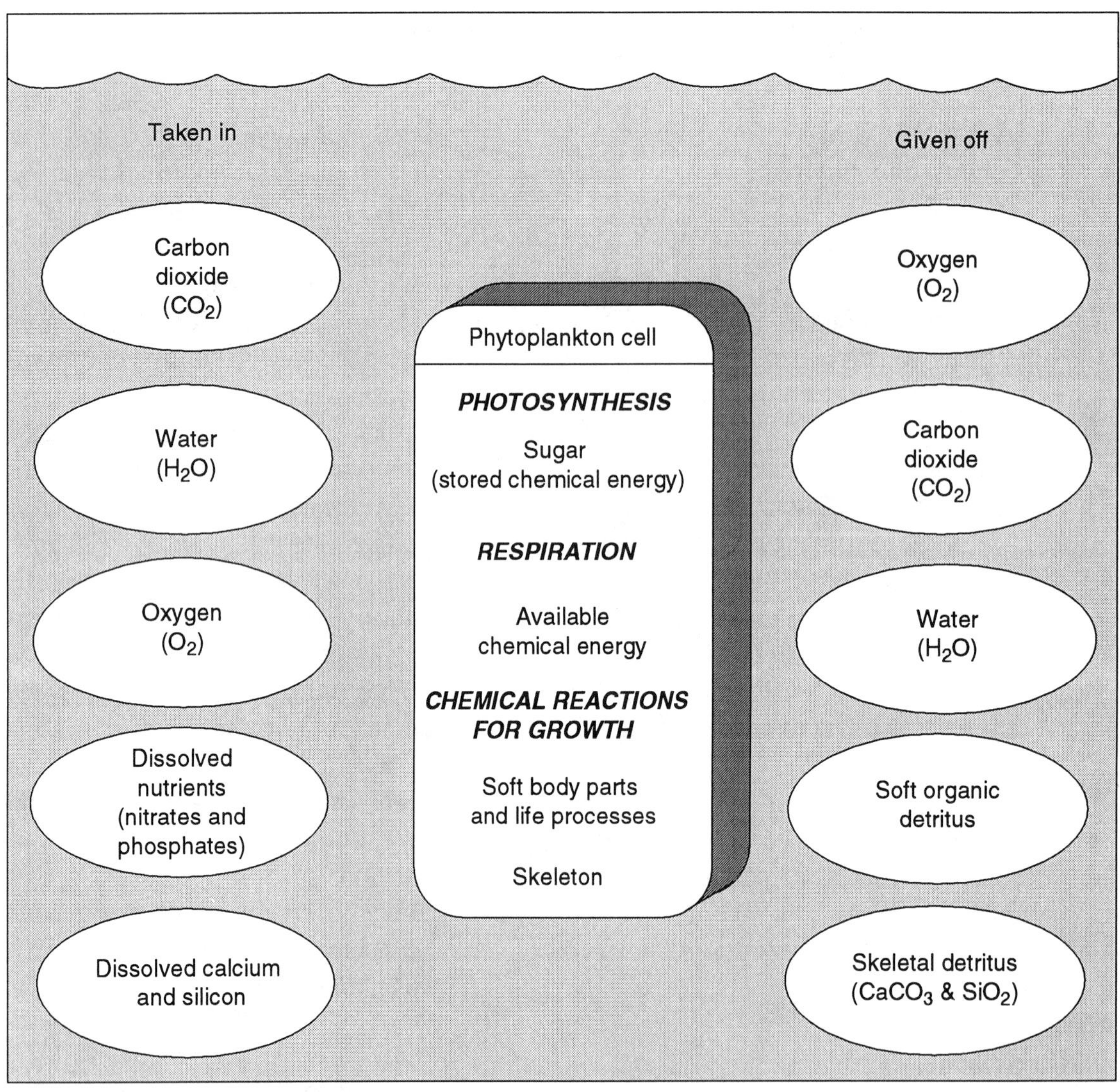

Fig. 5–6. Materials taken in and given off by a phytoplankton cell

Make the arrows point from the source to the marine snow.

c. In brown pencil, draw arrows starting from phytoplankton to show how their skeletons become biological sediments on the seabed. Make the arrows point to the seafloor sediments.

d. In blue pencil, indicate the sources of dissolved nutrients that are carried to the surface when water upwells (flows to the surface).

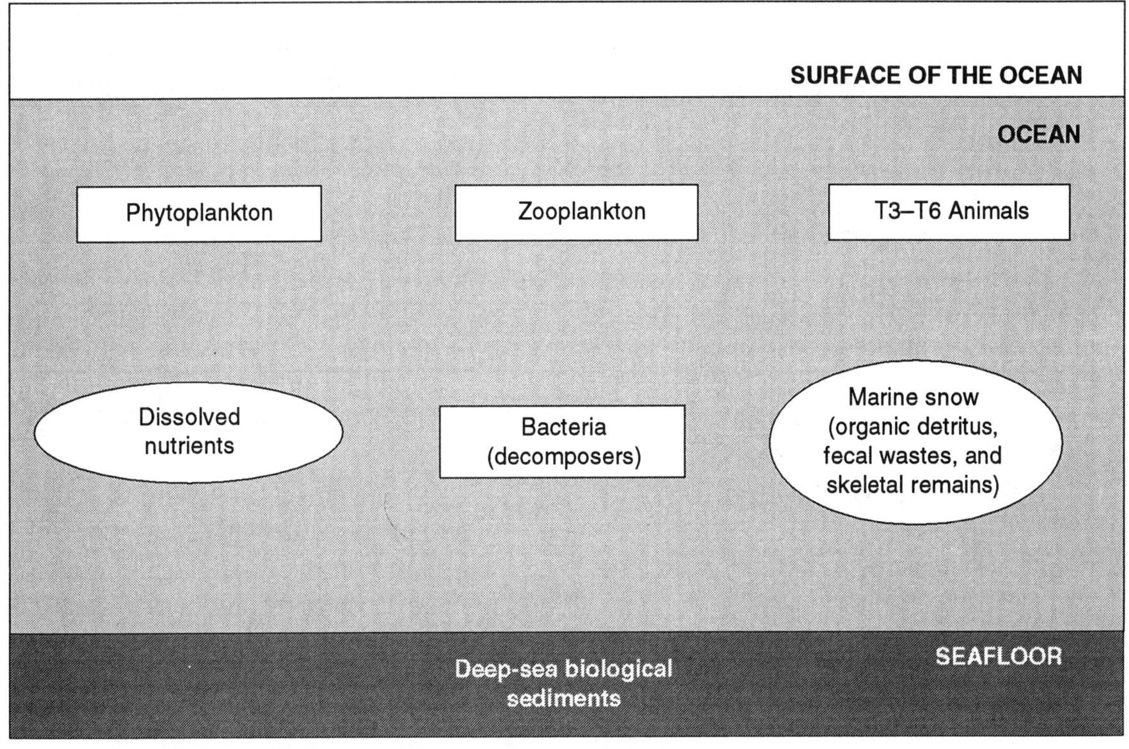

Fig. 5–7. Diagram of matter cycling in seawater

QUESTIONS

39. In what ways do phytoplankton modify the chemistry of seawater? Answer by referring to
    a. chemicals and materials taken in from seawater and given off into seawater by phytoplankton.
    b. interactions with other organisms.

40. How is marine snow related to feeding relationships among phytoplankton, zooplankton, larger animals, and bacteria?

41. What roles do phytoplankton play in the cycling of matter
    a. in food webs?
    b. in seawater?
    c. in marine snow?
    d. in the accumulation of particles on the seafloor?

42. What might explain why biological sediments (calcareous and siliceous muds) are greatest where phytoplankton are most abundant?

43. How could an increase in phytoplankton productivity remove more CO_2
    a. from the ocean?
    b. from the atmosphere?

44. One way to study the cycling of carbon dioxide (CO_2) in the atmosphere is to trace one of its elements, carbon (C). Starting with carbon dioxide in the atmosphere, describe or sketch answers to the following:
    a. How does carbon dioxide enter the ocean?
    b. How is carbon cycled in the ocean?
    c. What factors might increase the amount of atmospheric carbon dioxide entering the ocean?
    d. What ocean event removes carbon from food chains in the ocean?

45. In what ways might phytoplankton productivity be stimulated? What environmental conditions would foster rapid growth and reproduction? How could these conditions come about in the ocean?

46. If phytoplankton productivity could be increased, what are the likely consequences for
    a. the concentration of carbon dioxide in seawater?
    b. the concentration of carbon dioxide in the atmosphere?
    c. zooplankton populations?
    d. the ocean food chain?
    e. deep-sea sediment formation?

FURTHER INVESTIGATIONS

1. Using references, report to the class on the global importance of plankton for
    a. food, beginning at the bottom of the food chain.
    b. oxygen production through photosynthesis.
    c. absorption of carbon dioxide and possible ways to reduce global warming from the greenhouse effect.

2. Hold a debate to support or refute the following statements:
    a. There are no sessile land animals.
    b. In the ocean there are tremendous numbers of floating organisms, the plankton. On land, the equivalent would be organisms floating in the air. There are no "aerial plankton."

3. Using references, learn more about how the daily vertical migration of zooplankton is responsible for the changing levels of the "deep scattering layers" detected by sonar echo-sounders on ships. Explain how plankton might be related to "false-bottom" recordings.

4. Learn more about seafloor sediments that contain the remains of skeletal plankton. These include diatomaceous "ooze" and muds, foraminiferan "ooze," and radiolarian muds and oozes.
    a. Where are these found? What patterns, if any, appear in their distribution?
    b. Some of these deposits are mined commercially. What are they used for?
    c. Find out how geologists use the skeletal remains of plankton to determine the age of a given deposit, to seek evidence of changes in the earth's magnetic field, and to search for gas and oil.

5. Using models or mathematical examples,

demonstrate that smaller organisms float better than larger ones.

a. In water, two bodies fall at differing speeds, depending on the ratio of the weight of the falling body to its surface area. The surface area offers resistance to the water.
b. The surface area increases as the square of the radius of a body, but the volume increases as the cube of the radius of a body.
c. Would tropical plankton be larger or smaller than polar plankton? Explain your reasoning.

6. Recent studies point to the depletion of ozone in the upper atmosphere. Ozone blocks harmful ultraviolet rays from reaching the surface of the earth. How then might ozone depletion affect plankton? What might be the consequences? What actions might prevent serious ozone depletion? Use references.

7. Invite a bacteriologist or chemist from the local water department to speak about how the department tests water for harmful chemicals or organisms.

8. The concentration of carbon dioxide in the atmosphere increased during the 20th century. Use library references to learn about proposals to check further increases by
   a. adding nutrient chemicals to the ocean to stimulate phytoplankton productivity and
   b. launching satellites to beam sunlight onto dark polar waters during the winter.

9. How is information about plankton productivity useful in studying
   a. the total biological productivity of the oceans?
   b. open-ocean fish?
   c. fishing practices?

6. Ocean Color and Satellite Remote Sensing

Fishers and sailors have long noticed differences in ocean color and made up descriptive names like "Blue Pacific, "Vermilion Sea," and "Red Sea." When you look at the ocean, you see a color. Yet water in a beaker appears colorless. What gives the ocean its color?

Not surprisingly, the abundance of phytoplankton in the surface waters of the ocean is related to the color we see. Where there are few phytoplankton, the ocean looks blue; where phytoplankton are abundant, the ocean looks green. Occasional blooms of red-brown single-celled plankton called dinoflagellates can temporarily color the ocean red. Thus **ocean color** can often be used to indicate relative abundance of phytoplankton. In nearshore coastal waters where rivers empty into the ocean and freshwater runoff occurs, the water may be tinged with suspended particles of mud and clay, masking the color produced by plankton.

Oceanographers devised standards for measuring ocean color. One standard is the Forel–Ule Color Comparator. See Fig. 6–1. Each standard color is identified by a roman numeral, starting with deep-sea blue (I) and ending with a muddy yellowish-brown (XXI). The colors of offshore ocean water range from deep-sea blue (I) to green (X); coastal and inland waters range from green (XII) to brown (XXI). Yellow-green indicates dense phytoplankton populations.

QUESTIONS

1. How does the chlorophyll in phytoplankton interact with sunlight? Refer as needed to Topic 3 in Unit 3.

2. How do plankton change the apparent color of the ocean? What is the probable color where plankton are scarce? Where plankton are plentiful?

3. How could you use measurements of
   a. ocean color to indicate plankton populations?
   b. chlorophyll to indicate plankton populations?

Measuring Ocean Color

Directions for using a Forel–Ule Color Comparator are given in Activity 1 and illustrated in Fig. 6–2. Measuring water color also requires the use of a Secchi disk to determine **turbidity,** the reduction in water clarity caused by suspended particles, whether plankton or mud. The Secchi disk is lowered into the ocean until it almost disappears from view. In very clear waters of tropical oceans, the Secchi disk may not disappear until it is 40 m deep. In turbid coastal waters, the disk may disappear just a few meters down. See Fig. 6–1.

Fig. 6–1. Secchi disk

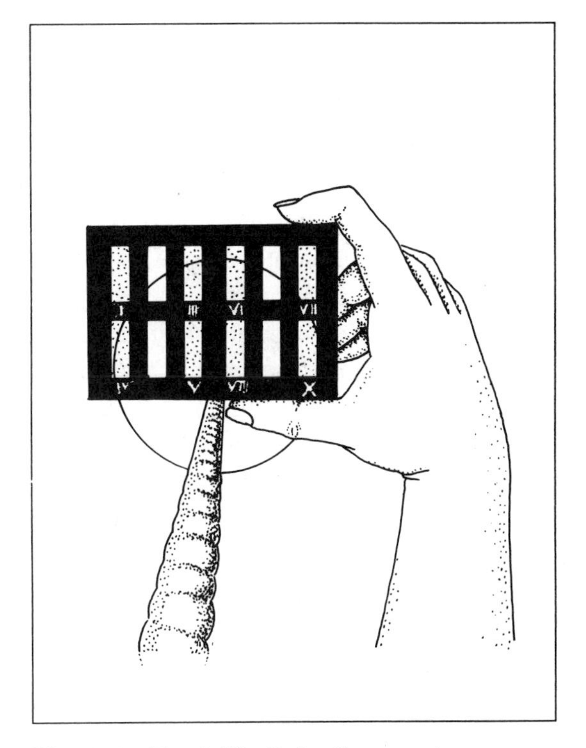

Fig. 6–2. Forel–Ule Color Comparator

ACTIVITY 1

Measure water color from a boat or dock.

MATERIALS

- copy of Workbook Table 6–1
- Secchi disk with lines at 1-m intervals
- Forel–Ule Color Comparator kit

PROCEDURE

1. From a boat, dock, pier, or offshore platform, observe water conditions. Describe the water color as it appears without the aid of the color comparator kit. Record your observations in Table 6–1.

2. Submerge a Secchi disk, white side up,

until you can barely see it. Keep it in this same place as you carry out Procedure 3.

3. Use the Forel–Ule Color Comparator to measure water color as follows:
   a. Shake the comparator before putting the distilled water ampoules into its empty viewing windows.
   b. Hold the comparator at arm's length as you look at the Secchi disk through the distilled water in the viewing windows.
   c. With the submerged Secchi disk as the background, compare the color of the water as seen through the distilled water in the viewing windows with the Forel–Ule standards. Find the color on the scale that most closely matches the water color, and note its number. In Table 6–1, record the number of the nearest Forel–Ule color scale.

4. Measure the depth of the Secchi disk. Record the depth by counting the meter marks as you haul in the line.

5. Complete Table 6–1.

Table 6–1. Water color and Secchi disk data Ⓦ

Observer's name:	Date:	Time:
Location:		
Description of boat, pier, or platform used:		
Weather conditions:		
Cloud cover/sunlight:		
Wind/wave conditions:		
Other characteristics of site:		
Description of water color:		
Secchi disk depth in meters:		
Measured water color (Forel–Ule color scale number):		

QUESTIONS

4. What is turbidity?
   a. How might turbidity be affected by the number, size, and shape of particles in water? By the way they reflect light?
   b. What human activities might affect turbidity of coastal waters?

5. What does the Secchi disk measure?
   a. What conditions might affect the depth at which the disk just disappears from view?
   b. How does the disk standardize water color observations from site to site?

6. How did your unaided observations of water color compare with your observations using the Secchi disk and the color comparator? How well did the standard color scale match the actual observed water color?

7. Plants may contain pigments besides chlorophyll. Remember that seaweeds and algae are classified as red, green, or brown according to their pigments. What might explain a greenish-brown ocean color?

8. **Red tides** are caused by dinoflagellate blooms that impart a reddish tinge to the water. What color(s) are these tiny organisms absorbing? What color(s) are they reflecting? How could the intensity of red color in the water indicate concentrations of these organisms?

9. How do sediments (suspended mud or clay particles) affect water color? What color would you use to describe mud? How could suspended particles of mud be distinguished from plankton?

10. How might organic detritus (marine snow) affect
    a. turbidity?
    b. ocean color?

Primary Productivity

Primary productivity in the open ocean is the rate of production of biomass made by phytoplankton in a given unit of time in a given volume of water. The rate of biomass production in a specific portion of the ocean changes throughout the year. In the North Atlantic, for example, primary productivity is greater in summer than in winter.

The amount of biomass in a volume of water at any one moment is called the **standing crop.** The standing crop includes the phytoplankton plus all the other organisms living at that time in that volume of water. If we know the biomass of the phytoplankton, we can estimate the biomass of the animals dependent on this food source.

Phytoplankton are eaten by herbivorous zooplankton. These zooplankton are eaten by larger carnivorous zooplankton and by fish and other ocean animals. Thus where plankton concentrations are high, so are populations of fish. Since ocean color changes with phytoplankton density, fishers can use ocean color to locate fish.

QUESTIONS

11. How might marine animals affect the

phytoplankton biomass? Would the animals increase, decrease, or have no effect on the biomass?

12. How is ocean color related to primary productivity?

13. What might explain the greater primary productivity in summer than in winter in the North Atlantic?

14. What are some practical and economic reasons for studying primary productivity in the ocean?

In Situ Research

Research ships allow oceanographers to collect plants, animals, and seawater and measure their characteristics. This kind of work is described as ***in situ*** (L. = at the site) observation. Modern shipboard research relies on navigational satellites to locate the sampling sites and relay information to other ships and onshore research stations. Buoys also collect *in situ* information about water conditions. Buoys can also send the information they gather to satellites, which relay it to ships or shore. See Fig. 6–3.

There is a problem with *in situ* research. Oceanographers on research ships must sail from site to site to collect and study samples of phytoplankton. Typically, they sample one site a day before moving to a new site—perhaps 400 km away. Plankton, however, inhabit huge areas of the ocean, and plankton blooms may occur in a few days. A research ship can gather only a small amount of information about large-scale changes in plankton populations. An example is the spring plankton bloom in the North Atlantic. Because a ship is just a speck in a vast and changing sea, researchers aboard a ship cannot satisfactorily study the sudden or widespread changes that mark shifts in phytoplankton biomass.

QUESTIONS

15. What are some possible explanations for rapid changes in plankton population? Suggest possibilities related to changes
    a. in the biological environment.
    b. in the physical environment.

Satellite Remote Sensing

Today ocean color can be studied on regional, oceanwide, and global scales by satellites equipped with automated devices called **remote sensors.** Some remote sensors are cameralike devices mounted on the satellites to record **ocean surface radiance,** light from the ocean surface.

One remote sensor, called the Coastal Zone Color Scanner (CZCS), measures the ocean surface radiance. Just like a camera, the scanner receives and records light. It receives light (ocean surface radiance) from four sources: **glint** (the reflected sunlight), **daylight** (the light we see in the sky), **reflected daylight** (the daylight reflected off the surface of the ocean), and **upwelled radiance** (the light transmitted from the euphotic zone into the atmosphere.) Only one of these sources, upwelled radiance, is the light that the scanner sees as ocean color. See Table 6–2.

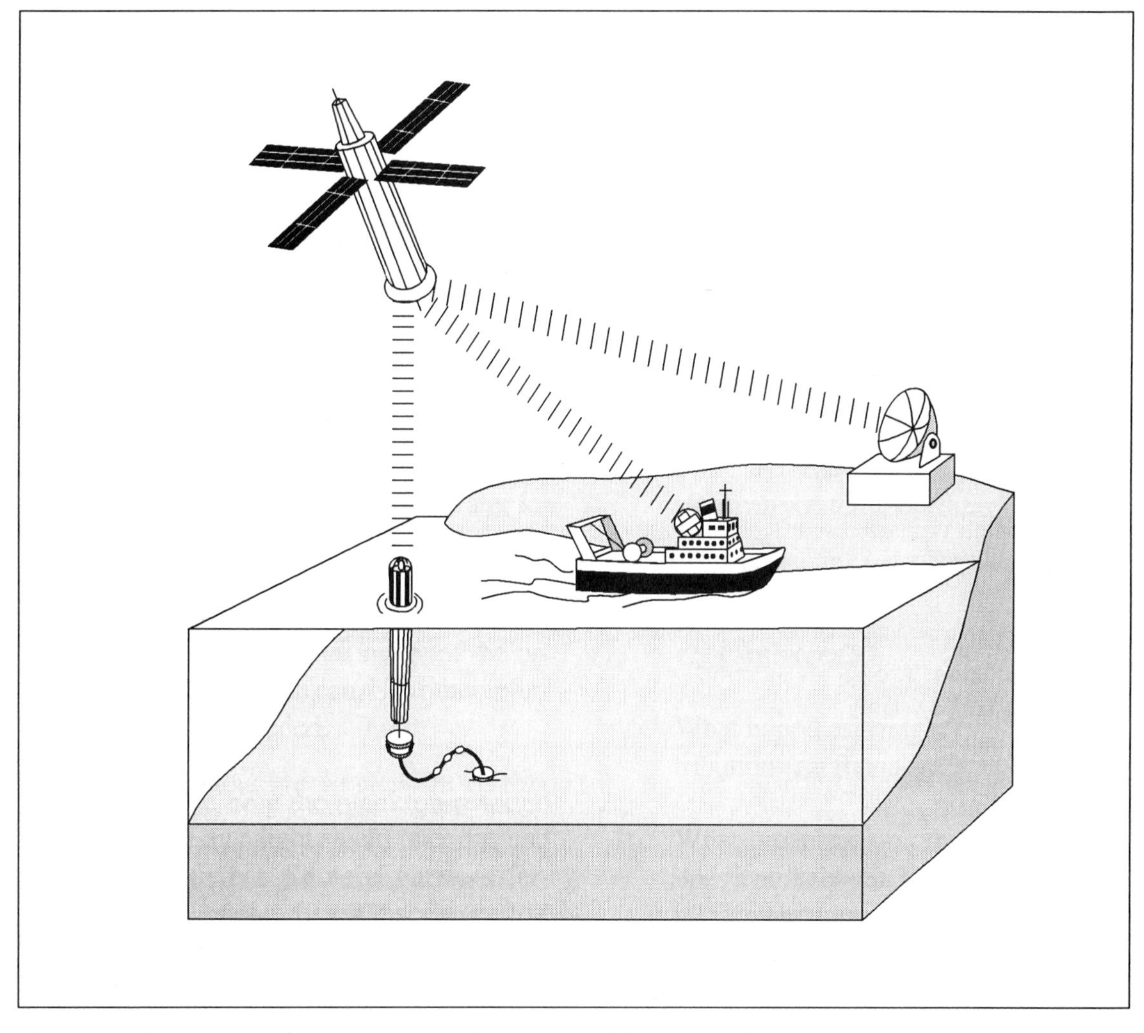

Fig. 6–3. Satellites aid in locating sampling sites and in transmitting data.

ACTIVITY 2

Make a diagram labeling the kinds of light received by remote sensors attached to a satellite.

MATERIALS

- copy of Workbook Fig. 6–4
- colored pencil

PROCEDURE

1. Read the terms in Table 6–2.
2. Using terms in Table 6–2,
   a. write a letter on each arrowhead in Fig. 6–4 to identify that type of light.
   b. Color the arrow that shows which light is measured as ocean color.

Table 6–2. Light coming to, entering, and reflecting from the ocean

A. ***Direct sunlight,*** also called ***incidental sunlight.*** Direct unscattered sunlight energy; white light.

B. ***Glint,*** also called ***sea surface reflection.*** Reflected direct sunlight; sunlight that bounces off the water's surface and is detected by the CZCS.

C. ***Daylight,*** also called ***atmospheric ambient light.*** Sunlight that reflects off and is scattered by air molecules, particles of dust, water droplets, and salt in the atmosphere. This produces the ambient (surrounding) **daylight** (or **skylight**) that we are familiar with. It accounts for about 90% of the light received by the CZCS.

D. ***Reflected daylight.*** Scattered atmospheric daylight that reflects off the surface of the ocean into the atmosphere and is detected by the CZCS.

E. ***Light transmitted into water.*** Light that penetrates the upper layers of the ocean, the **photic zone.** The light is transmitted into the ocean from daylight and, to a lesser extent, from direct sunlight.

F. ***Photic zone light.*** Light in the area from the surface of the ocean to the depth where there is no light. This region includes the **euphotic zone** (surface to about 80 m), where there is enough light for photosynthesis, and the **disphotic zone** (about 80 to 200 m), the distance that light penetrates the ocean. Photic zone light is absorbed, scattered, reflected, and transmitted by water molecules, plankton, and suspended particles.

G. ***Upwelled radiance.*** Light transmitted from the photic zone into the atmosphere. Satellite ocean-color instruments measure upwelled radiance at a constantly changing depth called "one optical depth," the depth where light drops to 37% of its intensity at the surface of the ocean. This depth changes with the amount of turbidity. It is this light that is recorded by the CZCS as **ocean color.**

H. ***Reflected photic zone light.*** Ambient light in the photic zone that reflects off the surface of the ocean back into the water.

I. ***Ocean surface radiance.*** All light received by the CZCS. Includes glint, daylight, reflected daylight, and upwelled radiance.

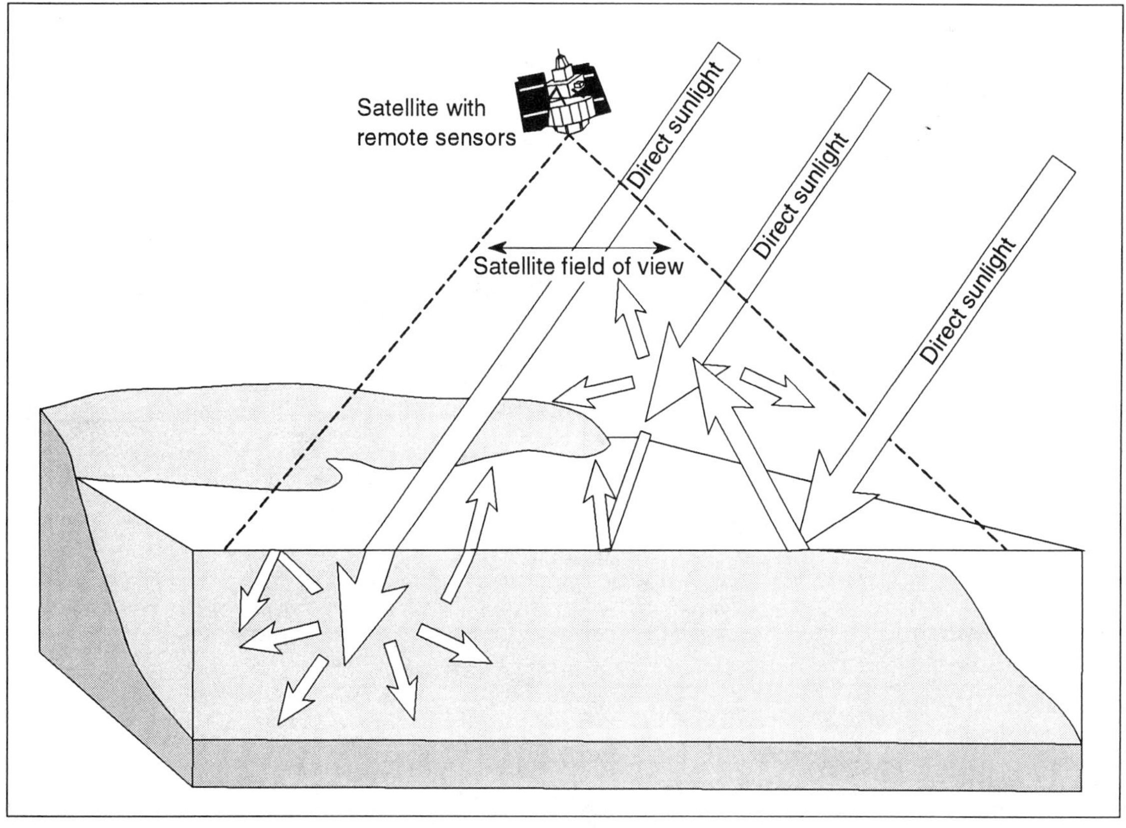

Fig. 6–4. Light received by a passive remote sensor attached to a satellite Ⓦ

QUESTIONS

16. How might light be scattered
    a. in the atmosphere by clean air? By smoke?
    b. in the ocean by clean water? By particles in the water?

17. Using the terms in Table 6–2, explain what humans see as
    a. daylight.
    b. light reflected from the surface of water.
    c. ocean color.

18. Answer the following questions in terms of absorbed and reflected light in different regions of the visible spectrum. Refer to Topic 3 in Unit 3, Plants, for information on the absorption spectrum of water and chlorophyll.
    a. If there were no phytoplankton in the water, what color would upwelled radiance be? Why?
    b. If there were large amounts of phytoplankton in the water, what color or colors would upwelled radiance be? Why?

Satellite Images

Measurement of ocean color (upwelled radiance) by satellite was first proven feasible by the Nimbus–7 research satellite. The satellite operated from 1978 to 1986, moving in a polar orbit—a path around the earth from pole to pole. See Fig. 6–5.

The satellite orbited at a height of 955 km (600 mi), much higher than planes fly. From this great height, its Coastal Zone Color Scanner had such a wide field of view that each image covered a swath (a strip) 800 km from north to south and 1,600 km from east to west. The images can be combined to form a maplike composite satellite image of a large area of the ocean. Several images can be combined to simulate a motion picture.

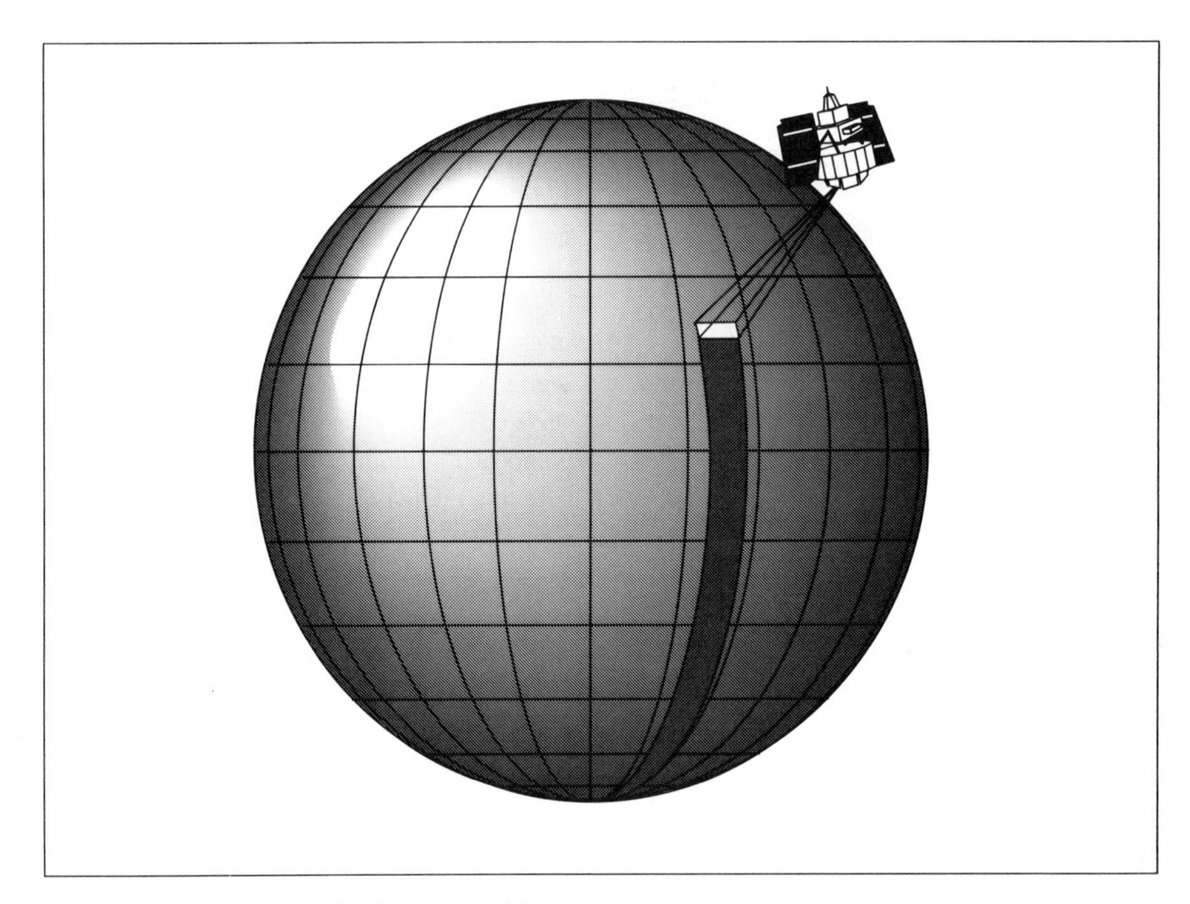

Fig. 6–5. Nimbus–7 satellite in a polar orbit

The Nimbus–7 satellite could make an image every 2 min, complete a full orbit every 104 min, and cover the globe in 2 ½ days. By slightly overlapping the images, it made continuous records of ocean color. See Fig. 6–6.

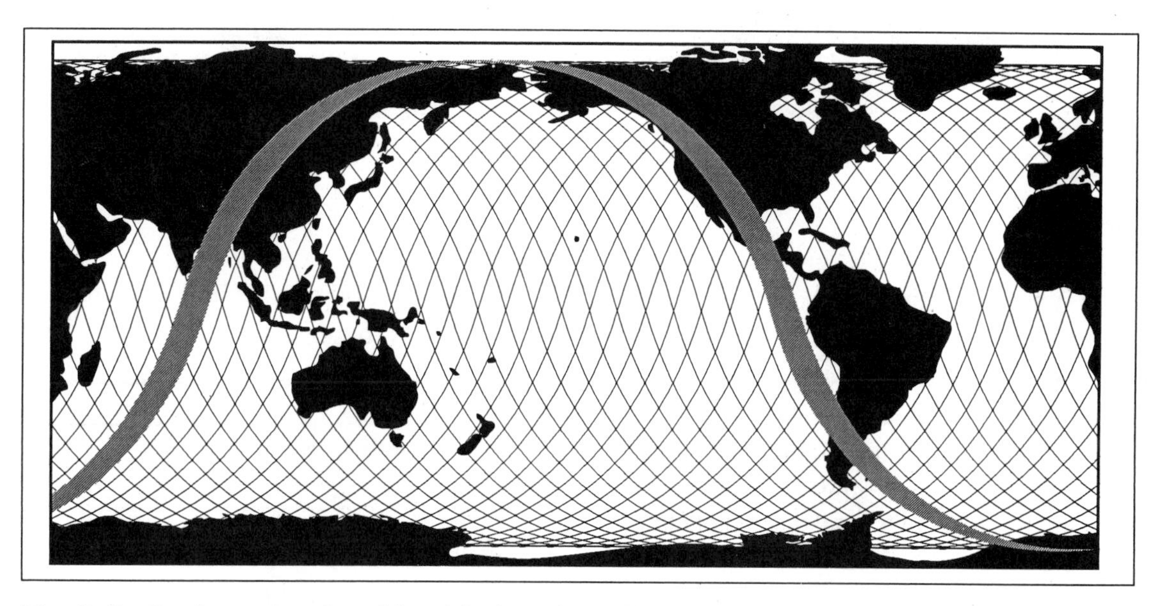

Fig. 6–6. Continuous imaging of the globe by polar-orbiting Nimbus–7 satellite (one orbit shown in gray)

Everywhere the satellite orbited, the remote sensor measured the intensity of upwelled radiance (ocean color). Using this data, a computer calculated the concentrations of chlorophyll pigments and plotted the values on a maplike image. It color-coded the image using a color key to distinguish relatively small changes in chlorophyll concentration from place to place. These satellite images are not photographs, and the colors used in the images are not intended to depict true ocean color (upwelled radiance).

Scientists wondered whether measurements made by remote sensing were as valid as *in situ* measurements. Using a method called ground truthing, they compared remote-sensing data with *in situ* data and found it just as accurate. Scientists can now get an updated picture of plankton in the ocean about once every 60 hours.

QUESTIONS

19. Satellite ocean-color images often use red to depict areas with very high chlorophyll concentration. If you were actually looking at an ocean area with a very high chlorophyll concentration, what color would you expect to see? (Refer as needed to Activity 1 in this topic.)

20. Satellites orbit the earth at much higher altitudes than planes fly. If identical Coastal Zone Color Scanners were attached to a satellite and to an airplane, both pointing toward the earth at the same angle and adjusted for the same angle of viewing, which would
    a. be able to "see" a larger area of the earth's surface? Use a sketch in your answer.
    b. be more capable of collecting con-

tinuous data? Explain.

c. be more expensive to operate? Explain.

d. require more advanced technology to operate?

21. What is meant by "ground truthing"? What would have to be done to determine the "ground truth" of a satellite's ocean-color data?

22. How would you compare satellite remote sensing with *in situ* research? What are the advantages and disadvantages of each?

Related Ocean Features

Ocean-color data obtained by Nimbus–7 over almost 8 years show that concentrations of phytoplankton pigment vary widely from place to place and time to time. Now, with satellite data, oceanographers can continuously study phytoplankton on a regional and oceanwide scale.

Oceanographers can also use ocean color to locate currents, eddies, areas of upwelling, and other **ocean features.** Most of these features cover 10,000 km^2 or less of ocean surface, appearing and changing within a few days or weeks. Some, like the spring plankton bloom in the North Atlantic, cover vast areas of the ocean.

Such features cover too large an area and change too rapidly for meaningful observation and measurement by shipboard research. Satellite data have revolutionized studying ocean features, expanding our understanding of large-scale ocean-basin and global events.

ACTIVITY 3

Interpret ocean-color images obtained from satellite data.

Produce false-color images of ocean color from satellite data.

MATERIALS

- copies of Workbook Figs. 6–7 and 6–8
- world atlas (optional)
- world globe (optional)
- colored pencils
- colored satellite ocean-color images (optional)

PROCEDURE

1. Look at the map in Fig. 6–7.
   a. Locate and name the ocean, lakes, and bays shown on the map. Label any features you find that are not already labeled.
   b. Locate the continent, islands, and other land features shown on the map. Label the features you find that are not already labeled.
   c. Locate the seaward edge of the continental shelf. The continental shelf is the submerged part of a continent that extends seaward 15 to 50 km. It slopes seaward to a depth of about 200 m.

2. Using Fig. 6–7 as a reference, look at the satellite image in Fig. 6–8.
   a. Landmasses are black. Locate the ocean and landmasses.
   b. Color-code the chlorophyll concentrations. (These colors are similar to the color code used in computer-drawn satellite images.)

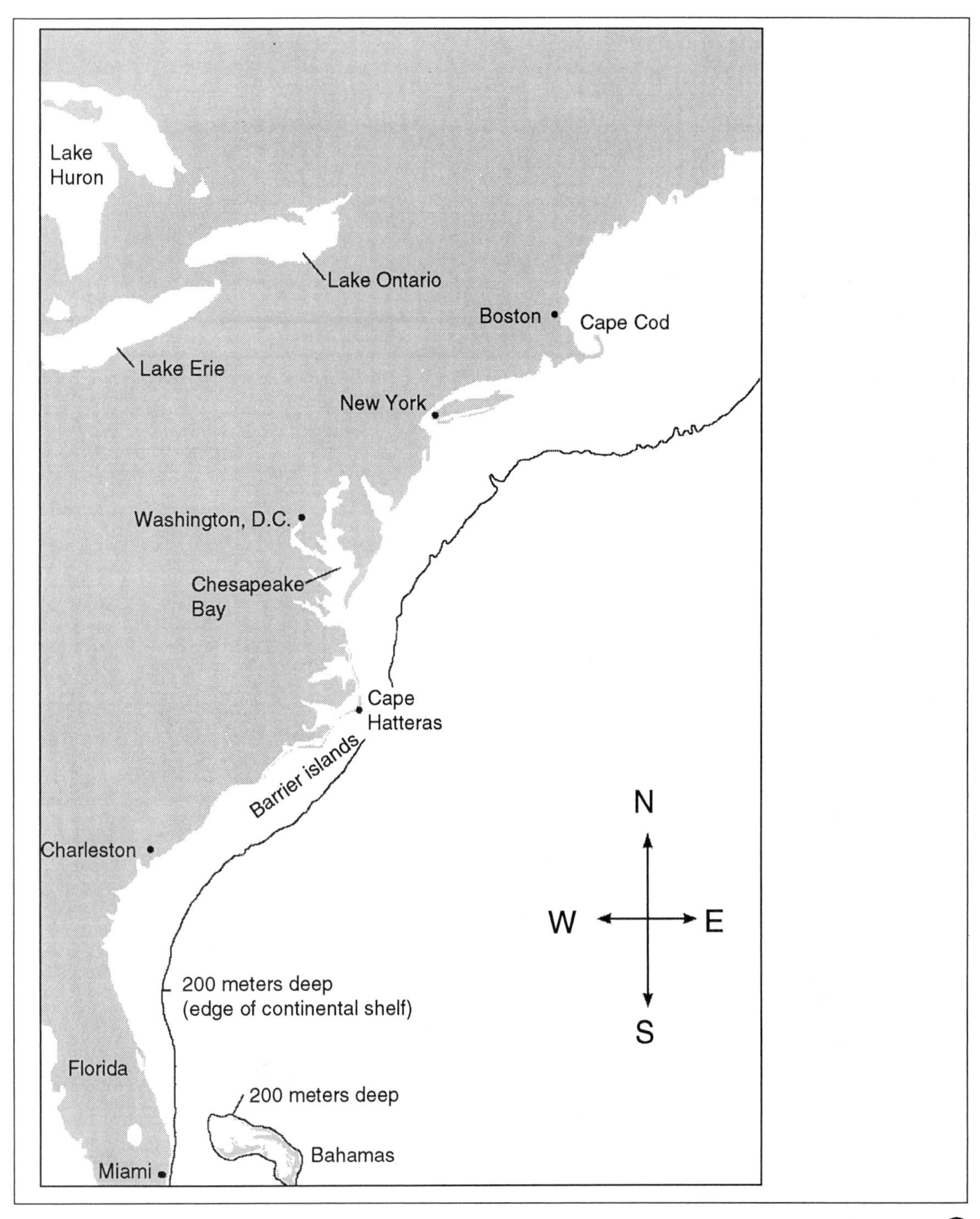

Fig. 6–7. The western North Atlantic

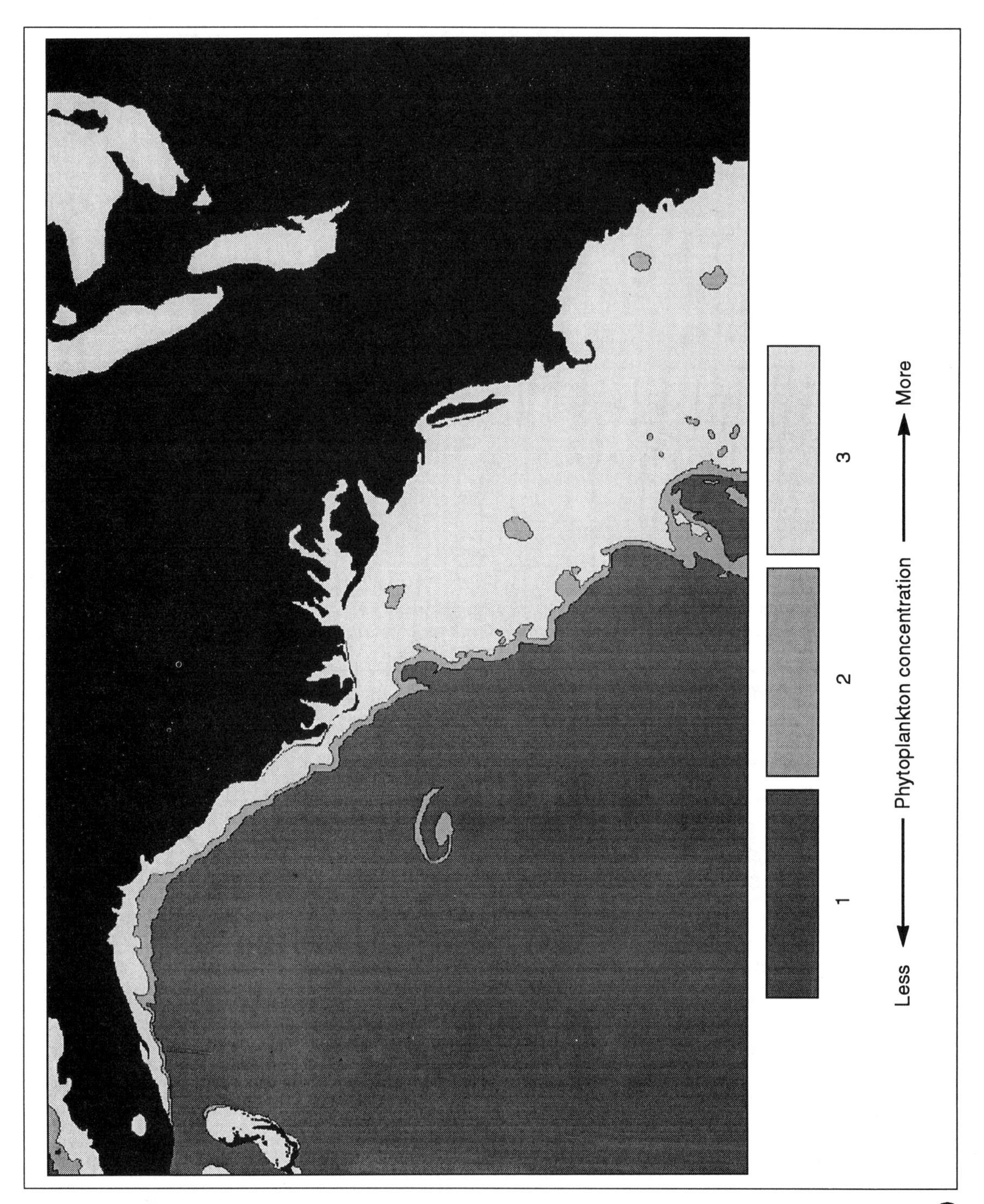

Fig. 6–8. Ocean-color image of the western North Atlantic
Source: Modified photograph from NASA's Coastal Zone Color Scanner remote satellite sensors

Examine the gray shading key, then color over the shades on the map to show the concentrations of phytoplankton as follows:

3 = red = greater than 1 mg/m^3
2 = yellow
1 = blue = less than 0.01 mg/m^3

3. After you have finished coloring Fig. 6–8, examine the color-coded satellite image for the ocean features listed in Table 6–3. Locate any features that might fit these descriptions, and label each feature in pencil, using its abbreviation.

Table 6–3. Ocean features that can be studied from ocean-color data

***Western ocean boundary currents* (WOBC).** Western ocean boundary currents are found on the western side of all ocean basins. These currents push one mass of water through another relatively nonmoving mass of water, like a fast river moving through a still lake. Examples are the Gulf Stream off the east coast of North America and the Kuroshio Current off Japan. These currents are composed of water that differs from its neighboring water in temperature, salinity, and other qualities, including ocean color.

***Eddies* (E).** Eddies are circular water currents that branch off from a western boundary current. These eddies move like whirlpools, gradually mixing with surrounding water until the two are indistinguishable. Ocean-color images provide information on how eddies and currents form and how they change over time. This knowledge is important in understanding the processes that enrich offshore waters with nutrients and plankton.

4. (Optional) If you have access to posters, prints, or slides of satellite ocean color images, analyze these as you did in Procedures 1 through 3. These images may show additional ocean features listed in Table 6–4.

Table 6–4. More ocean features that can be studied from ocean-color data

***Upwellings* (U).** Upward-moving currents that carry nutrient-rich water to the surface are called upwellings. Coastal upwellings vary from tens to hundreds of kilometers in length; equatorial upwellings are from hundreds to thousands of kilometers. Upwelling systems occur off the western coasts of the United States, Peru, and northwest Africa. Here the nutrient-rich upwelling provides the fertilizer for abundant phytoplankton growth, which in turn provides food for abundant growth of zooplankton and fish.

Table 6–4 *continued.* More ocean features that can be studied from ocean-color data

***El Niño events* (EN).** *El Niño* is a periodic climate change in the Pacific. During an *El Niño,* normal upwelling is suppressed and unusually warm water appears along the coasts of Ecuador and Peru. Phytoplankton populations drop and animals further up the food chain starve.

***Monsoons* (M).** Monsoons are wind systems that reverse seasonally, influencing large climatic regions, especially in the Indian Ocean. These wind reversals cause periodic upwelling conditions.

***River plumes* (RP).** River plumes are the discharge of sediment-laden river and estuary water into the ocean. Suspended material is highly reflective and readily observable in satellite images. Satellite studies are planned to determine whether the nitrates and phosphates discharged into coastal water from agricultural and urban sources enhance primary productivity. These studies will require understanding of nearshore sedimentary and circulatory processes. We will also need to understand how plumes form, mix with ocean water, and eventually dissipate.

***Seasonal phytoplankton blooms* (PB).** During the winter, especially in the North Atlantic, surface water becomes so cold that it sinks, causing vertical mixing of water. Deeper water rich in dissolved nutrients rises and mixes with surface water that is depleted of nutrients. When daily sunlight increases in the spring, conditions favor a rapid phytoplankton growth called a "spring phytoplankton bloom." The spring bloom is a major oceanic event that plays an important role in the global carbon cycle.

QUESTIONS

23. Where phytoplankton concentrations are high in the ocean, the actual ocean color is green.
    a. Examine the color-coded satellite image in Fig. 6–8. What color is used to depict ocean areas where phytoplankton concentrations are highest?
    b. Why might satellite ocean-color images be called "false-color images"? How is the satellite image different from a photograph?

24. In the satellite images, what are the areas(s) of greatest phytoplankton concentration? Of least concentration?

25. What ocean features did you identify in the satellite image?

26. What effect, if any, do the following appear to have on phytoplankton concentration?
    a. continental shelf
    b. the Bahamas islands
    d. eddies

e. bays and estuaries
f. large inland lakes
g. deep-ocean water

27. Bays, estuaries, and the Great Lakes are all biologically productive. What factors favor phytoplankton growth in these areas?

28. How could satellite ocean-color images be used by commercial fishing industries to improve their fish catch? From evidence in Fig. 6–8, where would you advise vessels to fish? Explain.

29. Phytoplankton productivity is largely related to the abundance of nutrients in the water. List all the events you can think of that might cause
    a. an increase in nutrients.
    b. a decrease in nutrients.

30. If you have access to other satellite ocean-color images, tell
    a. what ocean features each reveals.
    b. how these features may have formed.

31. Phytoplankton productivity is largely related to the abundance of nutrients in the water. What areas in the satellite images appear to have the most nutrients? Where might these nutrients have come from?

32. Which of the ocean features listed in Tables 6–3 and 6–4 are related to
    a. an increase or decrease in nutrients?
    b. changes in sunlight energy?
    c. other factors? Identify these.

33. How might you explain
    a. spring phytoplankton blooms in the North Atlantic?
    b. poor fish catches during an *El Niño*?
    c. abundant fish catches in upwelled areas?

34. How might a river plume discharging into the ocean affect phytoplankton growth? Describe what might happen when a river discharges into the ocean.

35. How could satellite data of the quantity of phytoplankton be used to
    a. detect ocean features?
    b. observe changes in the ocean environment?
    c. monitor global changes?

FURTHER INVESTIGATIONS

1. Learn about other satellite remote sensors and how they measure sea height, ocean surface temperature, sea surface winds, ice cover, and seafloor bathymetry.

2. Report on satellite research missions that study global oceanic and atmospheric conditions like those listed below. If possible, bring photographs and posters of satellite images to class.
    a. oceanic circulation
    b. atmospheric chemistry
    c. the ozone hole
    d. marine winds
    e. hydrologic (rain) cycles and rainfall patterns
    f. clouds and solar radiation

g. atmospheric carbon dioxide and other greenhouse gases
h. global heat transport
i. climate
j. human interactions

3. Relate the global oceanic and atmospheric phenomena in Further Investigation 2 to TV, radio, newspaper, and magazine reports about
   a. weather.
   b. climate changes.
   c. global environment.
   d. human impacts, such as oil spills.

4. Learn about satellite programs conducted by
   a. the National Aeronautics and Space Administration (NASA), including Seasat, the series of Nimbus satellites, and NASA's Earth Observing System (EOS); Upper Atmosphere Research Satellite; the TOPEX/Poseidon satellites (atmospheric chemistry and oceanic circulation); and proposed Earth Probe sensors.
   b. the U.S. Department of Defense, including GEOSAT (using altimetry), SALT (for measuring oceanic circulation), and the Navy Remote Ocean Sensing System (NROSS, for measuring ocean winds).
   c. the World Ocean Circulation Experiment (WOCE). This program uses satellites from the United States, Europe, and Japan.

5. Research and write a report on
   a. Europe's Remote Sensing Satellite ERS–1 (for ocean observations).
   b. Japan's Earth Resources Satellite JERS–1 (for global mapping of resources) and its Advanced Earth Observing Satellite.
   c. Canada's Radarsat (for sea-ice mapping).

6. Plan and conduct a demonstration for the class explaining
   a. geosynchronous orbits.
   b. polar orbits of a satellite.

Appendix A. Symbols, Abbreviations, and Units of Measure

1. SYMBOLS

X	multiplied by
÷	divided by
<	less than
=	equal to
>	greater than
/	divided by or per

2. MEASURES

International System (SI) Units		U.S. Customary Units	
mm	millimeter	in	inch
cm	centimeter	ft	foot
m	meter	yd	yard
km	kilometer (1,000 m)	mi	mile
mL	milliliter	oz	ounce (volume)
L	liter	qt	quart
		gal	gallon (U.S.)
g	gram	oz	ounce (mass)
kg	kilogram	lb	pound
˚C	degrees Celsius	˚F	degrees Fahrenheit

3. OTHER UNITS

atm	atmosphere
psi	pounds per square inch
cal	calorie
kcal	kilocalorie (1,000 calories)
nmi	nautical mile
kt	knots

Appendix B. Formulas

1. CIRCUMFERENCE

square	4L	L = length
rectangle	2L + 2W	W = width
circle	$\pi d = 2\pi r$	π = 3.14
		r = radius
		d = diameter

2. AREA

square	L X L
rectangle	L X W
circle	πr^2
sphere	$4\pi r^2$

3. VOLUME

cube	L X L X L
solid rectangle	L X W X H
sphere	$4/3\ \pi r^3$

4. CIRCULAR MEASURE

1 circle	= 360˚	(˚ = degree)
1 degree	= 60'	(' = minute)
1 minute	= 60"	(" = second)

5. OTHER UNITS

Density = mass/volume = g/cm^3 or g/mL

Joule (energy) = 1 newton/meter

Force = mass X acceleration = kg X m/sec/sec

Pressure = force/area

Appendix C. Scientific Notation

1. Numbers may be expressed in **powers of ten**. For example, 1,000,000 may expressed as 10^6, which means 10 X 10 X 10 X 10 X 10 X 10. In 10^6, the **base** is ten, and the **exponent** is 6.

one billion	=	1,000,000,000	=	10^9
one million	=	1,000,000	=	10^6
one thousand	=	1,000	=	10^3
one hundred	=	100	=	10^2
ten	=	10	=	10^1
one	=	1	=	10^0
one-tenth	=	0.1	=	10^{-1}
one-hundredth	=	0.01	=	10^{-2}
one-thousandth	=	0.001	=	10^{-3}
one-billionth	=	0.000000001	=	10^{-9}

2. Examples of converting numbers to powers of 10.

(a) 300	=	3 X 100	=	3×10^2
(b) 3,500	=	3.5 X 1,000	=	3.5×10^3
(c) 0.15	=	1.5 X 0.1	=	1.5×10^{-1}
(d) 0.05	=	5 X 0.01	=	5×10^{-2}

3. To multiply, add the exponents.

(a) $10^2 \times 10^3$	=	10^{2+3}	=	10^5
(b) 10 X 10	=	10^{1+1}	=	10^2
(c) $10^5 \times 10^3$	=	10^{5+3}	=	10^8
(d) $(3 \times 10^4)(2 \times 10^{-6})$	=	$6 \times 10^{4-6}$	=	6×10^{-2}
(e) $(4 \times 10^6)(2 \times 10^{-3})$	=	$8 \times 10^{6-3}$	=	8×10^3

4. To divide, subtract the exponents.

(a) $$\frac{10^3}{10^5} = 10^{3-5} = 10^{-2}$$

(b) $$\frac{4 \times 10^3}{2 \times 10^{-6}} = \frac{4}{2} \times 10^{3-(-6)} = 2 \times 10^{3+6} = 2 \times 10^9$$

(c) $$\frac{6.4 \times 10^{-2}}{1.6 \times 10^3} = \frac{6.4}{1.6} \times 10^{(-2)-3} = 4 \times 10^{-5}$$

Appendix D. Converting Units

1. LENGTH

Unit	cm	m	in	ft
1 cm	1	0.01	0.39	0.03
1 m	100	1	39.37	3.28
1 in	2.54	0.0254	1	0.08
1 fathom	182.88	1.83	72	6
1 mi	1.61×10^5	1.61×10^3	6.34×10^4	5,280
1 nmi	1.85×10^5	1.85×10^3	7.29×10^4	6,072

2. AREA

Unit	cm^2	m^2	km^2	in^2	ft^2	mi^2	nmi^2
1 cm^2	1	10^{-4}	10^{-10}	0.155	1.08×10^{-3}	3.85×10^{-11}	2.92×10^{-11}
1 m^2	10^4	1	10^{-6}	1,550	10.76	3.85×10^{-6}	2.92×10^{-7}
1 km^2	10^{10}	10^6	1	1.55×10^9	1.07×10^6	0.39	0.29
1 in^2	6.45	6.45×10^{-4}	–	1	6.94×10^{-3}	2.49×10^{-10}	1.88×10^{-10}
1 ft^2	929.03	0.09	–	144	1	3.59×10^{-8}	2.71×10^{-8}
1 mi^2	2.59×10^{10}	2.59×10^6	2.59	4.02×10^9	2.79×10^7	1	0.76

3. MASS

Unit	g	kg	lb	metric ton	ton
1 g	1	10^{-3}	2.21×10^{-3}	10^{-6}	1.1×10^{-6}
1 kg	1,000	1	2.21	10^{-3}	1.1×10^{-3}
1 lb (avdp)	453.59	0.45	1	4.54×10^{-4}	5×10^{-4}
1 metric ton	10^6	1,000	2,204.62	1	1.1
1 ton	907,184.7	907.2	2,000	0.91	1

4. VOLUME

Unit	m^3	cm^3	liter	in^3	ft^3	qt	gal
1 m^3	1	10^6	10^3	6.1×10^4	35.31	1.06×10^3	264.1
1 cm^3	10^{-6}	1	10^{-3}	0.06	3.53×10^{-5}	1.06×10^{-3}	2.64×10^{-4}
1 liter	10^{-3}	1,000	1	61.02	0.04	1.06	0.26
1 in^3	1.64	16.39	0.02	1	5.79×10^{-4}	0.02	4.33×10^{-3}
1 ft^3	2.83×10^{-2}	28,316.85	28.32	1,728	1	2.99	7.48
1 qt	9.47×10^{-4}	946.35	0.94	57.75	0.03	1	0.25
1 gal (U.S.)	3.79×10^{-3}	3,785.41	3.79	231	0.13	4	1

5. TEMPERATURE

Formulas

$$°C = \frac{°F - 32}{1.8} \qquad °F = (1.8 \times °C) + 32$$

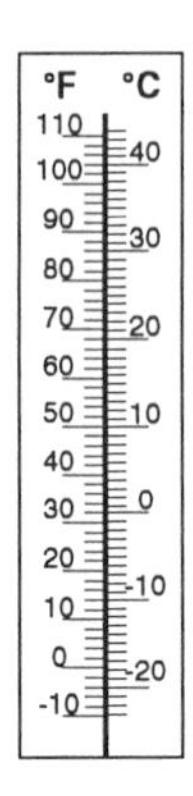

Conversion table

°C	°F
0	32
10	50
20	68
30	86
40	104
100	212

6. TIME

1 day	=	8.64×10^4 sec (mean solar day)	=	24 hr
1 year	=	8765.8 hr	=	3.156×10^7 sec (mean solar year)
1 aeon	=	10^9 yr (one billion years)		

Nautical time (expressed on a 24-hour clock)

Standard	Nautical
6 A.M.	0600 hr
9 A.M.	0900 hr
12 Noon	1200 hr
3 P.M.	1500 hr
6 P.M.	1800 hr
11:30 P.M.	2330 hr

7. SPEED

Unit	knots	mi/hr	km/hr	m/sec
1 knot	1	1.15	1.85	0.5
1 mi/hr	0.87	1	1.61	0.43
1 km/hr	0.54	0.62	1	0.27
1 m/sec	2	2.3	3.7	1

8. DENSITY

Unit	g/cm^3	g/L	kg/m^3	lb/ft^3	lb/gal
g/cm^3	1	10^3	10^3	62.4	8.35
g/L	10^{-3}	1	1	0.062	8.35×10^{-3}
kg/m^3	10^{-3}	1	1	0.062	8.35×10^{-3}
lb/ft^3	0.016	16.01	16.01	1	0.13
lb/gal	0.12	119.8	119.8	7.48	1

9. PRESSURE

Unit	atm	kg/cm^2	psi (lb/in^2)	in Hg	mm Hg
atm	1	1.03	14.7	29.92	760
kg/cm^2	0.968	1	14.22	28.96	735.56
psi	0.068	0.07	1	2.04	51.71
in Hg	0.03	0.035	0.491	1	25.4
mm Hg	1.31×10^{-3}	1.36×10^{-3}	0.019	0.039	1

10. ENERGY

1 cal = 4.18 Joule = 1.56×10^{-6} horsepower/hr

1 Joule = 0.239 cal = 3.73 horsepower/hr

Credits

Pages 25–39. Table 4–1 is modified from *Handbook of Hawaiian Fishes,* by W. A. Gosline and V. E. Brock. Honolulu, HI: University Press of Hawaii, 1960.

Pages 122–125. Tables 10–5, 10–7, 10–8, 10–9 use information from *Shark Watch,* by John Clark. New York, NY: Grosset & Dunlap, 1975.

Page 123. Table 10–6 uses information from *When Shark Eats Man,* by Victor Lipman. Honolulu, HI: *Honolulu* magazine, April 1983. Data collected in 1981 by George Balaz and Alan Kam, updated for the magazine in 1983.

Page 153. Fig. 2–6 is modified from *Animals Without Backbones,* second edition, by Ralph Buchsbaum. Chicago, IL: University of Chicago Press, 1976.

Page 167. Fig. 3–7 is modified from *Lower Animals,* by Martin Wells. New York, NY: McGraw-Hill, 1968.

Page 223. Fig. 6–5 is modified from *Living Invertebrates,* by Vicki and John Pearse and Mildred and Ralph Buchsbaum. Palo Alto, CA: Blackwell Scientific Publications, 1987.

Page 238. Fig. 6–12 is from *A Pictorial History of Sea Monsters and Other Dangerous Marine Life,* by James B. Sweeney. New York: Crown Publishers, 1973. It is a reproduction of a photo from the Forbes Collection at the Massachusetts Institute of Technology, Cambridge, MA.

Page 282. Fig. 9–2 is modified from *Living Invertebrates,* by Vicki and John Pearse and Mildred and Ralph Buchsbaum. Palo Alto, CA: Blackwell Scientific Publications, 1987.

Page 284. Fig. 9–4 is modified from *Living Invertebrates,* by Vicki and John Pearse and Mildred and Ralph Buchsbaum. Palo Alto, CA: Blackwell Scientific Publications, 1987.

Page 430. Fig. 6–8 is a modified photograph from NASA's Coastal Zone Color Scanner remote satellite sensors of the eastern coast of North America in May of 1981.

Index

Page numbers in *italics* indicate figures and tables.